The Meriden Britannia SILVER-PLATE TREASURY

The Complete Catalog of 1886-7 With 3,200 Illustrations

by

The Meriden Britannia Co.

With a New Introduction by

EDMUND P. HOGAN

Historian, The International Silver Company

Dover Publications, Inc., New York

Published in Canada by General Publishing Company, Ltd., 30 Lesmill Road, Don Mills, Toronto, Ontario.
Published in the United Kingdom by Constable and Company, Ltd., 10 Orange Street, London WC2H 7EG.

This Dover edition, first published in 1982, is an unabridged republication of the work originally published by the Meriden Britannia Co., Meriden, Connecticut, in 1886. A new Introduction has been written especially for the Dover Edition by Edmund P. Hogan.

Manufactured in the United States of America
Dover Publications, Inc., 180 Varick Street, New York, N.Y. 10014

Library of Congress Cataloging in Publication Data

Meriden Britannia Company.
The Meriden Britannia silver-plate treasury.

Reprint. Originally published: Catalogue: Meriden Britannia Company, 1886-7. Hartford: Case, Lockwood & Brainard Co., 1886.
1. Meriden Britannia Company—Catalogs. 2. Silver-plated ware, Victorian—United States—Catalogs. I. Title.
NK7240.M47 1982 739.2'3'02947467 82-9601
ISBN 0-486-24364-8

INTRODUCTION

by
EDMUND P. HOGAN

The Company

The Meriden Britannia Co. was founded in Meriden, Connecticut, in 1852, spearheaded by two enterprising Yankee peddlers, Horace C. and Dennis C. Wilcox, who had been selling under the name of H. C. Wilcox & Co. The founders also included I. C. Lewis, George R. Curtis, L. J. Curtis and W. W. Lyman of Meriden and Samuel Simpson and John Munson of Wallingford, Connecticut, makers of pewter and britannia (a pewterlike alloy) whose products the Wilcoxes had been selling.

In 1856, because it was felt that operations would be more efficient if all products were made in one place rather than in various small shops, a new three-story wooden factory was erected in Meriden. By that time the new process of electro-silverplating was growing in popularity, so additions to the new factory included a plating room in which 74 people worked.

It was not long before the demand for silverware far overshadowed that for britannia ware and it became evident that larger quarters were needed. In July 1863, on the first day of the Battle of Gettysburg, ground was broken for a brick factory four stories high, 500 feet long and 40 feet wide. The Meriden Britannia Co. was thus able to establish itself firmly as a silverware manufacturer.

Growth continued as sales climbed to over $2 million a year. Capital stock had been increased from the original $50,000 in 1852 to a whopping $1.1 million in 1879, when a new factory was built in Hamilton, Ontario, to serve the Canadian trade. In 1881 another large building was added to the Meriden complex.

A view of the company's works shows the first factory of 1856 on the left and the building of 1863 on the right.

A group photograph shows the leading figures in the company during the period 1855–60. Back row, left to right: Horace C. Wilcox, I. C. Lewis, George R. Curtis, Dennis C. Wilcox. Front row, left to right: John Munson, L. J. Curtis, Samuel Simpson, W. W. Lyman. Next to Lyman is W. H. Johnson, a young employee who found favor with management. He died in the Civil War.

The company was Meriden's largest manufacturer, employing the greatest number of people. To the townspeople it became affectionately known as the "Big Shop." It also had offices and display rooms in New York, Chicago, San Francisco and London.

The Meriden Britannia Co. issued large-format catalogs as early as 1877 but this, for the years 1886–7, was the last of the big ones. It shows over 300 classes of articles and includes approximately 3200 illustrations. With the possible exception of a Reed & Barton catalog for 1885, nowhere else can one find so broad a showing of Victorian silver plate.

Over 50 tons of paper were required for the entire run of 30,000 copies. These were sent to silverware dealers and wholesalers in the United States and abroad, not entirely without incident. For example, a dealer of the time related this tale:

> While located at a temporary address, a man interested in the silverware trade (at that time in the U.S. Army) sent for a catalog expecting to get a small pamphlet through the mail. What was sent, via Express, was a large, bound volume, about the size of a bound copy of *Harper's Weekly*. At that time, on the frontier, express was carried by mounted men at a heavy cost.
>
> He had changed stations twice before the book finally reached him and after having been carried several hundred miles by pony, it was delivered on payment of something a little over $15.00 for express charges, which I think would be a record price for a trade catalog.

A photograph taken in about 1873 shows company employees arranged in front of one of the buildings.

This catalog also represents the end of an era, the end of the late Victorian period. Tastes were changing and by the early 1890s the flamboyance and overornamentation characteristic of the 1870s and 1880s met with less favor. Designs became more restrained and in most cases such motifs as birds, bees and butterflies became passé. Although they are often derided, Victorian designs have a special charm of their own. They reflect an important period in the history of our country, marked by elegance and gracious living, a period the like of which we shall probably never see again.

The serious short financial panics of 1893, 1894 and 1896 made necessary broad reductions in lines, and the Meriden Britannia Co. never again offered so vast an assortment of silver-plated holloware as is represented in this catalog.

In 1898 the International Silver Co. was formed by the merger of more than a dozen silverware makers in the Meriden area. The Meriden Britannia Co. played a leading role in this organization and continued to operate as a division of the parent company. The trademark continued in use until about 1938.

The Catalog

The catalog is illustrated throughout with wood engravings. These pictures were actually engraved by hand onto the surface of blocks of fine-grained wood. It required a large measure of artistic ability to render the elaborate and highly embellished patterns so popular in 1886. Meriden Britannia Co. had its own wood-engraving department, in which six or eight men were steadily employed. But about 1890 the halftone process of printing came into general use and soon replaced the use of wood engravings. This was a mechanical process involving photography.

The great range of articles contained in the catalog and the great variety within each class is fascinating— 57 different designs for the then popular ice pitcher, 72 different dinner casters, 58 different card receivers— and this variety extends to many other articles such as cake baskets, jewel caskets and butter dishes.

The designers of Victorian silver plate displayed great imagination and, in many of the articles, a sense of humor. They found inspiration in nature; many articles are ornamented with flowers, twigs, coral, nuts, bees, birds, butterflies, squirrels, cows, boats, dogs, lizards and fish, as well as with little boys, girls, fairies and cherubs.

The catalog shows us how people lived in the last quarter of the nineteenth century—what they thought was necessary, or at least desirable, in a well-conducted home. In every situation pertaining to the serving of food and beverages, personal grooming and adornment and furnishings and ornaments for the home, there was silverware to make living more gracious and pleasant. Indeed, from children's cups and sets to crematory urns and casket hardware, the Meriden Britannia Co. was prepared to serve everyone in elegant style from the cradle to the grave.

Flatware

The process of silver plating by electricity was developed and perfected in this country by the Rogers brothers—William, Asa and Simeon—who first offered their wares in 1847. In 1862 all three brothers came to Meriden under contract to supervise the making of their famous product. The trademark "1847—ROGERS BROS." was established and henceforth all this silver plate was made by the Meriden Britannia Co. (and later by its successor, the International Silver Co.). It is still being made today.

Pages 396 to 447 show the patterns that were popular in 1886-7 and the numerous handsome serving pieces made in them. However, in such patterns as Assyrian Head, Arcadian and Embossed, the design on all pieces is not exactly the same. These variations made an interesting complete service.

Sterling Silver

Although the Meriden Britannia Co. was, at that time, primarily a silver-plate maker, it also made sterling-silver flatware. Seven patterns in 1847 Rogers Bros. silver plate were also available in sterling, while an additional two patterns were made in sterling only. This was more or less a "made-to-order" business, and the method by which these items were sold is clearly explained on page 429.

Simeon Rogers.

Asa Rogers.

William Rogers.

Telegraphic Code

Readers may wonder at the meaning of the words that appear in parentheses following the prices in the captions under each illustration. This is the telegraphic code, explained on page 4. In 1886 there was no nationwide telephone network as we know it today, but coincident with the rapid growth of the railroads and the invention of the telegraph, there was a widespread network of telegraph offices. Since the cost of messages was figured by the word, a code in which one word took the place of three, four or more obviously saved money. Users of the catalog were cautioned that "great care should be taken in the use of the right words, correctly spelled, etc. By this system, telegraph messages will be found very inexpensive. Night messages will reduce the cost."

Finishes

Many of the pieces illustrated are offered in a variety of finishes. By far, the most popular of these was chased. In *chasing,* the ornamentation was incised into the surface of the metal by small chisel-like tools and a small hammer. No metal was removed.

In the process of *engraving,* on the other hand, metal was actually cut away, through the use of a sharp hand tool.

The *satin* finish, which was very popular, deliberately produced a fine "pockmarked" surface against which the hand-engraving stood out in bright relief.

Gold inlay was not actually "inlaid"; parts of the design were plated with 24K gold. The contrast of gold and silver made a very attractive finish.

Niello was deep-line engraving in which the lines were filled with copper, lead and sulphur in borax, producing a type of black enamel that was fired and polished.

Old silver finish gave the surface a soft patina, the deep parts of the ornamentation being heavily oxidized.

For further information on Victorian silver plate, readers are referred to *American Silverplate*, by Dorothy T. and H. Ivan Rainwater, and *The Elegance of Old Silverplate* by Edmund P. Hogan.

For the sake of convenience, this reprint reproduces the catalog in $^3/_4$-size. The original, measuring approximately 12" x 16", weighed 13½ lbs. Material tipped into the original edition between pages 58 and 59, and 146 and 147, on slips measuring 4" x 6", are here reproduced on page 451.

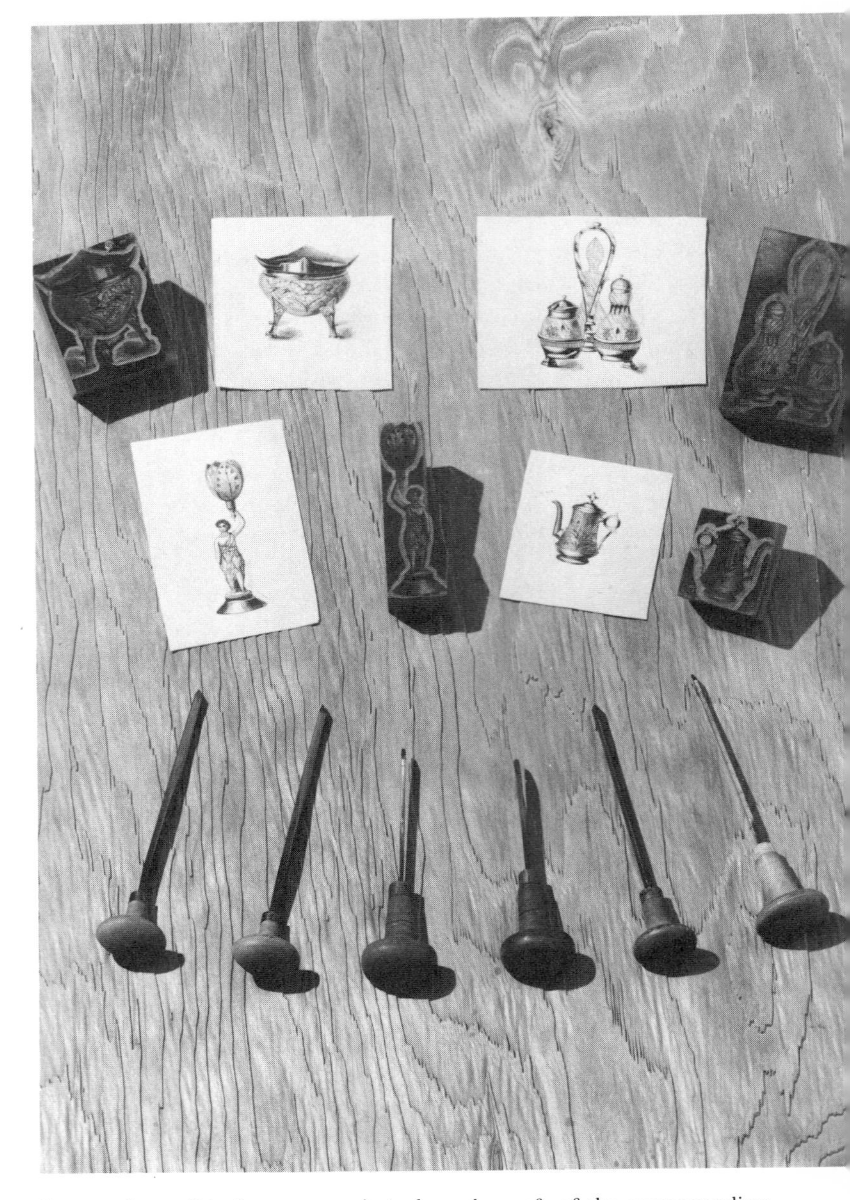

Engraved woodblocks, engraver's tools and proofs of the corresponding wood engravings.

The Meriden Britannia SILVER-PLATE TREASURY

The Complete Catalog of 1886-7 With 3,200 Illustrations

WORKS OF THE MERIDEN BRITANNIA CO. MERIDEN, CONN, U.S.A.
MANUFACTURERS OF ELECTRO GOLD AND SILVER PLATE.

Meriden Britannia Co.,

Meriden, Conn.

Gold and Silver Plate.

TRADE-MARK FOR SPOONS, FORKS, ETC.:

1847.–ROGERS BROS.–A 1. SECTIONAL PLATING }–XII.

WAREROOMS:

46 East 14th St., Union Square, New York;

147 State St., Chicago; 134 Sutter St., San Francisco;

7 Cripplegate Buildings, Wood St., E. C., London, England.

AND AT THE

Factories, Meriden, Conn., U. S. A.

Canada Factory: Hamilton, Ontario.

1886-7.

CATALOGUE

Meriden Britannia Company.

1886-7.

We have endeavored to make this the most complete Catalogue ever issued, embracing all latest designs both in ornamental and useful articles.

These goods are plated on both Nickel Silver and White Metal, the Nickel Silver, Silver Soldered ware being especially recommended for Hotel, Steamship, and Club use, and all places where hard usage is required.

Spoons, Forks, etc., are Stamped "**1847**.–ROGERS BROS.–A 1. ⊛," and when Sectionally plated, "**1847**.–ROGERS BROS.–XII. ⊛." These goods will be kept up to the high standard which this trade-mark has for so many years maintained.

Our facilities are of the best, the latest and most improved machinery being used, which, combined with skillful artists of long experience, enable us to produce artistic goods of the highest grade at a moderate price.

Estimates and designs for special or presentation pieces furnished when desired.

By the scale given under each heading the purchaser can determine the correct size of the articles illustrated.

Our long established reputation is in itself a guarantee for all goods manufactured by us.

HIGHEST HONORS

Awarded at all Fairs where we have exhibited, from World's Fair, 1853, to American Institute Fairs, 1873, 1874, and 1875; at the World's International Exhibition at Philadelphia, in 1876, and at New Orleans, 1885.

ADDRESSES.

All communications should be addressed to MERIDEN BRITANNIA CO., MERIDEN, CONN., U. S. A. Cable Address: IVESBIRD, NEW YORK.

DIRECCION.

Todas las comunicaciones deberáu dirijirse á MERIDEN BRITANNIA CO., MERIDEN, CONN., U. S. A. Direccion Telegráfica: IVESBIRD, NEW YORK.

Adressen.

Alle korespondenzen sollen an die Meriden Britannia Co., Meriden, Conn., U. S. A., adressirt sein. Kabl Adresse: Ivesbird, New York.

TELEGRAPHIC CODE.

EXPLANATION.

For convenience and economy in sending telegraphic orders we have adopted a system by which various WORDS represent our goods, and in this Catalogue you will find with each price a single word IN PARENTHESIS to be used as above.

In telegraphing, great care should be taken in the use of the right words, correctly spelled, etc.

By this system telegraph messages will be found very inexpensive. NIGHT messages will reduce the cost.

EXAMPLE:

Express WALK, ABIDE, ABLE, CELLAR, BARQUE, DUKE, ENACT, BUFFO, DEPEND. (Ten Words.)

WOULD READ LITERALLY:

Express one each, Nineteen Hundred Fifty-Eight Tea Set, Satin; No. Forty-Five, Twenty-Six Inch Chased Waiter; Nineteen Hundred Nineteen Urn, Chased; Thirty-One Chased Tilting Set; Seventy-Six Caster, Chased, Five No. Two Bottles; Eighteen Twenty-Two Basket, Chased, Gold Lined; Forty.-Nine Seventy Butter, Chased, Crystal Drainer; Two Hundred Eight Finger Bowl, Satin, Engraved; Fifteen Eleven Fruit Dish, Chased, Gold Lined.

TEN words represent SIXTY-FOUR; a saving of FIFTY-FOUR words.

In ordering FLAT WARE, *each word indicates one dozen* of the pattern it prefixes, in *extra plate.*

No. 9400. Buffalo Hunt.

Old Silver, Gold Inlaid, $325.00 (thyself). Old Silver, $315.00 (threshold).

Size, 15 x 27 inches. Height, 22 inches.

Trade Mark.
WHITE METAL.

GOLD AND SILVER PLATE.

Trade Mark.
NICKEL SILVER.

Prize Yacht.

No. 600. Engraved, ... $150.00 (scale).

(Height, 25 inches.)

ART WORK.

(ONE-THIRD SIZE.)

No. 6500. AURORA.

Old Silver, . . $92.00 (ZYMOTIC).
Gold Inlaid, . . 100.00 (ZOUNDS).

(Height, 25 inches.)

No. 6700. PSYCHE.

Old Silver, . . $87.50 (SAVANT).

(Height, 29 inches.)

No. 6800. HEBE.

Old Silver, . . $87.50 (SAUNTER).

(Height, 29 inches.)

GOLD AND SILVER PLATE.

No. 6600. KING FISHERS.

Old Silver, ... $75.00 (ZOOLOGY).
Old Silver, Gold Inlaid, . 85.00 (ZIGZAG).

(Height, 28 inches.)

No. 6900. CLEOPATRA.

Old Silver, . . $25.00 (YOUNGISH).
Old Silver, Gold Inlaid, 27.50 (YIELDING).

(Height, 16 inches.)

No. 7000. SEMIRAMIS.

Old Silver, . . $25.00 (YARDARM).
Old Silver, Gold Inlaid, 27.50 (WROUGHT).

(Height, 16 inches.)

GOLD AND SILVER PLATE.

No. 9100. HORSE.
Old Silver, $5.00 (SCALD.)
Old Silver, Gold Inlaid, 6.00 (SCAFFOLD).
(Height, 6 inches.)

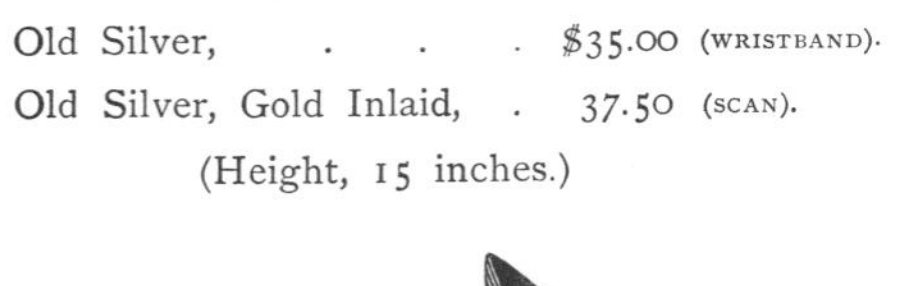

No. 6300. INDIAN SQUAW.
Old Silver, $35.00 (WRISTBAND).
Old Silver, Gold Inlaid, 37.50 (SCAN).
(Height, 15 inches.)

No. 6400. INDIAN CHIEF.
Old Silver, $35.00 (WRITHE).
Old Silver, Gold Inlaid, 37.50 (SCAMPER).
(Height, 16 inches.)

No. 7100. NEPTUNE.
Old Silver, $27.50 (WRITING).
Old Silver, Gold Inlaid, 30.00 (WRAITH).
(Height, 13 inches.)

No. 3100. SETTER DOG.
Old Silver, ... $5.50 (WOODNYMPH).
Old Silver, Gold Inlaid, 6.50 (SCARCE).
(Height, 3½ inches.)

No. 3150. BICYCLE.
Old Silver, . . . $12.00 (WORTHILY).
Old Silver, Gold Inlaid, . 13.50 (WORSHIP).
(Height, 7 inches.)

No. 3160. DOG AND BIRD.
Old Silver, . . . $5.00 (WORMWOOD).
Old Silver, Gold Inlaid, 6.00 (WORKBOX).
(Height, 5 inches.)

No. 6000. MARS.
Old Silver, ... $37.50 (WOODSCREW).
Old Silver, Gold Inlaid, . 40.00 (SCALPEL).
(Height, 16 inches.)

No. 6200. APOLLO.
Old Silver, . . $22.50 (SCALP).
(Height, 13 inches.)

No. 7200. AMPHITRITE.
Old Silver, ... $27.50 (WORKBAG).
Old Silver, Gold Inlaid, . 30.00 (WOOLSACK).
(Height, 15 inches.)

GOLD AND SILVER PLATE.

No. 3110. Wolf and Grouse.
Old Silver, ... $6.50 (scope).
Old Silver, Gold Inlaid, . 8.00 (witticism).
(Height, 4½ inches.)

No. 9500. Defeat.
Old Silver, . . . $12.00 (woodchuck).
Old Silver, Gold Inlaid, 13.50 (wonderful).
(Height, 10 inches.)

No. 3140. Buffalo.
Old Silver, ... $5.50 (scapula).
Old Silver, Gold Inlaid, . 6.50 (withy).
(Height, 4½ inches.)

No. 9600. Victory.
Old Silver, . . . $12.00 (wolverine).
Old Silver, Gold Inlaid, 13.50 (wizen).
(Height, 10 inches.)

No. 3130. Quail.
Old Silver, ... $8.00 (scandal).
Old Silver, Gold Inlaid, . 9.00 (withdraw.)
(Height, 7½ inches.)

No. 9200. Buffalo Hunt.
Old Silver, ... $23.50 (scabbard).
Old Silver, Gold Inlaid, . 25.00 (wistfully).
(Height, 9½ inches.)

TRADE MARK.
WHITE METAL.

TRADE MARK.
NICKEL SILVER.

VASES.

(HALF SIZE.)

No. 393.
Old Silver, . . . $14.00 (WITHSTAND).
Russian Gold Inlaid, . 20.00 (LEDGE).

No. 394.
Old Silver, . . . $18.00 (WITHOLD).
Russian Gold Inlaid, . 25.00 (LECTURE).

No. 395.
Old Silver, . . . $21.00 (WITCHING).
Russian Gold Inlaid, . 28.00 (LEEWARD).

No. 433. VINTAGE VASE.

Old Silver, . . . $35.00 (WISEACRE).
Old Silver, Gold Inlaid, . 40.00 (WIRINESS).

No. 396.
Old Silver, . . . $21.00 (WINGLESS).
Russian Gold Inlaid, . 28.00 (WINEPRESS).

No. 398.
Old Silver, . . . $32.50 (WINDAGE).
Russian Gold Inlaid, . 42.50 (LEEK).

PUNCH BOWLS.

(One-Third Size.)

No. 4. Capacity, 3 Gallons.
Engraved, Gold Lined, . $60.00 (outlay).

No. 5. Capacity, 2½ Gallons.
Engraved, Gold Inlaid and Gold Lined, . $115.00 (outfit).

No. 01. Capacity, 3 Gallons. Height, 30 inches.
Nickel Silver, Silver Soldered,
Repouseé and Engraved, Silver and Gold Inlaid.
Bowl, Gold Lined Complete, With Ladle, . $1,050.00. (volunteer).
(One-Fifth Size.)

No. 8. MOORISH GOLD INLAID PUNCH SET.

		Moorish, Gold Inlaid		Moorish, Old Silver.	
Nine Pieces complete,	-	$200.00	(TESTIMONY).	$161.50	(TEXT).
Bowl Separately,	- -	110.00	(TESTY).	95.00	(TEXTILE).

No. 22. XX GOLD INLAID BAR FENDER.

XX Gold Inlaid, $290.00 (THANE). Gold Lined, $265.00 (THANKFUL).

Trade Mark.
WHITE METAL.

GOLD AND SILVER PLATE.

Trade Mark.
NICKEL SILVER.

No. 6. Punch Bowl and Wine Cooler Combined.

Engraved, Gold Inlaid and Gold Lined, ... $275.00 (ottoman).

Capacity, 4 Gallons.

The above design may be used either for a Wine Cooler (to contain two quart and four pint bottles) or, when detached, for a Punch Bowl.

The article when complete, having a double wall, preserves the ice around the sockets containing the bottles (the ice being packed by removing the cover), or when desired, the whole interior construction may be removed, leaving the Gold Lined Punch Bowl ready for use, and protected from wear by the inner wall.

Other styles of ornamentation will be furnished if desired.

GOLD AND SILVER PLATE.

No. 1 Repousse. Capacity, 1½ Gallons.
Six Gold Lined Goblets, Complete, . . $96.00 (outlet).

No. 3. Punch Ladle.
Silver, Gold Inlaid and
Gold-Lined, . $20.00 (outgo).

No. 3. Punch Bowl. Capacity, 4 Gallons.
Engraved, Silver, Gold Inlaid and Gold Lined, . . $150.00 (outlast).

GOLD AND SILVER PLATE.

(ONE-THIRD SIZE.)

BAR SUGAR.

No. 10, . . $9.00 (PEDANT).

BAR SUGAR.

No. 7. Ten Half Pints, . $15.25 (PACIFIC).
No. 6. Fourteen Half Pints, 18.00 (PACKAGE).

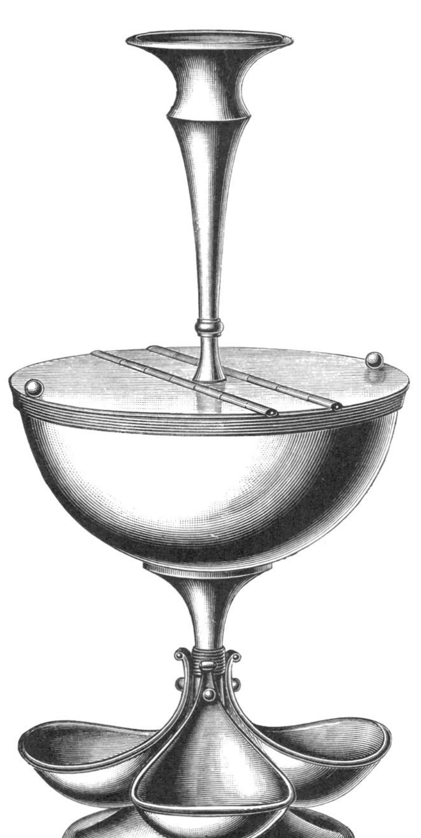

No. 9. BAR SUGAR.

Vase and Spice Cups, Gold Lined.
Plain, Ten Half Pints, $25.00 (PAGAN).

PATENT BEER PITCHER.

No. 100. Thirteen Half Pints, . $10.00 (OUTSET).

PATENT BEER PITCHER.

No. 50. Eleven Half Pints, . $10.00 (OUTSKIRT).

ICE TUBS.

(One-Third Size.)

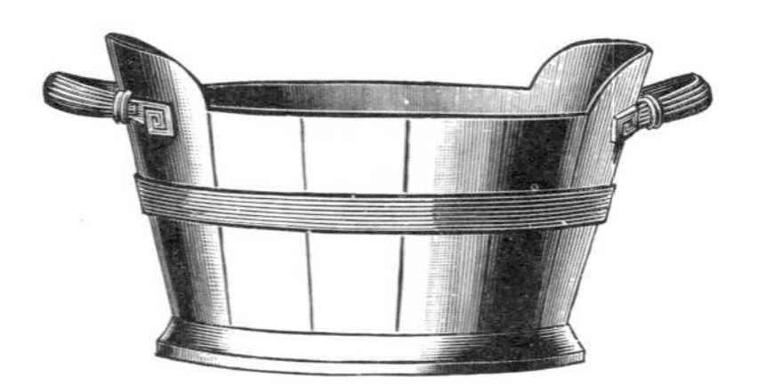

Ice Tub.

No. 21, ... $8.00 (paddock).
No. 20, with Bail (see No. 23), 7.50 (page).

Ice Tub.

No. 23, ... $15.00 (pageant).
No. 24, with Handles (see No. 21), 16.00 (pagoda).

No. 5. Ice Tub.

Plain, . . . $6.75 (packet).
Satin, . . . 6.75 (paddle).

No. 29.

Silver, . . . $7.50 (wintergreen)

No. 28.

Silver, . . . $9.00 (windfall).
Old Silver, . . 10.00 (whoop).
XX Old Silver, . 13.00 (wimble).
Gold Lined, $2.00 Extra.

No. 30.

Silver, . . . $8.50 (windrow).

No. 3. Ice Tub.

Plain, . . . $16.50 (padlock).

No. 27.

Silver, . . . $9.50 (willowy).
Old Silver, . . 11.00 (wildfire).
XX Old Silver, . 14.50 (wholesome).
Gold Lined, $2.00 Extra.

TRADE MARK.
WHITE METAL

WINE COOLERS.

TRADE MARK.
NICKEL SILVER.

(ONE-THIRD SIZE.)

No. 8.

Satin C, ... $15.00 (WHERRY).
Satin C, Old Silver, . . 17.50 (WHEREVER).
Satin C, XX Gold Inlaid, . 24.00 (WHERETO).

No. 6.

Engraved, . $16.50 (OUTWEIGH).

No. 2.

Plain, . . . $12.50 (OUTRUN).
Satin Shield, . . 12.50 (OUTSIDE).

No. 1.

Same as No. 2, only Plain Ring Handles.
Plain, . . . $11.00 (OUTSPREAD).

No. 10.

Chased, ... $27.50 (WHITENESS).
Moorish, Old Silver, . 30.50 (WHITEBAIT).
Moorish, Gold Inlaid, . 35.00 (WHIRLBONE).

No. 9.

Same as No. 10, Without Inside Lining.
Chased, ... $18.00 (WHIPSTOCK).
Moorish, Old Silver, . 21.00 (WHIPSAW).
Moorish, Gold Inlaid, . 25.50 (WHIPCORD).

No. 11.

Satin, . . . $15.00 (WHIFFLE).
Satin, Engraved, . 17.00 (WHETHER).

No. 5.

Plain, . . $16.75 (OUTPOST).

BOTTLE HOLDERS.

(ONE THIRD SIZE.)

No. 5. CLARET.

Satin C, . . .	$13.50	(WHEREON).
Satin C, Old Silver,	15.00	(WHEREOF).
Satin, XX Gold Inlaid,	18.50	(WHEREIN).

(For Quart Bottle.)

No. 20. SYPHON BOTTLE HOLDER AND CAP.

	HOLDER.	CAP.	
Moorish, Old Silver, .	$6.75	6.75	(WHALEMAN).
Moorish, Gold Inlaid, .	8.50	8.50	(WHALEBONE).

(Prices do NOT include Glass Bottle.)

No. 4.

Silver, ...	$13.50	(OVEN).
Old Silver, . .	15.00	(OVERDUE).
XX Gold Inlaid, .	18.50	(OVERSEE).

(For Quart Bottle.)

No. 1. BOTTLE HOLDER (CLOSED).

Plain, ...	$12.50	(OUTLOOK).
Hammered, . .	14.00	(WHEREAS).
Hammered, Old Silver,	15.00	(WHACK).

(For Quart Bottle.)

No. 1. SATIN ENGRAVED.

Satin Engraved, .	$14.50	(WHEELING).
Moorish, Old Silver,	16.00	(WHEATEN).
Moorish Gold, . .	20.00	(WHARFAGE).

No. 2. BOTTLE HOLDER (OPEN).

Plain, ...	$8.50	(OUTLINE).
Hammered, . .	9.25	(WHALER).
Hammered, Old Silver,	10.00	(WHELK).

(For Pint Bottle.)

Wine taken from the ice and placed in these felt lined Bottle Holders will retain its temperature, and the Cases present an elegant appearance.

Trade Mark.
WHITE METAL.

GOLD AND SILVER PLATE.

Trade Mark.
NICKEL SILVER.

No. 17. Bottle Waiter.

Single Plate. Quadruple Plate.
Satin, . $1.25 (whether). $1.75 (westward).
(Nos. 17 and 18 Half Size.)

No. 18. Bottle Waiter.

Single Plate. Quadruple Plate.
Satin, . $1.50 (wellbred). $2.00 (welcomer).
Hammered, 1.75 (weighty). 2.25 (weigher).

No. 16. Bottle Waiter.

Single Plate.
Per dozen, . . $5.25 (weird).
(One-Third Size.)

Ginger Ale or Soda Bottle Holder.
No. 7, . $3.75 (pease).
(Half Size.)

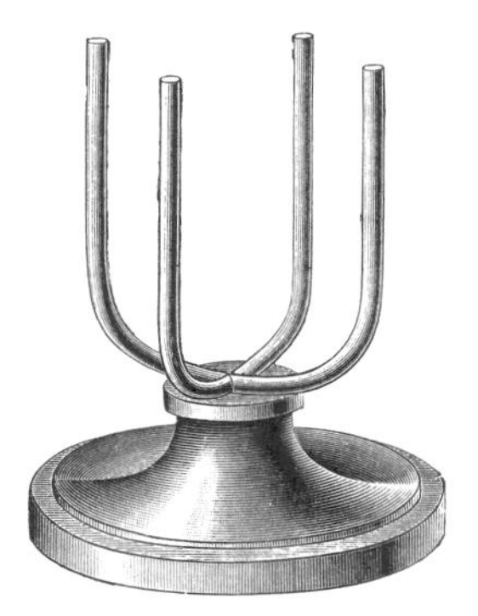

Ginger Ale Bottle Holder.
No. 13. Satin, . $2.00 (water).
(Half Size.)

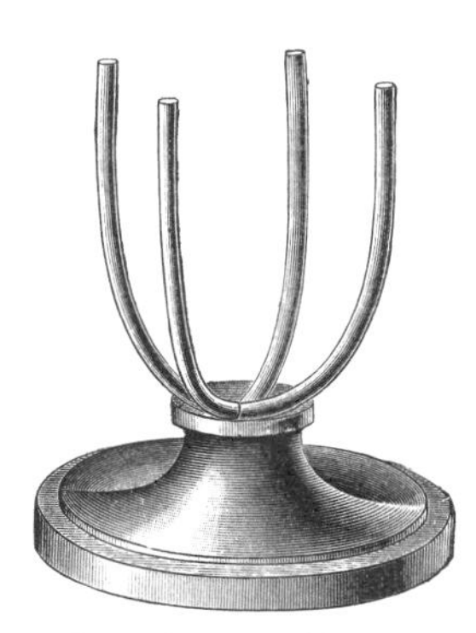

Soda Bottle Holder.
No. 14. Satin, . $2.00 (wavelet).
(Half Size.)

Bottle Holder.
No. 11. Reversible, . $4.25 (pebble).
(One-Third Size.)

Bottle Holder.
No. 05. Nickel Silver, Wood Bottom, . $8.00 (pecan).
(Half Size.)

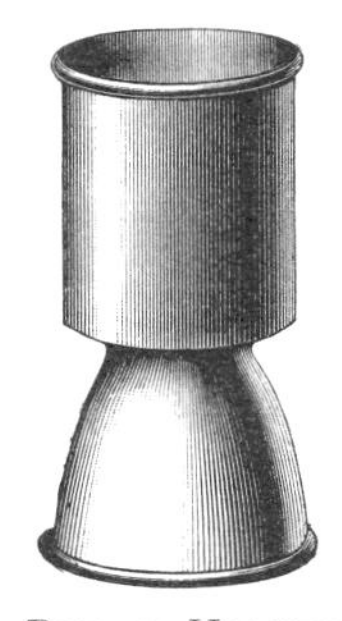

Bottle Holder.
No. 06. Nickel Silver, Reversible, . $7.50 (peculiar).
(One-Third Size.)

Burgundy Wine Basket.

No. 11½. For Pint Bottles. No. 9. For Quart Bottles.
Satin, . $12.50 (weed). $16.50 (waxwork).
(One-Third Size).

Bottle Holder.
No. 07. Nickel Silver, . $6.00 (weekly).
(Half Size.)

No. 15. Lager Beer Plate.
Single Plate.
Per Dozen, . $7.50 (pattern).
(Half Size.)

Burgundy Wine Basket.

	No. 12. For Pint Bottles.	No. 10. For Quart Bottles.
Plain, . . .	$11.00 (webbing).	$15.00 (wealthy).
Hammered, . .	12.50 (weasand).	17.00 (wayward).
Moorish Old Silver,	15.00 (wearer).	21.50 (waybill).
Moorish Gold Inlaid,	19.00 (weapon).	27.00 (weaker).

(One-Third Size.)

ALE MUGS, SODA HOLDERS, ETC.

No. 130. One-Half Pint.
Plain, . . . $2.75 (parrot).
With Glass Bottom, 3.25 (wadding).
(One-Third Size.)

No. 131. One Pint.
Plain, . . . $4.00 (parquet).
With Glass Bottom, 4.50 (waffle).
(One-Third Size.)

No. 54.
Plain, . $2.50 (parole).
(One-Third Size.)

No. 1.
Plain, . . $2.25 (peach).
Engine, . 2.75 (peak).
(Half Size.)

No. 55.
Plain, ... $3.00 (voucher).
Hammered, . . . 3.50 (voter).
Hammered, Gold Lined, 4.25 (vortical).
No. 57. One Size Smaller, 25c. Less.

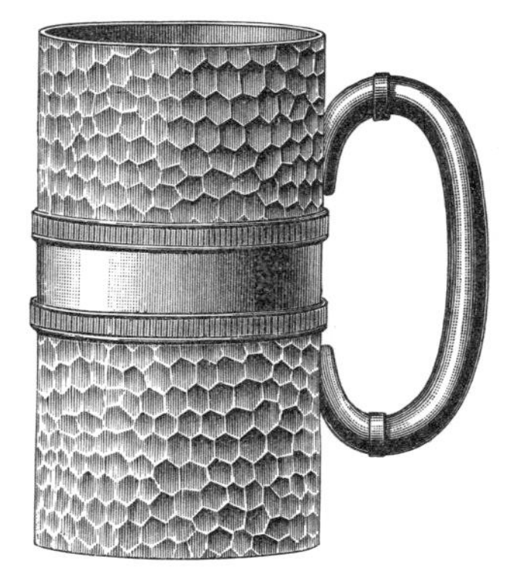

No. 56.
Hammered, . . . $4.00 (votive).
Hammered, Gold Lined, 4.75 (vouch).
(Half Size.)

No. 9, . $2.00 (peat).
(Half Size.)

No. 2. Medallion, . $2.00 (pavilion).
No. 02. Nickel Silver, 4.50 (pawn).
(Half Size.)

No. 6, . . $1.50 (pearl).
(Half Size.)

No. 8, . . $2.00 (peasant).
(Half Size.)

No. 20, . Sugar Sifter.
Plain, . $3.25 (patrol).
Engraved, 3.75 (patron).
(Half Size.)

No. 21. Sugar Sifter.
Silver, ... $4.25 (patty).
Silver, Gold Inlaid, . 5.00 (pave).
(Half Size.)

Sugar Sifter.
No. 22, . $4.75. (paving).
(Half Size.)

WHITE METAL.

GOLD AND SILVER PLATE.

NICKEL SILVER.

No. 4. Spice Dish.
Gold Lined, . . $12.00 (PASTIME).

Liquor Mixer.
No. 4. Two Half Pints, . $2.25 (PARSLEY).
No. 3. Three Half Pints, . 2.50 (PARSNIP).

No. 5. Spice Dish.
Gold Lined, . . $12.50 (PASTURE).

Punch Mug.
No. 10, . $3.50 (PASSPORT).

No. 1. Wine Thimble.
Silver, . . $1.25 (WAIF).
Gold Lined, . 1.50 (PASTRY).

Jigger.
No. 2. White Metal, . $1.25 (PASSWORD).
No. 01. Nickel Silver, . 3.50 (PASTE).

Punch Mug.
No. 12, . $3.25 (PASTERN).

Liquor Mixer.
Nickel Silver, Silver Soldered.
No. 04½. Three Gills, . $2.75 (PARTNER).
No. 03½. Four Gills, . 3.25 (PARTRIDGE).
No. 02½. Five Gills, . 3.50 (PASHA).
No. 01½. Seven Gills, . 4.00 (PASSIVE).
No. 06½. Seven Gills, . 4.50 (WAIST).
No. 07½. Eight Gills, . 5.25 (WAISTCOAT)

No. 01. Funnel.
Nickel Silver, Silver Soldered.
One Half Pint, . . $4.25 (SALUTE).
Two Half Pints, . . 5.00 (SAVAGE).
Three Half Pints, . . 6.00 (SALVE).
Four Half Pints, . . 6.75 (SALVO).

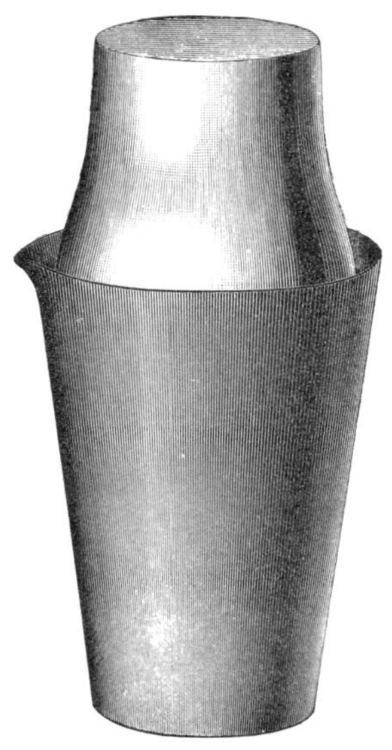

Liquor Mixer, complete.
Nickel Silver, Silver Soldered.
No. 08. Three Gills, . $5.00 (PARTAKE).
No. 09. Five Gills, . 7.75 (PARTIAL).
No. 010. Eight Gills, . 10.50 (PARTICLE).
No. 011. Twelve Gills, . 13.50 (PATISAN).
Capacity given of lower part only.

Trade Mark.
WHITE METAL.

BITTER TUBES.

Trade Mark.
NICKEL SILVER.

(Full Size.)

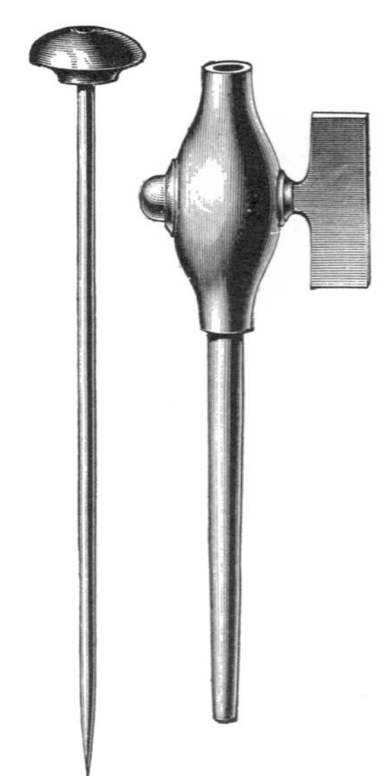

No. 1. Champagne Faucet.

Nickel Plated.

Per Dozen, . $13.50 (rapidity).

No. 1.
Per dozen, . $2.00 (parish).

No. 3.
Per dozen, . $2.50 (parch).

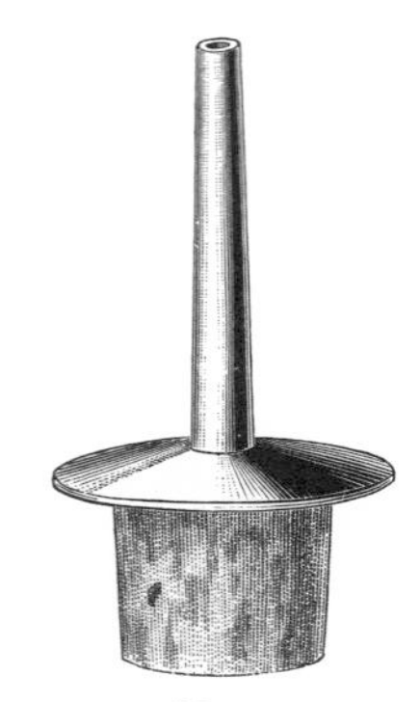

No. 2.
Per dozen, . $3.00 (pardon).

BAR STRAINERS.

(One-Third Size.)

No. 9, . . $2.00 (waterproof).

No. 6, . $3.25. (parody).

No. 4.
Metal Handle, . . . $3.00 (park).
No. 040. Nickel Silver, . 5.00 (waterline).

No. 8, . . $3.75 (parley).

Nickel Silver, Silver Soldered.
No. 0100, . $4.75 (watercure).

Nickel Silver, Silver Soldered.
No. 070. Walrus Ivory Handle, . $5.00 (parlance).

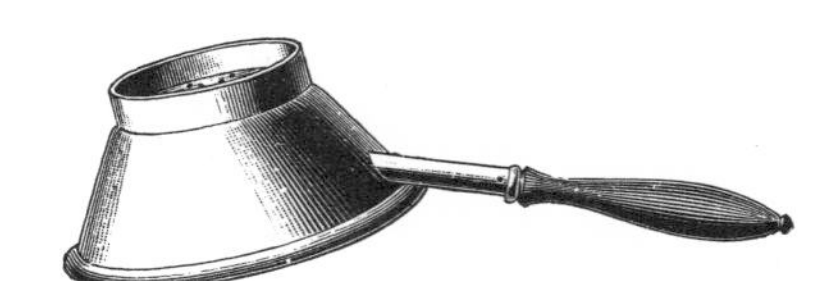

Nickel Silver, Silver Soldered.
No. 050. Ebony Handle, . $4.50 (parlor).

Nickel Silver, Silver Soldered.
No. 060, . $5.50 (watermark).

GOLD AND SILVER PLATE.

No. 50. Cork Screw.
Hammered Old Silver, $3.50 (volition).
(Half Size.)

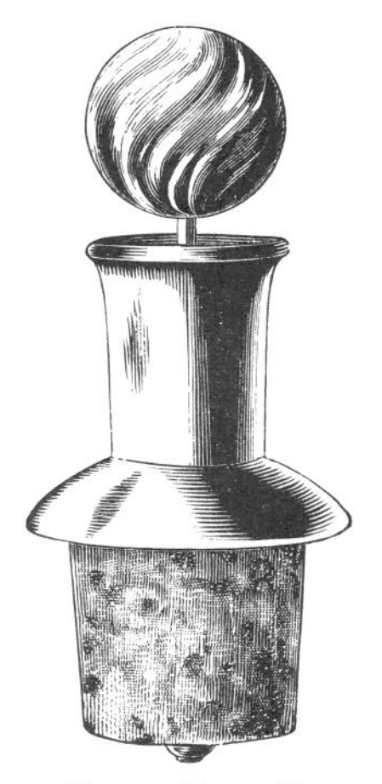

No. 1. Glass Ball Stopple.
Per dozen, . $4.50 (panacea).
(Full Size.)

No. 2. Glass Ball Stopple.
Per dozen, . $4.50 (pamphlet).
(Full Size.)

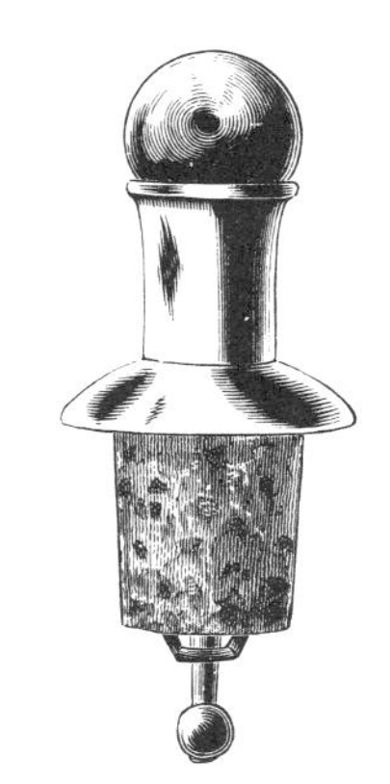

No. 3. Glass Ball Stopple.
Per dozen, . $4.50 panel).
(Full Size.)

HAVILAND'S PATENT STOPPLES.

(Full Size.)

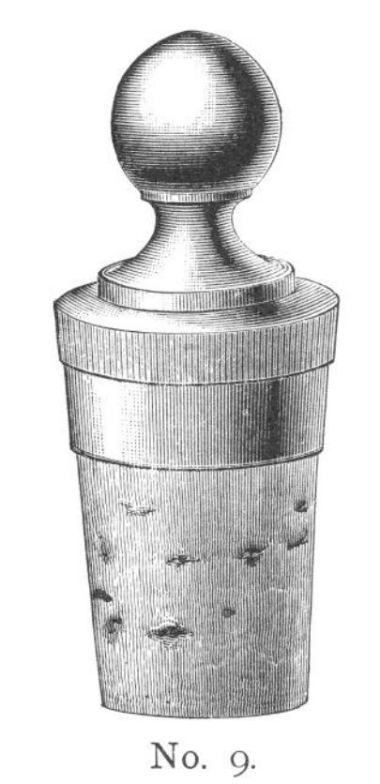

No. 9.
Per doz., $10.50 (transition).

No. 1.
Per doz., $5.00 (panic).

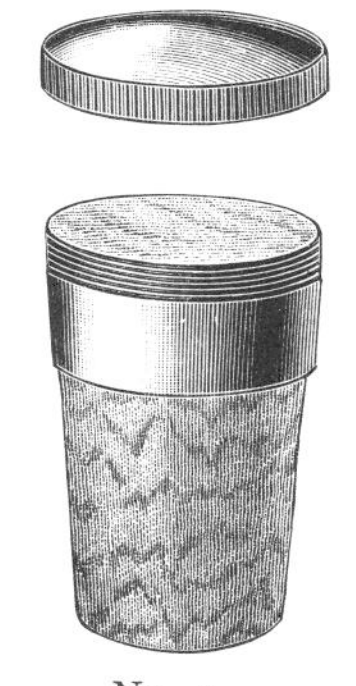

No. 5.
Per doz., $4.00 (pannier).

No. 6.
Per doz., $3.00 (panoply).

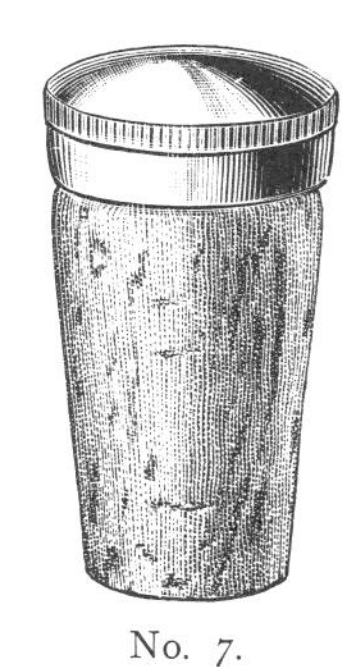

No. 7.
Per doz., $2.00 (pansy).

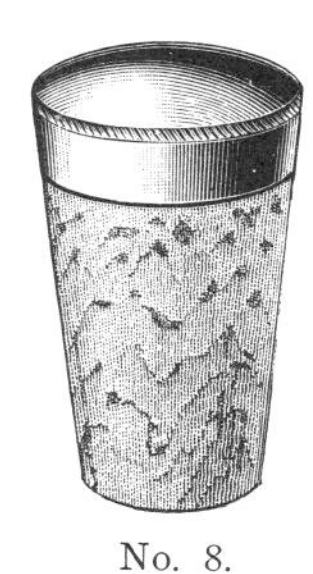

No. 8.
Per doz., $1.50 (panther).

No. 11. Shield.
Per doz., $10.50 (tranship).

No. 5. Thistle.
Per doz., $13.00 (pantry).

No. 13.
Per doz., $12.00 (transform).

No. 12. Ring.
Per doz., $12.00 (transact).

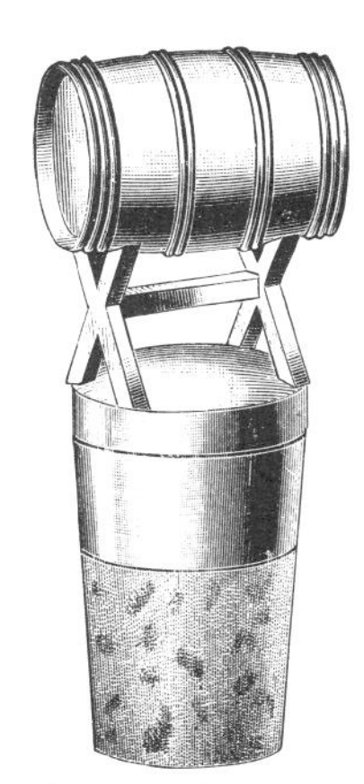

No. 6. Barrel.
Per doz., $14.00 (paragon).

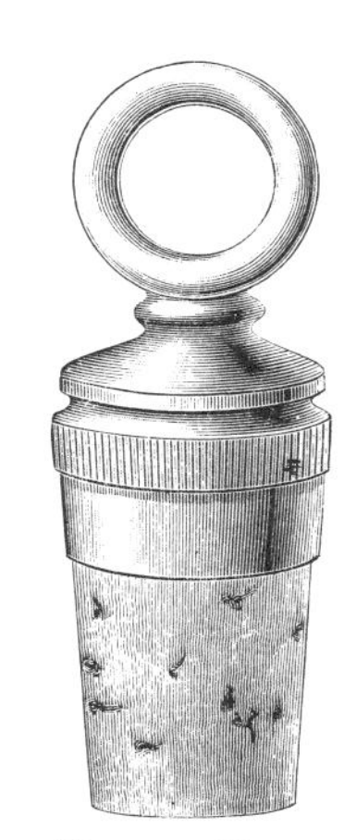

No. 10. Ring.
Per doz., $10.50 (traction).

BISCUIT JARS.

(ONE-THIRD SIZE.)

No. 7, . $9.00 (PERFORM).

No. 33. Crystal, . $6.00 (WATERCART).

No. 29, . $11.50 (PERVADE).

No. 30, . $12.00 (PETAL).

No. 34. Porcelain, . $13.50 (WATCHMAN).

No. 32, . $13.50 (PESTLE).

No. 26, . $13.50 (PERMIT).

No. 27, . $13.50 (PERIL).

No. 21. Three Half Pints, . $6.00 (PERCH).
No. 20. Seven Half Pints, . 8.00 (PERCHANCE).
No. 19. Eleven Half Pints, . 10.00 (PERCOLATE).

GOLD AND SILVER PLATE.

No. 37, . . $12.00 (WHATEVER).
Rose and Gold Decoration.

No. 39, . . $13.50 (WHIMSICAL).

No. 36, . . $10.50 (WELLBEING).

No. 38, . . $13.50 (WELL-BORN).
Rose and Gold Decoration.

No. 31, . . $7.50 (WHILOM).

No. 35, . . $13.50 (WEARINESS).

Trade Mark.
WHITE METAL.

GOLD AND SILVER PLATE.

Trade Mark.
NICKEL SILVER.

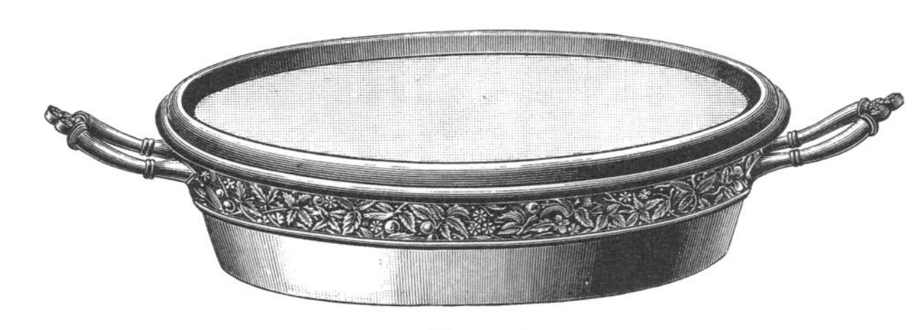

No. 118.
9 inch, Seven Half Pints, . $7.50 (YOKEMATE).

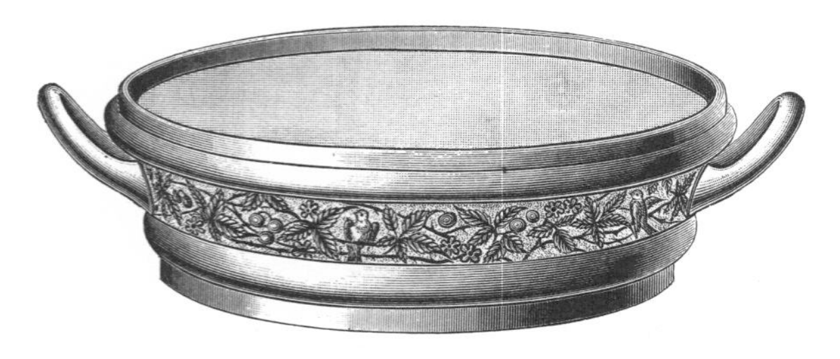

No. 121.
9 inch, Seven Half Pints, . . $9.25 (YEOMANRY).
9 inch, Seven Half Pints, Old Silver, 10.25 (VEHICULAR).

No. 119
8 inch, Seven Half Pints, . $8.25 (WORSHIPER).

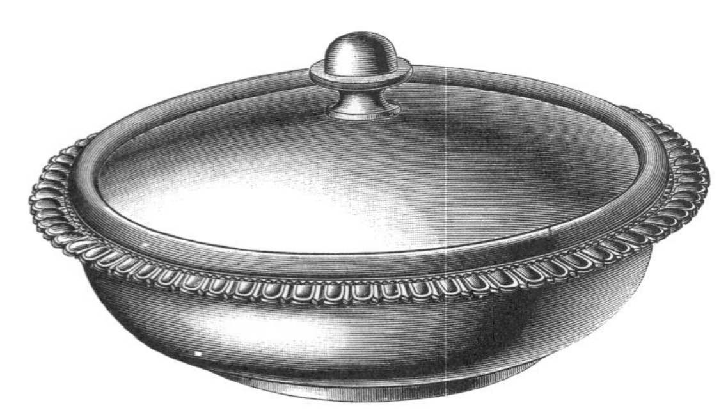

No. 114.
Plain, 9 inch, Seven Half Pints, . $15.00 (WORLDLING).
Chased, 9 inch, Seven Half Pints. . 16.50 (WOOL-PACK).

No. 115.
Embossed, 9 inch, Seven Half Pints, . . $17.00 (WORKABLE).
Embossed, Old Silver, 9 inch, Seven Half Pints, 18.50 (WOOD-CRAFT).

No. 122.
Plain, 9 inch, Seven Half Pints, . $14.00 (WOMANISH).
Chased, 9 inch, Seven Half Pints, . 15.50 (WHIRLWIND).

No. 117.
9½ inch, Eight Half Pints, . . $16.00 (WITTINGLY).
9½ inch, Eight Half Pints, Old Silver, 17.00 (WHIRLPOOL).

TRADE MARK.
WHITE METAL.

BAKING DISHES.

TRADE MARK.
NICKEL SILVER.

PORCELAIN LINED, WITH PLATED RECEPTACLE.

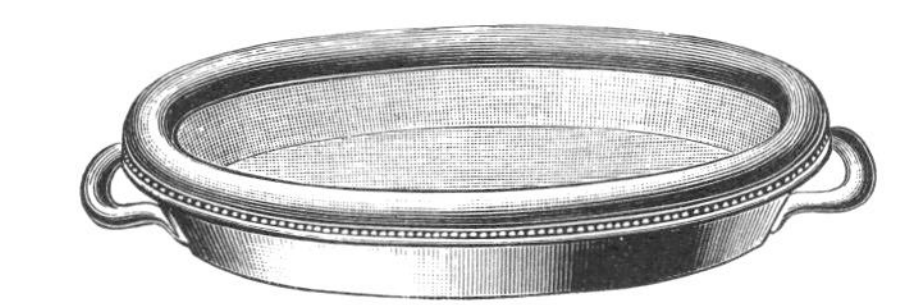

EGG DISH.

No. 3. 6 inch, ... $3.00 (MEMOIR).
No. 2. 7 inch, ... 3.25 (MEMENTO.)

PIE DISH.

No. 2, 10 inch, ... $6.00 (MEMBRANE).

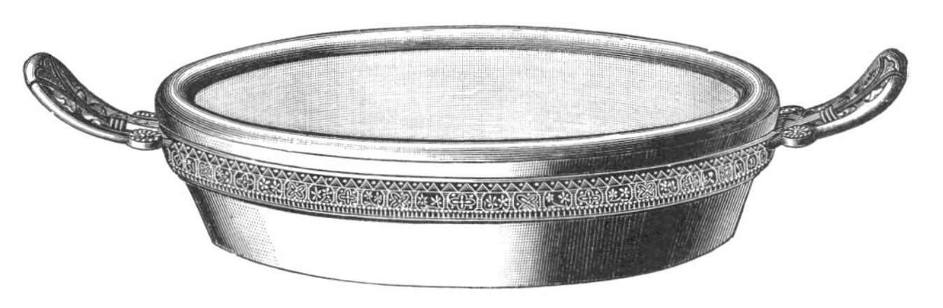

No. 84½. 9 inch, Six Half Pints, . $7.50 (METAPHOR).
No. 84. 9½ inch, Eight Half Pints, . 8.00 (MESSAGE).

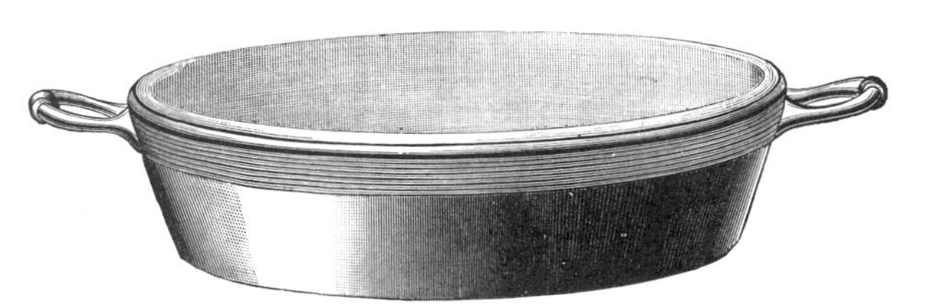

No. 81½. 9 inch, Six Half Pints, . $6.75 (MEMORY).
No. 81. 9½ inch, Eight Half Pints, . 7.50 (MENACE).

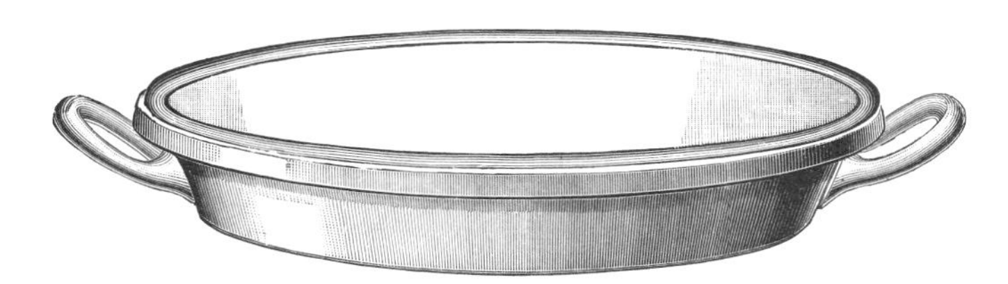

No. 113. Oval, 10 inch, Six Half Pints, . $10.50 (WARLIKE).

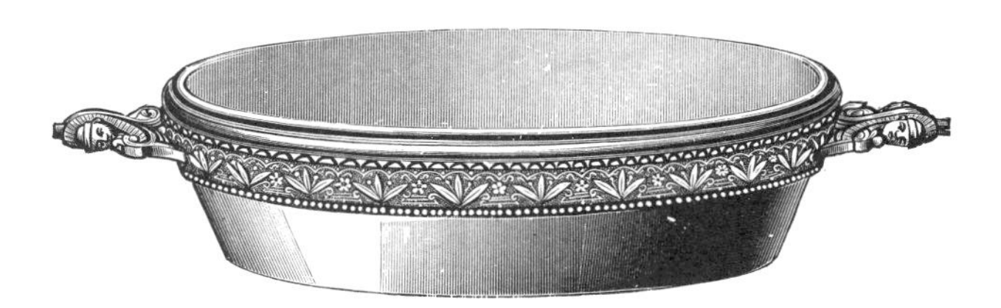

No. 82½. 9 inch, Six Half Pints, . $6.75 (MEND).
No. 82. 9½ inch, Eight Half Pints, . 7.50 (MENTAL).

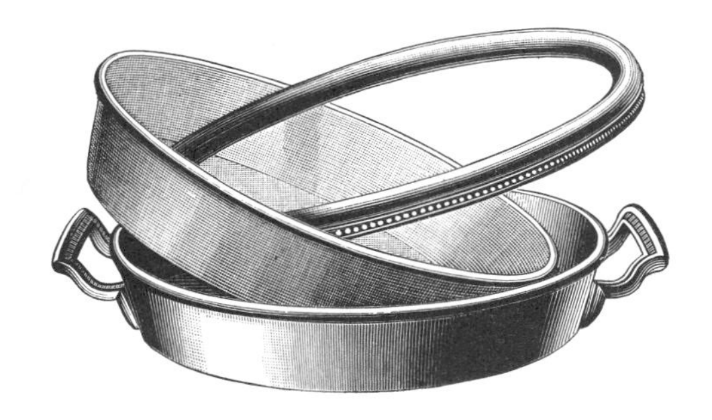

Above Cut shows the different parts of a Baking Dish.

No. 24. 7 inch, Five Half Pints, . $7.25 (MERCER).
No. 3. 8 inch, Five Half Pints, . 7.50 (MENTION).
*No. 23. 8 inch, Eight Half Pints, . 8.00 (MERCHANT).
No. 22. 9 inch, Ten Half Pints, . 8.50 (MERCURY).
No. 21. 10 inch, Thirteen Half Pints, 10.00 (MERCY)
No. 20. 11 inch, Eighteen Half Pints, 11.50 (MERGE).
*No. 23 Dish is same diameter as No. 3 but deeper.

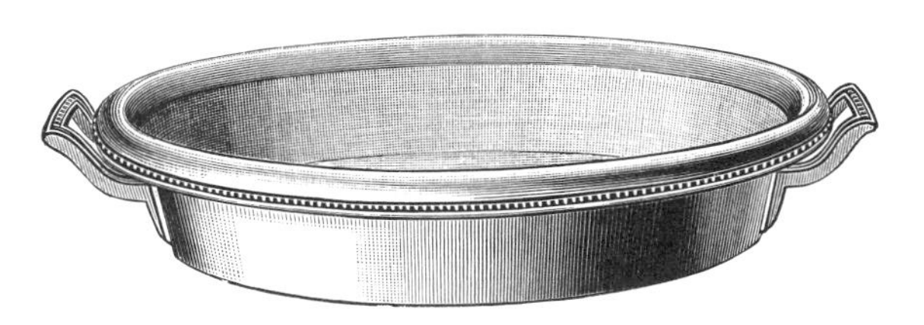

No. 2½. ROUND.

No. 2½. 9 inch, Eight Half Pints, . . $8.25 (MERINO).
No. 2. 9½ inch, Nine Half Pints, . . 9.00 (MERIT).
No. 1. 12 inch, Fourteen Half Pints, . 10.50 (MERMAID).

ABOVE STYLE IN OVAL.

No. 12. 10 inch, Six Half Pints, . . $10.50 (WASHING).
No. 11. 12 inch, Eight Half Pints, . 11.25 (WARWHOOP).
No. 10. 14 inch, Ten Half Pints, . 12.00 (WARRANT).

GOLD AND SILVER PLATE.

MERIDEN B COMPANY
Trade Mark.
NICKEL SILVER.

No. 33.

Plain, 8 inch, Five Half Pints, . . . $11.25 (meteor).
Chased, 8 inch, Five Half Pints, . . . 14.00 (method).

No/76.

Plain, 9 inch, Six Half Pints, . . . $15.00 (midway).

No. 87. Oval.

Plain, 8½ inch, Four Half Pints, . . . $13.50 (mislay).

No. 90. Hammered and Applied, X X Gilt.

9 inch, Six Half Pints.

Plain, ... $16.00 (minared).
Hammered, ... 18.50 (mode).
Hammered and Applied, ... 21.00 (model).
Hammered and Applied, X X Gilt, . . . 23.50 (moderate).

No. 32.

Plain, 9½ inch, Eight Half Pints, ... $12.00 (metre).
Chased, 9½ inch, Eight Half Pints, . . . 15.00 (metrical).

No. 32½.

No. 33½. 8 inch, Five Half Pints, . . $12.50 (mobile).
No. 32½. 9½ inch, Eight Half Pints, . . 13.50 (mock).

GOLD AND SILVER PLATE.

		Plain.	Hammered.
No. 103.	Six Half Pints,	$12.00 (NORSE).	$14.50 (NORTH).
No. 104.	Seven Half Pints,	14.00 (NORTHERN).	17.00 (NOSEGAY).
No. 105.	Nine Half Pints,	16.00 (NOSTRUM).	19.50 (NOTABLE).

		Plain.	Hammered.
No. 96.	Five Half Pints,	$11.50 (NOTARY).	$13.00 (NOTCH).
No. 97.	Six Half Pints,	12.00 (NOTE).	14.00 (NOTED).
No. 94.	Seven Half Pints,	13.50 (NOTICE).	15.50 (NOTIONAL).
No. 95.	Eleven Half Pints,	16.50 (NOURISH).	19.00 (NOVEL).

OVAL.

	Plain.	Chased.
No. 86. 8½ inch, Four Half Pints,	$12.00 (MIRTH).	$13.00 (MISDATE).

OVAL.

	Plain.	Hammered.
No. 101. 10 inch, Six Half Pints,	$14.00 (NORMAN).	$16.50 (WANDERER).

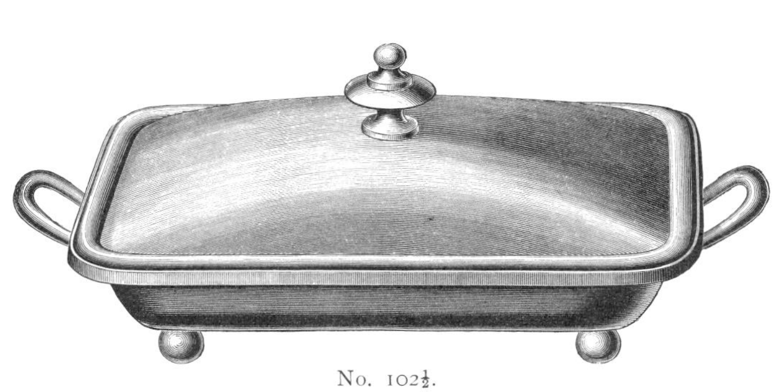

No. 102½.

	Plain.	Hammered.
Seven Half Pints,	$20.00 (NOVELTY).	$23.00 (NOVICE).

No. 102. Same as above, only with foot like No. 100.

Seven Half Pints,	$20.00 (WANTING).	$23.00 (WARHORSE).

No. 80. OVAL.

Plain, 12 inch, Seven Half Pints, ... $17.50 (MISSAL).

No. 83. Same as No. 80, without Border.

Chased, ... $18.00 (MISSION).

No. 100.

Silver, Five Half Pints, ... $21.00 (NUDGE).

X Gold Inland, Five Half Pints, . . . 24.00 (NUGGET).

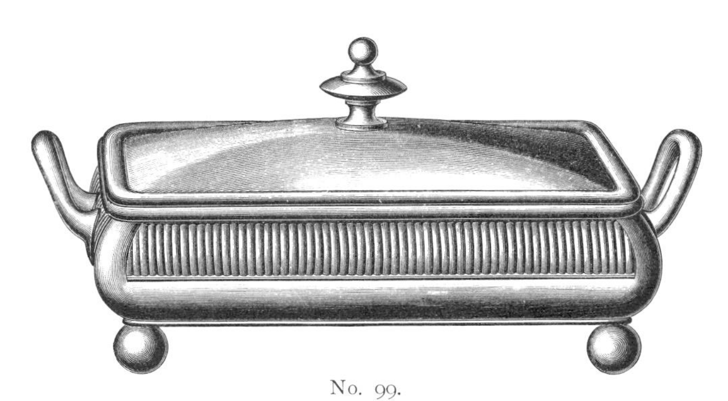

No. 99.

Plain, Five Half Pints, ... $20.00 (NULLIFY).

GOLD AND SILVER PLATE.

No. 109. Plain, 8 inch, Six Half Pints, . . $13.50 (WARFARE).
No. 109. Hammered, 8 inch, Six Half Pints, . 14.50 (WAREHOUSE).
No. 110. Plain, 9 inch, Seven Half Pints, . 15.00 (WALLET).
No. 110. Hammered, 9 inch, Seven Half Pints, 16.50 (WALKER).

No. 111. Plain, 8 inch, Six Half Pints, . . $13.50 (WARDROBE).
No. 111. Hammered, 8 inch, Six Half Pints, . 14.50 (WARDSHIP).
No. 112. Plain, 9 inch, Seven Half Pints, . 15.00 (WAKEFUL).
No. 112. Hammered, 9 inch, Seven Half Pints, 16.50 (WAISTBAND).

No. 98.

Silver, Seven Half Pints, ... $16.50 (NOVIATE).
Old Silver, Seven Half Pints, ... 18.00 (NOWISE).
XX Gold Inlaid, Seven Half Pints, . . . 23.50 (NOZZLE).

No. 85.

Plain, 9 inch, Six Half Pints, ... $16.00 (MIGRATE).
Chased, 9 inch, Six Half Pints, . . . 17.50 (MILCH).

No. 0200.

Nickel Silver, Silver Soldered.

8 inch, Five Half Pints, ... $36.00 (WAGONER).

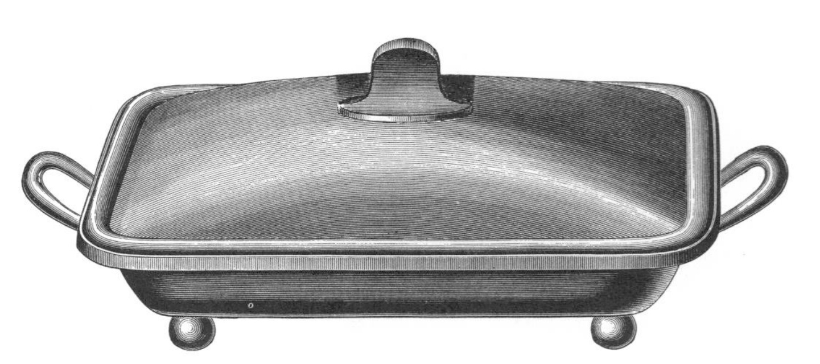

No. 0210.

Nickel Silver, Silver Soldered.

11 inch, Seven Half Pints, ... $54.00 (WAFTAGE).

GOLD AND SILVER PLATE.

No. 123.

Plain, 9 inch, Seven Half Pints, . $14.50 (TRANSLATOR).

No. 124.

Embossed, 9 inch, Seven Half Pints, . . . $16.00 (TURBULENT).

Embossed, Old Silver, 9 inch, Seven Half Pints, . 17.50 (TUNEFUL).

No. 120.

Satin, $8\frac{3}{4}$ inch, Seven Half Pints, . . . $15.50 (TURGENT).

Satin, Engraved, $8\frac{3}{4}$ inch, Seven Half Pints, . 18.00 (TUMID).

No. 116. Oval.

Plain, 11 inch, Eight Half Pints, . $17.50 (UNHURT).

Quilted, 11 inch, Eight Half Pints, . 19.00 (UNITEDLY).

CAKE BASKETS.

No. 1912.

Plain, ... $7.00 (URGENTLY).

Chased, ... 8.00 (UPHOLD).

Chased, Gold Lined, . 10.00 (UNLATCH).

No. 1913.

Satin, ... $7.50 (UPSTART).

Satin, Chased, ... 8.50 (UPHILL).

Satin, Chased, Gold Lined, . 10.50 (UTTERLY).

WHITE METAL.

GOLD AND SILVER PLATE.

NICKEL SILVER.

No. 1915.

Satin, Old Silver, . . . $10.00 (WALLEYE).
Satin, Old Silver, Gold Lined, 12.00 (TIMEPIECE).

No. 1914.

Satin, Old Silver, . . . $9.50 (TIMIDITY).
Satin, Engraved, Old Silver, 10.50 (TOGGLE).

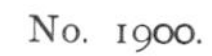

No. 1900.

Satin, ... $11.50 (TOLERABLE).
Satin, Engraved, ... 12.50 (TOLLMAN).
Satin, Engraved, Gold Lined, . . 14.50 (TOMBOY).
Satin, Engraved, XX Gold Inlaid, . 16.50 (TONSORIAL).

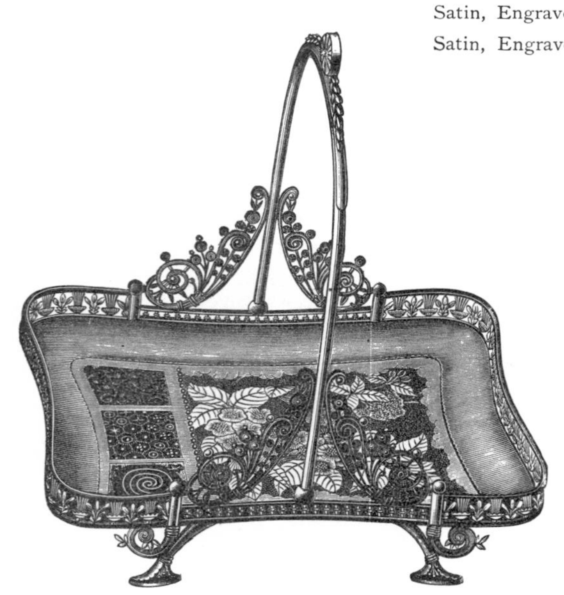

No. 1917.

Satin, ... $12.50 (TOOTHSOME).
Etched, Old Silver, . . 14.00 (HOUSEMAID).
Etched, X Gold Inlaid, . . 16.50 (HYGIENE).

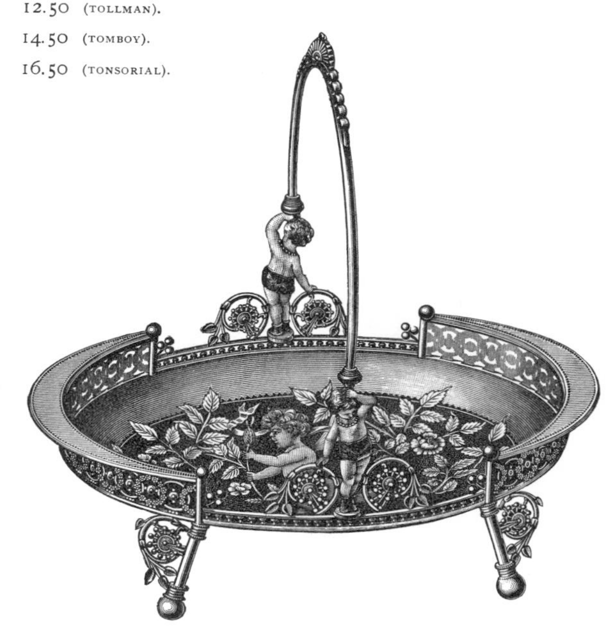

No. 1918.

Satin, ... $13.50 (TIDELOCK).
Etched, ... 15.00 (HUMANELY).
Etched, X Gold Inlaid, . 17.50 (HURTLE).

MERIDEN. B. COMPANY. TRADE MARK. NICKEL SILVER.

CAKE BASKETS.

(ONE-THIRD SIZE).

No. 1875.

Chased, . . . $10.50 (HOTHOUSE).
Chased, Gold Lined, 12.50 (HOTSPUR).

No. 1903.

Satin, ... $13.50 (VOCATION).
Moorish, ... 14.50 (VOCALIST).
Moorish, Old Silver, . . 16.00 (VIVID).
Moorish, Gold Inlaid, . 20.00 (VISUAL).

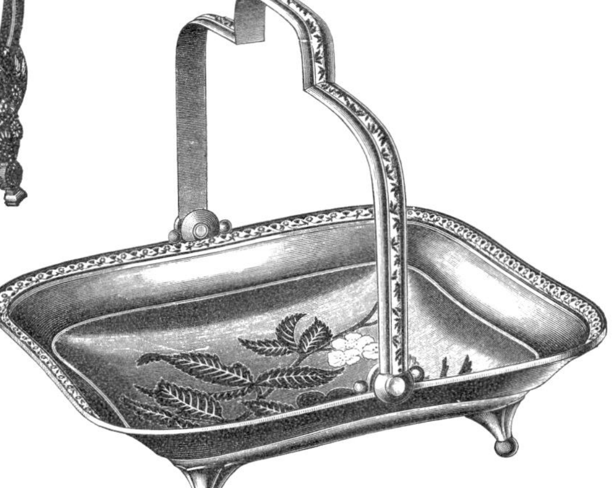

No. 1876.

Satin, ... $10.00 (INFALLIBLE).
Plum Chased, ... 11.00 (INFANTA).
Satin, Chased, ... 11.00 (INFERENCE).
Rose Embossed, XX Gold Inlaid, 15.50 (INFINITE).

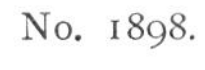

No. 1898.

Satin, ... $10.00 (VIRTUAL).
Satin, Gold Lined, . 12.00 (VINEYARD).
Pearl, Hammered, . 11.00 (VICINAGE).
Pearl, XX Gold Inlaid, 14.00 (VISITOR).

No. 1895.

Intaglio, Chased, Old Silver, . $15.00 (VILLAGER).
Intaglio, Chased, XX Gold Inlaid, 19.00 (VICTORINE).

No. 1904.

Satin, ... $15.00 (VICARIOUS).
Moorish, ... 16.00 (VIBRATION).
Moorish, Old Silver, . 17.50 (VESTMENT).
Moorish, Gold Inlaid, . 22.00 (VERONICA).

GOLD AND SILVER PLATE.

No. 1889. 9 INCH.

Chased, ... $7.50 (HYSSOP).
Chased, Gold Lined, . 9.00 (HYSTERIA).
Chased, X Gold Inlaid, 10.00 (IDEALIST).

No. 1890. 11 INCH.

Chased, ... $11.00 (IDENTIFY).
Chased, Gold Lined, . 13.00 (IDYL).
Chased, X Gold Inlaid, 14.00 (INEXPERT).

No. 1878.

Satin, ... $11.50 (INSULAR).
Satin, Engraved, . . . 12.50 (INSURANCE).
Satin, Engraved, XX Gold Inlaid, 16.50 (INSURGENT).

No. 1910.

Satin, ... $7.50 (VERNAL).
Satin, Engraved, . . 8.50 (VERIFY).
Satin Engraved, Gold Lined, 10.50 (VERITABLE).

No. 1894.

Satin, ... $12.50 (VERBOSE).
Satin, Embossed, . . . 13.50 (VERACITY).
Satin, Embossed, XX Gold Inlaid, 17.50 (VERMILION).

No. 1842.

Plain, ... $15.00 (DOUBLE).
Feather Chased, . . 16.00 (DOUBLET).
Feather Chased, Gold Lined, 18.00 (DOUBLOON).

No. 1842.

Niello and Silver, . . $16.00 (DOUBTLESS).
Niello and Gold, . . 19.00 (DOUBT).

GOLD AND SILVER PLATE.

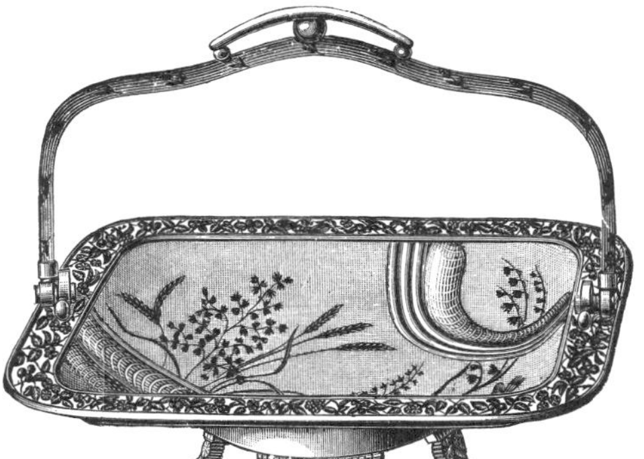

No. 1902.

Satin, ... $10.50 (VENTILATE).
Satin, Engraved, . . 11.50 (VENEERING).
Satin, Engraved, Gold Lined, 13.50 (VELVETEEN).

No. 1888.

Satin, ... $9.50 (HUGELY).
Satin, Engraved, ... 10.50 (HUMDRUM).
Satin, Chased, XX Gold Inlaid, 14.50 (HYPERBOLE).

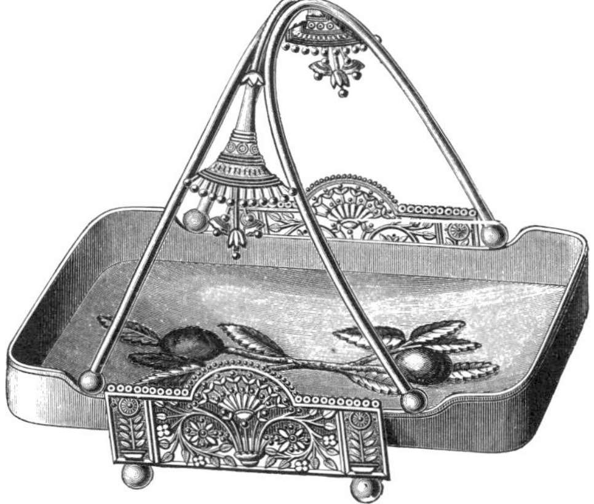

No. 1883.

Satin, Chased, ... $12.00 (INFLAME).
Satin, Chased, Gold Lined, . 14.00 (INFLATE).
Satin, Chased, XX Gold Inlaid, 15.00 (INFLECT).

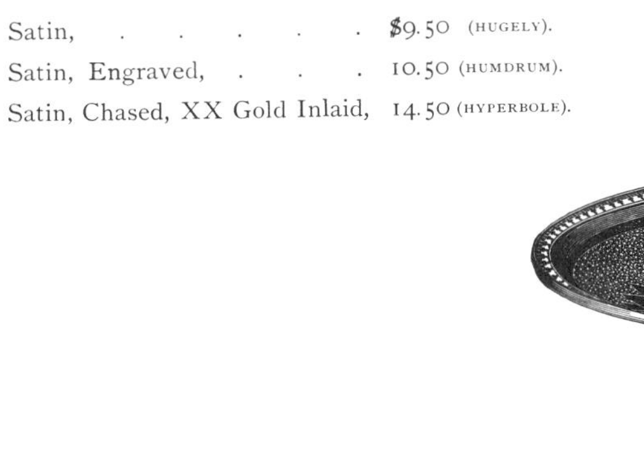

No. 1879.

Satin, ... $10.00 (HOUSING).
Satin, Engraved, ... 11.00 (HOWDAH).
Satin, Engraved, XX Gold Inlaid, 16.00 (HOWITZER).

No. 1868.

Silver, ... $12.00 (DOGEART).
Silver, Gold Lined, ... 14.00 (DOGE).
Silver, Gold Inlaid and Gold Lined, 16.00 (DOGMA).

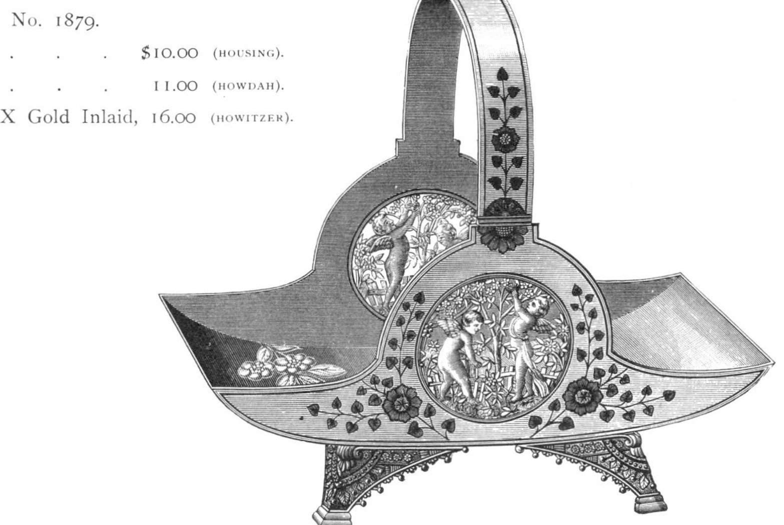

No. 1869.

Silver, ... $14.00 (DOGMATIC).
Silver, Gold Lined, ... 16.00 (DOIT).
Silver, Gold Inlaid and Gold Lined, . 18.00 (DOLCE).

GOLD AND SILVER PLATE.

No. 503. Bread Basket.

Chased, ... $10.00 (intention).

Chased, Gold Lined, . 12.00 (intercede).

No. 501. Bread Basket.

Satin, Engraved, . . . $9.50 (intellect).

Satin, Engraved, Gold Lined, 11.50 (intensity).

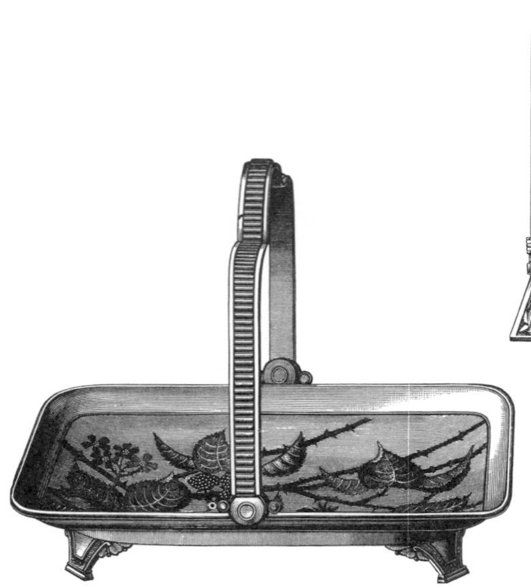

No. 1882.

Satin, ... $10.00 (velocity).

Satin, Engraved, . . . 12.00 (vedette).

Satin, Engraved, XX Gold Inlaid, 16.00 (vehemence).

No. 1816.

Plain, . . . $9.50 (duly).

Chased, . . . 10.50 (dumb).

Chased, Gold Lined, 12.50 (dumpling).

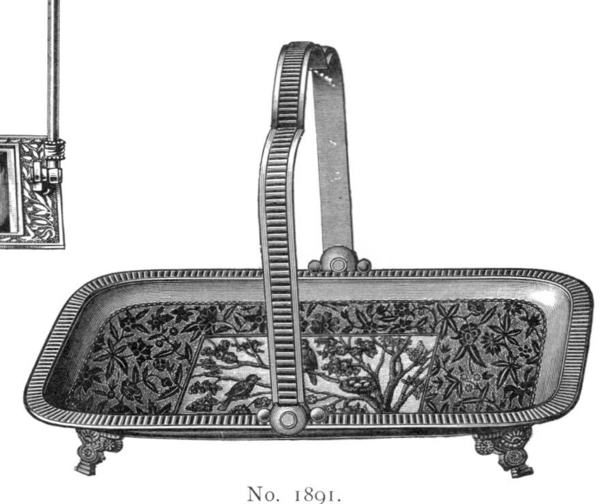

No. 1891.

Satin, ... $10.50 (intaglio).

Chased D, ... 12.50 (intact).

Chased, XX Gold Inlaid, 15.50 (integral).

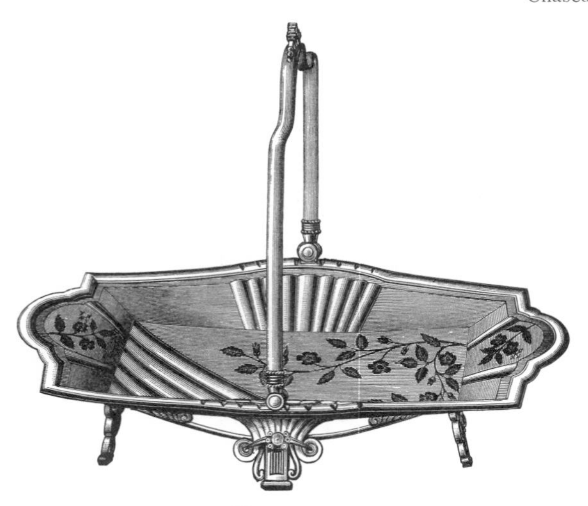

No. 1901.

Satin, Engraved, . . $12.00 (vassalage).

Moorish, Old Silver, . 13.00 (vaudeville).

Moorish, Gold Inlaid, . 16.50 (vascular).

No. 1852.

Plain, ... $12.50 (dough).

Chased, ... 13.50 (doughnut).

Chased, Gold Lined, . . . 15.50 (doughty).

Chased, Gold Inlaid and Gold Lined, 17.50 (dove).

WHITE METAL

GOLD AND SILVER PLATE.

NICKEL SILVER.

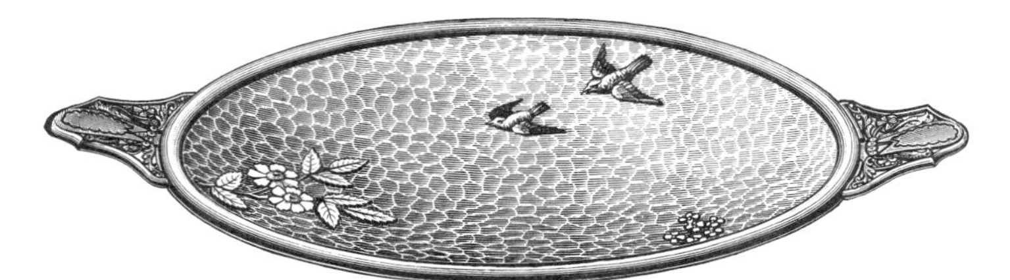

No. 502. BREAD BASKET.

Hammered, Old Silver,	$9.50	(VARIATION).
Hammered and Applied, Old Silver,	10.50	(VAPORIZE).
Hammered and Applied, Gold Inlaid,	13.00	(VANGUARD).

No. 500. BREAD BASKET.

Satin, Chased,	$9.00	(VALVULAR).
Chased, Gold Lined,	11.00	(VALUATION).

No. 1892.

Plain,	$7.00	(VALERIAN).
Satin,	7.00	(VALENTINE).
Satin, Gold Lined,	9.00	(VAGUELY).

No. 1863.

Plain,	$6.50	(EFFORT).
Chased,	7.50	(EFFUSE).
Chased, Gold Lined,	9.50	(EGOIST).

No. 1846.

Plain,	$12.50	(DRAG).
Chased,	13.50	(DRAGON).
Chased, Gold Lined,	15.50	(DRAIN).

No. 1897.

Plain,	$6.00	(VACILLATE).
Chased,	6.50	(VACCINE).
Chased, Gold Lined,	8.50	(VACATE).

No. 1873.

Embossed, Chased,	$8.25	(INTERLACE).
Embossed, Chased, Gold Lined,	10.25	(INTERLINK).

TRADE MARK.
WHITE METAL.

GOLD AND SILVER PLATE.

TRADE MARK.
NICKEL SILVER.

No. 1908.

Satin, ... $8.00 (UTENSIL).

Satin, Engraved, . . . 9.00 (USEFUL).

Satin, Engraved, Old Silver Border, 10.00 (UPROOT).

No. 1909. SAME STYLE, OVAL.

Satin, ... $12.00 (UPLIFT).

Satin, Engraved, . . . 13.00 (UPLAND).

Satin, Engraved, Old Silver Border, 14.00 (USURPER).

No. 1907.

Plain, . . . $7.50 (UNSEEN).

Gold Lined, . . 9.50 (UNSEAT).

No. 1855.

Chased, . . . $12.50 (DREAM).

Russian Gold Inlaid, . 16.50 (DREAR).

No. 1874.

Silver, . . $10.50 (INTERDICT).

Gold Lined, . 12.50 (INTERFERE).

No. 1872.

Plain, ... $11.00 (INFLEXIBLE).

Chased, ... 12.00 (INFLUENCE).

Chased, X Gold Inlaid and Gold Lined, 16.00 (INEXTINCT).

No. 1870.

Chased, ... $12.50 (INFREQUENT).

Chased, Gold Lined, . . . 14.50 (INFURIATE).

Chased, X Gold Inlaid and Gold Lined, 16.00 (INFUSION).

TRADE MARK.
WHITE METAL.

GOLD AND SILVER PLATE.

TRADE. MARK.
NICKEL SILVER.

No. 1877.

Satin, ... $10.50 (UPHEAVE).
Satin, Engraved, . . . 11.50 (UNYOKE).
Satin, Engraved, XX Gold Inlaid, 15 50 (UPHOLSTER).

No. 1850.

Plain, . . . $8.00 (EARLY).
Chased, . . . 9.00 (EARN).
Chased, Gold Lined, 11.00 (EARNEST).

No. 1853.

Hammered, . . . $12.00 (DOVETAIL).
Hammered, Chased, . . 13.00 (DOWAGER).
XX Gilt, Hammered, Chased, 16.00 (DOWER).

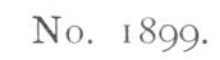

No. 1899.

Satin, ... $11.00 (UNDAUNTED).
Hammered, ... 12.00 (UNCOUPLE).
Satin, X Gold Inlaid, . . 14.00 (UNCONCERN).
Hammered, X Gold Inlaid, . 15.00 (UNCLOSE).

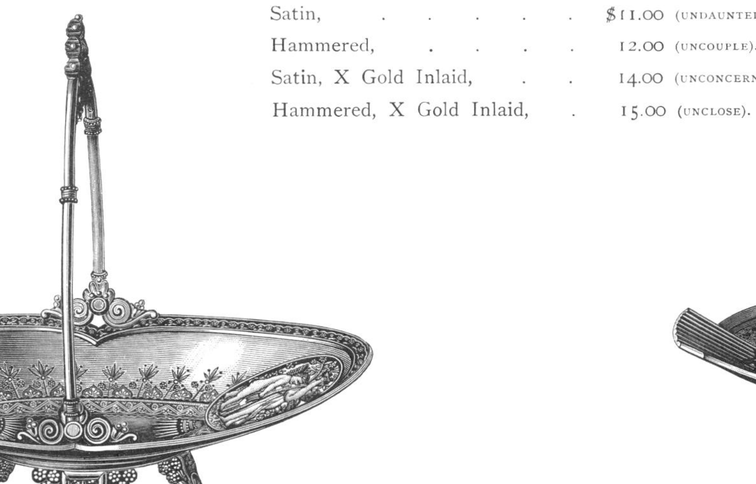

No. 1845.

Plain, ... $10.50 (DRAPE).
Chased, ... 11.50 (DRAPERY).
Chased, Gold Lined, . . . 13.50 (DRAWBACK).

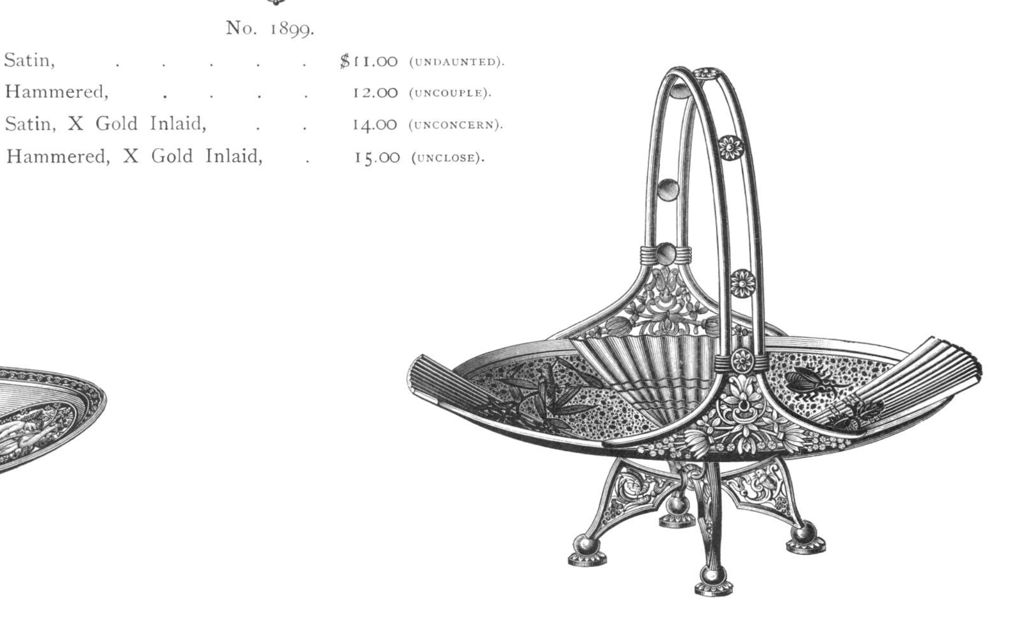

No. 1854.

Chased, ... $13.50 (DOVECOT).
Chased, Gold Inlaid, . . . 15.50 (DOWEL).

TRADE MARK.
WHITE METAL.

GOLD AND SILVER PLATE.

TRADE MARK.
NICKEL SILVER.

No. 1849.

Plain, ... $6.75 (EAGLE).
Chased, . . . 7.75 (EARL).
Chased, Gold Lined, . 9.75 (EARLDOM).

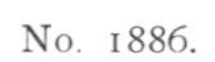

No. 1886.

Plain, ... $7.75 (INTRUDE).
Chased, ... 8.50 (INTUITION).

No. 1843.

Plain, ... $7.50 (DRAKE).
Chased, ... 8.50 (DRAM).
Chased, Gold Lined, . 10.50 (DRAMA).

No. 1885.

Plain, ... $6.50 (INUNDATE).
Plain, Gold Lined, . 8.50 (INVECTIVE).

No. 1893.

Satin, ... $6.75 (UNWIND).
Chased, ... 7.75 (UNWARY).
Satin, Chased, . . 7.75 (UNVEIL).
Satin, Chased, Gold Lined. 9.75 (UNTWIST).

No. 1884.

Silver, ... $7.00 (INTERVIEW).
Gold Lined, . . . 9.00 (INTESTATE).
Gold Inlaid and Gold Lined, 10.00 (INTONE).

No. 1881.

Silver, . . . $7.00 (INVEIGLE).
Old Silver, . . 8.00 (UNWRAP).
Gold Lined, . . 9.00 (INVERSE).

TRADE MARK.
WHITE METAL.

GOLD AND SILVER PLATE.

TRADE MARK.
NICKEL SILVER.

No. 1871.

Silver, ...	$6.00	(UNSADDLE).
Old Silver, . . .	7.00	(UNSCREW).
XX Gold Inlaid, . .	10.00	(UNSHEATHE).

No. 1887.

Satin, ...	$5.00	(INVESTMENT).
Chased, . . .	5.50	(INVIOLATE).
Satin, Chased, . .	5.50	(INVOCATE).

No. 1851.

Plain, ...	$6.50	(DUTY.)
Chased, ...	7.50	(DWARF).
Chased, Gold Lined, .	9.50	(DWELL).

No. 1848.

Plain, ...	$6.00	(DWINDLE).
Gold Lined, . .	8.00	(DYE).

No. 1847.

Plain, ...	$6.50	(DUDGEON).
Chased, ...	7.50	(DUE).
Chased, Gold Lined, .	9.50	(DUEL).

No. 1822.

Plain, ...	$6.75	(DUENNA).
Chased, ...	7.75	(DUET).
Chased, Gold Lined, .	9.75	(DUKE).

No. 1880.

Plain, ...	$6.25	(INTRIGUE).
Chased, . . .	7.00	(INTRODUCE).

GOLD AND SILVER PLATE.

No. 1896.

Plain, ... $5.50 (UNRAVEL).
Chased, . . . 6.00 (UNMASK).
Chased, Gold Lined, . 8.00 (UNLIKE).

No. 1633.

Plain, ... $5.00 (EIGHTH).
Chased, ... 5.50 (ETHER).
Chased, Gold Lined, . 7.50 (EJECT).

No. 1803.

Plain, ... $5.00 (EDGE).
Chased, ... 5.50 (EDGING).
Chased, Gold Lined, . 7.50 (EDIBLE).

CAKE BASKETS.

NICKEL SILVER, SILVER SOLDERED.

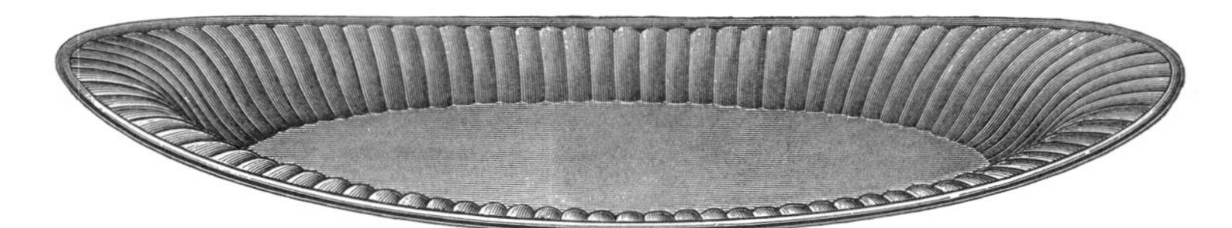

No. 0112. Bread Dish.

Plain, Fluted, . . . $20.00 (TOPKNOT).
Satin, Fluted, . . . 20.00 (TOPICAL).

No. 0106.

Silver, . . . $21.00 (REPLY).

No. 0102.

Silver, . . . $23.00 (REPRESENT).

GOLD AND SILVER PLATE.

No. 0105.

Embossed, . . $17.50 (UNHINGE).

Satin, Embossed, . 17.50 (UNCTION).

No. 0103.

Satin, ... $15.50 (UNAWARE).

Satin, Engraved, . 18.50 (UNAPTLY).

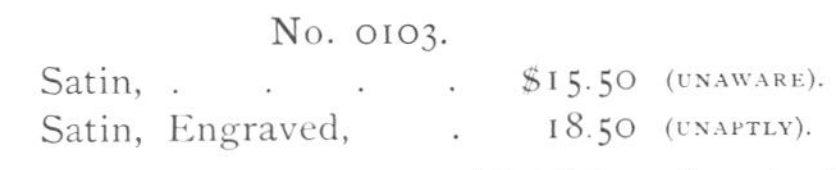

No. 0104. Same as 0103, with higher Standard.

Satin, ... $15.50 (UNANIMOUS).

Satin, Engraved, . 18.50 (UNGUENT).

No. 0107.

Satin, . . . $21.00 (UNFURL).

Satin, Engraved, . 23.50 (UNEASY).

No. 0100.

Plain, ... $16.50 (REPORT).

No. 0101. With Plain Standard, 15.00 (REPOSE).

No. 0110.

Satin, . . . $21.00 (UNEVEN).

Satin, Engraved, . 23.50 (UNDINE).

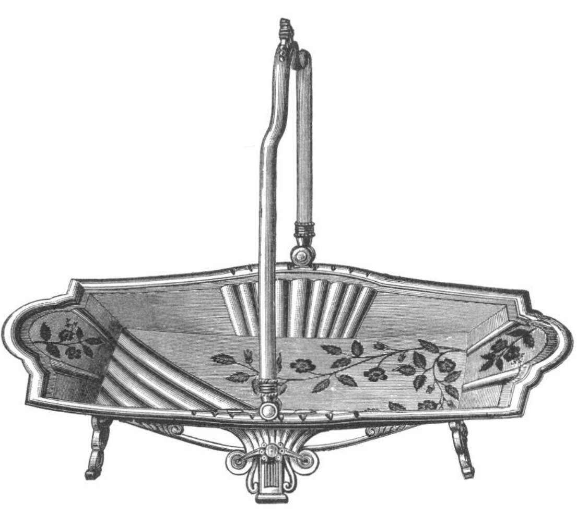

No. 0108.

Satin, ... $22.00 (UNLACE).

Satin, Engraved, . . . 25.00 (UNIONIST).

No. 0111.

Satin, ... $22.00 (UNIVERSE).

Satin Engraved, ... 25.00 (UNIFORM).

NICKEL SILVER, SILVER SOLDERED.

TRADE MARK.
WHITE METAL.

BUTTER DISHES.

TRADE MARK.
NICKEL SILVER.

(ONE-THIRD SIZE.)

No. 5011.
With Patent Crystal Drainer.

Plain, ... $10.50 (ULTIMATE).
Chased, ... 11.50 (ULTERIOR).

No. 4996. ROUND.
With Patent Crystal Drainer.

Plain, ... $10.50 (JACOBIN).
mbossed, Chased, 11.50 (JACONET).

No. 4997. OVAL.

Plain, ... $11.00 (JAGUAR).
Chased, . . . 12.00 (JANITOR).

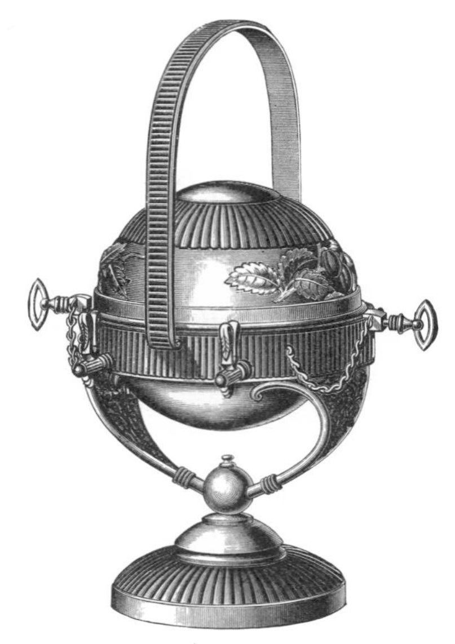

No. 4994. ROUND.
With Patent Crystal Drainer.

Plain, ... $10.50 (JANGLE).
Chased, ... 11.50 (JAPANESE).

No. 4995. OVAL.

Plain, ... $11.00 (JASPER).
Chased, ... 12.00 (JAVELIN).

No. 5012.
With Patent Crystal Drainer.

Plain, ... $11.50 (UMBRELLA).
Satin, Engraved, . 12.50 (UMBRAGE).

PATENT CRYSTAL DRAINER.

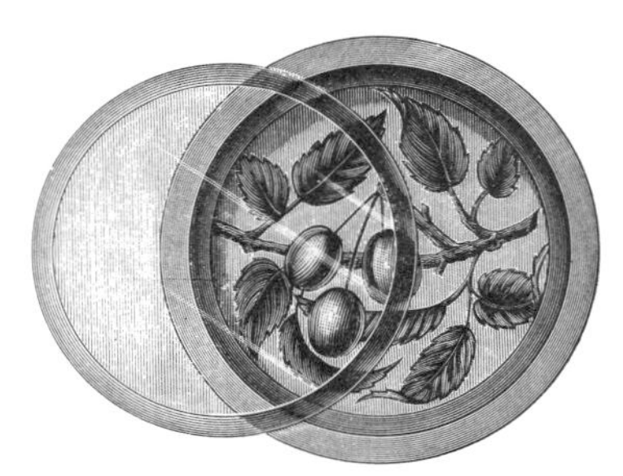

The object of this Embossed Chased Drainer is to make the Dish more elegant. The removable Plate Glass prevents it ever becoming defaced by contact with the knife, or action of the salt butter, and shows clearly the ornamental plate, which will retain its original finish for an indefinite period.

Butter Dishes not listed with the Patent Drainer can be furnished with them at 25 cents extra, but no deduction will be made when plain Drainer is substituted.

No. 4979. REVOLVING.
OVAL.

Plain, ... $9.75 (ENDORSE).
Chased, ... 10.75 (ENDOW).

No 4978. REVOLVING.
With Patent Crystal Drainer.

Plain, ... $8.75 (ENCROACH).
Chased, ... 9.75 (ENDANGER).

GOLD AND SILVER PLATE.

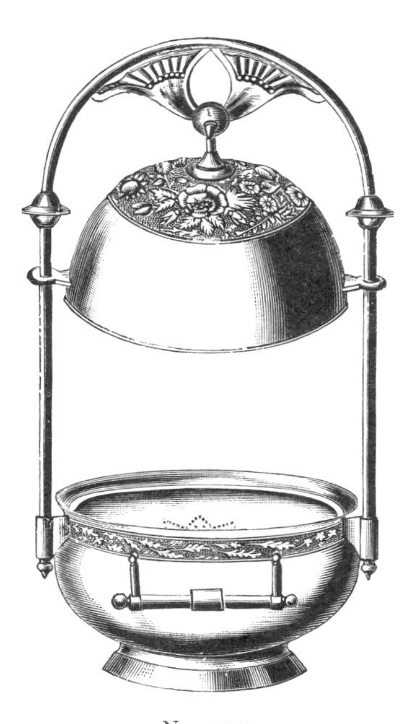

No. 4941.

Embossed, . $8.00 (EMPERIL).

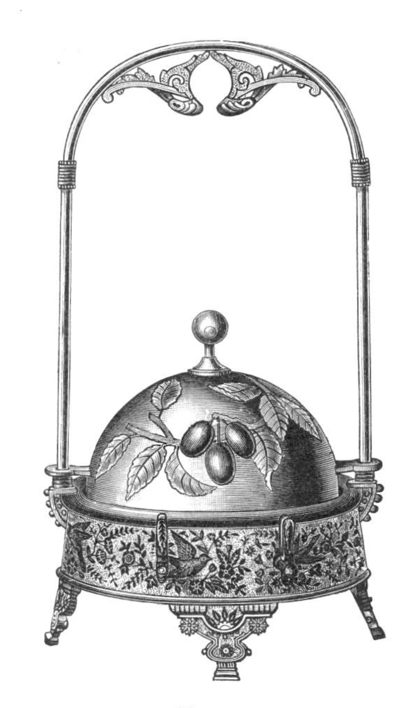

No. 4993.

With Patent Crystal Drainer.

Plain, . . $8.50 (IRRADIATE).
Embossed, Chased, 9 50 (ISINGLASS).

No. 4992.

With Patent Crystal Drainer.

Plain, . . $8.50 (INVOLVE).
Embossed, Chased, 9.50 (IODINE).

No. 4940.

With Patent Crystal Drainer.

Plain, . . $8.00 (EMPLOY).
Chased, . . 9.00 (EMPORIUM).

No. 4972.

With Patent Crystal Drainer.

Satin, . . $9.25 (SUBJUGATE).
Chased, . . 10.25 (EMIGRATE).

No. 4965.

With Patent Crystal Drainer.

Plain, . . $8.75 (EMOTION).
Chased, . . 9.50 (EMPALE).

GOLD AND SILVER PLATE.

No. 5003.

Plain, ... $6.00 (TYPICAL).
Chased, . . . 7.00 (TYMBAL).
Satin, Chased, . . 7.00 (TWINGE).

No. 5013. FLUTED.
With Patent Crystal Drainer.

Plain, . . . $6.50 (TOUCHSTONE).
Satin, . . . 6.50 (TORTUOUS).

No. 5004.

Plain, . . . $6.75 (TYMPANUM).
Satin, Engraved, . 7.75 (TWISTER).

No. 5002.

Plain, ... $7.50 (JULIAN).
Chased, . . . 8.50 (JUMBLE).

No. 5006.

Plain, ... $7.75 (TYPHOON).
Satin, Engraved, . . 8.75 (TWOFOLD).

No. 5005.

Plain, ... $7.00 (TWILIGHT).
Chased, . . . 8.00 (TURQUOIS).
Satin, Chased, . . 8.00 (TURNPIKE).

No. 5014. FLUTED.
With Patent Crystal Drainer.

Plain, . . . $6.75 (TUSCAN).
Satin, . . . 6.75 (TURNSTILE).

No. 5009.
With Patent Crystal Drainer.

Plain, . . . $8.25 (TURNKEY).
Chased, . . . 9.00 (TURBOT).
Satin, Chased, . . 9.00 (TORTOISE).

No. 5001.
With Patent Crystal Drainer.

Plain, . . . $7.00 (JOYOUS).
Hammered, . . 8.00 (JUBILEE).

No. 5010.
With Patent Crystal Drainer.

Plain, ... $8.75 (TURGID).
Chased, . . . 9.50 (TORPOR.)
Satin, Chased, . . 9.50 (TORMENT).

GOLD AND SILVER PLATE.

No. 7. CHEESE DISH.
Ruby Glass Cover, . $8.50 (TRACERY).

No. 3. CHEESE DISH.
Engraved, . . $9.00 (EMERALD).

No. 6. CHEESE DISH.
Ruby Glass Cover, . $9.50 (TURBID).

No. 4990.
With Patent Crystal Drainer.
Plain, . . . $7.00 (ESSAY).
Chased, . . . 8.00 (ESSAYIST).

No. 4969.
Plain, . . $6.50 (ENJOY).
Chased, . . 7.00 (ENLARGE).

No. 4988.
With Patent Crystal Drainer.
Plain, . . . $5.50 (ESCALOP).
Chased, . . 6 50 (ESCAPADE).

No. 4999.
Plain, . . . $5.25 (JUDICIAL).
Chased, . . . 6.00 (JUGGLER).

No. 4998.
Plain, . . . $5.00 (JOSTLE).
Chased, . . . 6.00 (JOVIAL).

No. 4971. REVOLVING.
OVAL.
Chased, . . . $9.50 (ENCHANT).

No. 5008.
Plain, . . . $7.25 (TRIANGLE).
Chased, . . . 7.75 (TRESTLE).

No. 4970. REVOLVING.
With Patent Crystal Drainer.
Chased, . . . $8.50 (ENACT).

GOLD AND SILVER PLATE.

No. 4968.

Plain, . . . $6.00 (ENOUGH).

Chased, . . . 6.50 (ENQUIRE).

No. 4986.

Plain, . . . $5.50 (ERUDITE).

Chased, . . . 6.50 (ESCALADE).

No. 4961.

Plain, . . . $5.00 (ENGLISH).

Chased, . . . 5.50 (ENGRAVE).

No. 5016.

With Patent Crystal Drainer.

Plain, . . . $7.50 (TONNAGE).

Satin, Engraved, . 8.50 (TONIC).

No. 4984.

Plain, . . . $5.00 (ESCORT).

No. 4984.

Chased, . . . $5.50 (ESCHEW).

Satin, Engraved, . 6.00 (TOUGHEN).

No. 4967.

Plain, . . . $4.75 (ENFORCE).

Chased, . . . 5.25 (ENGAGE).

No. 4946½.

Plain, . . . $5.50 (ENTREAT).

Chased, . . . 6.50 (ENTRY).

No. 4966.

Plain, . . . $4.50 (ENDUE).

Chased, . . . 5.00 (ENDURE).

No. 5015.

With Patent Crystal Drainer.

Plain, . . . $7.00 (TOMPION).

Satin, Engraved, . 8.00 (TOKAY).

TRADE MARK.
WHITE METAL.

GOLD AND SILVER PLATE.

TRADE MARK.
NICKEL SILVER.

No. 4951.

Plain, . . $4.00 (ENTWIST).

Engraved, . 4.50 (ENVELOP).

No. 4932½.

Plain, . . $4.75 (ENSUE).

Chased, . . 5.25 (ENTAIL).

No. 4932.

Plain, . . $3.50 (ENVIRON).

Chased, . . 4.00 (ENVOY).

No. 4946.

Chased, . . $5.00 (EQUIP).

No. 4947.

Plain, . . $3.75 (EPILOGUE).

Chased, . . 4.50 (EPITAPH).

No. 4947½.

Plain, . . $5.00 (ENTIRE).

Chased, . . 5.75 (ENTITLE).

No. 53.

Plain, . . $4.00 (JOGGLE).

Satin S., . . 4.50 (JOINER).

Chased, . . 5.00 (JOIST).

No. 4946.

Plain, . . $4.00 (EQUATION).

No. 4943.

Chased, . . $5.50 (EPIC).

No. 4943½. Bail Handle.

Chased, . . $6.75 (EPICURE).

No. 4944½.

Plain, . . $6.25 (ENSIGN).

Chased, . . 6.75 (ENSLAVE).

No. 4956.

Plain, . . $5.00 (EPOCH).

Chased, . . 5.50 (EQUAL).

GOLD AND SILVER PLATE.

No. 01865.

Tête-à-Tête, . $8.50 (REVENGE).

No. 0832.

Plain, . . $10.50 (TRAPEZE).
Satin, . . 10.50 (TRANSHIP).

No. 0837.

Plain, . . $13.50 (TRAVERSE).
Satin, . . 13.50 (TRAPPINGS).

No. 0833.

Plain, . . $11.00 (TRELLIS).

No. 0835.

Plain, . . $16.50 (TREFOIL).
Satin, . . 16.50 (TREATY).

No. 0838.

Plain, . . $13.50 (TRIBE).
Satin, . . 13.50 (TRENCHER).

No. 0839.

Plain, . . $13.50 (TRIBLET).
Satin, . . 13.50 (TREPAN).

No. 0840.

Satin, . . $16.50 (TRANSPOSE).
Satin, Engraved, 18.50 (THERMAL).

NICKEL SILVER, SILVER SOLDERED.

GOLD AND SILVER PLATE.

BUTTER DISH.

No. 0834, . $15.00 (REVIEW).

BUTTER DISH.

No. 0830, . . . $14.50 (REVILE).
No. 0831, Smaller, . 10.50 (TIARA).

BUTTER DISH.

No. 0836, . $16.50 (REVISE).

INDIVIDUAL BUTTER PLATES.

(FOR INDIVIDUAL SALTS SEE INDEX S.)

(ONE-THIRD SIZE.)

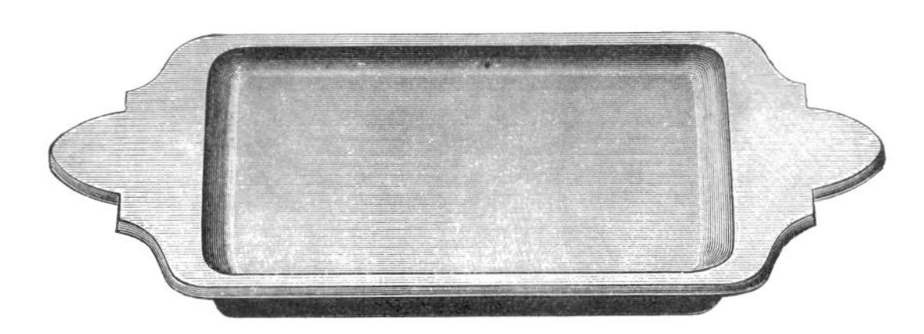

No. 02.

Plain, . . per dozen, $15.00 (THEATER).
Gold Lined, . per dozen, 18.00 (THRALDOM).

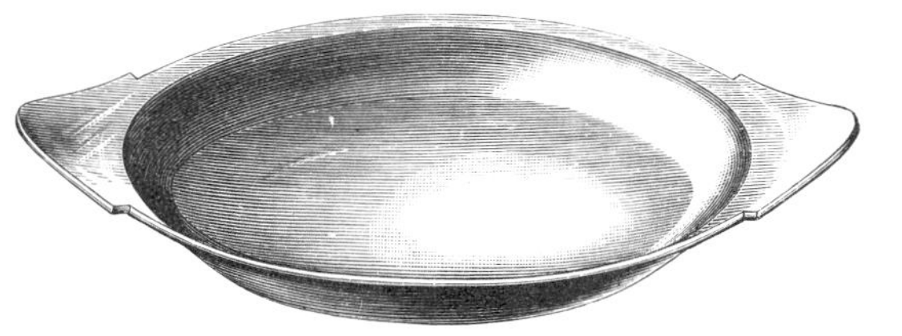

No. 01.

Silver Lined, . per dozen, $13.50 (CREAKING).
Gold Lined, . . per dozen, 16.50 (CREAM).

No. 05.

Plain, . per dozen, $10.50 (THORNY).
Satin, . per dozen, 10.50 (THIRDLY).
Gold Lined, per dozen, 13.50 (THINKING).

No. 03.

Silver Lined, . per dozen, $13.50 (CREATURE).
Gold Lined, . per dozen, 16.50 (CREDENCE).

No. 04.
With Glass Protector.

Embossed, Chased, . . per dozen, $15.00 (JUNIPER).
Embossed, Chased, Gold Inlaid, per dozen, 18.00 (JUPITER).
(Full Size.)

Plush or Morocco Cases, for ½ dozen, . $4.50 extra (THICKET).
Plush or Morocco Cases, for 1 dozen, . 6.00 extra (THESPIAN).

NICKEL SILVER, SILVER SOLDERED.

GOLD AND SILVER PLATE.

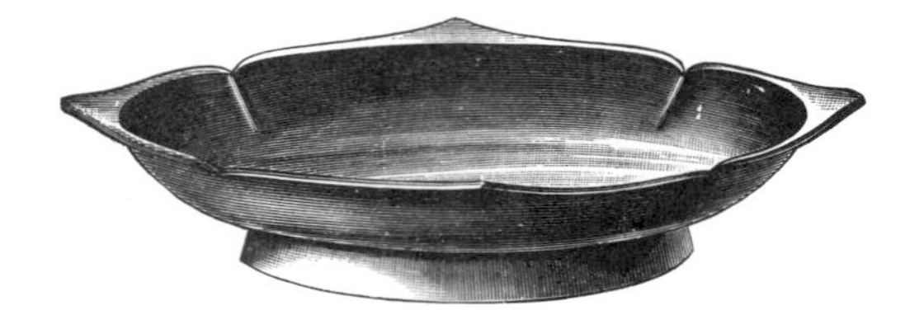

No. 3.

Gold Lined, . per dozen, $13.50 (CRICKET).

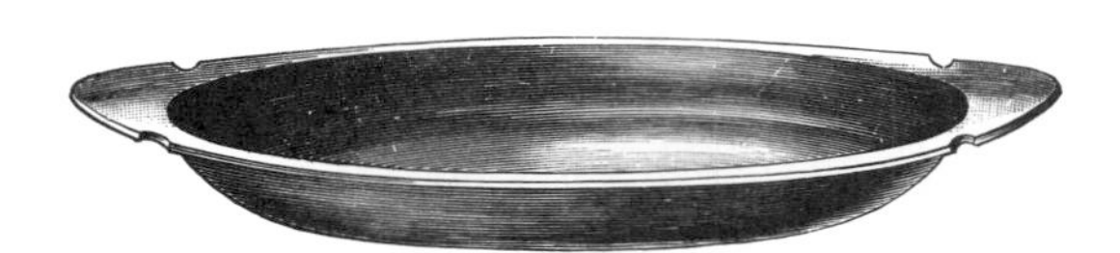

No. 4. OVAL.

Gold Lined, . per dozen, $13.50 (CREOLE).

No. 1600.

Gold Lined, Plain, . per dozen, $12.00 (CRESCENT).
Gold Lined, Chased, . per dozen, 14.00 (CRESS).

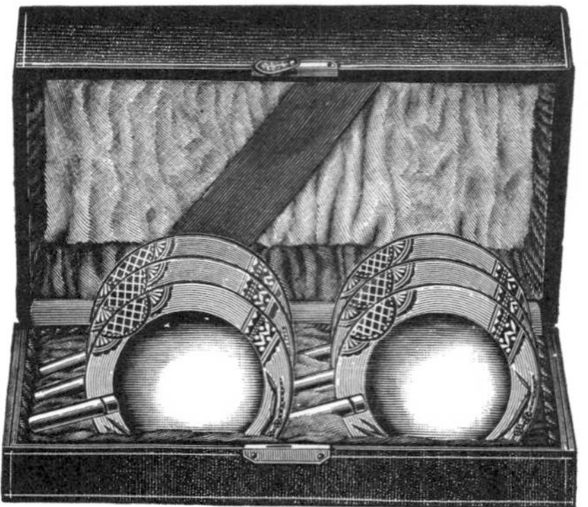

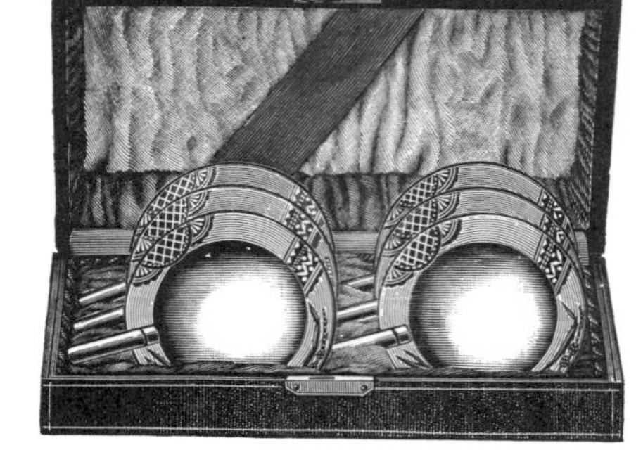

No. 1601.

Engraved, Gold Lined, per dozen, $18.00 (CRIB).

Plush Case for ½ dozen, . $4.50 extra (TIPSTAFF).
Plush Case for 1 dozen, . 6.00 extra (TINMAN).

No. 1605.

With Glass Protector.

Chased, . . per dozen, $15.00 (SUBJOIN).
Chased, Gold Inlaid, per dozen, 18.00 (SUBJECTION).

Plush Case for ½ dozen, . $4.50 extra (TITHE).
Plush Case for 1 dozen, . 6.00 extra (TITHING).

No. 1602.

Silver Lined, . per dozen, $12.00 (CREDITOR).
Gold Lined, . per dozen, 15.00 (CREED).

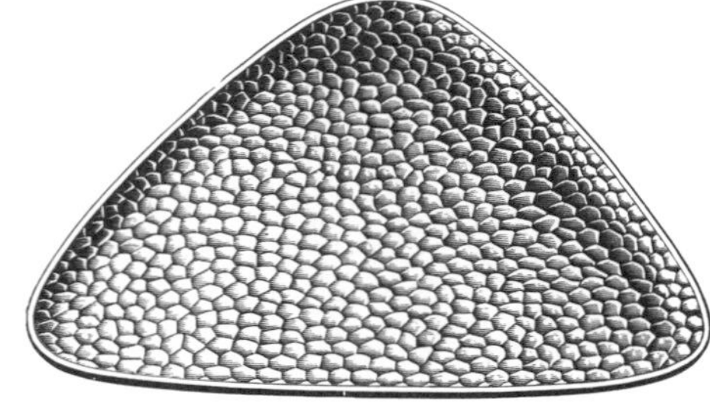

No. 1604.

Hammered, ... $9.00 (TOCSIN).
Hammered, Gold Lined, per dozen, 12.00 (CRESSET).

No. 1603.

Gold Lined, . per dozen, $12.00 (CREMONA).

Plush or Morocco Cases for ½ dozen, . $4.50 extra (TINCTURE).
Plush or Morocco Cases for 1 dozen, . 6.00 extra (TIMELY).

Trade Mark.
WHITE METAL.

GOLD AND SILVER PLATE.

Trade Mark.
NICKEL SILVER.

BUTTER DISHES.

No. 5019.

With Patent Crystal Drainer.

Satin, . . . $6.50 (TRADEWIND).
Engraved, . . . 7.50 (TRACKAGE).
Satin, Engraved, . 7.50 (TRAGICAL).

No. 5017.

With Patent Crystal Drainer.

Plain, . . . $5 50 (TRAINER).
Chased, . . . 6.50 (TOWNHALL).

Decorated China Base.

No. 5020.

With Patent Crystal Drainer.

Satin, . . . $8.50 (TORVISM).
Engraved, . . . 9.50 (VINERY).
Satin, Engraved, . 9.50 (TOPSAIL).

No. 5018.

With Patent Crystal Drainer.

Plain, . . . $8.00 (TOWNSHIP).
Chased, . . . 9.00 (TOWLINE).

CONFECTIONERY TRAYS.

(One-Third Size.)

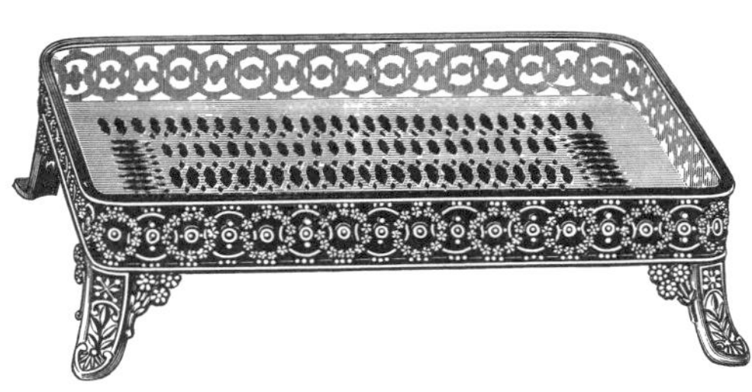

No. 50.

Old Silver, 8 inch, . $10.00 (TRANSCRIBE).
Old Silver, 10 inch, . 13.00 (TRAMMEL).

No. 229. Compotier.

Satin, ... $8.00 (PRAWN).
Satin, Gold Lined, ... 9.00 (PRACTICAL).
Satin, Gold Lined, Old Silver Border, 10.00 (POTENTATE).

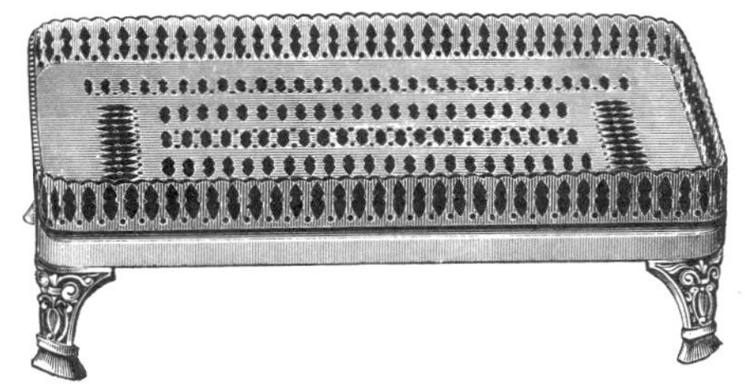

No. 040. Nickel Silver

8 inch, . . . $12.00 (TRANSACTION).
10 inch, . . . 15.00 (TRAMP).

Trade Mark.
WHITE METAL.

GOLD AND SILVER PLATE.

Trade Mark.
NICKEL SILVER.

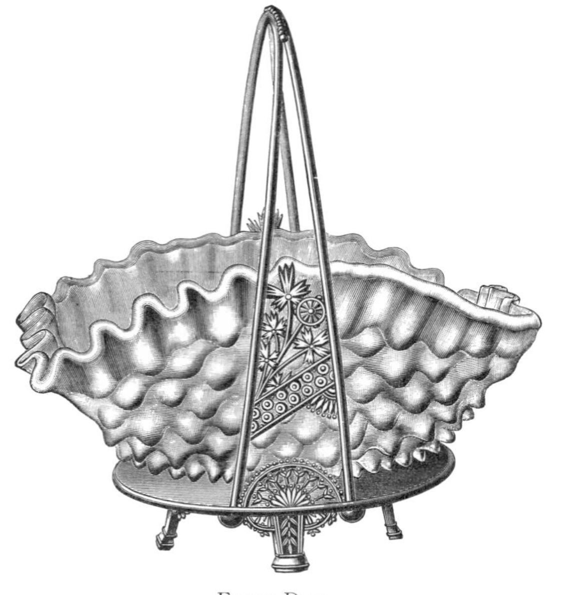

Fruit Dish.
No. 1615, . . $13.50 (steamboat).

No. 272. Berry Dish.
Assorted Colors, . . $8.00 (stationary).

No. 1052. Epergne.
Crystal, . . $21.00 (stateroom).

No. 1616. Fruit Dish.
Peach Glass, . . $15.75 (stainless).

No. 1617. Fruit Dish.
Ruby, . . $10.50 (stability).

BERRY DISHES.

(ALSO SEE FRUIT DISHES.)

(ONE-THIRD SIZE.)

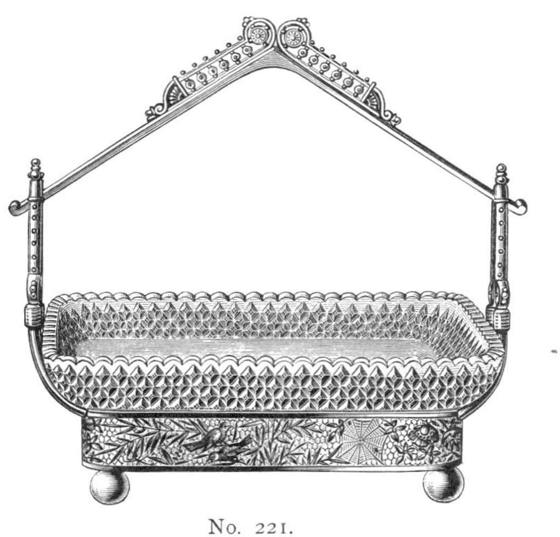

No. 221.
Fine Cut Glass.
Silver, ... $22.00 (DEXTERITY).
Silver, Gold Inlaid, . 24.00 (DIADEM).

No. 222.
Ruby or Blue, Fine Cut Glass.
Silver, ... $20.50 (DIAGONAL).
Silver, Gold Inlaid, . 22.50 (DIAGRAM).

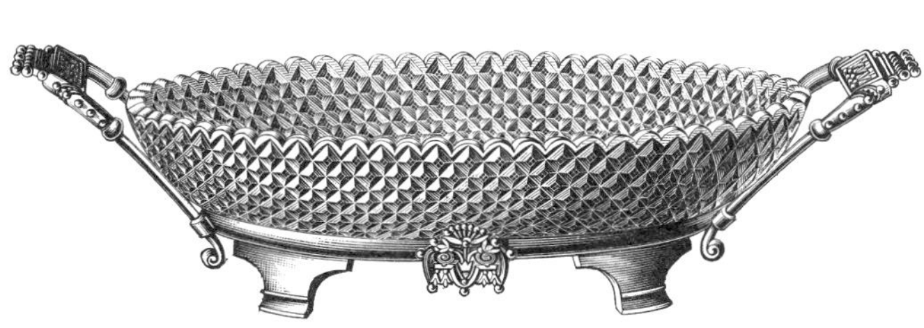

No. 214.
Fine Cut Glass, . $25.00 (DEVOUT).

No. 1517. ICE CREAM DISH.
Fine Cut Glass.
Crystal Cut, Gold Inlaid, ... $40.00 (DIAMETER).
Ruby or Blue, Cut, Gold Inlaid, . 45.00 (DIAMOND).

No. 236.
Fine Cut Glass.
Silver, ... $34.00 (DILATION).
Silver, Gold Inlaid, . 38.00 (DILIGENCE).

No. 238.
Fine Cut Glass.
Silver, ... $30.00 (DIGHT).
Silver, Gold Inlaid, . 34.00 (DIGIT).

TRADE MARK.
WHITE METAL.

GOLD AND SILVER PLATE.

TRADE MARK.
NICKEL SILVER.

No. 233.
Silver, . . $15.50 (DIGESTION).
Silver, Gold Inlaid, 17.50 (DIGGER).

No. 223.
Ruby or Blue Fine Cut Glass.
Silver, ... $22.00 (DEW).
Silver, Gold Inlaid, . 24.00 (DEXTER).

No. 252.
Fine Cut Glass.
Silver, ... $20.00 (HOLSTER).
Silver, Gold Inlaid, . 22.00 (HOMAGE).

No. 1544. ICE CREAM DISH.
Silver, . . . $16.50 (DIGNITARY).

No. 212.
Fine Cut Glass, . . $32.00 (DICTION).

No. 231. Cut Glass.
Silver, . . . $19.50 (DIFFRACT).
Silver, Gold Inlaid, . 21.50 (DIFFUSIVE).

GOLD AND SILVER PLATE.

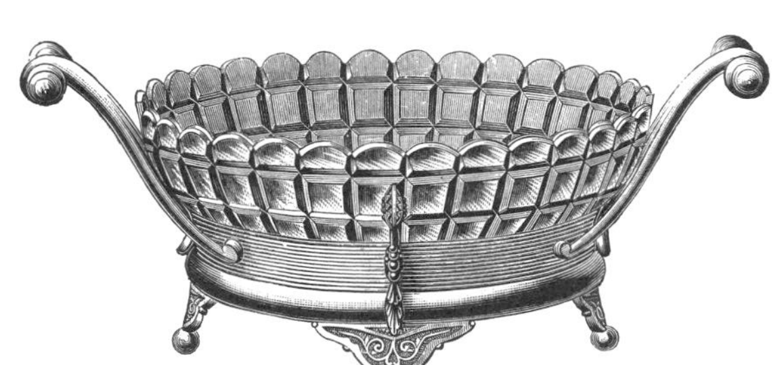

No. 176.
Cut Glass, . $12.00 (DEVOTE).

No. 215.
Cut Glass, . . $15.00 (DIAL).

No. 266, . . $8.75 (TIGHTEN).
Assorted Colors

No. 255. Ruby, . $11.50 (TICKING).

No. 263, . . $8.50 (TILLAGE).
Assorted Colors.

No. 270. BERRY SET.
Complete, . . $21.00 (SUBDUE).
Assorted Colors.

No. 184, . $13.00 (DIGRESS).

No. 205, . $14.00 (DIGNIFY).

GOLD AND SILVER PLATE.

No. 251, ... $10.00 (HOOK).

No. 264, ... $10.75 (THEBAN).
With Six Individual Dishes, complete, 12.25 (TESTATE).
Assorted Colors.

No. 269, ... $14.50 (TESTATOR).
With Six Individual Dishes, complete, 16.00 (TERSELY).

No. 261, ... $16.50 (TERRAPIN).
Silver and Gold Inlaid, . . 19.00 (TERMINATE).

No. 268, ... $12.00 (TENANTRY).
With Six Individual Dishes, complete, . 13.50 (TENACITY).
Assorted Colors.

GOLD AND SILVER PLATE.

No. 265, . . $9.50 (SUBDIVIDE).
Assorted Colors.

No. 254, . . $10.00 (PREMIUM).

No. 241, . . $8.50 (BALSAM).
Assorted Colors.

No. 249, . $8.00 (BANDAGE).
Assorted Colors.

No. 208, . . $12.50 (DIFFER).

No. 224, . . $9.75 (DIMENSION).

No. 240, . . $9.00 (BANANA).
Assorted Colors.

No. 271, . . $10.50 (PREMISE).
Assorted Colors.

GOLD AND SILVER PLATE.

No. 186.
Crystal, . . $9.00 (DILUTE).
Ruby, . . 9.75 (DIME).

No. 202.
Crystal, . . $7.50 (DISBURSE).
Ruby, . . 8.25 (PREPARE).

No. 226, . . $6.50 (BALCONY).

No. 161, . . $6.00 (DIP).

No. 162, . . $7.00 (DIPLOMA).

No. 191, . . $8.00 (DIMINISH).

No. 199, . . $9.50 (DIRE).

No. 211, . . $9.00 (DIMPLE).

GOLD AND SILVER PLATE.

No. 242, . . $6.50 (AWNING).

No. 262. Ruby, . $7.50 (STROPHE).

No. 227.
Crystal, . . $7.00 (BANISH).
Ruby, . . 7.75 (STUBBLE).

No. 256. With Spoon, $6.50 (WRONG).
Assorted Colors.

No. 246, . . $7.50 (BALLOT).

No. 244, . . $6.50 (AXIOM).

No. 192, . . $8.00 (DINNER).
Assorted Colors.

No. 243, . . $7.50 (BALLAD).

GOLD AND SILVER PLATE.

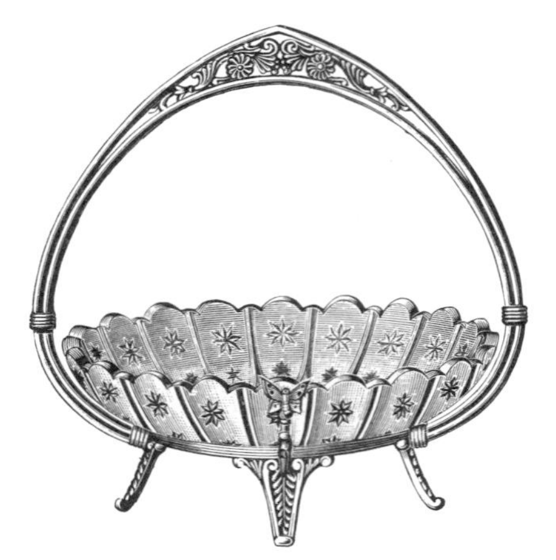

No. 195, . . $4.25 (DISARM).

No. 248, . . $7.00 (AZURE).

No. 155. Round, 6 inch, . $3.25 (DISCORD).
No. 156. Round, 8 inch, . 4.50 (DISCOUNT).

No 175, . . $4.75 (DISCLAIM).

No. 179, . . $6.75 (DISCOLOR).

No. 173, Oval, . . $5.50 (DISCERN).

No. 258, . . $4.25 (STRIVE).

No. 216, Silver, . $6.50 (DISCARD).

CALL BELLS.

(HALF SIZE, EXCEPTING NOS. 31, 33, 34, 36, 38, 39, AND 40, ONE-THIRD SIZE.)

(PRICES PER DOZEN.)

No. 31. REVOLVING.
Bronze Base, . $25.25 (TRIDENT).

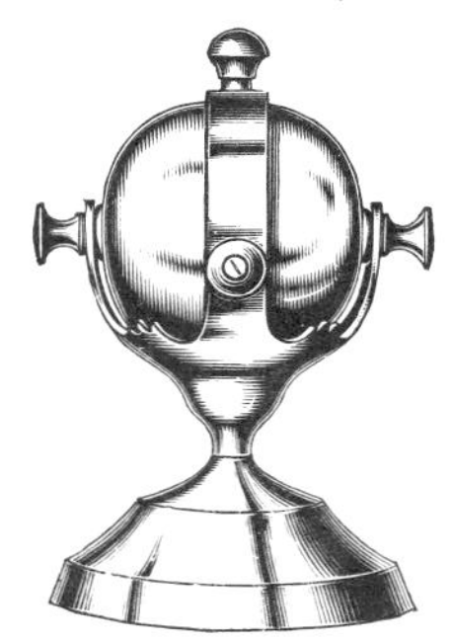

No. 36. REVOLVING.
Plated Base, . $32.00 (TRENT).

No. 33. REVOLVING.
White Base, . $31.50 (TRIPLET).

No. 38. REVOLVING.
Bronze Base, . . $19.00 (TROPIC).
No. 39. REVOLVING.
Silver and Bronze Base, $20.00 (TROPHY).

No. 45. EMBOSSED.
Old Silver Base, $24.50 [illegible]

No. 34. REVOLVING.
Rosewood Base, $32.00 (TRIPOD).

No. 40. REVOLVING.
White Base, . $21.00 (TROTTER).

No. 44. EMBOSSED.
Old Silver Base, $26.00 (STOUTLY).

No. 9200.
Bronze Base, $7.50 (STEWARD).

No. 9404.
Gilt Base, $15.00 (STEVEDORE).

No. 7175. With Guard (STIGMATIC).
No. 7100. Without Guard, $12.00 (STEELYARD).
Bronze Base.

No. 9403.
Nickel Base, $11.00 (STRATEGY).

No. 9300.
Bronze Base, $8.00 (STRAWBERRY).

No. 9402, . $10.00 (STICKLER).

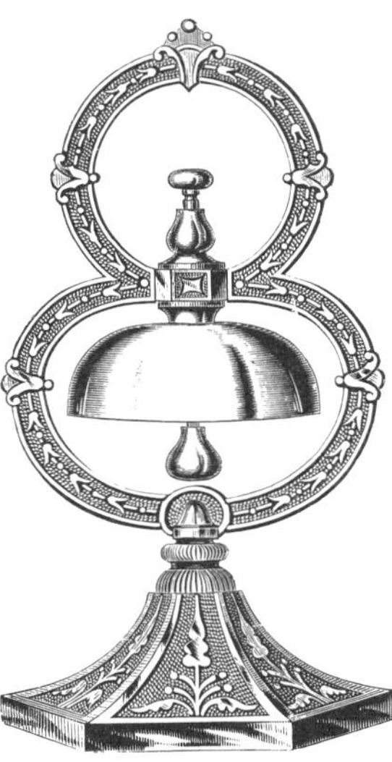

No. 8450. Bronze Frame.
Bronze Base, $16.00 (TRIFLING).

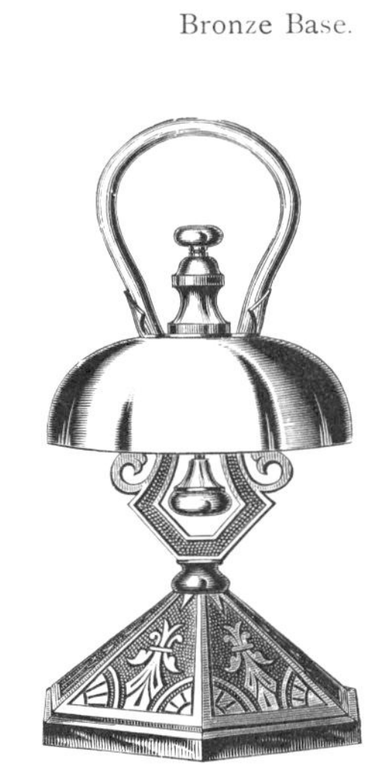

No. 8350. With Guard (TRIER).
Bronze.
No. 8300. Without Guard, $16.00 (STRENUOUS).

No. 6900.
Bronze Base, $15.00 (TUFT).

No. 7300.
Nickel and Verde Base, $20.00 (TRUSTEE).

GOLD AND SILVER PLATE.

No. 4300.
Black Base, $26.00 (TRUCK).

No. 7600. Silver Plated Frame.
Black Base, . $42.00 (TUMBLE).

No. 8700. Gilt Frame.
Black Base, . $20.00 (TRINAL).
No. 8600. (Larger.)
Gilt Frame, . $26.00 (TRIMLY).

No. 4600. Extra Finish, all Plain.
White Base, . $24.00 (TRUDGE).
No. 4500. Octagon Base.
Black Base, . $24.00 (TRUCKMAN).

No. 7850. Gilt Frame.
Black Base, . . $40.00 (TRIENNIAL).

No. 4400. HOTEL.
Gilt Base, . . $60.00 (TRUCKAGE).
Plated Base, . . 60.00 (TRUCKLE).

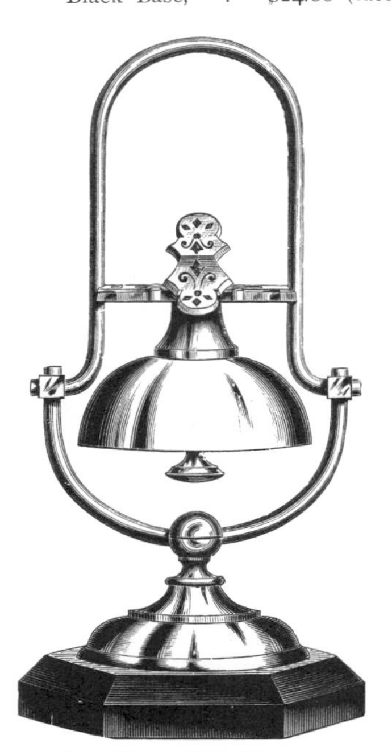

No. 8500. Gilt Frame.
Black Base, . . $38.00 (TRIMNESS).

No. 9100.
Gilt Base, . . $54.00 (STEADFAST).

No. 2400. HOTEL.
Black and Gold Base, . $54.00 (STATIONER).
White Marble Base, . 56.00 (TROCHE).

No. 8900.
Gilt Base, . . $30.00 (STATELY).

For material tipped into the original edition between pages 58 and 59, see page 451.

TRADE MARK.
WHITE METAL.

GOLD AND SILVER PLATE.

TRADE MARK.
NICKEL SILVER.

No. 6700.
Nickel Plated and Verde.
Black Base, . $12.00 (TRUTH).

No. 8050. With Guard (TRIBUTARY).
No. 8000. Without Guard, $11.00 (SPRINGER).
Bronze Base.

No. 8150. With Guard (TRIBUTE).
No. 8100. Without Guard, $12.00 (TRICK).
Bronze Base.

No. 3000.
Bronze Base, Fancy, $10.00 (TROT).
Gilt Base, . . 13.50 (TROUBADOUR).

No. 6850. With Guard (SPREAD)
No. 6800. Without Guard.
Nickel Plated and Verde.
Fancy Base, . $15.00 (TRUTHFUL).

No. 9050. With Guard (SPORTIVE).
No. 9000. Without Guard, $18.00 (SPLINTER).
Gilt Base.

No. 6450. With Guard (SOLVENT).
No. 6400. Without Guard (SOLITUDE).
Nickel Plated and Verde.
Black Base, . $16.00 (SPARKLE).
Gilt Base, . 17.00 (SOLICIT).
(Two-Thirds Size.)

No. 3250. With Guard (SPANKER).
No. 3200. Without Guard, $16.50 (TROUBLE).
Plated Base.

No. 1300.
Plain Beaded Base, $18.00 (TRINE).

No. 2700.
Bronze Base, Fancy, $13.50 (TROMBONE).

No. 2800.
Bronze Base, Fancy, $10.50 (TROOP).

No. 1900.
Black Base, . $19.00 (SORREL).
Black and Gold Base, 21.00 (SORGHUM).
Black and Pearl Base, 22.00 (SONOROUS).

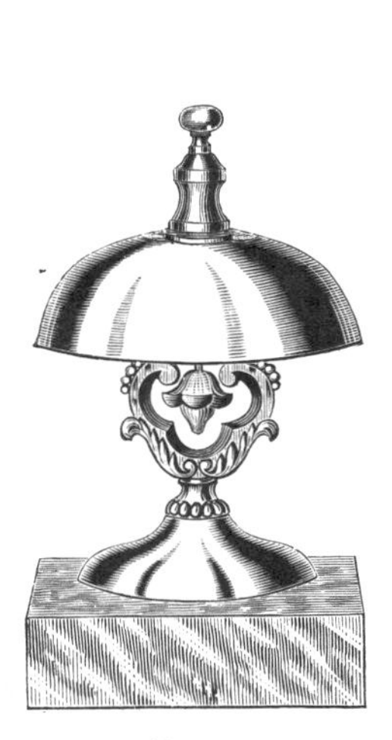

No. 2200.
White Marble Base, $18.50 (TROD).

No. 2250. With Guard.
White Marble Base, $18.50 (SONGSTRESS).

No. 6500. Hand.
Black Base, $36.00 (TUCKER).

No. 5400. Tulip Top.
Bronze Base, $25.00 (TRUMPERY).

No. 2900. Fancy.
Bronze Base, $12.00 (TROPICAL).

GOLD AND SILVER PLATE.

No. 050.
Pear Shape, $7.00 (TURMOIL).

No. 070
Pear Shape, $6.00 (TUNE).

No. 080, $7.50 (TUNNEL).

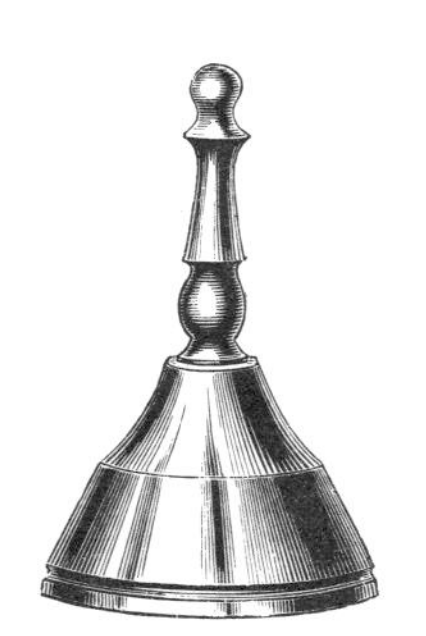

No. 098, $7.00 (TWINKLE).

No. 0102, $10.00 (TYRANT).
Gold Plated, 12.00 (TYRO).

No. 091, $7.00 (TURRET).

No. 093, $9.00 (TWANG).

No. 094, $16.00 (TWIG).

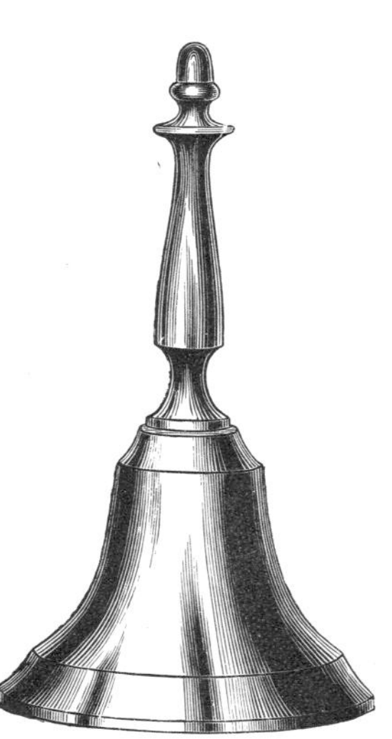

No. 0101, $16.00 (TYPE).

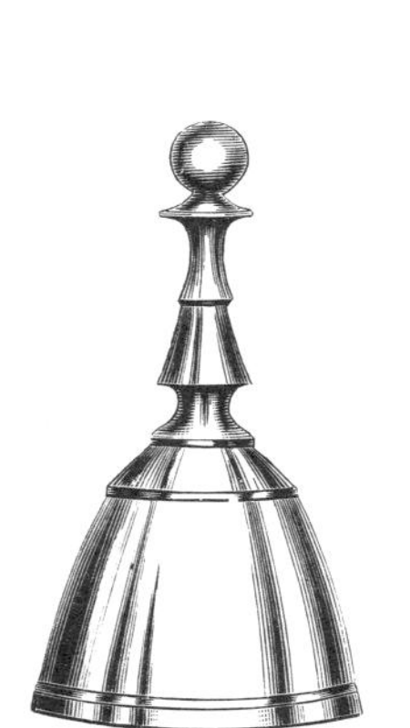

No. 090. Extra Finish.
Plated, . $16.00 (TURNER).
Real Bronze, 15.00 (TURNIP).

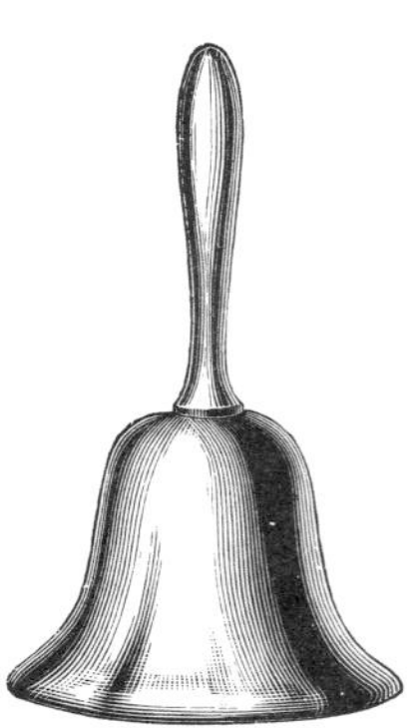

No. 086, $10.00 (TURKEY).

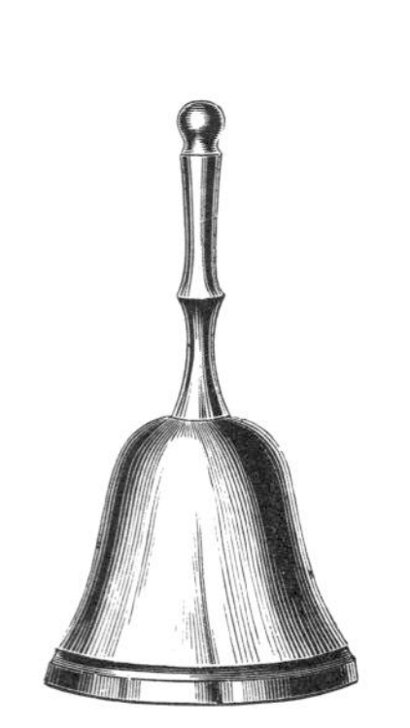

No. 092, $8.00 (TUTOR).

NICKEL SILVER, SILVER SOLDERED.

(PRICES FOR EACH.)

No. 022.
Embossed, . . $6.00 (PROMENADE).
Embossed, Old Silver, 6.50 (PROLONG).
Embossed, Gold Inlaid, 7.00 (PROLOGUE).

No. 024.
Silver,. . $4.75 (PROJECTILE).
Old Silver, 5.25 (PROHIBIT).
Gold Inlaid, 6.00 (PRESIDENT).

No. 023.
Embossed, . . $6.50 (PROFUSION).
Embossed, Old Silver, 7.00 (PRODUCTIVE).
Embossed, Gold Inlaid, 7.50 (PRODIGAL).

No. 025.
Silver, . $5.00 (PROBATION).
Old Silver, 5.50 (PROBABLE).
Gold Inlaid, 6.50 (PRISONER).

BUTTON HOOKS, SHAVING BRUSHES, ETC.

(FULL SIZE.)

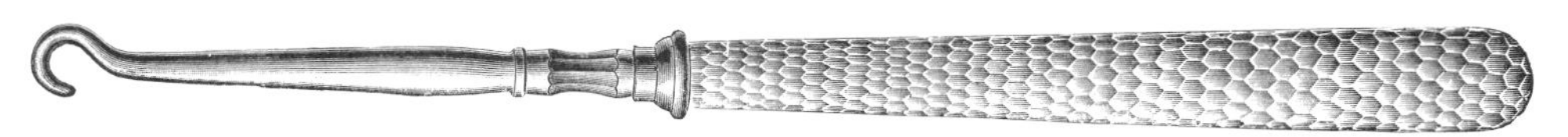

No. 3. BUTTON HOOK.
Satin, $1.75 (REMAND). Satin, Engraved, $2.00 (REMAIN). Hammered, Old Silver, $2.00 (REMEDY).

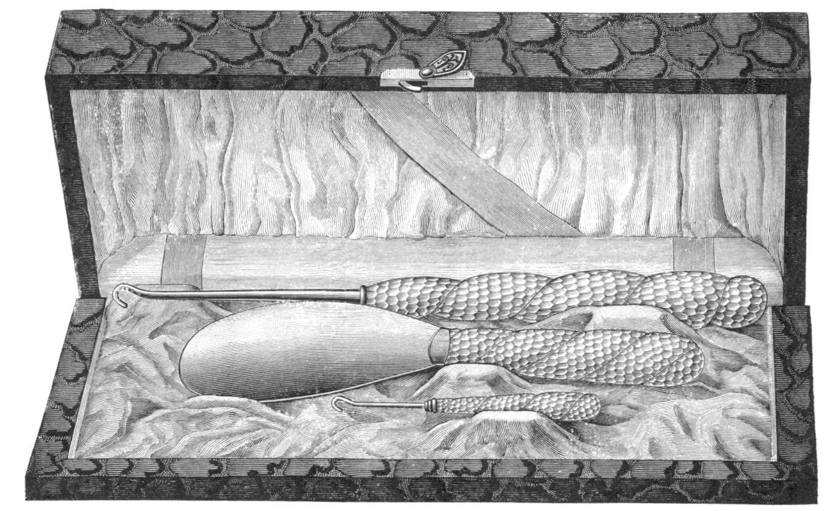

No. 2. GLOVE.
Satin, Engraved, . $1.50 (REMARK).
Hammered, Old Silver, 1.50 (REMIND).

PLUSH CASE, CONTAINING ONE EACH:
No. 5 Hammered, Old Silver Button Hook, . $3.00 (RELIANCE).
No. 5 Hammered, Old Silver Shoe Horn, . . 3.00 (REGISTRY).
No. 1 Hammered, Old Silver Glove Buttoner, . 1.50 (REGATTA).
Complete, in Case, ... 11.50 (REGULATION).
(Half Size.)

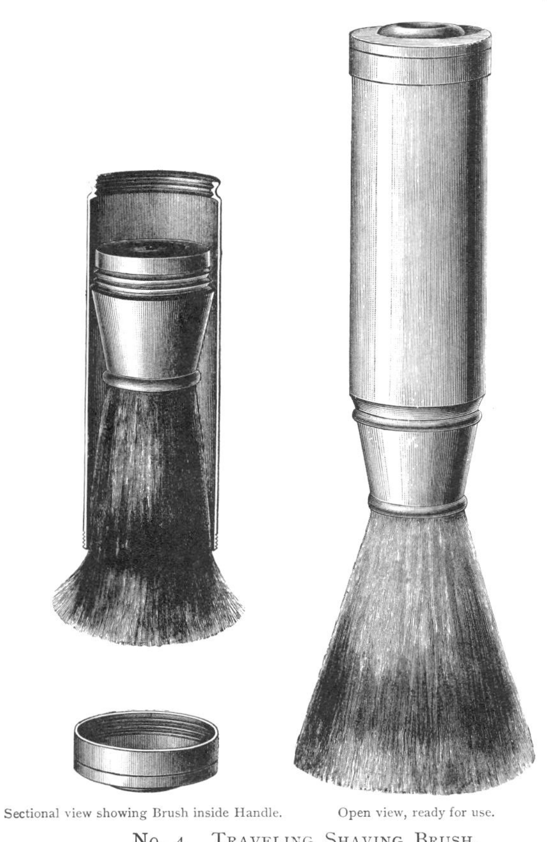

Sectional view showing Brush inside Handle. Open view, ready for use.

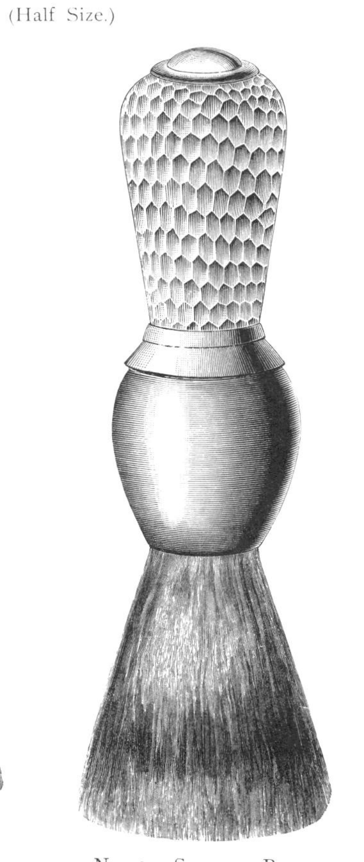

No. 4. Arabesque.
Old Silver, $2.25 (RELATION).

No. 4. TRAVELING SHAVING BRUSH.
Satin, ... $3.75 (REINSURE).
Hammered, Old Silver, 4.25 (RELEVANT).

No. 2. SHAVING BRUSH.
Satin, ... $3.50 (RELENT).
Hammered, Old Silver, 4.00 (RELAPSE).

No. 6. Moorish.
Hammered, Old Silver, $3.00 (REGARD).
Moorish, Old Silver, . 3.50 (REISSUE).
No. 6. SHOE HORN TO MATCH.
Hammered, Old Silver, $3.00 (RELIC).
Moorish, Old Silver, . 3.50 (RELISH).

GOLD AND SILVER PLATE.

No. 6. Moorish, Old Silver Whisk Broom.

Satin, ...	$2.75	(RABBLE).
Arabesque, Old Silver, .	3.00	(REMISS).
Hammered, Old Silver, .	3.00	(REMNANT).
Moorish, Old Silver, .	3.25	(REMODEL).

(Half Size.)

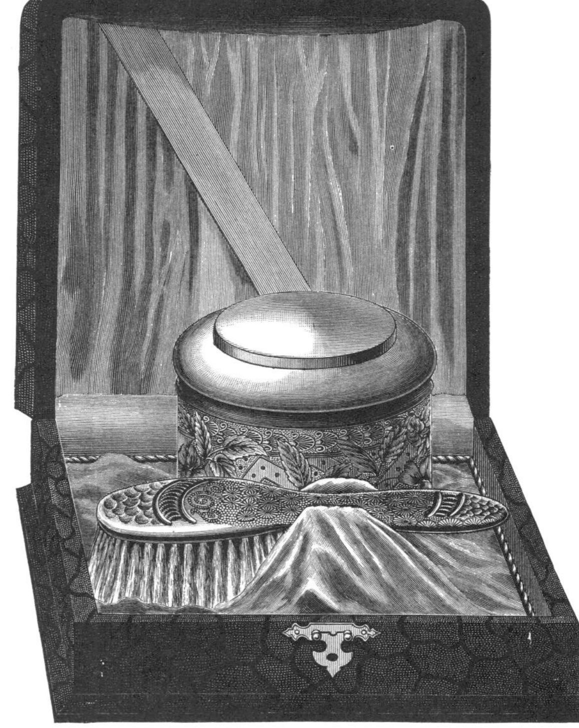

Plush Case, containing Infant Hair Brush and Puff Box.

Complete, ...	$14.25	(REPAST)
No. 400 Brush—Moorish, Old Silver,	3.75	(REPAY).
No. 9 Puff Box—Old Silver, . .	6.00	(RENTAL).
Plush Case, ...	4.50	(REMOUNT).

(Half Size.)

No. 5. Hammered Whisk Broom.

Satin, ...	$2.75	(REPAIRER).
Arabesque, Old Silver, .	3.00	(RENTROLL).
Hammered, Old Silver, .	3.00	(RENEWAL).
Moorish, Old Silver, .	3.25	(RENDITION).

(Half Size.)

No. 45. Whisk Broom Holder.

Enameled Copper, Old Silver Pockets, $9.00 (REMORSE).

(Price does not include Broom.)

(One-Third Size.)

No. 30. Whisk Broom Holder.

Old Silver, ...	$9.75	(REMOTE).
Old Silver, Gold Inlaid, .	10.75	(REMOVE).

(Price does not include Broom.)

(One-Third Size.)

Trade Mark.
WHITE METAL.

BRUSHES, COMBS, ETC.

(Half Size.)

Trade Mark.
NICKEL SILVER.

No. 010. Back Comb.
Silver, . . . $2.50 (GARMENT).
Silver, Gold Inlaid, 3.00 (GARNER.)

No. 011. Back Comb.
Satin, Engraved, ... $2.50 (GARNET).
Satin, Engraved, Gold Inlaid, 3.00 (GARNISH).

No. 012. Back Comb.
Silver, . . . $1.75 (GARB).
Gilt, . . . 2.00 (GARDEN).

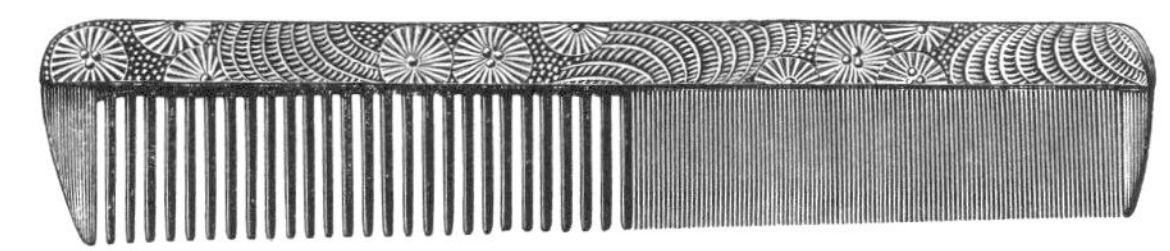

No. 40. Moorish, Old Silver Comb.
Satin, . . . $3.25 (REALIZE). Hammered, Old Silver, $3.50 (RAWHIDE).
Arabesque, Old Silver, 3.50 (RECITAL). Moorish, Old Silver, . 3.75 (REACTION).
Embossed, . . . $4.00 (RECAPTURE).

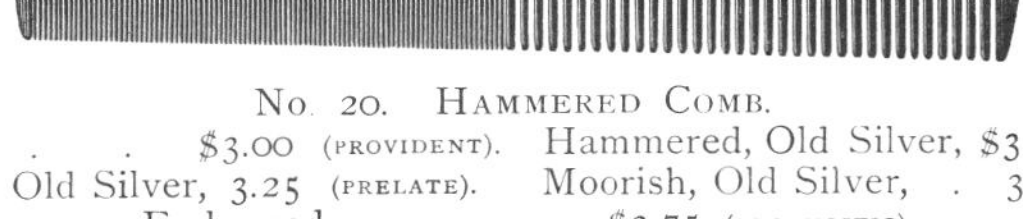

No. 20. Hammered Comb.
Satin, ... $3.00 (PROVIDENT). Hammered, Old Silver, $3.25 (PRIDE).
Arabesque, Old Silver, 3.25 (PRELATE). Moorish, Old Silver, . 3.50 (PREFIX).
Embossed, . . . $3.75 (PROGNOSTIC).

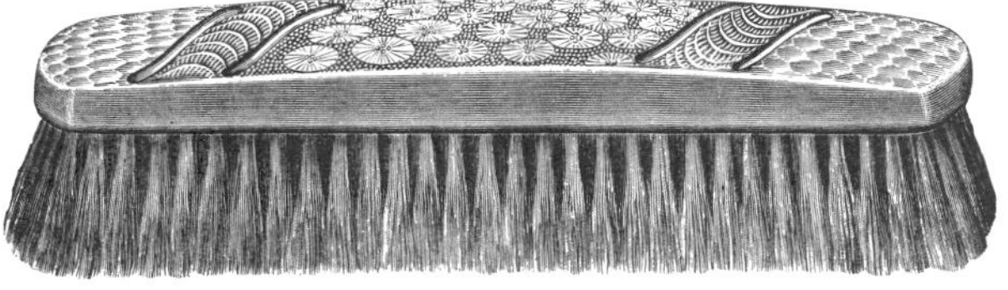

No. 300. Embossed Hair Brush.
Satin, . . $5.50 (PRIMARY). Arabesque, Old Silver, $6.00 (PRESUMER).
Satin, Engraved, 6.00 (PREFECT). Hammered, Old Silver, 6.00 (PROFUSELY).
Embossed, . 8.00 (PRODUCT). Moorish, Old Silver, . 6.50 (PRINCELY).

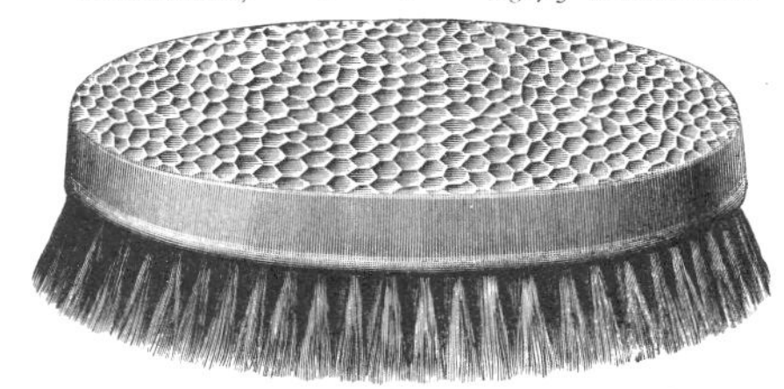

No. 500. Hammered Military Hair Brush.
Satin, . . $6.50 (REALITY). Hammered, Old Silver, $7.00 (READING).
Satin, Engraved, 7.00 (REASONER). Moorish, Old Silver, . 7.50 (RAVENOUS).

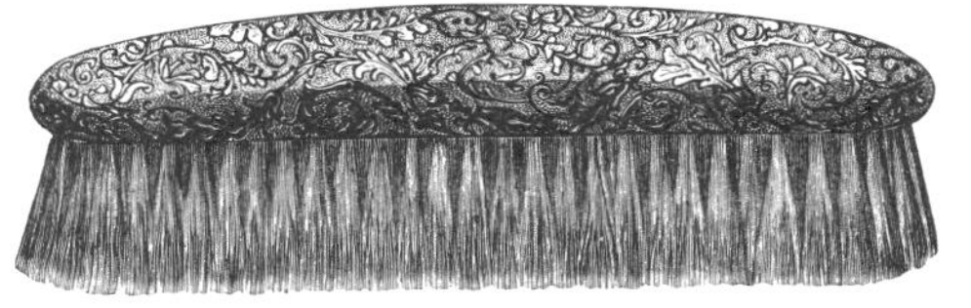

No. 200. Moorish, Old Silver Clothes Brush.
Satin, ... $5.50 (PRESSURE). Hammered, Old Silver, $6.00 (RAVAGE).
Satin, Engraved, . 6.00 (PRELUDE). Moorish, Old Silver, . 6.50 (RAVELIN).
Arabesque, Old Silver, 6.00 (PRESAGE). Embossed, ... 8.00 (RAWNESS).

No. 100. Arabesque, Old Silver Hat Brush.
Satin, ... $4.75 (PRESENCE). Hammered, Old Silver, $5.25 (PRIME).
Satin, Engraved, . 5.25 (PREPENSE). Moorish, Old Silver, . 5.75 (PRESTO).
Arabesque, Old Silver, 5.25 (PREMIER). Embossed, ... 7.00 (PREMISE).

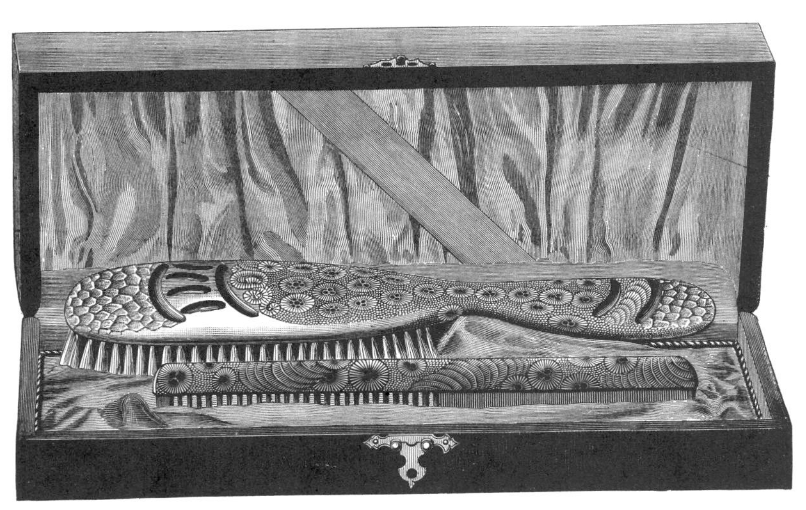

Hair Brush and Comb in Plush Case, complete, $14.75 (RATHER).
No. 300 Moorish, Old Silver Hair Brush, . 6.50 (RATTLE).
No. 40 Moorish, Old Silver Comb, ... 3.75 (RATIO).
Plush Case, ... 4.50 (RASH).

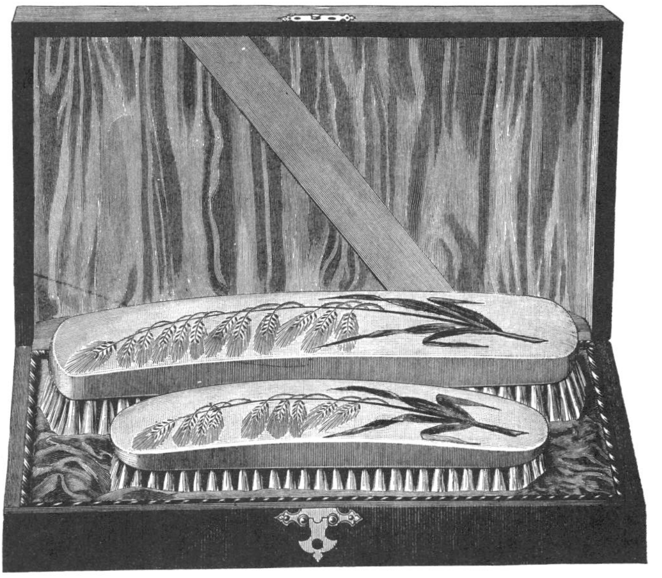

Hat and Clothes Brush in Plush Case, complete, $15.75 (QUIVER).
No. 100 Satin, Engraved Hat Brush, . . . 5.25 (QUOTA).
No. 200 Satin, Engraved Clothes Brush, . . 6.00 (QUONDAM).
Plush Case, ... 4.50 (QUICKSTEP).

GOLD AND SILVER PLATE.

No. 4.
Silver, . $3.25 (GAMBOL).
Gilt, . . 3.50 (GAMBREL).

No. 50. Hammered Old Silver Manicure Set, Seven Pieces in Plush Case, $21.50 (REFUTE).

Cream Boxes, . each, $2.00 (REGALIA).
Nail File, . . . 2.75 (REGALE).
Cuticle Knife, . . 2.75 (REGAIN).
Polisher, . . 4.00 (REFUSAL).
Scissors, . each, 1.75 (REFUGE).
Plush Case, . 4.50 (REDTOP).

No. 2.
Silver, . $2.75 (GANGWAY).
Silver and Gold, 3.00 (GAPE).

No. 4.
Silver, . . $2.75 (GAMUT).
Silver and Gold Inlaid, 3.00 (GANG).

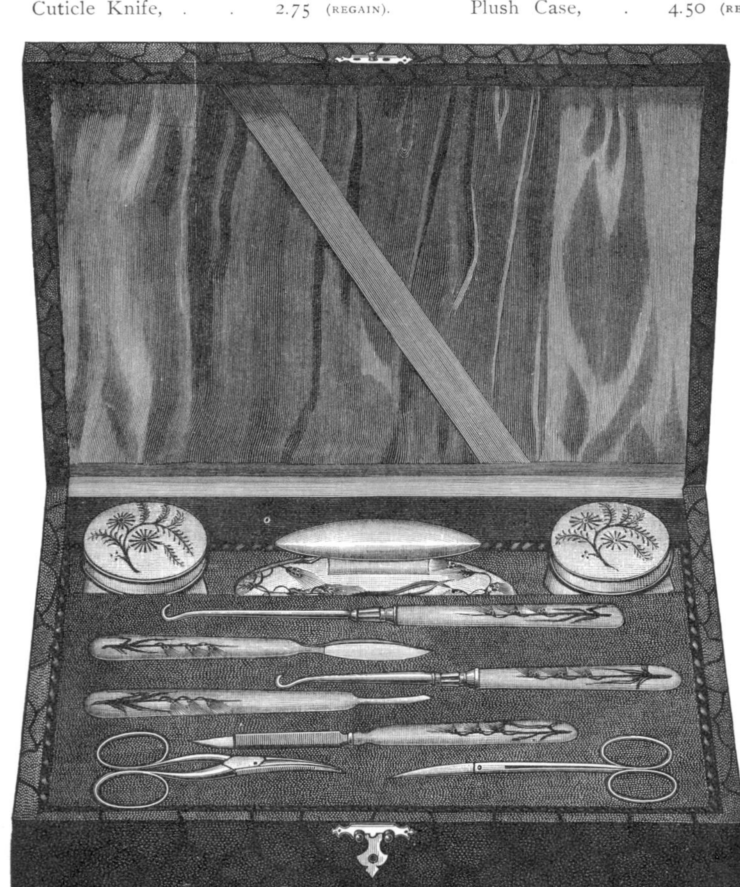

No. 6.
Silver, . . $2.25 (GARGLE).
Silver and Gold Inlaid, 2.50 (GARLAND).

No. 51. Satin Engraved Manicure Set, Ten Pieces in Plush Case, . . $28.75 (RAPPER).

Cream Boxes, . each, $2.00 (REFRESH).
Scissors, . . each, 1.75 (REFRACT).
Nail File, . . . 2.75 (REFORM).
Polisher, . $4.00 (REDNESS).
Cuticle Knife, 2.75 (REENACT).
Corn Knife, 2.75 (REFINERY).
No. 2 Glove Button Hook, $1.50 (REFEREE).
No. 3 Button Hook, . 2.00 (RECOGNIZE).
Plush Case, . . . 5.50 (REFLEX).

GOLD AND SILVER PLATE.

(FULL SIZE.)

EMBOSSED. MOORISH.

No. 17 INK ERASERS.
Embossed, Old Silver, . $2.75 (TEASER).
Moorish, Old Silver, . 3.00 (TASTEFULLY).

No. 7. GLOVE BUTTONER.
Embossed, Old Silver, $1.25 (TAPERING).

No. 8. BUTTON HOOK.
Embossed, Old Silver, $1.50 (SWEAL).

No. 17 LETTER OPENER.
Embossed, Old Silver, $3.00 (TALMUD).

No. 7. SHOE HORN.
Silver, . . $2.00 (SUBLIME).
Etched, Old Silver, 2.50 (SUBSALT).
(Half Size.

No. 17 PAPER KNIFE.
Embossed, Old Silver, $3.50 (TEMPLAR).

No. 9. BUTTON HOOK.
Embossed, Old Silver, $2.00 (TEDDER).

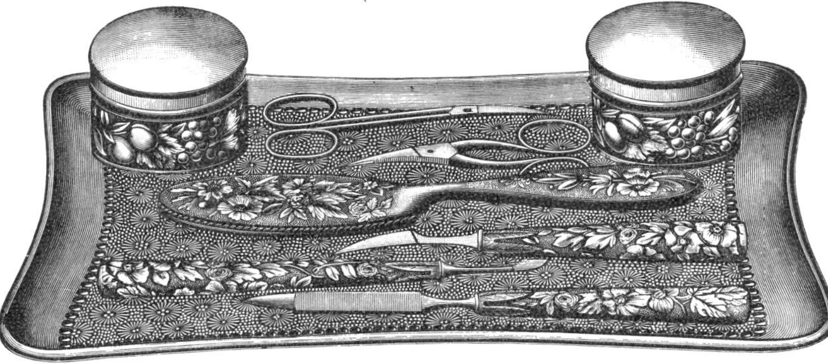

No. 52. MANICURE SET. Embossed, Old Silver.
Nine Pieces with Tray, . . . $25 50 (THIRSTY).

Nail File, . . $2.25 (THINLY).
Polisher, . . 3.75 (THEREAT).
Cuticle Knife, . . $2.25 (THEREON).
Corn Knife, . . . 2.25 (THANKLESS).
Scissors, . . each, $1.75 (THICKNESS).
Cream Boxes, . " 2.00 (TEUTONIC).

No. 115—9 inch Tray. Moorish, Old Silver, $7.50 (TERRIFY). (Half Size.)

GOLD AND SILVER PLATE.

(CANDELABRA ONE-THIRD SIZE.)

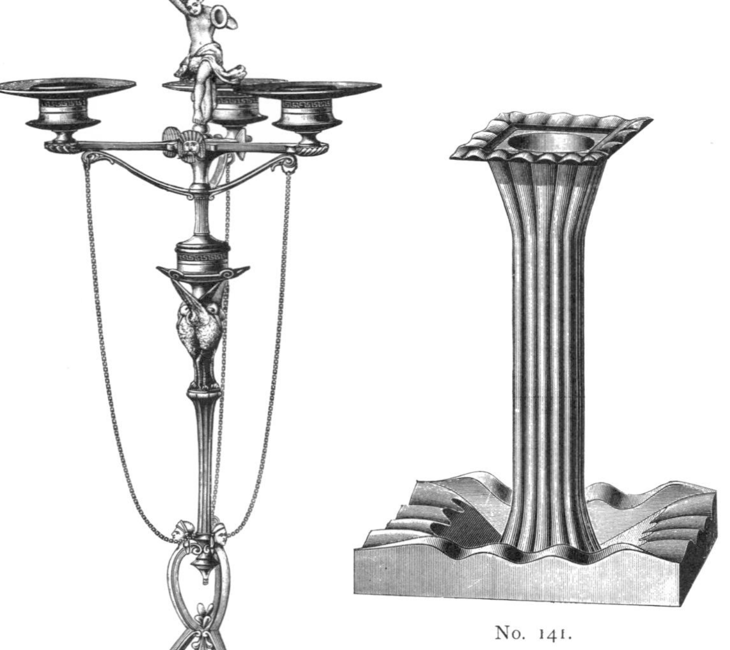

No. 141.
Silver, . . $6.50 (SUCCEED).
Old Silver, . 7.00 (SUCTION).
(Half Size.)

No. 140. CANDLESTICK.
Silver, . . $5.50 (SUFFICIENT).
Old Silver, . 6.00 (SUMMER).
(Half Size.)

No. 47.
Silver, Gold Inlaid, . $25.00 (TAILORESS).

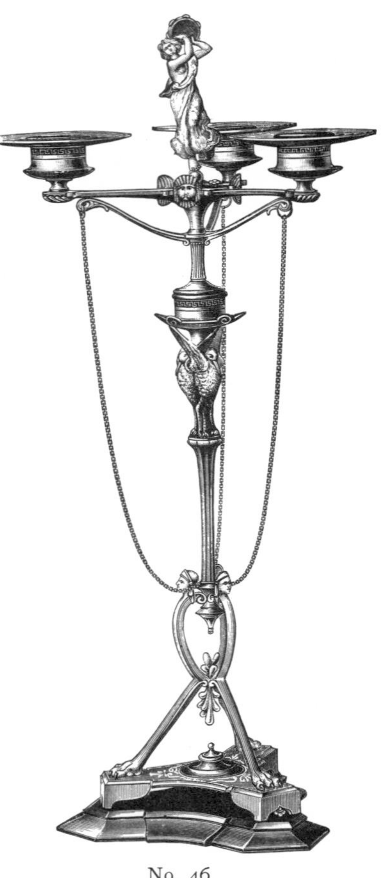

No. 46.
Silver, Gold Inlaid, . $25.00 (TABLATURE).

No. 048. FOUR-LIGHT.
Nickel Silver, Hard Soldered.
Silver, . . $73.00 (TEMPTATION).
Old Silver, . 75.00 (TAMENESS).

No. 45.
Silver, . . . $15.00 (TALMUDIC).
Silver, Gold Inlaid, . 17.00 (TALLYMAN).

No. 43. VASE CANDELABRA.
Satin, Engraved, . . . $17.50 (TALESMAN).
Satin, Engraved, XX Gold Inlaid, 22 50 (TALKATIVE).

Trade Mark.
WHITE METAL.

CANDLESTICKS, CANDELABRA, ETC.

(One-Third Size.)

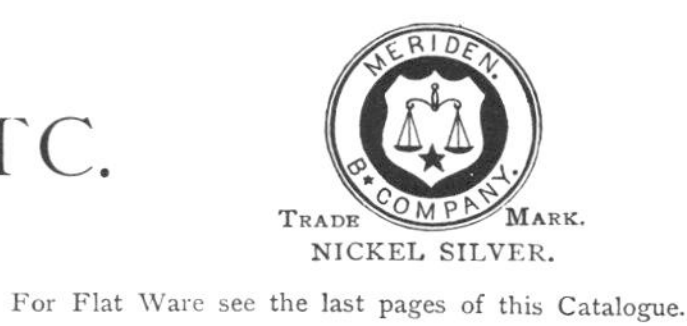

Trade Mark.
NICKEL SILVER.

For Flat Ware see the last pages of this Catalogue.

For Spoons, Forks, Knives, etc., see last pages of this Catalogue.

No. 28.
Five Lights, . . $48.00 (loyal).
(One-Third Size.)

No. 134.
Old Silver, ... $15.00 (tempest).
Old Silver, Gold Inlaid, 17.50 (temerity).
(Half Size.)

No. 135.
Old Silver, ... $15.00 (teaching).
Old Silver, Gold Inlaid, 17.50 (taurus).
(Half Size.)

GOLD AND SILVER PLATE.

No. 35.
Five Light, . . $50.00 (TEMPORAL).

No. 26.
Three Light . . $24.00 (LURK).
Five Light, . . 33.00 (LUSCIOUS);

No. 38.
Three Light, . . $24.00 (UPRISE).
Five Light, . . 33.00 (UPROAR).

No. 42. HAMMERED.

	Three Light.		Five Light.	
Plain,	$24.00	(RACKET).	$33.50	(RADIAL).
Plain, Old Silver,	25.00	(RADIANCE).	35.00	(RADIATE).
Hammered, Old Silver,	28.00	(RADICAL).	38.00	(RAID).
Hammered, Old Silver, XX Gold Inlaid,	32.00	(RAJAH).	42.00	(RARITY).

No. 24.

Three Light,	$33.00	(LOZENGE).
Five Light,	36.00	(LUCID).
Seven Light,	39.00	(LUCK).

No. 40.

Three Light, . . $23.00 (QUININE).
Five Light, . . 30.00 (QUINTET).

No. 27.

Three Light, . . $24.00 (LUSTRE).
Five Light, . . 33.00 (LUSTY).

No. 37.

Three Light, . . $22.50 (UNICORN).
Five Light, . . 30.00 (UNION).

No. 39. (HEIGHT, 20 INCHES.)

Three Light, . . $23.50 (UNIQUE).
Five Light, . . 31.00 (UNISON).

No. 39 has arms like No. 38 (page 66), with base and sockets like No. 37.

No. 101.

Silver, ... $9.50 (LURCH)
Gilt, ... 10.50 (LURE).
Gold and Steel Finish, 11.50 (LURID)

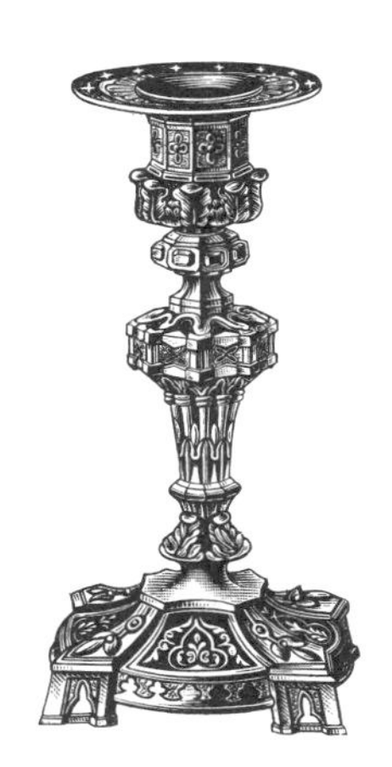

No. 128.

Old Silver, . . $6.50 (MAROON).
Old Silver, Gold Inlaid, 8.00 (TELESCOPE).

No. 115.

Silver, . . . $9.50 (LUNAR).
Gilt, . . . 10.50 (LUNCH).
Gold and Steel Finish, 11.50 (LUNCHEON).

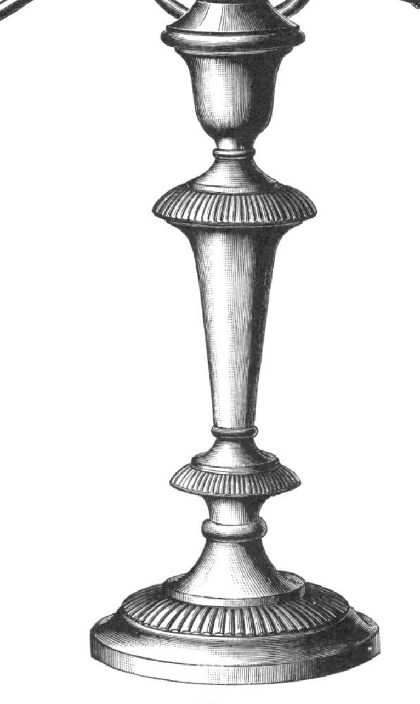

No. 41.

Three Light, . . . $22.50 (UNITE).
Five Light, . . . 30.00 (UPRIGHT)

No. 33.

Silver, ... $18.00 (MACE)
Silver, Gold Inlaid, . 21.00 (MACHINE).

No. 34.

Silver, ... $20.00 (LUTE).
Silver, Gold Inlaid, . 23.50 (LUXURIANT).

GOLD AND SILVER PLATE.

No. 98.
Old Silver, . $7.00 (MANGER).
Gold Inlaid, . 8.00 (MANGO).

No. 97.
Silver, . . . $7.00 (MAGNET).
Gilt, . . . 8.00 (MAGNIFY).
Gold and Steel Finish, 9.00 (MAGNOLIA).

No. 114.
Silver, . . . $4.50 (MAGPIE).
Gilt, . . . 5.00 (MAIN).
Gold and Steel Finish, 5.50 (MAINTAIN).

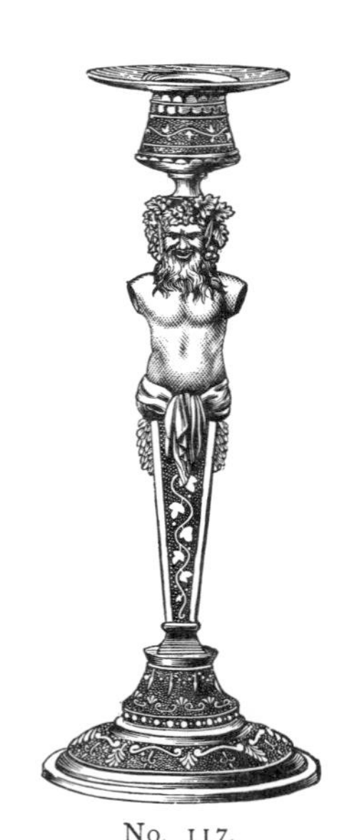

No. 117.
Old Silver, . $6.75 (MANFUL).

No. 36.
Three Light, . . $20.00 (TARPAULIN).
Five Light, . . 25.00 (TARLATAN).

No. 31.
Silver, ... $13.50 (LUXURY).
Silver, Gold Inlaid, . 16.00 (LYCEUM).

No. 32.
Silver, ... $17.00 (LYNX).
Silver, Gold Inlaid, . 20.00 (LYRE).

GOLD AND SILVER PLATE.

No. 136.
Enameled Copper Base,
Old Silver Mountings, $4.50 (TANGIBLE).
(Half Size.)

No. 137. CANDLESTICK AND MATCH HOLDER.
Enameled Copper Base, Old Silver Mountings, $6.75 (TANYARD).
(Half Size.)

No. 138. CANDLESTICK AND MATCH HOLDER.
Enameled Copper Base, Old Silver Mountings, $7.50 (TANTALIZE).
(Half Size.)

One Pair, Closed. No. 130. TRAVELING CANDLESTICKS. Single, Open.
(Full Size.)

Silver, . . per pair, $4.00 (MARVEL).
Hammered, . per pair, 5.00 (TANNERY).

No. 3. Height, 9 inches, $5.00 (QUERY).
No. 5. Height, 10 inches, 5.75 (QUEST).

No. 11. Height, 10 inches, $6.50 (QUESTION).
No. 10. Height, 11 inches, 7.00 (QUIET).
No. 9. Height, 12 inches, 7.50 (QUILL).

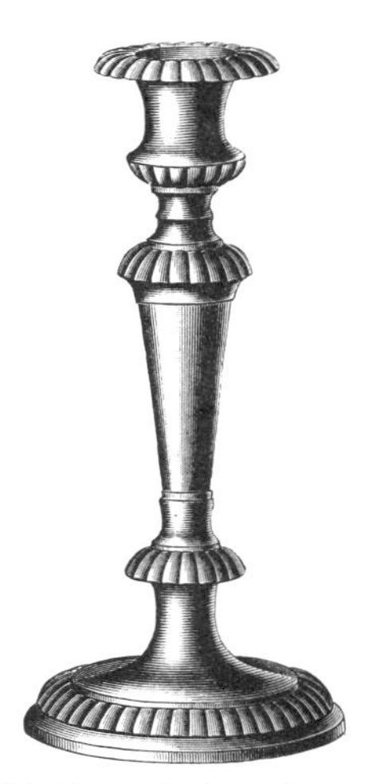

No. 2. Height, 9 inches, $4.50 (QUILT).
No. 4. Height, 10 inches, 5.25 (QUINCE).

GOLD AND SILVER PLATE.

No. 127.

Old Silver, . . . $3.00 (MARAUD).

Old Silver, Gold Inlaid, 3.75 (TAMARIND).

No. 125.

CANDLESTICK AND MATCH BOX.

Gold and Steel Finish, . $7.50 (MAMMON).

No. 126.

Old Silver, . . . $3.00 (MARINE).

Old Silver and Gold Inlaid, 3.75 (TALLYHO).

No. 109.

Silver, . . . $4.00 (MANIFEST).

Gold and Steel Finish, 5.00 (MANIKIN).

No. 132.

Silver, ... $4.00 (TAMPION).

Silver, Gold Inlaid, . 5.00 (TAMBOURINE).

No. 110

Silver, . . . $4.00 (MARBLE).

Gold and Steel Finish, 5.00 (MARGIN).

No. 107.

Silver, . . . $3.50 (MAJOR).

Gold and Steel Finish, 4.50 (MALT).

No. 108.

Silver, . . . $3.50 (MANKIND).

Gold and Steel Finish, 4.50 (MANNER).

No. 94.

Silver, . . . $3.50 (MANTEL).

Gold and Steel Finish, 4.50 (MANTILLA).

No. 111.

Silver, . . . $4.00 (MARK).

Gold and Steel Finish, 5.00 (MARLINE).

No. 113.

Silver, . . . $5.00 (MADRIGAL).

Gold and Steel Finish, 6.00 (MAGIC).

No. 129.

Silver, . . $6.25 (MARSHAL).

Silver, Gold Inlaid, 7.25 (MARTEN).

No. 131.

Silver, . . $3.50 (TACKLING).

Silver, Gold Inlaid, 4.00 (TACTILE).

CARD TABLES.

(ONE-THIRD SIZE.)

No. 7800.

Old Copper, ... $80.00 (TALENTED).
Old Silver, ... 85.00 (TACTICIAN).
Old Silver, XX Gold Inlaid, . 100.00 (TABULATE).

No. 7700.

Hammered and Applied, Old Silver, . $75.00 (TALBOT).
Hammered and Applied, XX Gold Inlaid, 90.00 (ANGUISH).

The Ornamental Tops of these Tables are protected by beveled Plate Glass.

No. 7500.

Old Silver, ... $65.00 (TALISMAN).

Damascene and Applied, XX Gold Inlaid, 75.00 (ANGLER).

The Ornamental Top of this Table is protected by beveled Plate Glass.

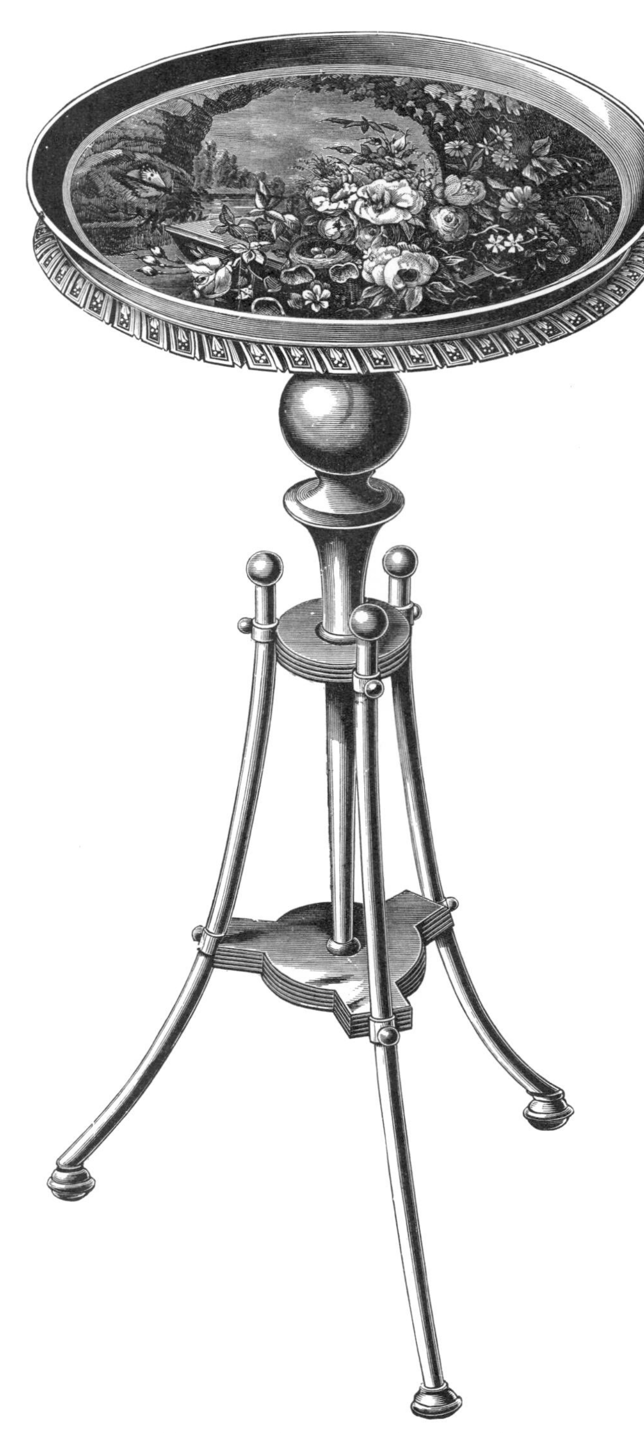

No. 7400. DECORATED PORCELAIN TOP.

Gold and Steel Finish, . . . $45.00 (SAXON).

(Assorted Decorations.)

No. 7600.

Hammered and Applied, Old Silver, . $70.00 (SYSTEM).

Hammered and Applied, XX Gold Inlaid, 80.00 (ANGULAR).

The Ornamental Top of this Table is protected by beveled Plate Glass.

No. 6900.

Height, 35 inches.

Old Silver, Gold Inlaid, . . $125.00 (SAYING).

CARD RECEIVERS.

(One-Third Size.)

No. 226. Enameled Copper.

Old Silver Centre, . . $12.00 (syntax).

XX Gold Inlaid Centre, . 13.50 (syndicate).

No. 225.

Old Silver, . . . $11.50 (synopsis).

Old Silver, XX Gold Inlaid, 13.00 (symphony).

No. 227. Enameled Copper.

Old Silver Centre, . . $12.00 (symmetry).

XX Gold Inlaid Centre, . 13.50 (symbol).

No. 228. Enameled Copper.

Old Silver Centre, . . $15.00 (sylvan).

XX Gold Inlaid Centre, . 16.50 (sycamore).

No. 193.

Silver, Gold Lined, . . . $20.00 (hilarity).

Silver, Gold Inlaid and Gold Lined, 23.00 (hillock).

No. 200.

Old Silver, . . . $18.00 (memorial).

Old Silver, XX Gold Inlaid, 20.00 (mentor).

GOLD AND SILVER PLATE.

No. 213.

Silver, . . $9.00 (SWORD).
Silver, Gold Inlaid, 10.50 (SWIVEL).
(Non-Tarnishable.)

No. 5. PLAYING CARD CASE.
Holding Two Packs.
Silver, Gold Inlaid, . $7.50 (PREAMBLE).
(Non-Tarnishable.)

No. 214.

Satin, Engraved, . . $8.50 (SWIFTLY).
Satin, Engraved, Gold Inlaid, 10.00 (SWARTHY).
(Non-Tarnishable.)

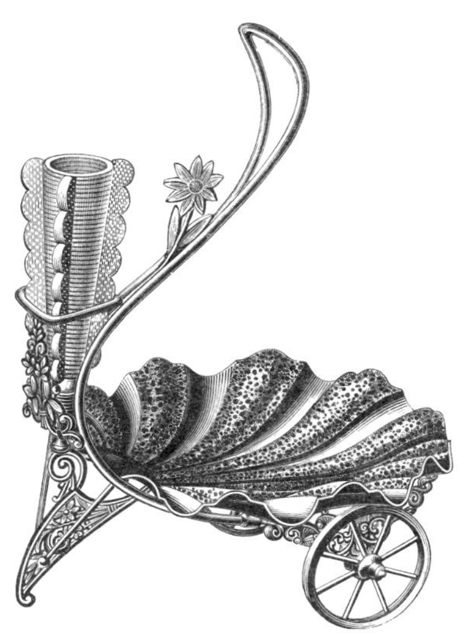

No. 176.

Silver, . . . $7.50 (HAMMER).
Gold Lined, . . 8.50 (HAMPER).

No. 174.

Chased, . . . $10.00 (HABIT).
Niello and Gold, . 11.50 (HACK).

No. 157.

Plain, Gold Lined, . . $8.00 (SUSPENSION).
Damascene, Gold Lined, . 9.00 (HARMONY).

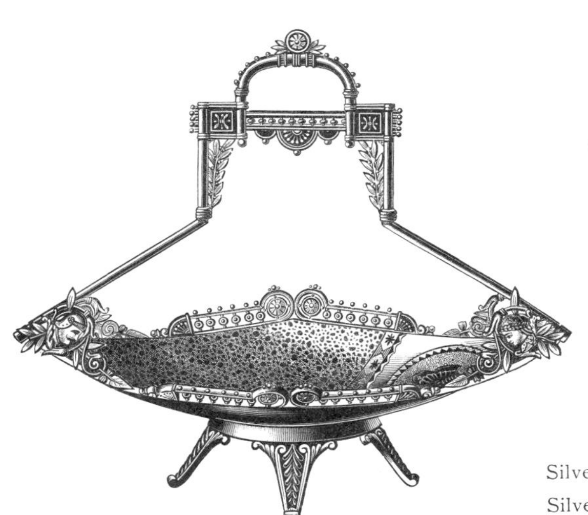

No. 181.

Silver, ... $7.50 (GUARDIAN).
Silver, Gold Inlaid, . 8.50 (GUAVA).

No. 192.

Silver, Gold Lined, . . $10 50 (HERRING).
Silver, Gold Inlaid and Gold Lined, 12.50 (HESPER).

No. 183.

Chased, ... $8.00 (GRUMBLE).
Chased, Gold Lined, ... 9.00 (GUANO).
Chased, Gold Inlaid and Gold Lined, 9.50 (GUARANTEE).

GOLD AND SILVER PLATE.

No. 220.

Enameled Copper, Old Silver Standard, $6.50- (SURGICAL).

(Non-Tarnishable).

No. 211.

Chased, . . $6.00 (SURFEIT).

Chased, Gold Inlaid, 7.50 (SUPREME).

No. 221. MIRROR CENTRE.

Enameled Copper, Old Silver Standard, $7.50 (SUPINE).

(Non-Tarnishable.)

No. 215.

Old Silver, Brocade, Chased, . $7.50 (SUPERNAL).

Brocade, Chased, X Gold Inlaid, 9.00 (SUPERBLY).

(Non-Tarnishable).

No 222.

Enameled Copper, Old Silver Mountings, $6.50 (SUNSHINE).

(Non-Tarnishable.)

No. 207.

Hammered and Applied, . . $8.50 (MEDIUM).

Hammered and Applied, Gold Inlaid, 10.00 (MEDLEY).

(Non-Tarnishable.)

No. 224.

Chased, Old Silver, . $8.50 (SURCINGLE).

Chased, X Gold Inlaid, 10.50 (SUPERSEDE).

(Non-Tarnishable.)

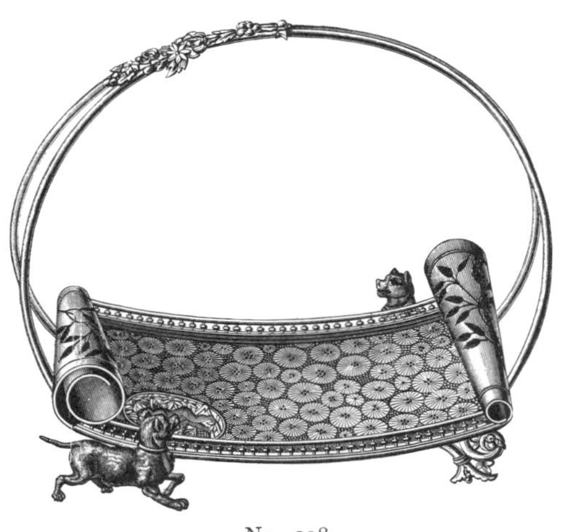

No. 218.

Moorish, Old Silver, . $12.00 (SUNLIGHT).

Moorish, Gold Inlaid, . 13.50 (SUNBEAM).

(Non-Tarnishable.)

No. 217.

Satin, ... $8.00 (SUPPORTER).

Satin, Gold Inlaid, . 10.00 (SUPERSCRIBE).

(Non-Tarnishable.)

No. 219.
Hammered, Chased, . . . $9.00 (SUMMIT).
Hammered, Chased, Gold Inlaid, 10.50 (SUMMARY).
(Non-Tarnishable.)

No. 194.
Satin, Engraved, . . . $8.50 (HIRSUTE).
Satin, Engraved, Gold Inlaid, 10.50 (HIST).

No. 229.
Satin, ... $8.00 (PRAWN).
Satin, Gold Lined, . . . 9.00 (PRACTICAL).
Satin, Gold Lined, Old Silver Border, 10.00 (POTENTATE).

No. 189.
Moorish, Old Silver, . $11.00 (HEXAGON).
Moorish, Gold, Inlaid, . 13.00 (HIATUS.)
(Non-Tarnishable.)

No. 212.
Old Silver, . . $6.50 (SUFFUSE).
Old Silver, Gold Inlaid, 8.00 (SUITABLE).
(Non-Tarnishable.)

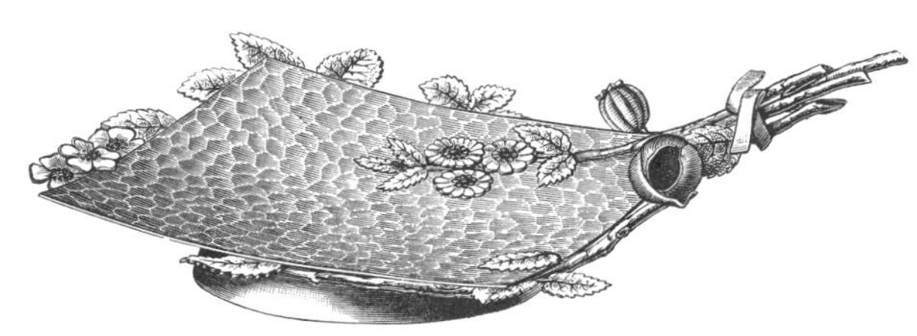

No. 188.
Hammered, Old Silver, . . $10.00 (HIBERNAL).
Hammered, Old Silver, Gold Inlaid, 12.00 (HICKORY).
(Non-Tarnishable.)

No. 182.
Chased, ... $7.00 (GROWTH).
Chased, Gold Lined, . . . 8.00 (GRUDGE).
Chased, Gold Inlaid and Gold Lined, 8.50 (GRUFFLY).

No. 201.
Chased, . . $7.00 (MORALIST).
Chased, Gold Inlaid, 8.50 (MORDANT).

No. 199.
Old Silver, . . $8.50 (MEAL).
Old Silver, Gold Inlaid, 10.00 (MEANDER).
(Non-Tarnishable.)

GOLD AND SILVER PLATE.

No. 206.

Silver, ... $6.50 (MEAD).
Silver, Gold Inlaid, . 7.50 (MEADOW).
(Non-Tarnishable.)

No. 198.

Old Silver, ... $6.50 (MEDICAL).
Old Silver, Gold Inlaid, . 8.00 (MEDICINE).
(Non-Tarnishable.)

No. 155.

Chased, ... $6.00 (HANDY).
Chased, Gold Inlaid, . 7.50 (HANGER).

No. 205.

Old Silver, ... $7.00 (MEED).
Old Silver, Gold Inlaid, . 8.00 (MELEE).
(Non-Tarnishable.)

No. 72

Satin, Gold Lined, . $9.50 (HAVOC).

No. 204.

Old Silver, ... $6.50 (MAYOR).
Old Silver, Gold Inlaid, . 8.00 (MAZE).
(Non-Tarnishable.)

No. 187.

Gold Lined, ... $9.50 (HINGE).
Gold Inlaid and Gold Lined, 10.50 (HINT).

No. 195.

Satin, Engraved, ... $11.50 (HISTORY).
Satin, Engraved, Gold Inlaid, . 13.50 (HITCH).

GOLD AND SILVER PLATE.

No. 209.
Chased, . . $4.50 (SUBURBAN).
Chased, Gold Lined, 5.50 (SUBSIDIZE).
(Non-Tarnishable.)

No. 210.
Brocade, Chased, . . $4.75 (SUBTRACT).
Brocade, Chased, Gold Lined, 5.75 (PRECEDENT).
(Non-Tarnishable.)

No. 208.
Brocade, Chased, . . $4.50 (SUBSISTENCE).
Brocade, Chased, Gold Lined, 5.25 (PRECAUTION).
(Non-Tarnishable.)

No. 196.
Silver, . . $5.00 (MELLOW).
Silver, Gold Lined, 6.00 (MELODY).

No. 147.
Plain, Gold Lined, . $5.50 (HELMET).
Chased, . . . 5.50 (HELP).
Chased, Gold Lined, . 6.00 (HELVE).

No. 197.
Silver, . . $5.50 (MELON).
Silver, Gold Lined, 6.50 (MELT).

No. 130.
Chased, . . $5.00 (HARVEST).
Chased, Gold Lined, 6.00 (HASP).

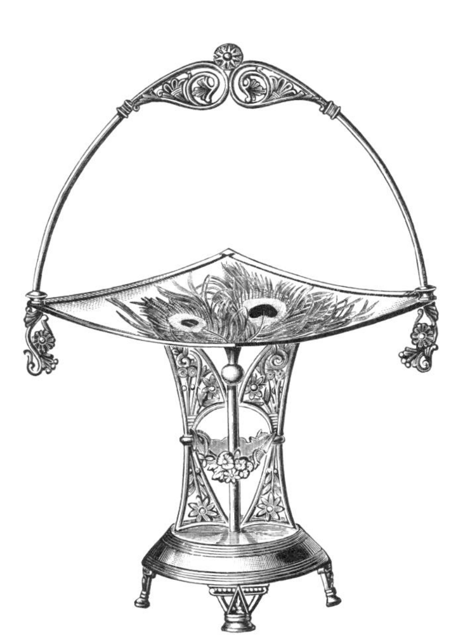

No. 162.
Silver and Gold Inlaid, . $7.50 (HARE).

No. 111.
Old Silver, . . $6.25 (HEAVY).
Old Silver, Gold Lined, 6.75 (HECTOR).

GOLD AND SILVER PLATE.

No. 154.

Brocade, Chased, . . $5.00 (HELD).
Brocade, Chased, Gold Lined, 5.75 (HELM).

No. 153. OVAL.

Plain, . . . $5.00 (HEMLOCK).
Gold Lined, . . 5.50 (HEMP).

No. 152. ROUND.

Plain, . . . $4.50 (HENCE).
Gold Lined, . . 5.00 (HEPTAGON).

No. 141.

Chased, ... $4.50 (HERALD).
Chased, Gold Lined, . 5.50 (HERB).

No. 139.

Plain, . . . $4.50 (HERO).
Gold Lined, . . 5.00 (HEROINE).

No. 158.

Engraved, ... $6.50 (HALYARD).
Engraved, Silver, Gold Inlaid, 7.50 (HAMLET).

No. 223.

Chased, ... $6.50 (SUBMERGE).
Chased, Silver and Gold Inlaid, 7.50 (SUBLET).
(Non-Tarnishable.)

No. 175.

Niello, . . . $7.50 (HACKNEY).
Niello and Gold, . 9.00 (HADDOCK).

No. 148.

Plain, Gold Lined, . $6.50 (HEARTH).
Chased, . . . 6.50 (HEARTY).
Chased, Gold Lined, . 7.00 (HEATH).

No. 149.

Plain, . . . $6.00 (HASSOCK).
Plain, Gold Lined, . 6.50 (HASTEN).

Trade Mark.
White Metal.

CARD CASES AND PORTEMONNAIES.

(ALSO SEE PAGE 77.)

(Half Size.)

Trade Mark.
Nickel Silver.

No. 2. Card Case.
Silver, ... $3.50 (grown).
Old Silver, . . 4.00 (precision).
Silver, Gold Inlaid, 5.00 (grub).

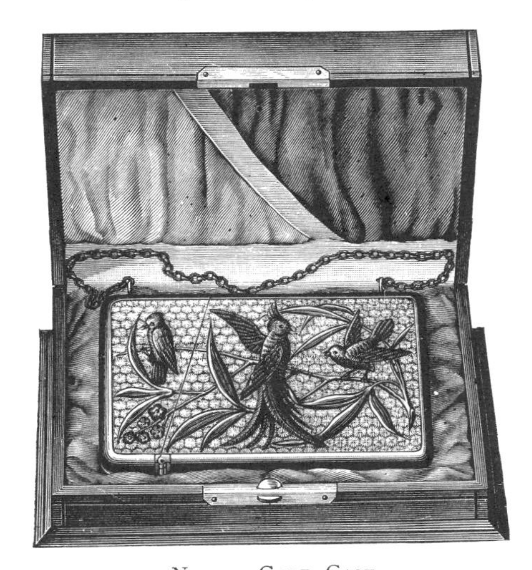

No. 4. Card Case.
Silver, ... $3.50 (gruel).
Old Silver, . . 4.00 (precisely).
Silver, Gold Inlaid, 5.00 (gruff).
Plush or Morocco Cases, $2.50 extra (guard).

No. 3. Card Case.
Silver, ... $3.50 (guess).
Old Silver, . . 4.00 (precipitate).
Silver, Gold Inlaid, 5.00 (guest).

No. 030. Nickel Silver.
Satin, Engraved, . $7.25 (groom).
No. 030½. With Chain on side.
Satin, Engraved, . $7.25 (groove).

No. 031½. Nickel Silver.
Satin, Engraved, . $7.25 (grope).

No. 031. Nickel Silver.
Satin, Engraved, . $7.25 (grot).

Plush or Morocco Cases for above, $2.50 extra (group).

No. 032½. Nickel Silver.
Satin, Engraved, . $7.25 (grow).
No. 032. With Chain on end.
Satin, Engraved, . $7.25 (growl).
Plush or Morocco Case, $2.75 extra (precinct).

No. 050. Portemonnaie.
Satin, Engraved, . $9.50 (grind).
Silver, Gold Inlaid, 10.50 (grip).

No. 053 Portemonnaie.
Satin, Engraved, . $9.50 (grocer).
Silver, Gold Inlaid, 10.50 (grocery).

No. 051. Portemonnaie.
Satin, Engraved, . $9.50 (grit).
Silver, Gold Inlaid, 10.50 (groat).

No. 052. Portemonnaie.
Satin, Engraved, . $9.50 (grist).
Silver, Gold Inlaid, 10.50 (gristle).

Plush or Morocco Cases for above, $3.00 each, extra (groats).

COMBINATION CASTERS.

(One-Third Size.)

No. 2125. Caster.
Showing Caster and Fruit Dish separately.
Chased, 6 No. 93 Bottles, . $27.00 (coach).
Chased, 6 No. 95 Bottles, . 28.50 (coal).
With No. 3 Bell Handle, $2.00 extra (coarse).

No. 2125. Fruit Dish, Gold Lined.

No. 2162. Bowl Gold Lined.
Plain, 6 No. 20 Bottles, ... $21.50 (giaour).
Hammered, 6 No. 20 Bottles, . . . 24.00 (gibe).
Hammered and Applied, 6 No. 20 Bottles, . 25.50 (giddy).
Hammered and Applied, XX Gilt, 6 No. 20 Bottles, 27.00 (gift).

No. 2130.
Bowl Gold Lined.
Chased, 5 No. 12 Bottles, . $18.00 (coast).

No. 2154.
Chased, 6 No. 98 Bottles, . $26.00 (codger).
With Bowl Gold Lined, . 28.00 (codify).

No. 2163.
Bowl Gold Lined.
Plain, 6 No. 19 Bottles, . 22.50 (coercion).

DINNER CASTERS.

(ONE-THIRD SIZE.)

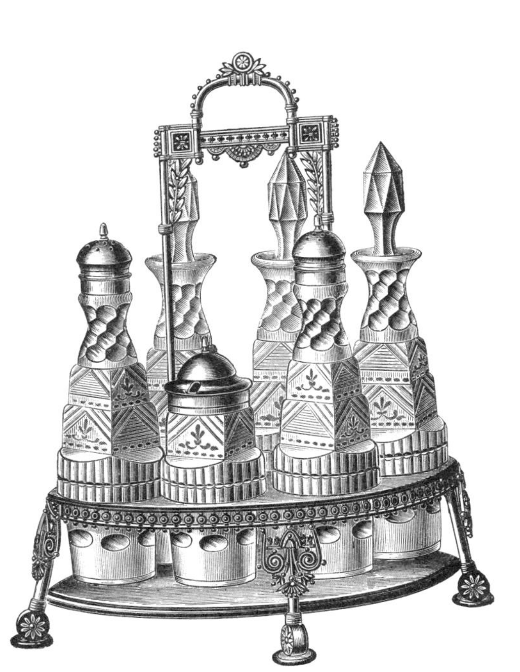

No. 2156.

6 No. 98 Bottles, . $22.00 (COPPER).
6 No. 16 Bottles, . 17.00 (COPPERAS).

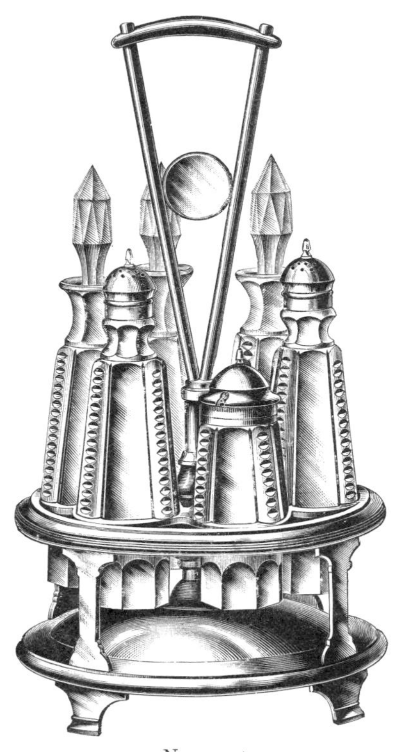

No. 2145.

6 No. 97 Bottles, . $21.00 (CODDLE).
6 No. 13 Bottles, . 14.50 (COERCE).

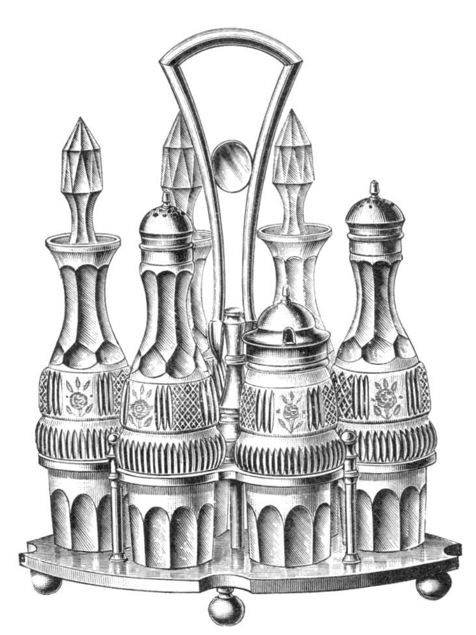

No. 2137.

6 No. 95 Bottles, . $19.00 (COBWEB).

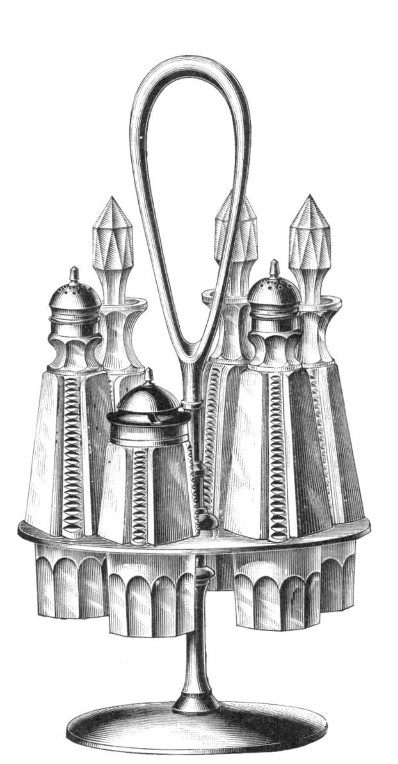

No. 2102½.

6 No. 97 Bottles, . $22.00 (COCKLOFT).
6 No. 11 Bottles, . 15.50 (COCKPIT).

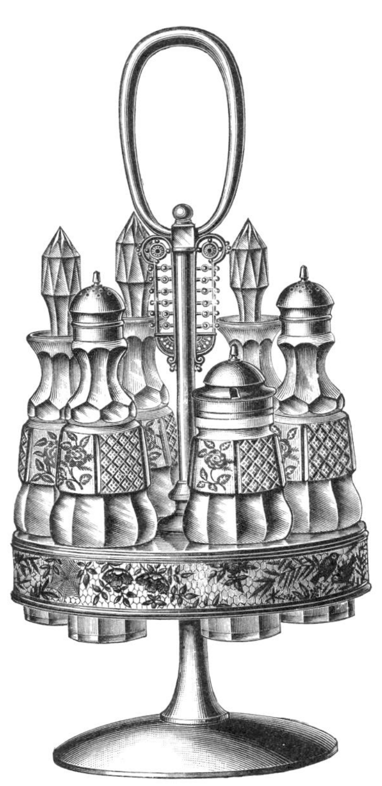

No. 2152.

6 No. 94 Bottles, . $24.00 (COCOA).
6 No. 16 Bottles, . 19.00 (COCOON).

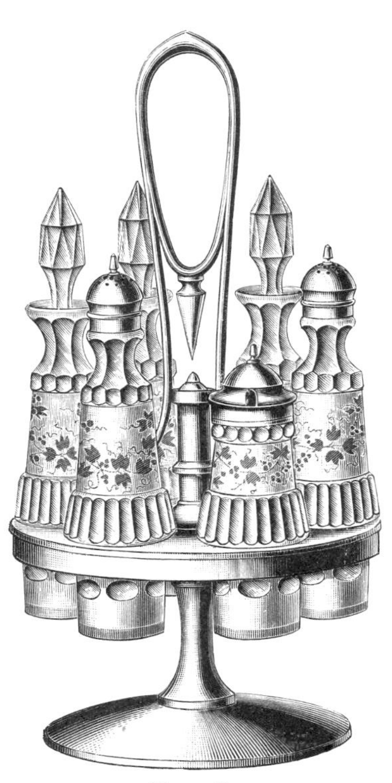

No. 2083.

6 No. 90 Bottles, . $21.00 (COD).
6 No. 11 Bottles, . 18.00 (CODE).

GOLD AND SILVER PLATE.

No. 2167.
Plain, 6 No. 21 Bottles, . . $11.00 (GEYSER).
Satin, Engraved, 6 No. 21 Bottles, 12.50 (ROSEWATER).

No. 2168.
6 No. 11 Bottles, . $12.50 (GIANT).

No. 2166.
6 No. 17 Bottles, . $10.75 (GEWGAW).

No. 2144.
Plain, 6 No. 11 Bottles, . $12.50 (COFFEE).
Chased, 6 No. 11 Bottles, . 13.50 (COFFER).
Chased, 6 No. 95 Bottles, . 20.00 (COG).

No. 2153.
Chased, 6 No. 16 Bottles, . $19.00 (COBBLER).
Chased, 6 No. 98 Bottles, . 24.00 (COCHINEAL).

No. 2133½.
Plain, 6 No. 16 Bottles, . $14.50 (COGENCY).
Chased, 6 No. 16 Bottles, . 15.50 (COGNATE).
Chased, 6 No. 11 Bottles, . 14.00 (COHESION).

GOLD AND SILVER PLATE.

No. 323.
4 No. $21\frac{1}{2}$ Bottles, . $8.50 (SAWYER.)

No. 2173.
Plain, 6 No. 23 Bottles, . $10.00 (SAWMILL).
Chased, 6 No. 23 Bottles, . 10.75 (SAWDUST).
Bottles with assorted colors, $0.25 extra (SAVANNA).

No. 324.
4 No. 11 Bottles, . $9.00 (SCHOOLBOY).

No. 2147.
Plain, 5 No. 11 Bottles, . $8.75 (COLOR).
Plain, 6 No. 11 Bottles, . 9.75 (COLT).
Chased, 5 No. 11 Bottles, . 9.50 (COLON.)
Chased, 6 No. 11 Bottles, . 10.50 (COLONY).

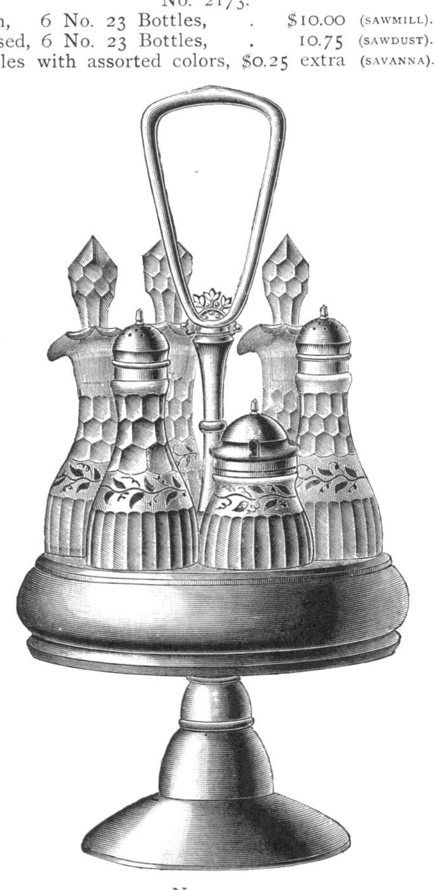

No. 2179.
Plain, 6 No. $73\frac{1}{2}$ Bottles, . $8.00 (SAWFIT).
With Class A Bottles, $0.50 less (SCAPULAR).

No. $2142\frac{1}{2}$.
Plain, 5 No. 16 Bottles, . $10.25 (SCHOLASTIC).
Chased, 5 No. 16 Bottles, . 11.00 (SCUTCHEON).
Chased, 6 No. 16 Bottles, . 11.75 (SCRUPULOUS).
With No. 13 Bottles, $1.50 less (SCRUTINIZE).

No. 2181.
6 No. 103 Bottles, . $25.50 (SATIRIZE).

No. 2148. 5 No. 96 Bottles, . $14.50 (COBALT).
No. 2149. 6 No. 96 Bottles, . 16.00 (COBBLE).

No. 2182.
6 No. 104 Bottles, . $27.50 (SATIRICAL).

No. 2161.
Plain, 6 No. 20 Bottles, . $9.75 (COINAGE).
Chased, 6 No. 20 Bottles, . 10.50 (COLLATION).

No. 2141. No. 4 BELL HANDLE.
5 No. 13 Bottles, . $10.50 (SATIN).
6 No. 13 Bottles, . 11.00 (COMMUTE).
Without Bell Handle, $2.00 less (SATCHEL).

No. 2174.
Plain, 6 No. 11 Bottles, . $9.25 (SATIATE).
Chased, 6 No. 11 Bottles, . 10.00 (SATELLITE).

GOLD AND SILVER PLATE.

No. 2169.
Plain, 5 No. 17 Bottles, $5.75 (SARACEN).
Chased, 5 No. 17 Bottles, 6.25 (SARABAND).

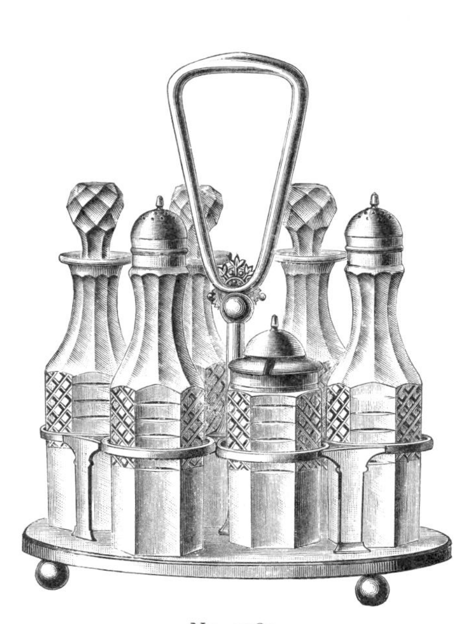

No. 2180.
6 No. 102 Bottles, . $24.00 (SAPPHIC).

No. 2171.
Plain, 5 No. 22 Bottles, $6.25 (SAPPER).
Chased, 5 No. 22 Bottles, 7.00 (SAPORIFIC).

No. 2175.
Chased, 6 No. 14 Bottles, . $8.50 (SANDEHEIM).

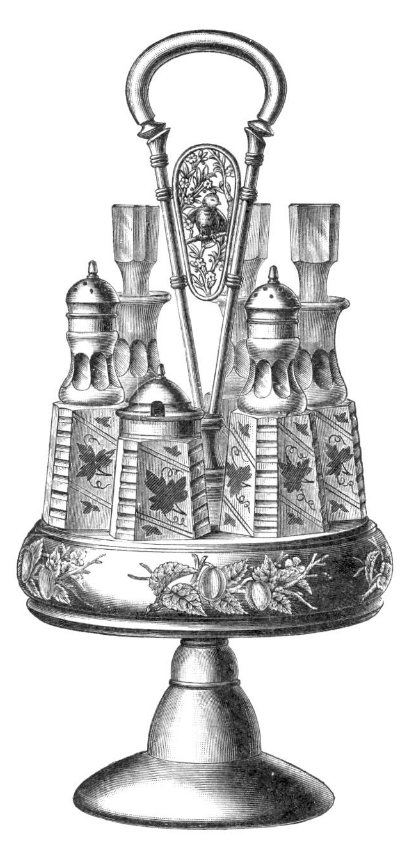

No. 2165.
Plain, 5 No. 18 Bottles, . $7.00 (BANQUET.)
Chased, 5 No. 18 Bottles, . 7.50 (BANTER).
Plain, 6 No. 18 Bottles, . 7.50 (BANYAN).
Chased, 6 No. 18 Bottles, . 8.00 (BARBICAN).

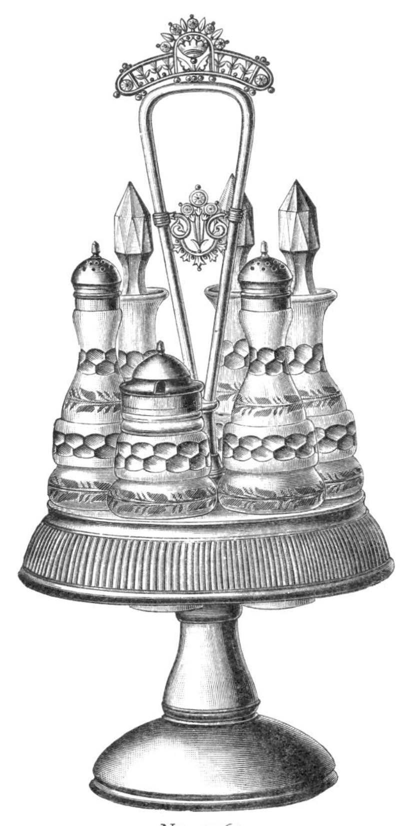

No. 2164.
5 No. 11 Bottles, . $7.75 (BANKER).
6 No. 11 Bottles, . 8.50 (BANNER).

GOLD AND SILVER PLATE.

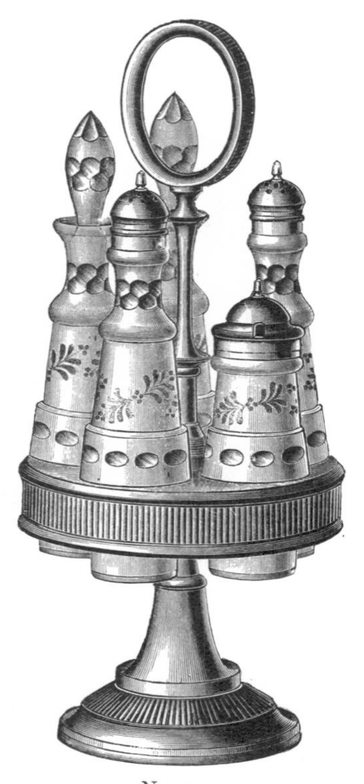

No. 71.
5 No. 14 Bottles, $6.25 (CORONA).

No. 2150. 5 No. 96 Bottles, $14.50 (COCKADE.)
No. 2151. 6 No. 96 Bottles, 16.00 (COCKLE).

No. 77.
Plain, 5 No. 23 Bottles, . $5.75 (SAILCLOTH).
Chased, 5 No. 23 Bottles, . 6.25 (SAGENESS).

No. 67. With No. 7 Bell Handle.
Plain, 6 No. 12 Bottles, . $8.75 (COLORED).
Chased, 6 No. 12 Bottles, . 9.50 (COMFIT).
Without Bell Handle, $1.50 less.

No. 2160.
Plain, 5 No. 15 Bottles, . $6.50 (COPYIST).
Chased, 5 No. 15 Bottles, . 7.00 (COQUET).
Plain, 6 No. 15 Bottles, . 7.00 (COQUETRY).
Chased, 6 No. 15 Bottles, . 7.50 (CORAL).

No. 75½. Chased Base.
Plain, 6 No. 2 Bottles, . $6.00 (GLANDULE).
Chased, 6 No. 2 Bottles, . 6.50 (GLARE).

No. 75. Plain Base.
Plain, 6 No. 2 Bottles, . $5.50 (GLARING).
Chased, 6 No. 2 Bottles, . 6.00 (GLAUBER).

GOLD AND SILVER PLATE.

No. 2178.

Plain, 6 No. 24 Bottles, . $8.75 (SACKCLOTH).
Chased, 6 No. 24 Bottles, . 9.25 (RUTHLESS).

No. 327.

Satin, 5 No. 23 Bottles, . $6.75 (RURALIST).
Chased, 5 No. 23 Bottles, . 7.25 (RUNAWAY).
Satin, Chased, 5 No. 23 Bottles, 7.25 (RUNLET).

No. 2177.

Plain, 5 No. 24 Bottles, . $7.50 (RUBBLE).
Chased, 5 No. 24 Bottles, . 8.00 (ROYALTY).

No. 2172.

Plain, 5 No. 21 Bottles, . $7.25 (RUSTICATE).
Chased, 5 No. 21 Bottles, . 8.00 (RUSHLIGHT).

No. 60$\frac{3}{4}$.

5 No. 23 Bottles, . $5.75 (RUNNER).
6 No. 23 Bottles, . 6.25 (RUGGEDLY).

No. 2170.

Plain, 5 No. 22 Bottles, . $7.00 (ROYALISM).
Chased, 5 No. 22 Bottles, . 7.50 (ROWLOCK).

No. 57.
Plain, 5 No. 12 Bottles, . $5.00 (CONCERN).
Chased, 5 No. 12 Bottles, . 5.50 (CONCERT).

No. 63.
Plain, 5 No. 13 Bottles, . $6.00 (CONDUCT).
Chased, 5 No. 13 Bottles, . 6.50 (CONE).

No. 55.
Chased, 5 No. 12 Bottles, . $7.00 (COMPLETE).
Chased, 6 No. 12 Bottles, . 7.50 (COMPLEX).

No. 66.
Chased, 5 No. 12 Bottles, . $5.50 (CONDIGN).

No. 35½.
Chased, 6 No. 11 Bottles, . $9.00 (COMPLY).

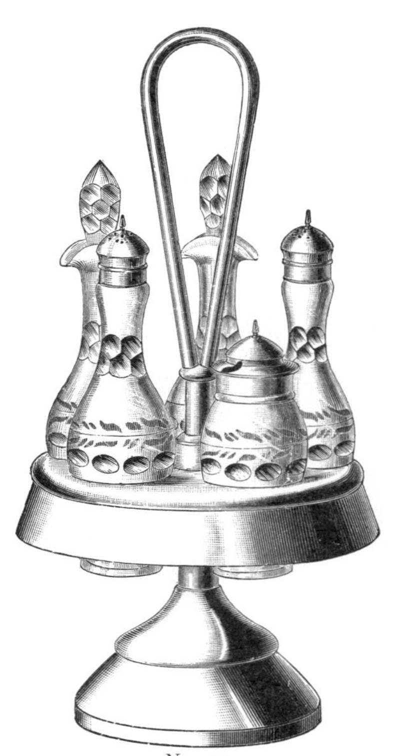

No. 35.
Plain, 5 No. 2 Bottles, . $6.00 (COMPORT).
Plain, 6 No. 2 Bottles, . 6.50 (COMPOSE).
Chased, 5 No. 2 Bottles, . 6.50 (COMPOUND).
Chased, 6 No. 2 Bottles, . 7.00 (COMPRESS).

GOLD AND SILVER PLATE.

No. 67.

Plain, 5 No. 12 Bottles, . $6.00 (CONCRETE).
Plain, 5 No. 13 Bottles, . 6.50 (CONCUR).

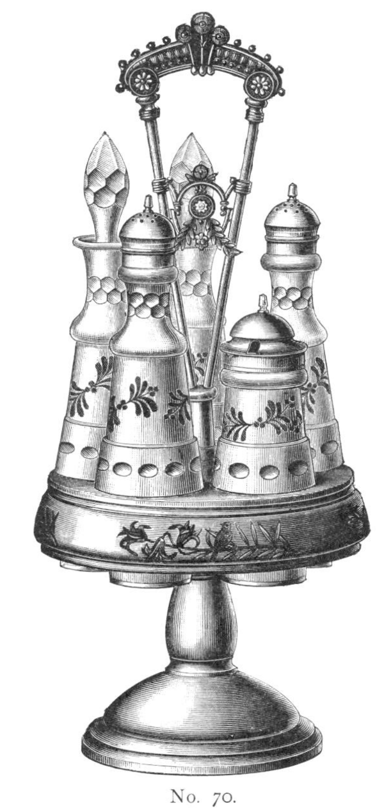

No. 70.

Plain, 5 No. 14 Bottles, . $5.50 (CORBAN).
Chased, 5 No. 14 Bottles, . 6.00 (CORBEL).

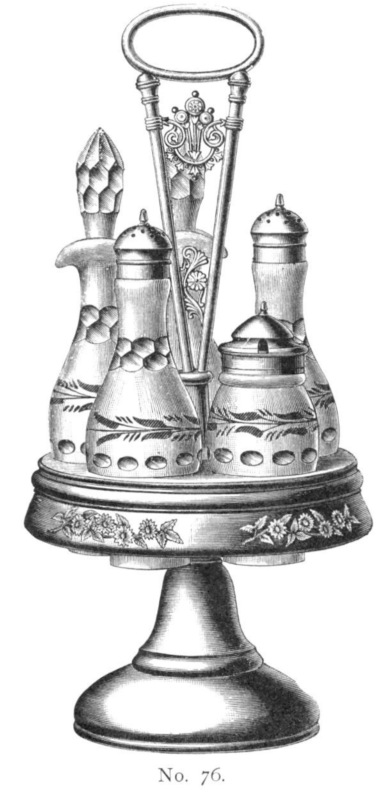

No. 76.

Plain, 5 No. 2 Bottles, . $5.00 (BARBECUE).
Chased, 5 No. 2 Bottles, . 5.50 (BARQUE).

No. 64.

Plain, 5 No. 13 Bottles, . $6.75 (CONCLUDE).
Chased, 5 No. 13 Bottles, . 7.25 (CONCORD).
Chased, 6 No. 13 Bottles, . 7.75 (CONCOURSE).

No. 74.

Plain, 5 No. 14½ Bottles, . $5.75 (COLONEL).
Chased, 5 No. 14½ Bottles, . 6.25 (COLONIST).

No. 67.

Chased, 5 No. 12 Bottles, . $6.50 (CONCH).
Chased, 5 No. 13 Bottles, . 7.00 (CONCISE).

TRADE MARK
WHITE METAL.

GOLD AND SILVER PLATE.

TRADE MARK.
NICKEL SILVER.

No. 60¾.
5 No. 14 Bottles, . $5.00 (COPY).
6 No. 14 Bottles, . 5.50 (COPYER).

No. 326.
Plain, 5 No. 2 Bottles, . . $5.00 (SAGACITY).
Satin, Chased, 5 No. 2 Bottles, 5.50 (SADDLEBOW).

No. 325.
Plain, 4 No. 2 Bottles, . . $4.50 (SADDLERY).
Satin, Chased, 4 No. 2 Bottles, 5.00 (SACKING).

No. 65.
Plain, 5 No. 12 Bottles, . $5.00 (CONDENSE).
Chased, 5 No. 12 Bottles, . 5.50 (CONDEMN).

No. 49.
Plain, 4 No. 2 Bottles, $4.00 (CONSTRAIN).
Chased, 4 No. 2 Bottles, 4.50 (CONSTRUCT).

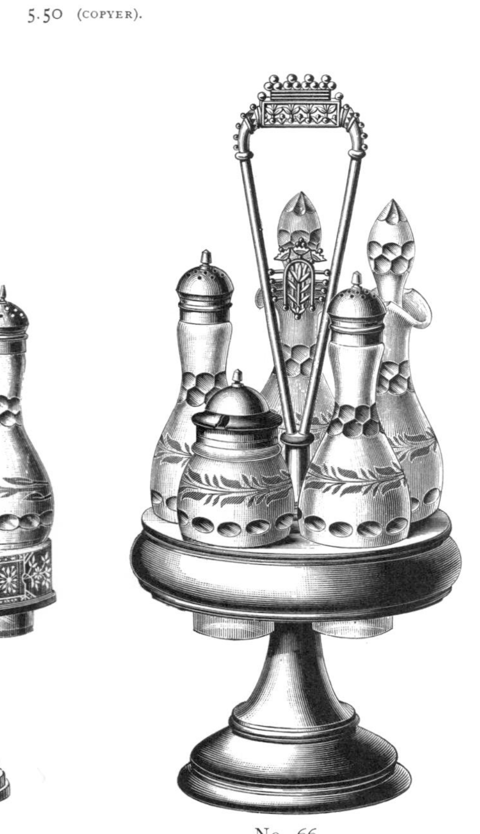

No. 66.
Plain, 5 No. 2 Bottles, $5.00 (CONFECT).
Chased, 5 No. 2 Bottles, 5.50 (CONDIGN).

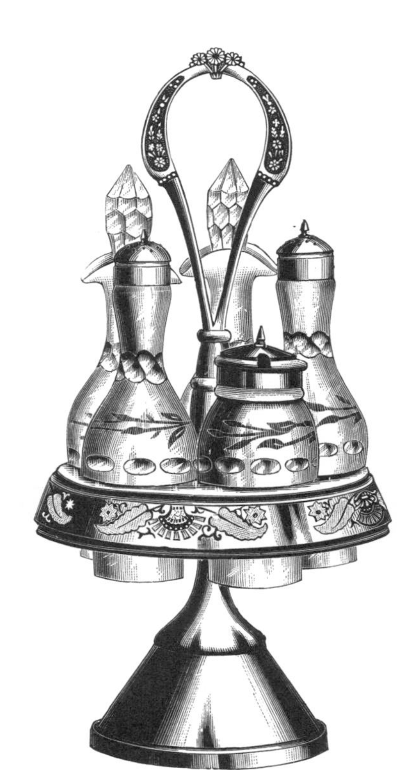

No. 42.
Plain, 5 No. 2 Bottles, $5.00 (CONNECT).
Chased, 5 No. 2 Bottles, 5.50 (CONNIVE).
Plain, 6 No. 2 Bottles, 5.50 (CONNECTED).
Chased, 6 No. 2 Bottles, 6.00 (CONNIVED).

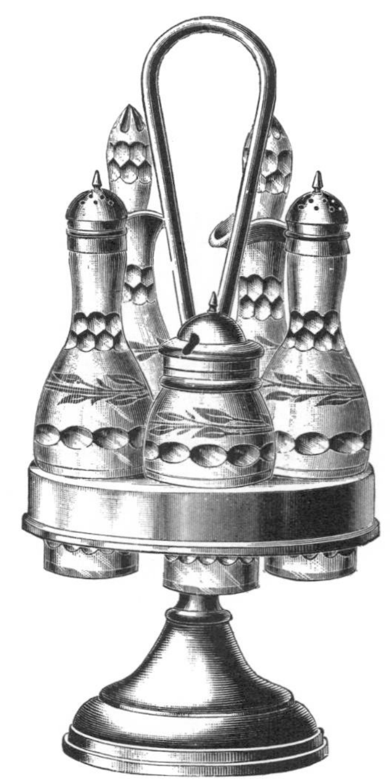

No. 50.
Plain, 5 No. 2 Bottles, $4.50 (CONQUER).
Chased, 5 No. 2 Bottles, 5 00 (CONSCRIPT).
For style of Chasing, see No. 49.

No. 68½.

Plain, 4 No. 12 Bottles, . $3.75 (GIRDER).

Chased, 4 No. 12 Bottles, . 4.25 (GIRTH).

No. 69. WITH No. 6 BELL HANDLE.

Plain, 5 No. 14 Bottles, . $5.75 (GIRANDOLE).

Chased, 5 No. 14 Bottles, . 6.25 (GIRD).

No. 68.

Plain, 4 No. 2 Bottles, . $3.75 (CONSIGN).

Chased, 4 No. 2 Bottles, . 4.25 (CONSIGNEE).

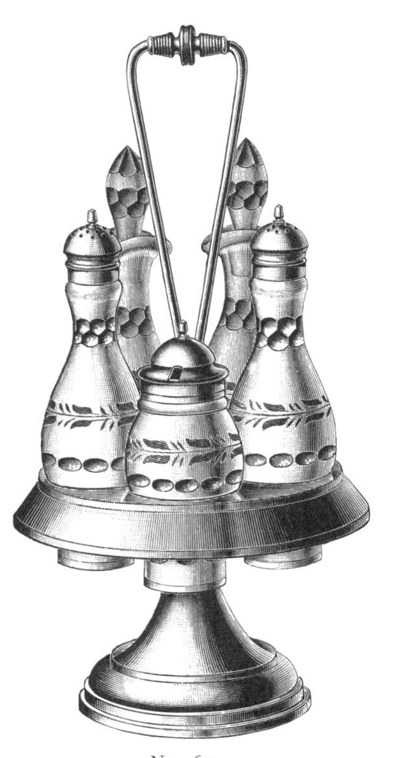

No. 69.

Plain, 5 No. 2 Bottles, . $4.25 (CONIC).

No. 69½.

Plain, 5 No. 2 Bottles, . $4.25 (GIRAFFE).

Chased, 5 No. 2 Bottles, . 4.75 (GIPSY).

No. 69.

Chased, 5 No. 2 Bottles, . $4.75 (CONICAL).

NICKEL SILVER CASTERS.

(One-Third Size.)

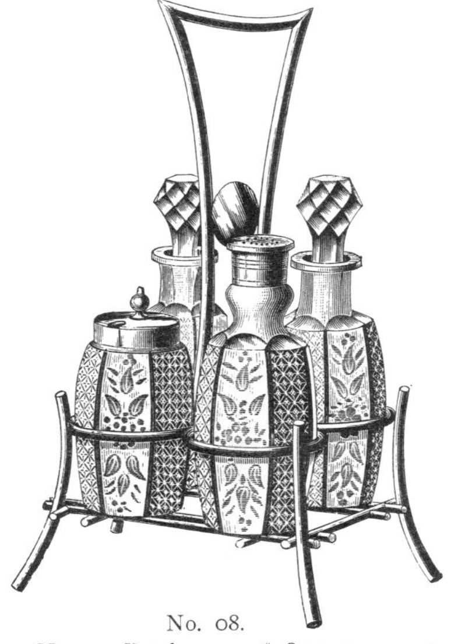

No. 08.
4 No. 91 Bottles, . $18.00 (reindeer).
4 No. $91\frac{3}{4}$ Bottles, . 15.00 (passage).

No. 013.
6 No. 73 Bottles, . $18.00 (rotation).

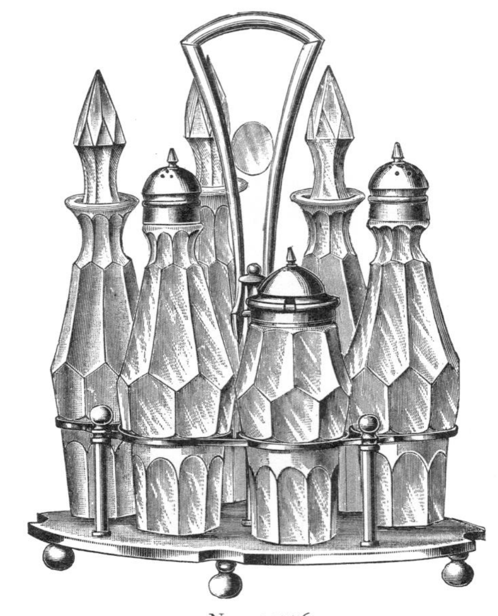

No. 02776.
6 No. $87\frac{1}{2}$ Plain Bottles, . $35.00 (rejoice).

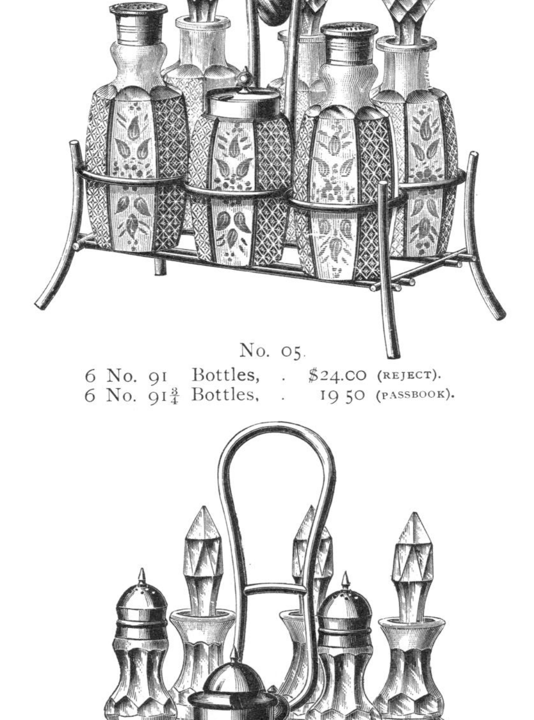

No. 05.
6 No. 91 Bottles, . $24.00 (reject).
6 No. $91\frac{3}{4}$ Bottles, . 19 50 (passbook).

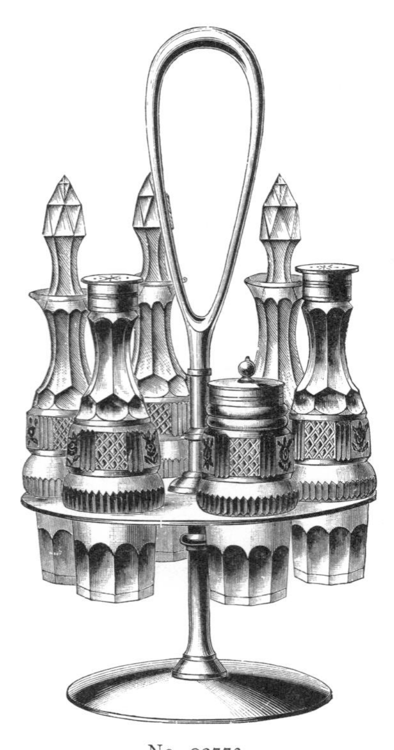

No. 02773.
6 No. 95 Bottles, . $26.00 (regret)

No. 02774.
6 No. 99 Bottles, . $26.00 (regulate).

No. 016.
6 No. 93 Bottles, . $18.00 (regimen).

NICKEL SILVER, SILVER SOLDERED.

GOLD AND SILVER PLATE.

No. 021.
2 No. 09 Bottles, $7 50 (ROTATORY).

No. 010.
3 No. 010 Bottles, $7.50 (REJOIN).

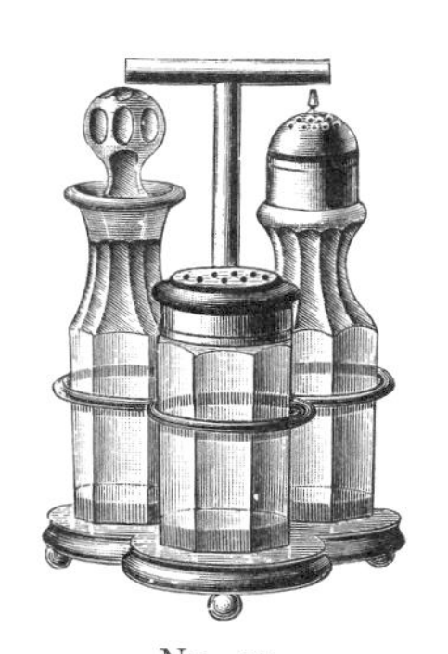

No. 07.
3 No. 09 Bottles, $9.00 (REKINDLE).

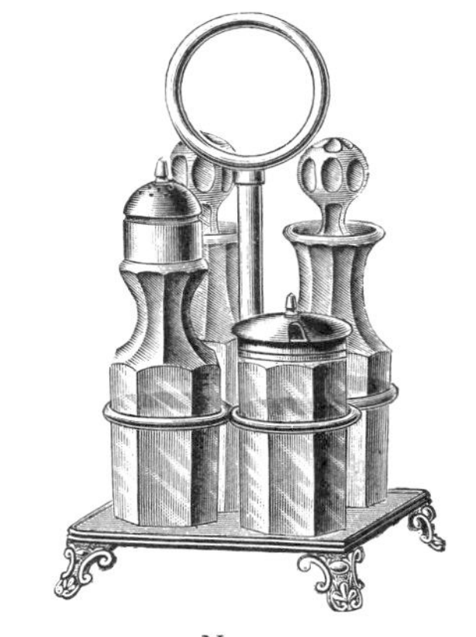

No. 09.
4 No. 09 Bottles, $12.00 (REJOINDER).

No. 012.
4 No. 68 Bottles, . $10.50 (REIGN).

No. 031.
4 No. 74 Bottles, . $1300 (ROMANCER).

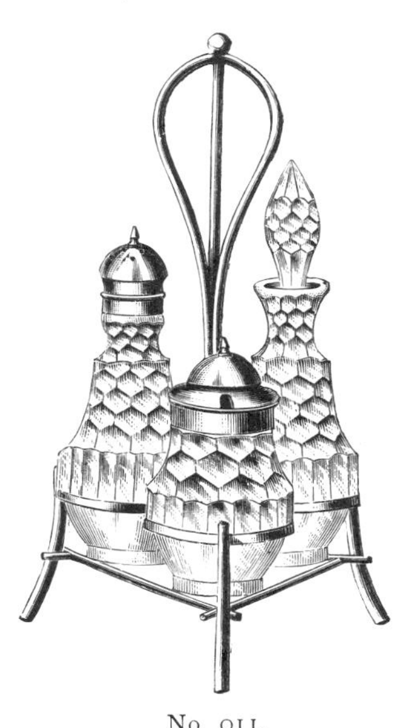

No. 011.
3 No. 68 Bottles, . $9.00 (REHEARSE).

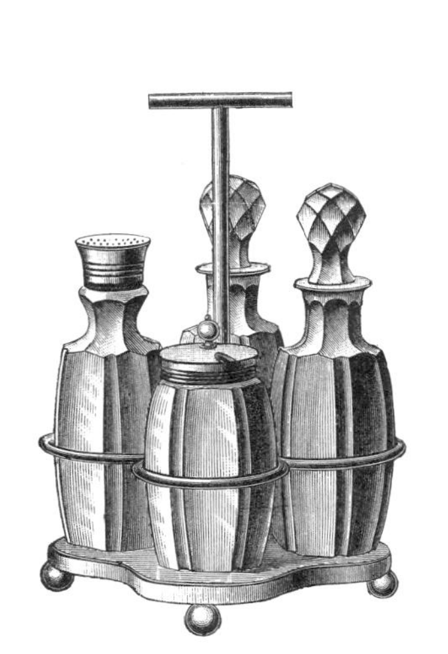

No. 028.
4 No. $91\frac{1}{2}$ Bottles, $16 50 (ROMANTIC).

No. 029.
4 No. $96\frac{1}{2}$ Bottles, $18.00 (ROLLCALL).

No. 027.
4 No. 70 Bottles, $14.50 (ROSEMARY).
4 No. 72 Bottles, 16.50 (ROOFLESS).

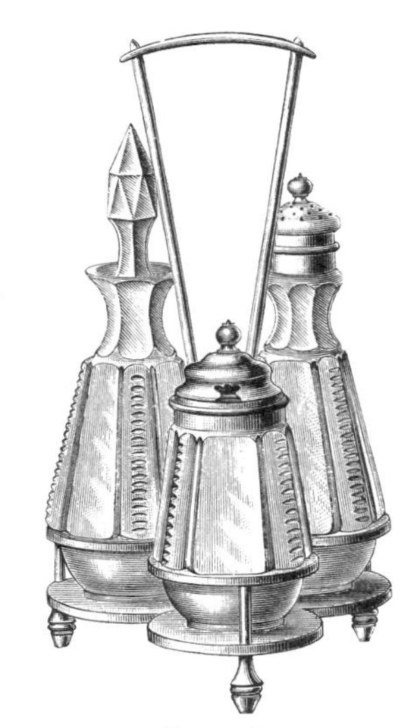

No. 026.
3 No. 72 Bottles, $13.50 (RELATE).
3 No. 70 Bottles, 12.00 (ROOFTREE).

NICKEL SILVER, SILVER SOLDERED.

DINNER CASTER BELL AND VASE HANDLES.

(ONE-THIRD SIZE.)

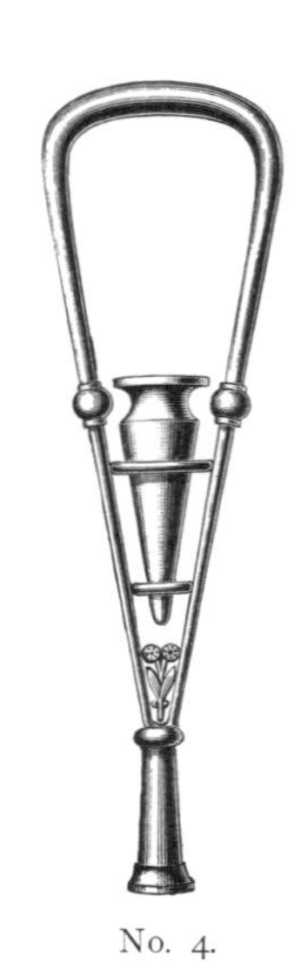

No. 4.
Vase, . $0.75 extra (ROCKSALT).

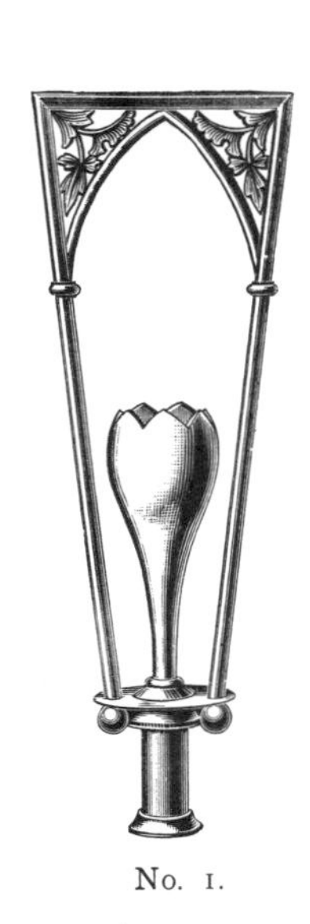

No. 1.
Vase, . $1.50 extra (RIPRAP).

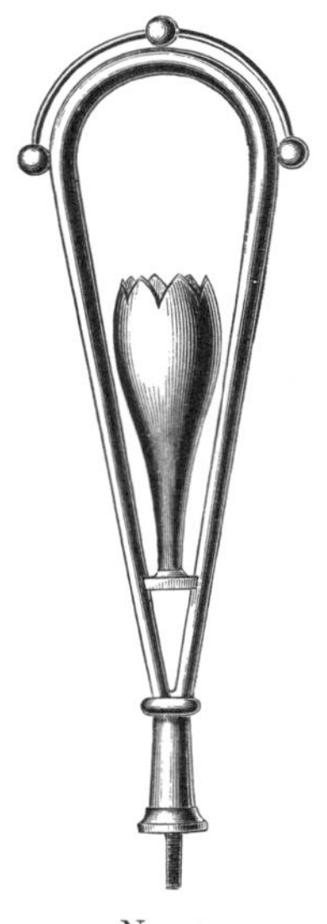

No. 3.
Vase, . $1.50 extra (RISIBLE).

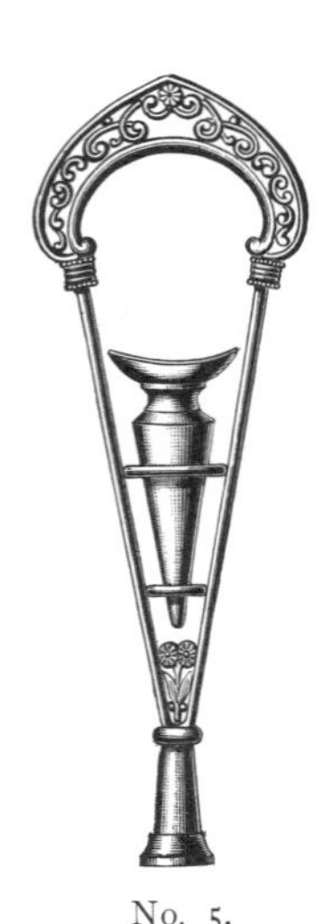

No. 5.
Vase, . $0.75 extra (RIGHTNESS).

Casters sold with these Handles will be charged EXTRA as above.

THE FOLLOWING ARE PRICES FOR VASE HANDLES SOLD SEPARATELY.

No. 1.	No. 3.	No. 4.	No. 5.
Vase, . $3.00 (RINGDOVE).	Vase, . $3.00 (RINGBOLT).	Vase, . $2.25 (RIGOROUS).	Vase, . $2.25 (RIGMAROLE).

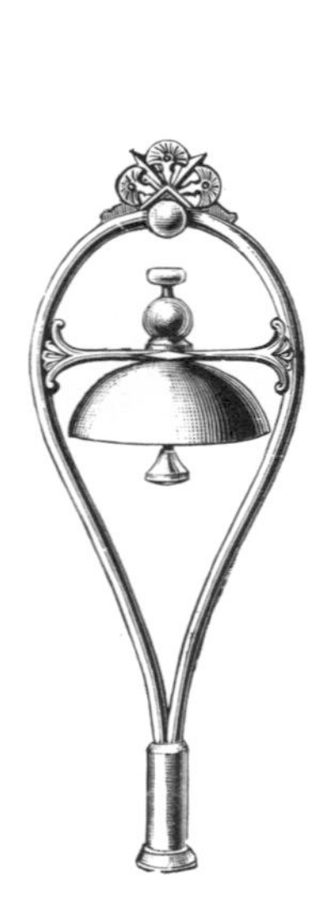

No. 2.
Bell, $1.50 extra (RIGIDNESS).

No. 3.
Bell, $2.00 extra (RIFLEMAN).

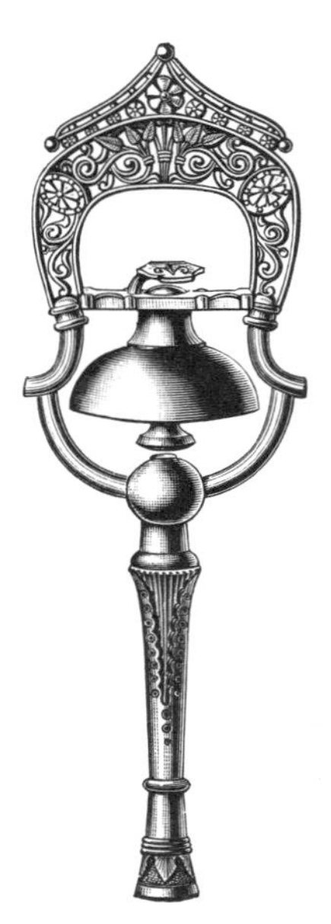

No. 5.
Bell, $2.00 extra (RIDICULE).

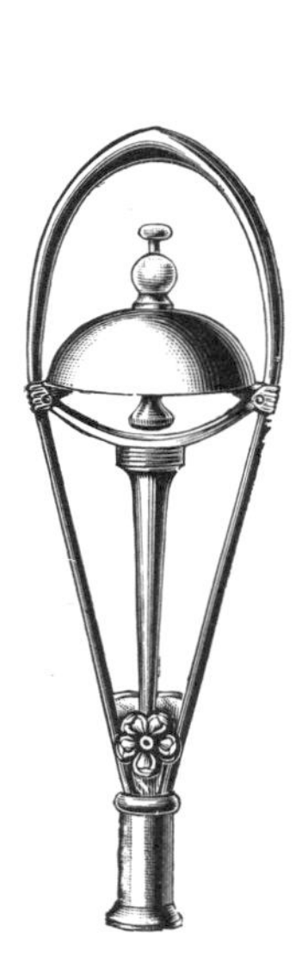

No. 4.
Bell, $2.00 extra (RIDGEPOLE).

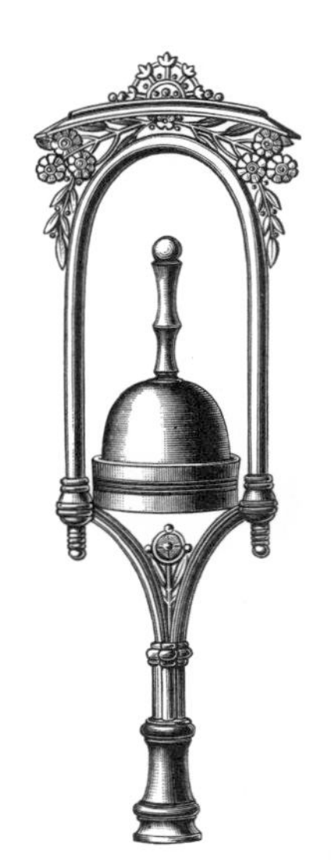

No. 7. Bell, or Toothpick Holder, $1.50 extra (RIDDLE).

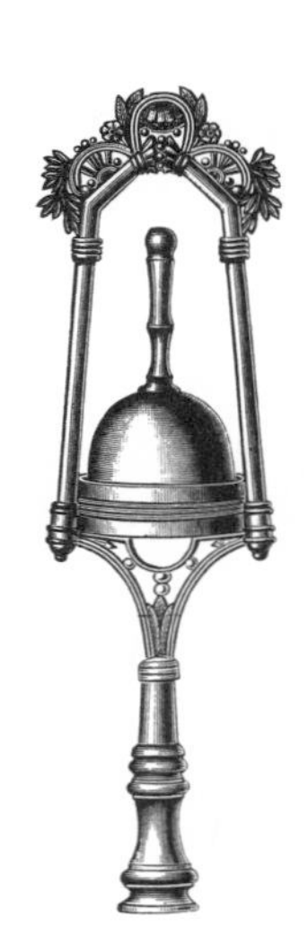

No. 6.
Bell, $1.50 extra (RICHNESS).

Casters sold with these Handles will be charged EXTRA as above.

THE FOLLOWING ARE PRICES FOR BELL HANDLES SOLD SEPARATELY.

No. 2.	No. 3.	No. 4.	No. 5.	No. 6.	No. 7.
Bell, $3.00 (REVOCABLE).	Bell, $3.50 (REVISION).	Bell, $3.50 (RHYMSTER).	Bell, $3.50 (RHOMBIC).	Bell, $3.00 (REVOLUTION).	Bell, 3.00 (REVOLVER).

DINNER CASTER BOTTLES.

(PRICES PER DOZEN.)

(ONE-THIRD SIZE.)

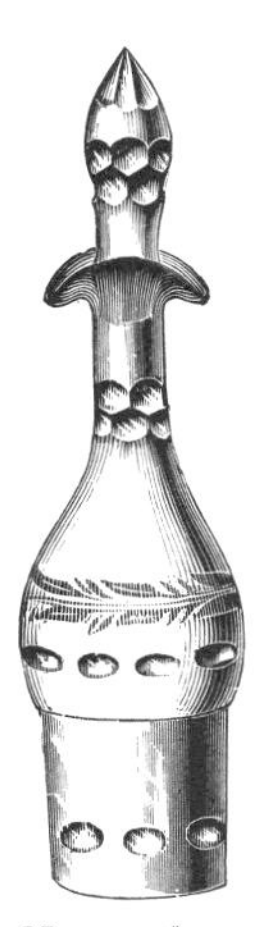
No. 2, $4.50.

No. 14½, $5.25.

No. 12, $4.50.

No. 14, $4.50.

No. 11, $5.75.

No. 13, $5.25.

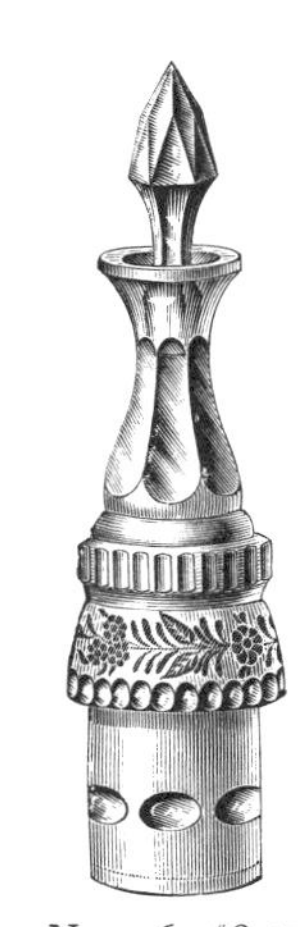
No. 16, $8.50.

No. 17, $5.25.

No. 18, $7.00.

No. 19, $7.00.

No. 20, $9.00.

No. 21, $6.00.

No. 22, $5.75.

No. 23, $7.00.

No. 24, $7.50.

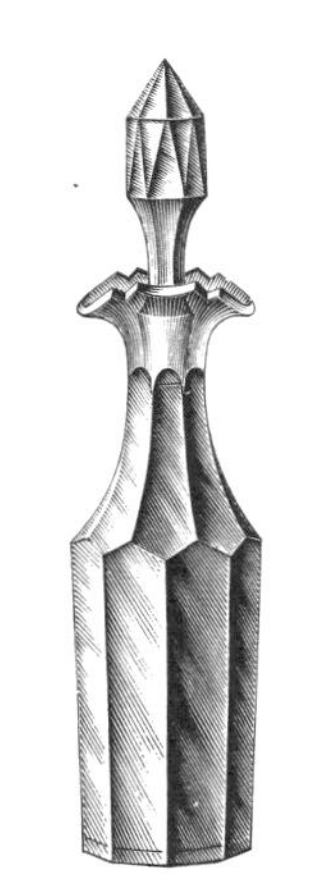
No. 96, $15.00.

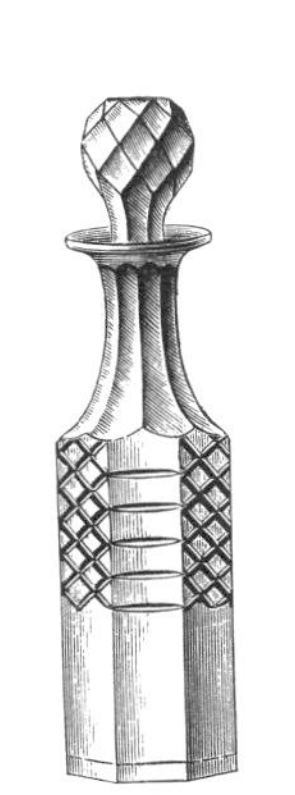
No. 102, $30.00.

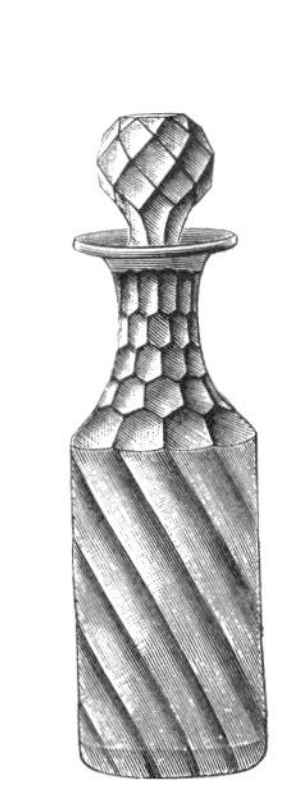
No. 104, $30.00.

No. 95, $18.00.

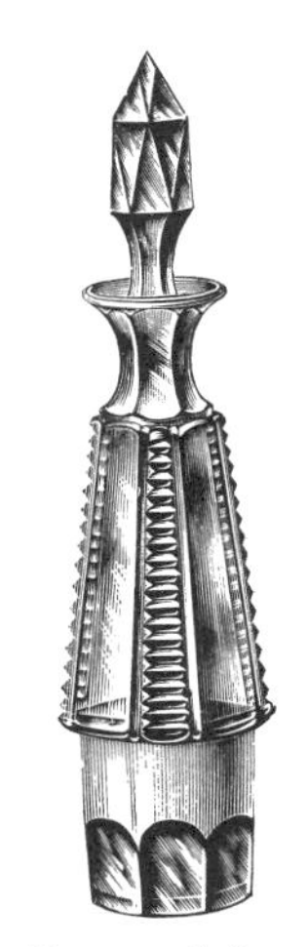
No. 97, $18.00.

No. 98, $18.00.

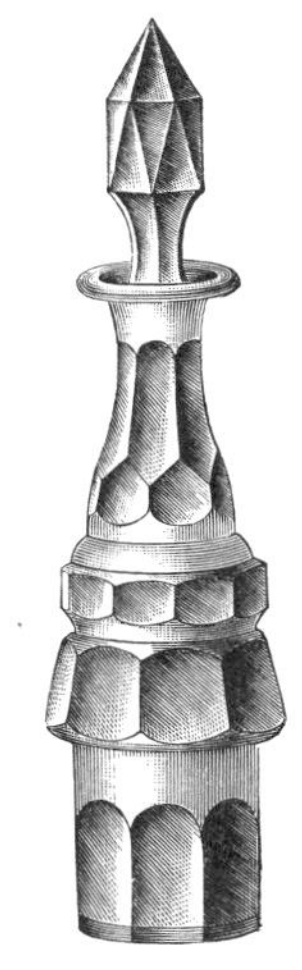
No. 99, $20.00.

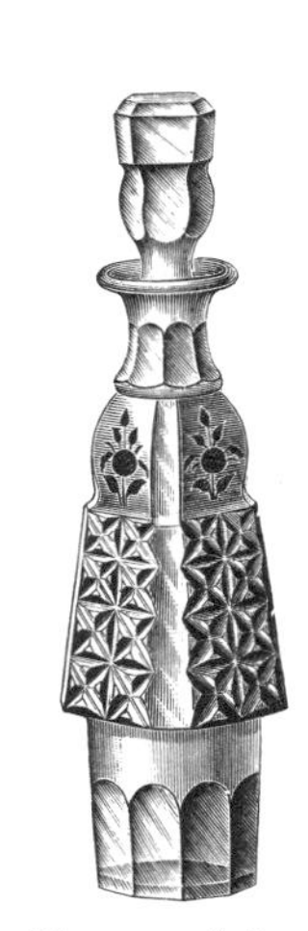
No. 101, $18.00.

BOTTLES INTERCHANGED IN CASTERS AS FOLLOWS:

CLASS A. Nos. 2, 02½, 12, and 14,	Without extra charge.
Nos. 14½ and 17,	$0.25 per Caster more than Class A.
Nos. 11, 13, 15, 18, 19, 21, and 22,	.50 per Caster more than Class A.
No. 23. Crystal,	.75 per Caster more than Class A.
Nos. 24, Crystal, and 23, Colored,	1.00 per Caster more than Class A.
Nos. 16 and 20,	$2.00 per Caster more than Class A.
Nos. 96 and 90,	3.50 per Caster more than Class A.
Nos. 94, 95, 97, 98, 99, and 101,	7.00 per Caster more than Class A.
Nos. 91, 102, 103, and 104,	12.00 per Caster more than Class A.

BREAKFAST CASTERS.

(One-Third Size).

No. 280.
3 No. 70 Bottles, . $6.50 (consult).

No. 300.
4 No. 73 Bottles, . $9.00 (corduroy).

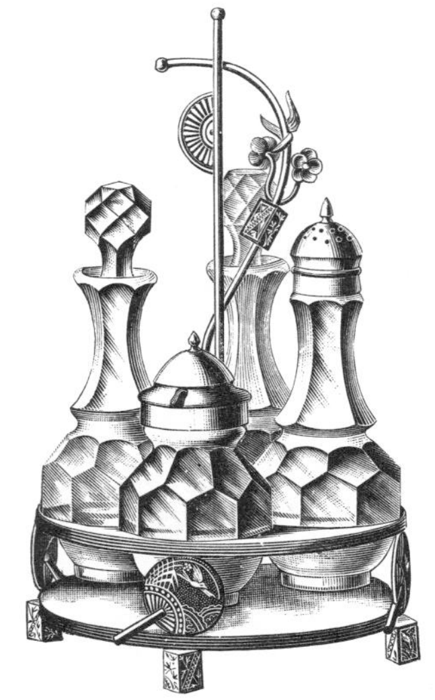

No. 281.
4 No. 70 Bottles, . $7.75 (content).

No. 297.
4 No. 73 Bottles, . $9.00 (cordon).

No. 331.
2 No. 74 Bottles, and Salt, . $9.50 (revere).

No. 301.
Plain, 4 No. 73 Bottles, . $10.50 (cord.)
Chased, 4 No. 73 Bottles, . 11.50 (cordage).

No. 313.
4 No. 74 Bottles, . $9.50 (gland).

No. 283.
4 No. 70 Bottles, . $9.00 (contrary).

No. 293.
4 No. 64 Bottles, . $7.75 (contend).

GOLD AND SILVER PLATE.

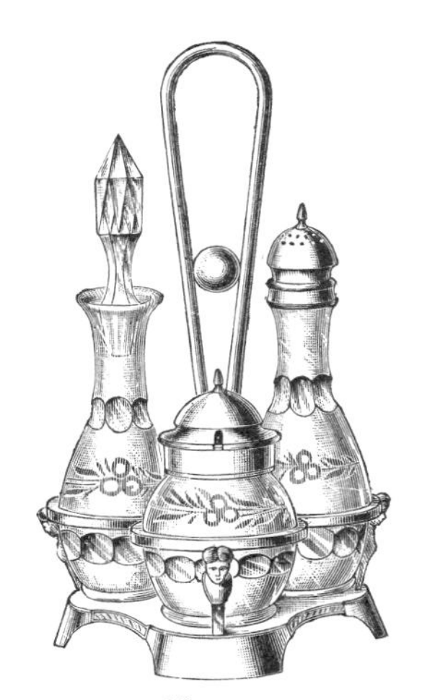

No. 250.
3 No. 145 Bottles, . $5.00 (CONVOKE).

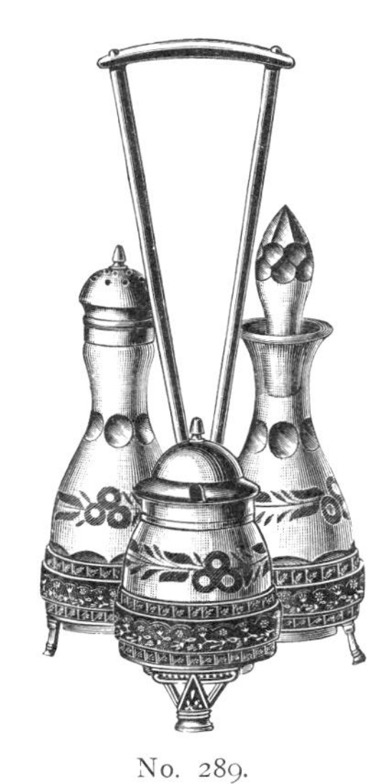

No. 289.
3 No. 145 Bottles, . $5.25 (CONTOUR).

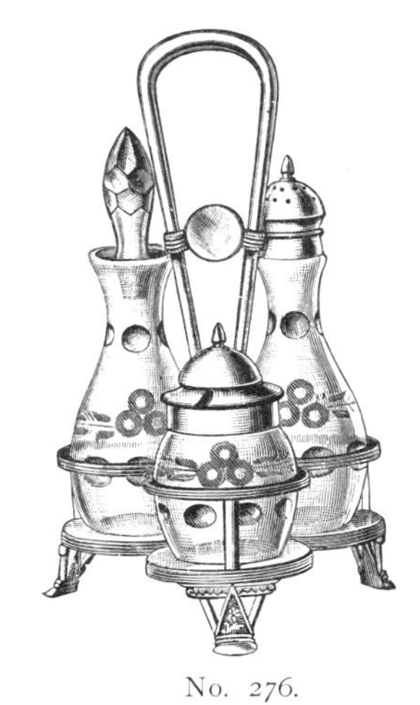

No. 276.
3 No. 145 Bottles, . $5.00 (CONVENE).
No. 277. 4 No. 145 Bottles, . 5.50 (CONVERT).

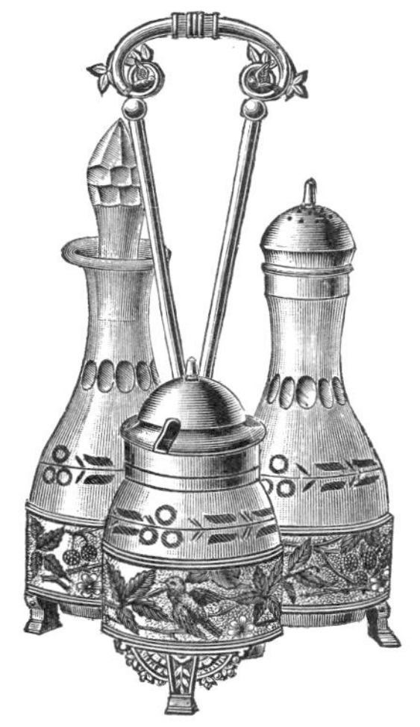

No. 332.
3 No. 145 Bottles, $4.25 (REVERSION).

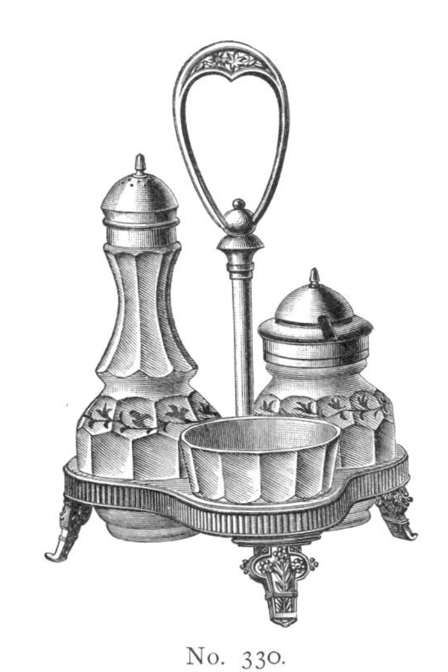

No. 330.
2 No. 70 Bottles and Salt, $8.00 (REVERSAL).

No. 287.
3 No. 145 Bottles, $5.25 (CONTINUE).

No. 333.
4 No. 145 Bottles, $5.00 (REVELER).

No. 288.
4 No. 145 Bottles, $6.25 (CONTORT).

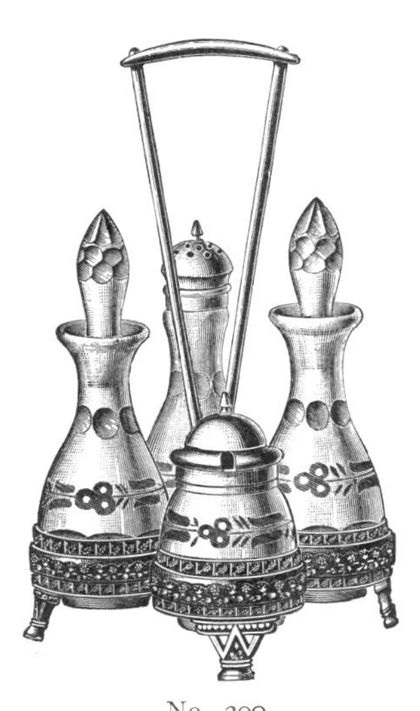

No. 290.
4 No. 145 Bottles, $6.25 (CONTEXT).

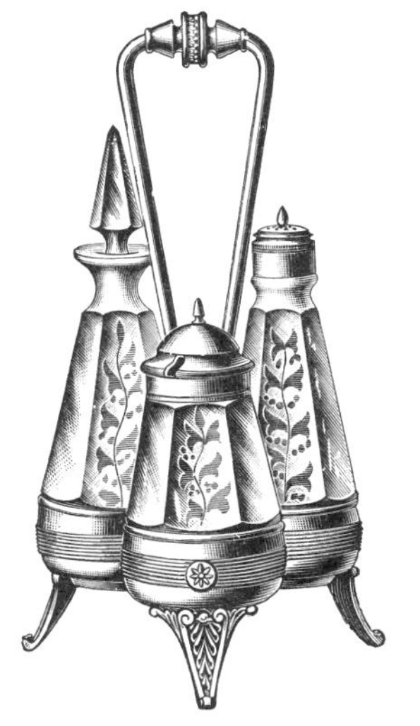

No. 272.
3 No. 145 Bottles, $4.50 (CONTRIVE).
3 No. 71 Bottles, 6.00 (CONTRAST).

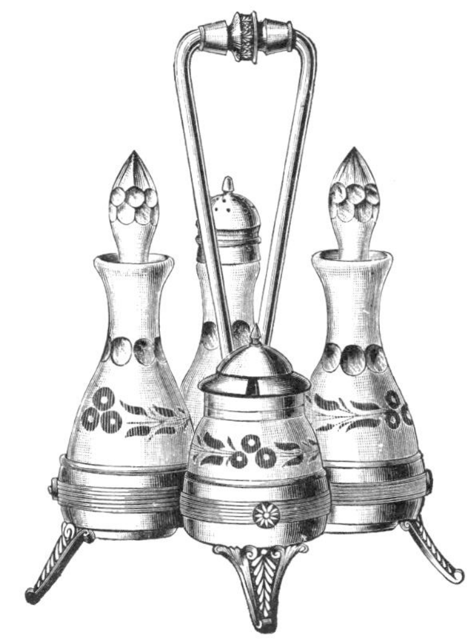

No. 273.
4 No. 145 Bottles, $5.00 (CONVEY).
4 No. 71 Bottles, 7.00 (CONVINCE).

GOLD AND SILVER PLATE.

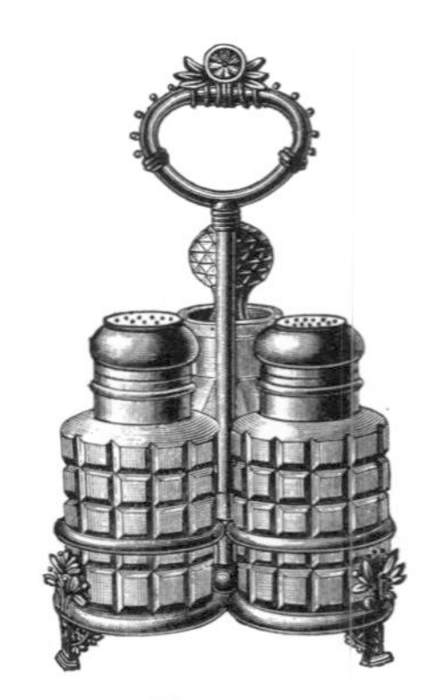

No. 321.
3 No. 732 Bottles, . $7.00 (REVERENCE).

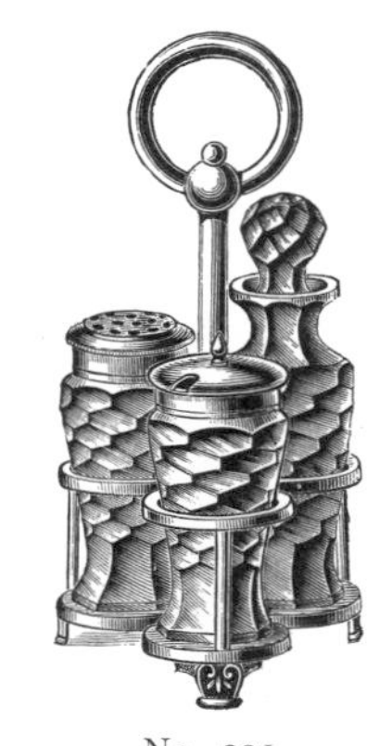

No. 291.
3 Bottles, . $7.00 (CONVOY).

No. 322.
4 No. 732 Bottles, . $8.50 (RETRACE).

No. 68.
Per doz., . $11.50.

No. 70.
Per doz., . $12.50.

No. 320.
4 No. 725 Bottles, . $8.50 (REVENGER).
Assorted Colors.

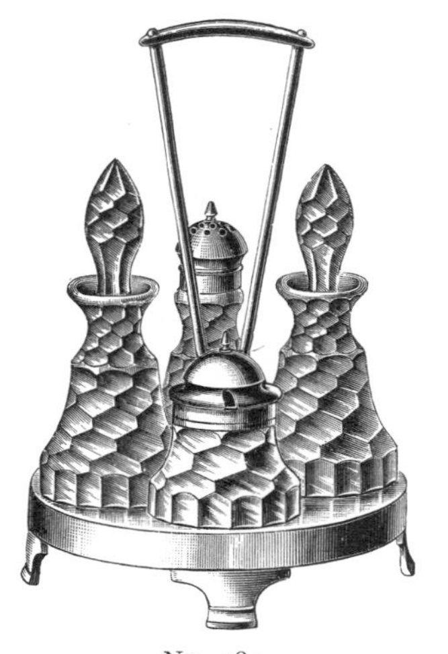

No. 282.
4 No. 68 Bottles, . $7.00 (CONTRACT).

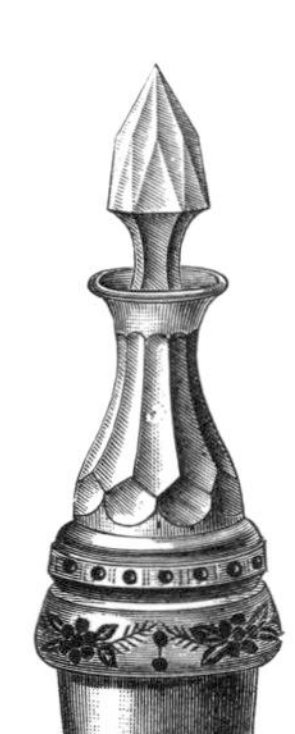

No. 73.
Per doz., . $8.00.

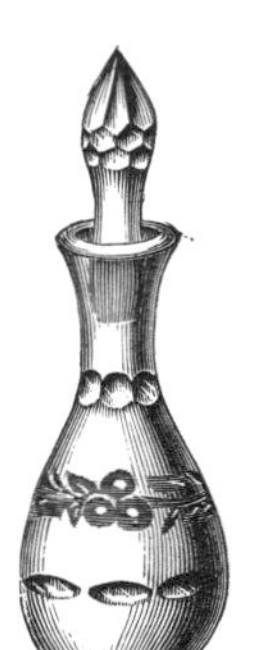

No. 145.
Per doz., . $5.50.

No. 319.
4 No. 731 Bottles, . $9.50 (RETRENCH).

No. 314.
4 No. 74 Bottles, . $9.50 (GLADIATOR)

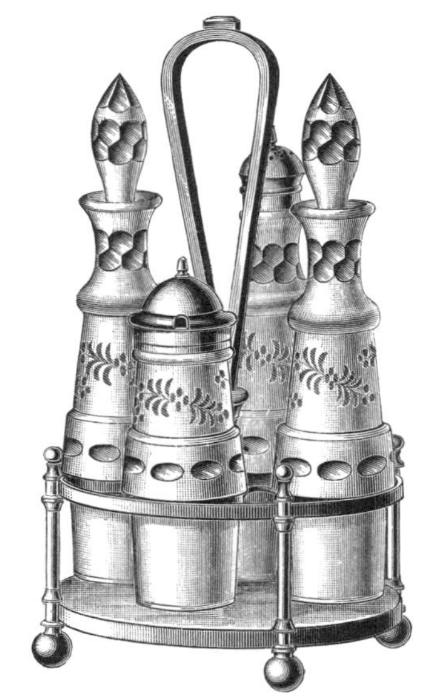

No. 244.
4 No. 14 Bottles, . $6.50 (COOPER).
No. 246.
5 No. 14 Bottles, . 7.00 (COOPERAGE).

No. 254.
4 No. 68 Bottles, . $7.50 (COPAL).

GOLD AND SILVER PLATE.

No. 329.

2 No. 010 Bottles and Salt, . $7.75 (RETINUE).

No. 302.

Silver, 3 No. 725 Bottles, . $7.50 (COPPICE).

No. 328.

2 No. 723 Bottles and Salt, . $7.25 (RETICENT).

No. 266.

3 No. 09 Bottles, $6.50 (CONTAIN).

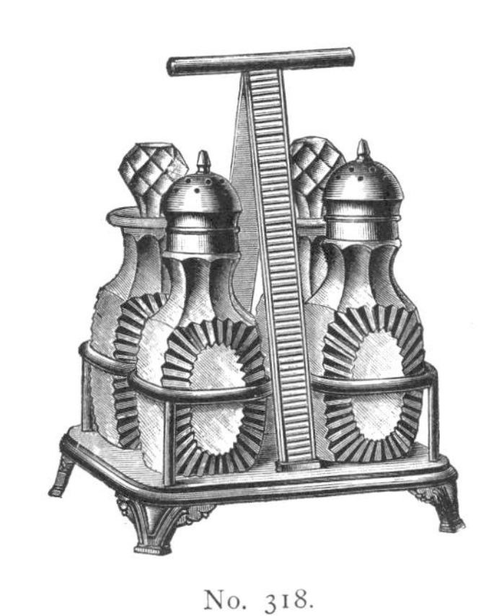

No. 318.

4 No. 729 Bottles, $10.00 (RETARD).

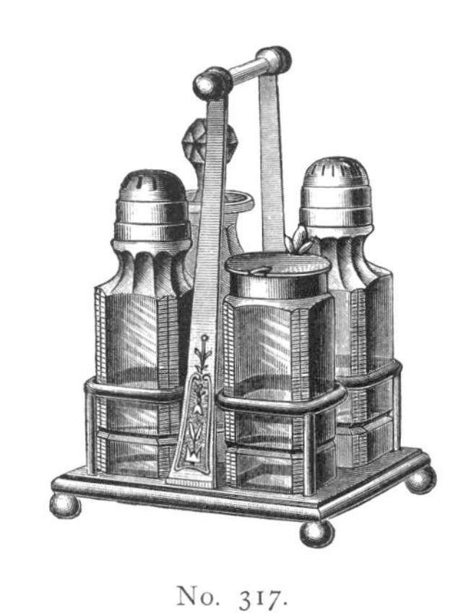

No. 317.

4 No. 730 Bottles, $10.00 (RETAINER).

No. 279.

3 Bottles, . $5.00 (CONTACT).

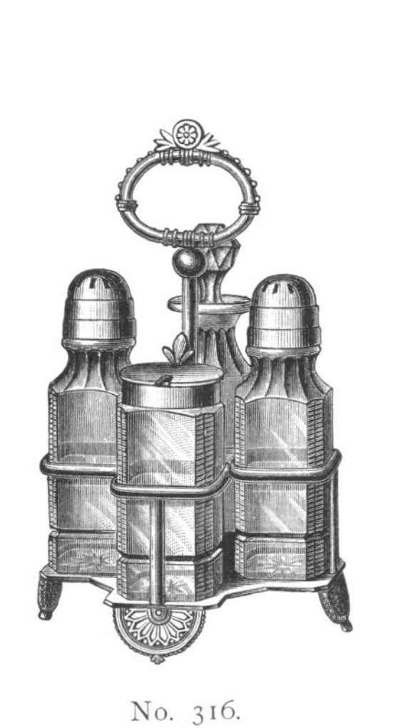

No. 316.

4 No. 730 Bottles, $9.50 (GLANCE).

No. 310.

4 No. 727 Bottles, $8.50 (GLADSOME).

No. 267.

3 No. 09 Bottles, $7.50 (COOL).

No. 315.

4 No. 726 Bottles, $8.50 (RETENTIVE).

TRADE MARK.
WHITE METAL.

INDIVIDUAL CASTERS.

(HALF SIZE.)

MERIDEN.
B. COMPANY.
TRADE MARK.
NICKEL SILVER.

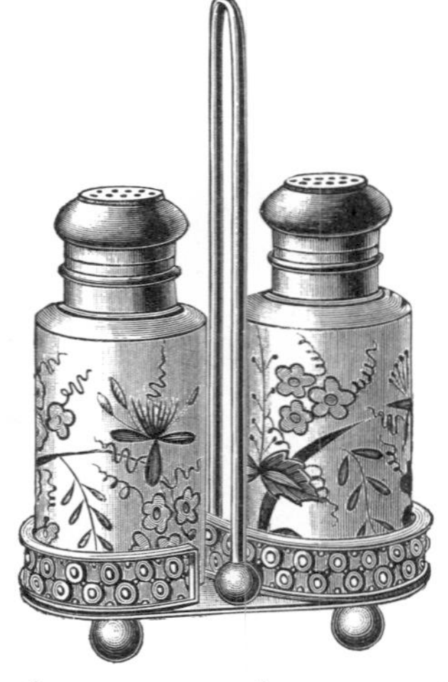

No. 60, . . $2.75 (RESTLESS).

No. 50, . . $3.00 (RESPONDENT).

No. 48, . . $2.75 (RESPONSIVE).

No. **22**, Gold Lined, $5.00 (CORRIDOR).

No. 52, . . $4.75 (RESPECTFUL).

No. 32.

Gold Lined, . . $6.75 (ARMINIAN).

Silver and Gold Inlaid, 7.50 (ARMISTICE).

No. 51, . . $3.00 (RESPECTIVE).

No. 53, . . $6.00 (RESOLUTION).

No. 49, . . $3.00 (RESISTANCE).

GOLD AND SILVER PLATE.

No. 65, . $3.00 (PECTORAL).
Cut Glass.

No. 58, . $5.00 (RESERVATION).

No. 62, . $3.50 (PEELER).

No. 57, . $3.50 (RESINOUS).

No. 61, . $3.50 (PEDANTRY).

No. 46, . $2.50 (RESIGNED).

No. 56, . $3.50 (RESERVED).

No. 63, . $3.75 (PENSION).

No. 64, Longwy, . $6.25 (PENSIONER).

No. 55, . $5.75 (RESIDENCE).

GOLD AND SILVER PLATE.

No. 25.
Silver, . . $5.00 (CORUSCATE).
Silver, Gold Inlaid, 5.75 (COSEY).

No. 41.
Gold Lined, . $7.00 (ARTIFICE).
Silver, Gold Inlaid, 7.50 (ARBITER).

No. 29.
Gold Lined, . $6.25 (CORSAIR).
Silver, Gold Inlaid, 7.00 (CORSELET).

No. 39.
Gold Lined, . $4.50 (AREOLA).

No. 14.
Gold Lined, . $4 50 (COTTAGE).

No. 12.
Gold Lined, . $4.25 (CORRECT)

No. 36.
Gold Lined, . $4.00 (ARGONAUT).

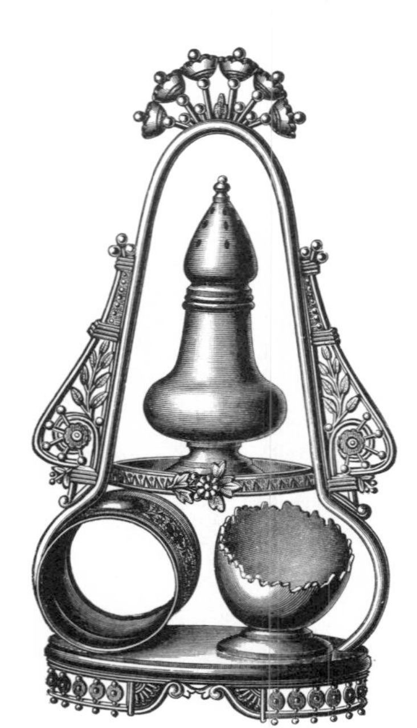

No. 33.
Gold Lined, . $7.00 (ARMOR).
Silver, Gold Inlaid, 8.00 (ARNICA).

No. 34.
Gold Lined, . $7.00 (ARIAN).
Silver, Gold Inlaid, 8.00 (ARMADA).

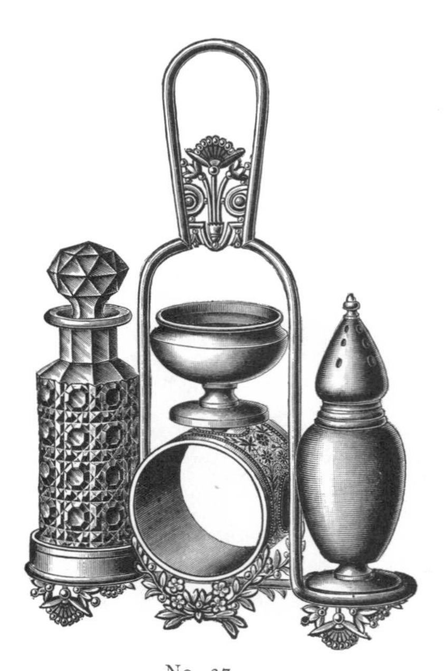

No. 37.
Gold Lined, . $7.00 (ASCETIC).

GOLD AND SILVER PLATE.

No. 21.
Gold Lined, . $4.75 (COSTUME).

No. 31.
Gold Lined, . $6.00 (COST).
Silver, Gold Inlaid, 6.75 (COSTLY).

No. 20.
Gold Lined. . $4.50 (COUGH).

No. 27.
Gold Lined, . $5.50 (CORSET).

No. 24.
Gold Lined, . $5.75 (CORRUGATE).

No. 23.
Gold Lined, . $5.25 (CORVETTE).

No. 28.
Gold Lined, . $6.00 (CORRUPT).

No. 19.
Gold Lined, . $4.00 (CORTEGE).

No. 17.
Gold Lined, . $6.00 (COUCH).

No. 40.
Gold Lined, . $6.50 (PENCIL).

No. 30.
Gold Lined, . $5.00 (COSMETIC).
Silver, Gold Inlaid, 5.75 (COSSET).

WINE CASTERS.

(ONE-THIRD SIZE.)

MERIDEN B. COMPANY.
TRADE MARK.
NICKEL SILVER.

No. 71, . . $20.00 (DEBIT).

No. 500. CLARET JUG.
Old Silver Mountings.
Fine Cut Glass, $25.00 (RESEAT).

No. 79, . . $25.00 (DEARTH).

No. 82, . . $75.00 (RESEARCH).

No. 81, . . $40.00 (REQUITAL).

GOLD AND SILVER PLATE.

No. 85.
Old Silver Border, . $20.00 (REPUBLICAN).

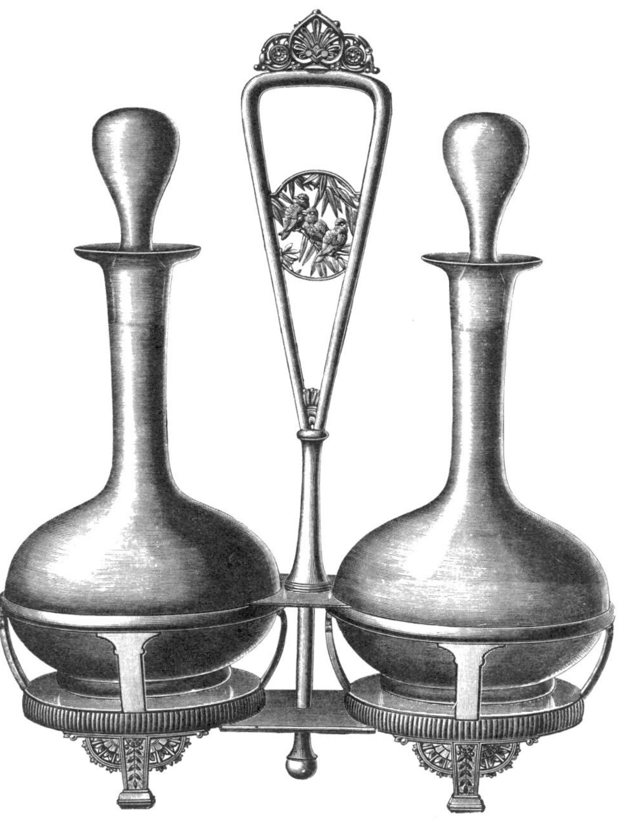

No. 86.
Ruby, Polka Dot, . . $24.00 (REPORTER).

No. 78. BARREL.
6 Wine Cups, complete.
Gilt, . . . $20.00 (DEBAR).

No. 69, . . $45.00 (DEBASE).

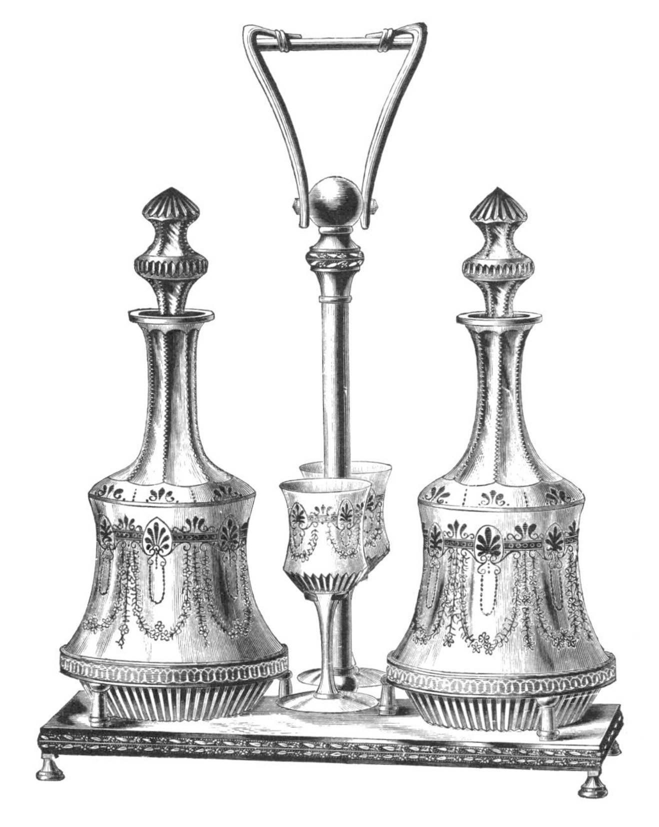

No. 0102, . $60.00 (REDOUND).
Nickel Silver, Silver Soldered.

GOLD AND SILVER PLATE.

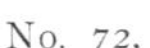

No. 72, . $30.00 (DEBONAIR).

No. 80, $32.00 (DEBARK).

No. 501. Claret Jug.
Cut Glass, . . $12.50 (REPLEVY).

No. 77. Lock Wine, . . $25.00 (DEBATE).

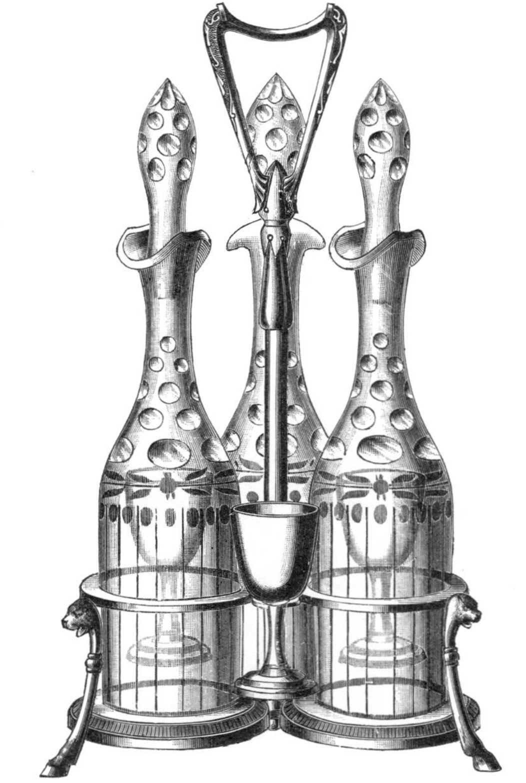

No. 60. 3 Bottles, with Goblets, . $27.00 (DEBRIS).
No. 59. 3 Bottles, without Goblets, 18.00 (DEBT).
No. 62. 2 Bottles, with Goblets, . 19.00 (DEBTOR).
No. 61. 2 Bottles, without Goblets, 14.00 (DEBUT).

CELERY STANDS.

(ONE-THIRD SIZE.)

No. 60.
Ruby, Decorated, $10.50 (REPLENISH).

No. 63.
Venetian Thread Glass, $8.50 (PAYABLE).
Assorted Colors.

No. 59.
Decorated, . $9.50 (REFINE).
Assorted Colors.

No. 55, . $8.50 (DAMSON).

No. 53, . $11.00 (DANCE).
Crystal Cut.

No. 61.
Decorated, . $12.50 (REPEL).
Assorted Colors.

No. 57.
Crystal, Cut, . $10.50 (REPEATER).

No. 62.
Crystal, Engraved, . $11.00 (REPEAT).

No. 58.
Decorated, . $10.50 (REPLACE).
Assorted Colors.

No. 44, . $7.00 (DARK).

No. 52, . $6.00 (DAPPER).

No. 39, . $6.00 (DAPPLE).

No. 51, . $7.75 (DANDLE).

CELERY TRAY.

No. 56, . $6.75 (DARKEN).

No. 49, . $6.50 (DART).

No. 50, . $7.00 (DARE).

No. 38. Block Cut, $14.00 (DANGER).

No. 40, . $7.00 (DARLING).

WHITE METAL.

PICKLE CASTERS.

(ONE-THIRD SIZE.)

TRADE MARK.
NICKEL SILVER.

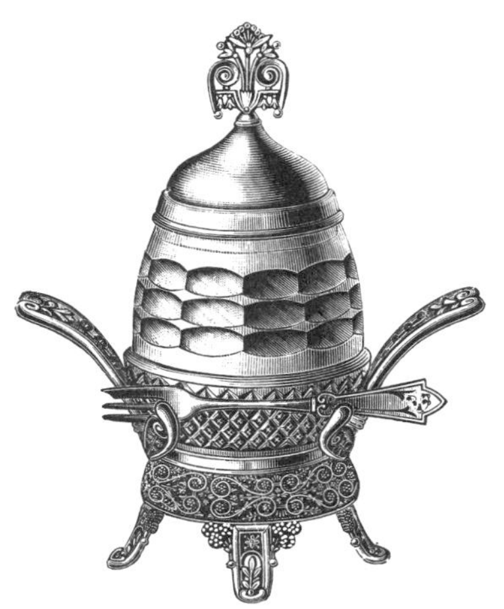

No. 178. Cut Glass, $9.00 (CRITERION).

No. 229.
Cut and Engraved, $6.00 (PAY-DAY).
Old Silver, . 6.75 (PAYMENT).

No. 233, . $3.50 (PAVEMENT).

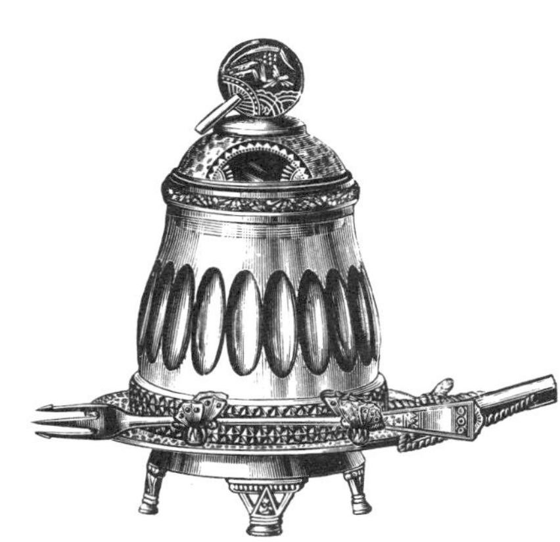

No. 159. Cut Glass, $9.00 (CRITIC).

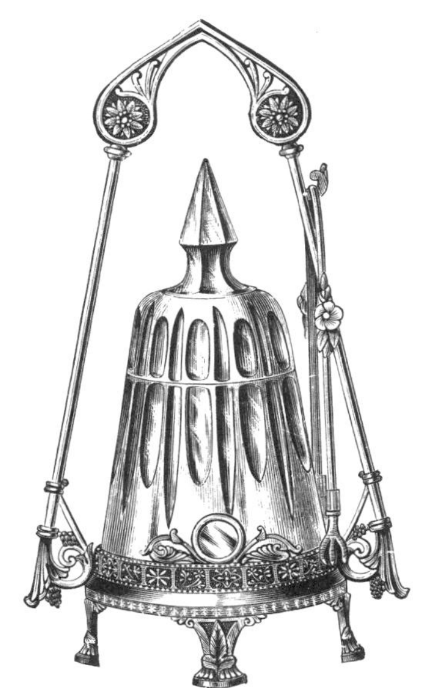

No. 153. Cut Glass, $9.50 (CRITICISE).

No. 228.
Pomona Art Glass, $6.00 (PACKHORSE).

No. 217.
Decorated, $6.00 (PACKMAN).
Assorted Colors.

No. 309. COMBINATION.
5 Bottles, . $15.00 (PAGANISM).

No. 218. Decorated, . $10.00 (PAGING).
Gold Inlaid, . . 11.50 (PAINTER).
Assorted Colors.

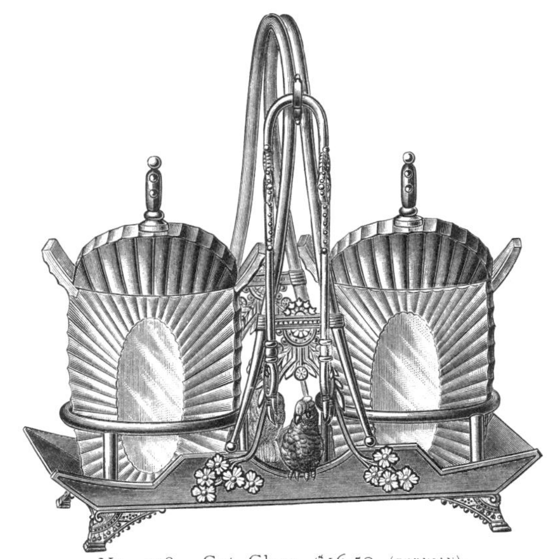

No. 198. Cut Glass, $16.50 (GORDIAN).

No. 192, . $10.50 (CULMINATE).
Gold Inlaid, . 13.00 (CULPABLE).

GOLD AND SILVER PLATE.

No. 230.
Assorted Colors, . $3.50 (PAPYRUS).

No. 216.
Colored, . $6.00 (PALACE).

No. 231.
Decorated, . $6.50 (PALADIN).
Assorted Colors.

No. 224.
Ruby, . $5 50 (PANDEAN).

No. 200.
Crystal, . $12.00 (PANORAMA).

No. 196.
Decorated, . $7.50 (CRITICISM).
Assorted Colors.

No. 197, . $10.50 (PANDORE).

No. 215, . $10.00 (GOODLY).

No. 225.
Assorted Colors, . $10.00 (PANTHEON).

No. 226. 3 Bottles.
Assorted Colors, . $10.75 (PANTOMIME).

GOLD AND SILVER PLATE.

No. 164. With Gilt Spoon, $7.50 (CROCUS).
Also used as Sugar or Jelly Dish.

No. 202. Pickle or Olive Dish.
Decorated Porcelain, . . $6.50 (PARTING).

Marmalade.
No. 400, . $7.00 (GOLDEN).

No. 201, . $8.00 (PARSON).

No. 176.
Patent Slide Cover, $5.50 (CRUPPER).

No. 222.
Crystal, . . $4.75 (PALMY).
Assorted Colors, 5.00 (PAMPER).

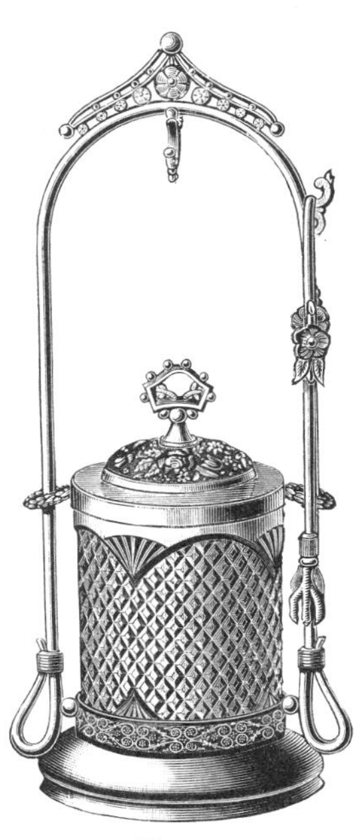

No. 172.
Patent Slide Cover, $4.00 (CRUMBLE).

No 175, . $7.25 (CRINKLE).

No. 193, . $12.00 (CULPRIT).

No. 199, . $8.00 (CROFT).

No. 185, . $10.25 (CRIPPLE).

GOLD AND SILVER PLATE.

No. 227, . $5.00 (PARABLE).
Pomona Art Glass.

No. 156, . $5.00 (CROOKED).

No. 223, . $5.00 (PARADISE).
Assorted Colors.

No. 212, . $3.75 (GRACEFUL).

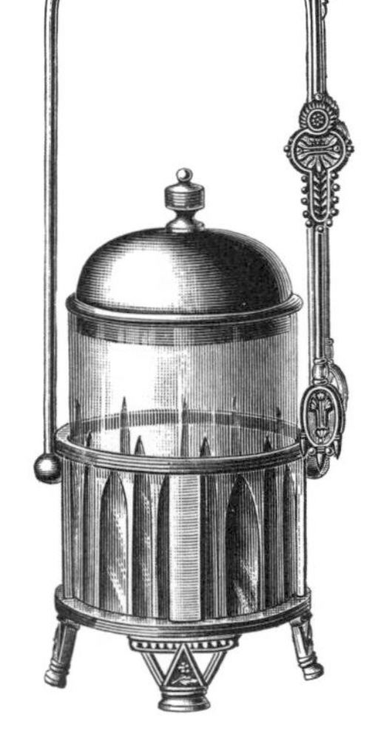

No. 157½, . $5.00 (CRONY).

No. 168, . $6.00 (CROCHET).

No. 195, . $6.75 (CROZIER).

No. 221.
Crystal, . $4.00 (PARAFFINE).
Assorted Colors, 4.25 (PARALLEL).

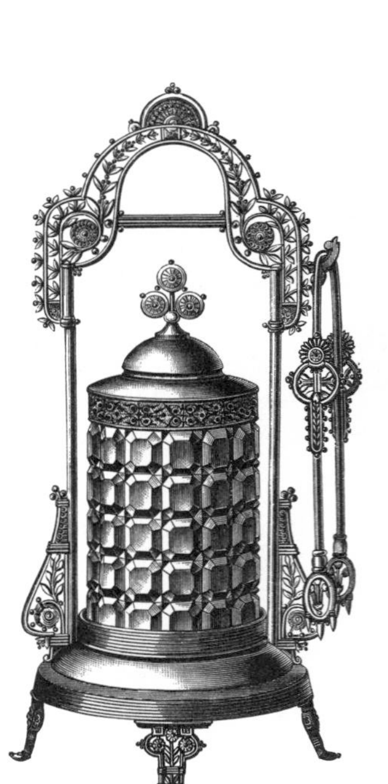

No. 210, . $5.00 (BASTILE).

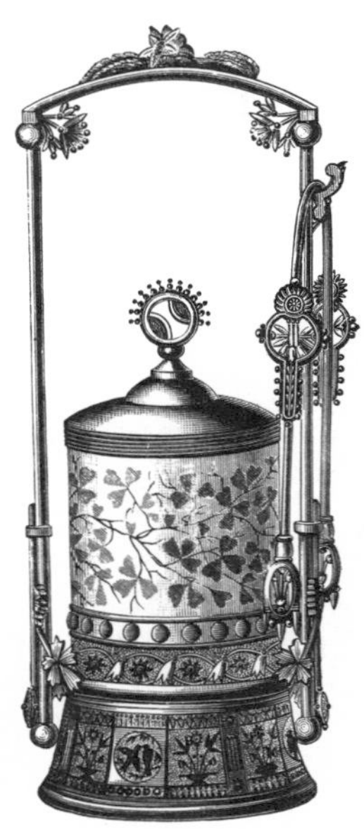

No. 206, . $3.75 (BASTION).

TRADE MARK.
WHITE METAL.

GOLD AND SILVER PLATE.

TRADE MARK.
NICKEL SILVER.

No. 203, . $3.00 (BARROW).

No. 205, . $3.50 (BASHAW).

No. 207, . $3.50 (BATTEN).

No. 219.
Crystal, . $3.00 (PARENT).
Assorted Colors, 3.25 (PARIAN).

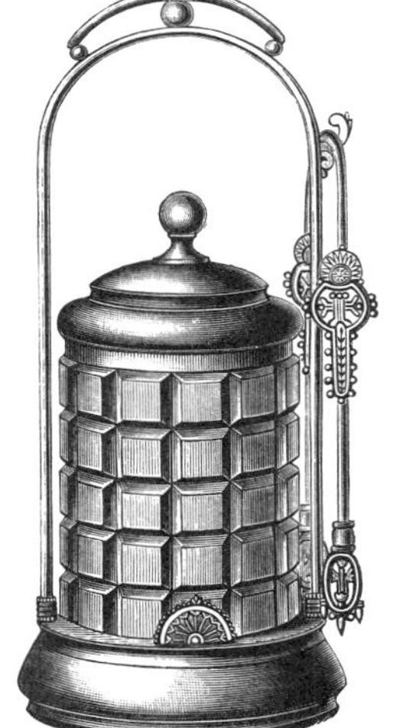

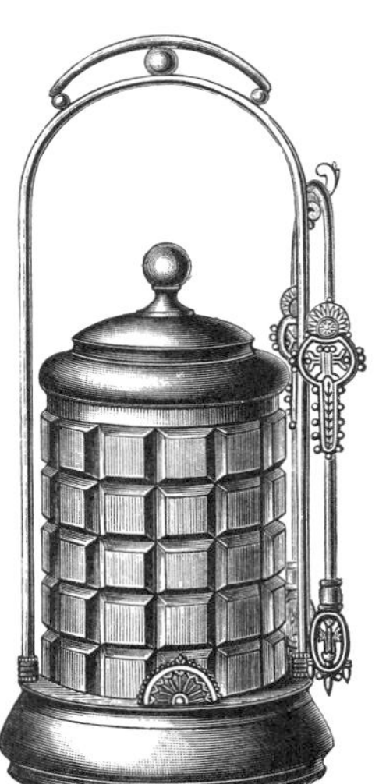

No. 211, . $3.50 (GOLDFISH).

No. 208, . $4.00 (BASIL).

No. 204, . $3.25 (BASALT).

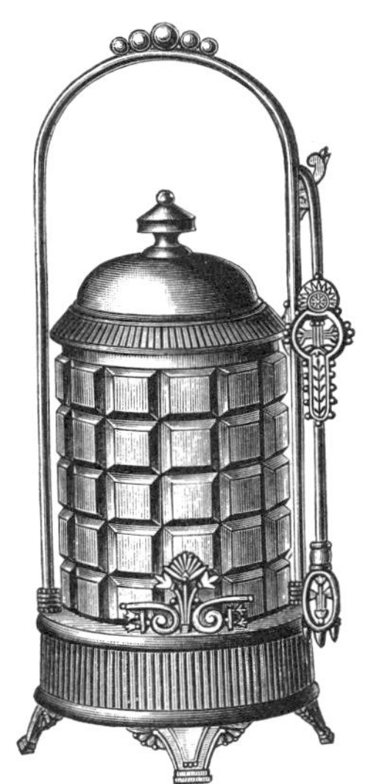

No. 213, . $4.00 (GOSSAMER).

No. 209, . $4.50 (BASSO).

No. 220, . $3.25 (PARSEE).

No. 166, . $9.00 (CROSSBOW).

No. 131, . $7.50 (CRUISE).

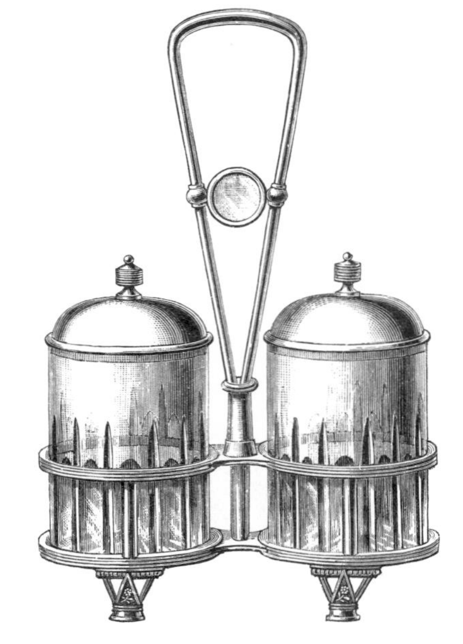

No. 157, . $9.00 (CROOK).

No. 169, . $12.00 (CRUSTY).

No. 179, . $8.00 (CRUSADE).

No. 180, . $12.00 (CRIMSON).

Trade Mark.
WHITE METAL.

GOLD AND SILVER PLATE.

Trade Mark.
NICKEL SILVER.

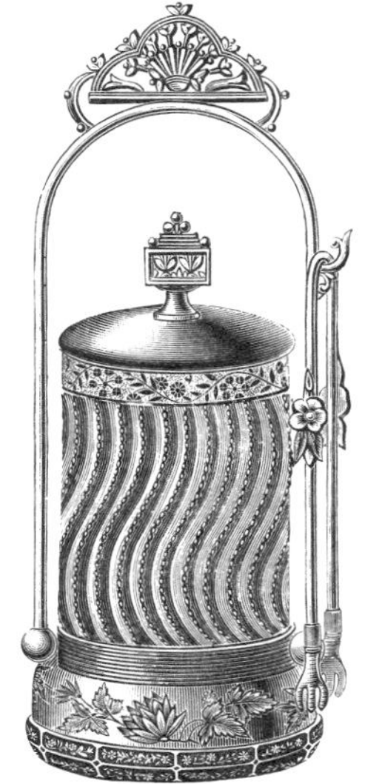

No. 232, . $3.75 (PARTICULAR).

No. 137, . $3.00 (CRUTCH).

No. 11, . $3.00 (CURABLE).

No. 6, . $5.00 (CUDGEL).

No. 148, . $4.00 (CROUP).

No. 3½. Single Plate, $1.87 (PATIENT).
No. 3. Without Fork, 1.50 (CUDDY).
This article does not bear our trade-mark.

No. 4. Single Plate, $4.00 (CUIRASS).
This article does not bear our trade-mark.

No. 140. 2 Bottles, . $6.75 (CROWBAR).

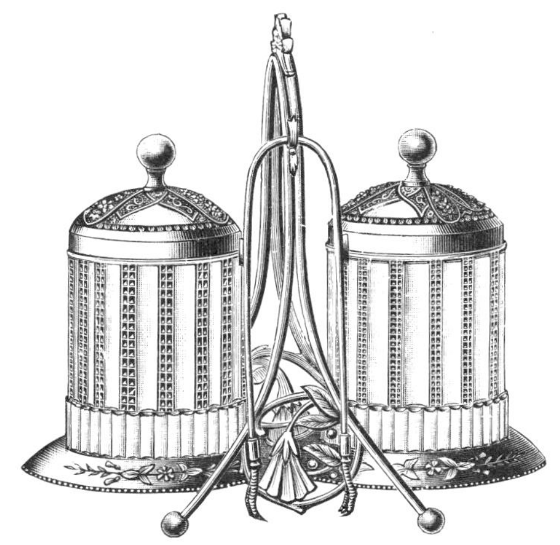

No. 10½. Plated Chased Covers, $6.50 (CUBIT).
No. 10. Glass Covers, . . 6.00 (CUCKOO).

No. 12, . $5.00 (CUPPING).

NICKEL SILVER PICKLE CASTERS.

(ONE-THIRD SIZE.)

No. 06.
Satin Engraved, $17.50 (PARAPET).

No. 017, . $11.50 (PARAMOUNT).

No. 014, . $18.50 (RENT).

No. 04, . . $13.50 (REPACK).
X Glass, . . 18.75 (REPAIR).

No. 015, . $19.00 (REPARTEE).

NICKEL SILVER SALAD CASTERS.

(ONE-THIRD SIZE.)

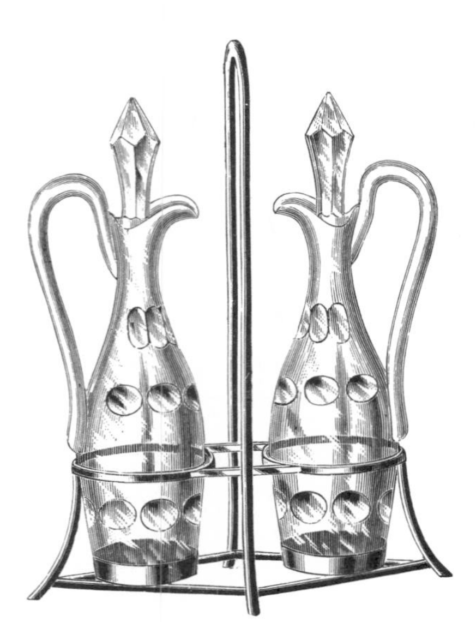

No. 02, . $10.50 (RELAY).

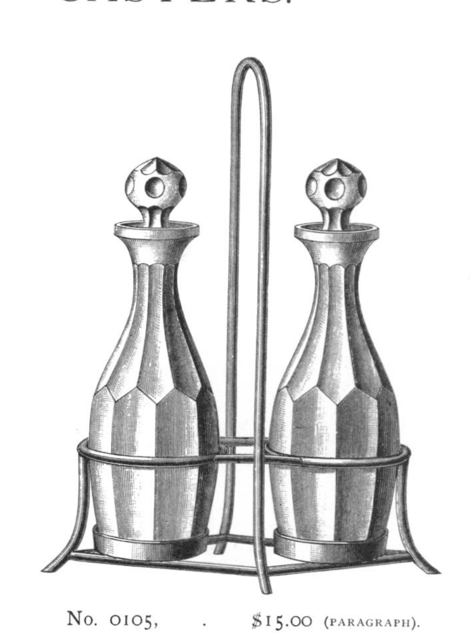

No. 0105, . $15.00 (PARAGRAPH).

NICKEL SILVER, SILVER SOLDERED.

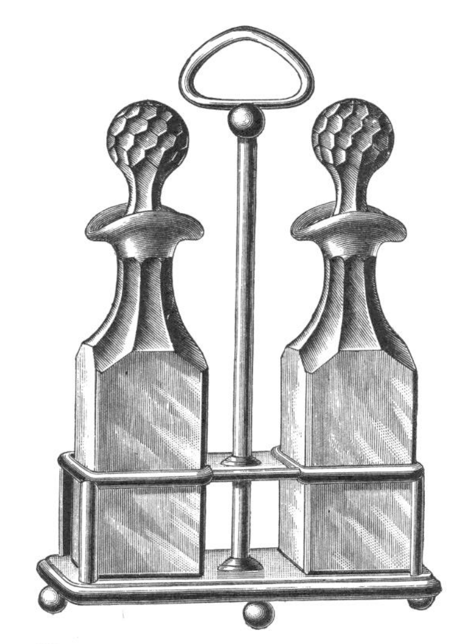

No. 0113, . $21.00 (PATHETIC).

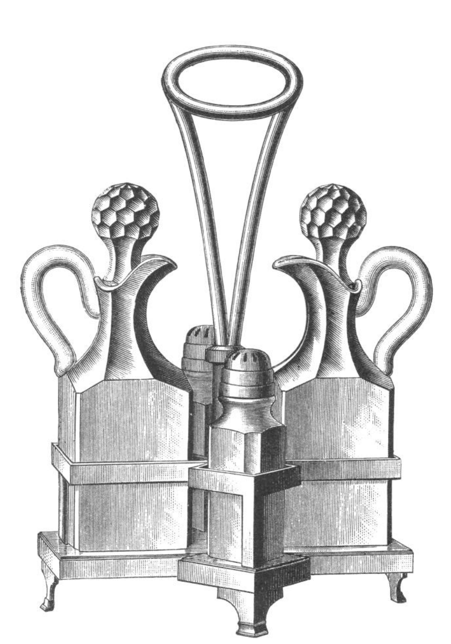

No. 0118, . $48.00 (PATHLESS).

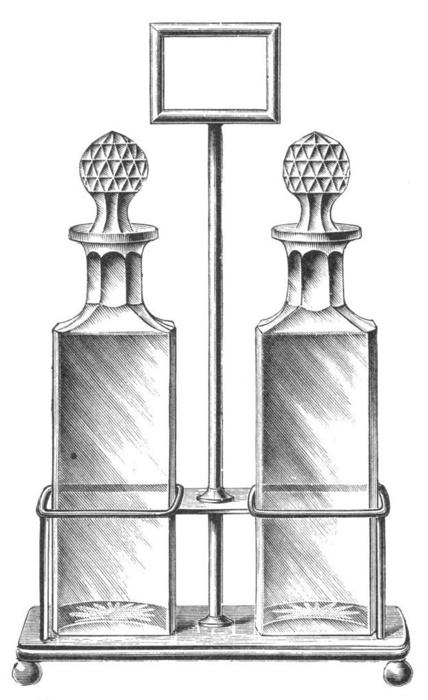

No. 0112, . $20.00 (RELEASE).

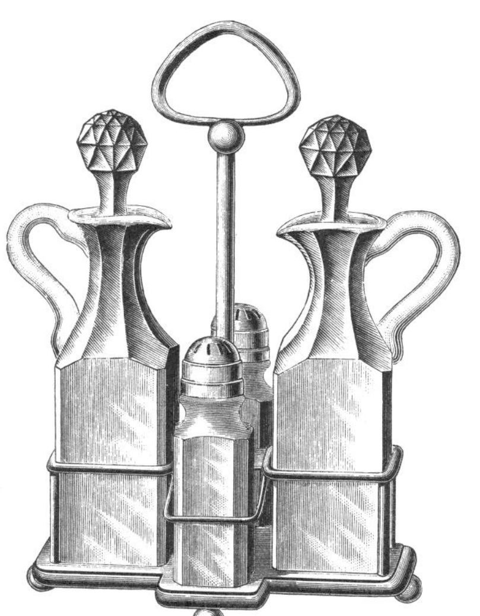

No. 0114, . $31.00 (PATHOS).

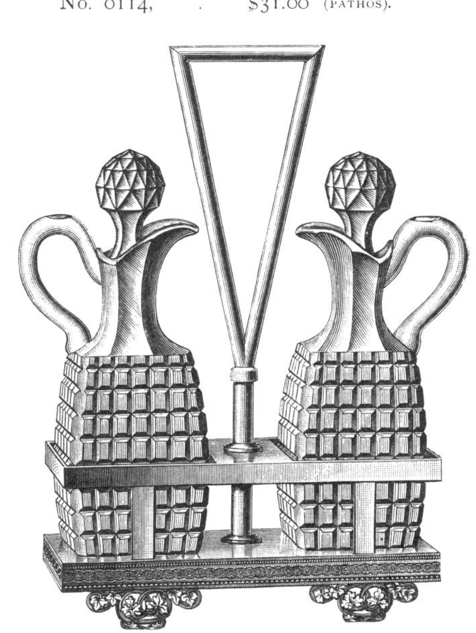

No. 0115, . $37.50 (PATHWAY).

No. 0120, . $42.50 (PATIENCE).

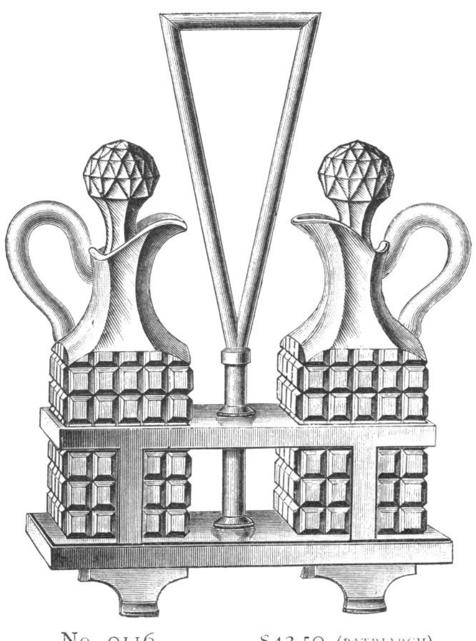

No. 0116, . $42.50 (PATRIARCH).

NICKEL SILVER, SILVER SOLDERED.

WHITE METAL SALAD CASTERS.

(One-Third Size.)

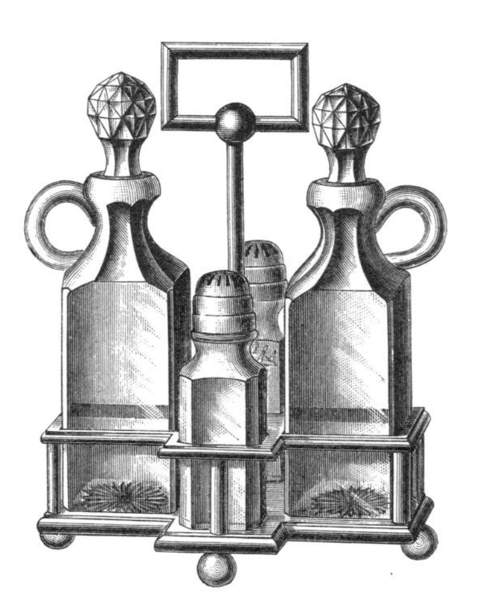

No. 18, . $19.50 (greet).

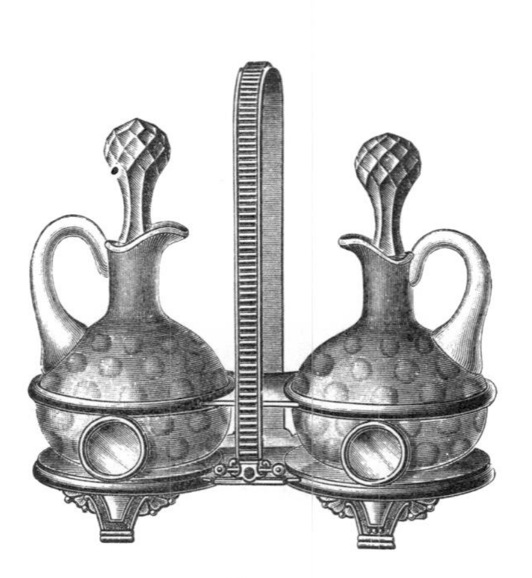

No. 24.
Amberina, . $9.00 (parboil).

No. 31.
Ruby, . $10.50 (parchment).

No. 22, . $16.50 (greeting).

No. 19, . $16.00 (grenade).

No. 14. Without Salt and Pepper, . $16.50 (dancer).
No. 16. With Salt and Pepper, . 21.00 (davit).

GOLD AND SILVER PLATE.

No. 29.
Ruby, . $9.00 (PATERNAL).

No. 27.
Ruby, . $8.50 (PASTURAGE).

No. 32.
Rose, Decorated, . $12.00 (PARTY).

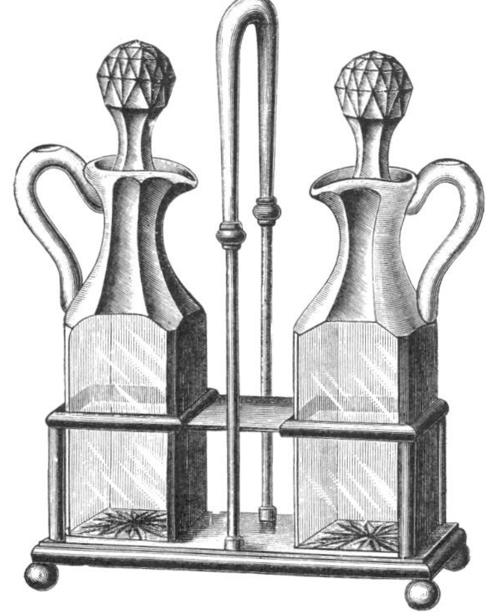

No 23, . $15.00 (PATCH).

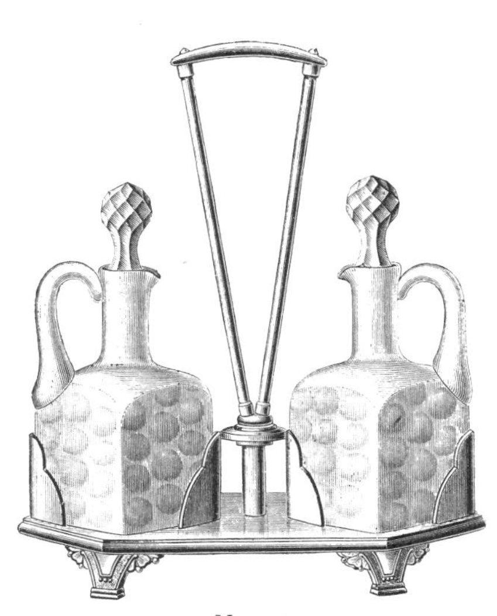

No. 25.
Crystal, . $10.00 (PASSENGER).

No. 30.
Ruby, . $10.50 (PASSION).

No. 33. CORALINE BOTTLES.
Silver, . . $12.00 (PASTIL).
Old Silver, . 13.00 (PASSOVER).

No. 34. CORALINE BOTTLES.
Silver, . $12.50 (PASSABLE).

GOLD AND SILVER PLATE.

No. 10. SAUCE BOTTLE HOLDER.

For Worcestershire Sauce, . $6.00 (DALE).

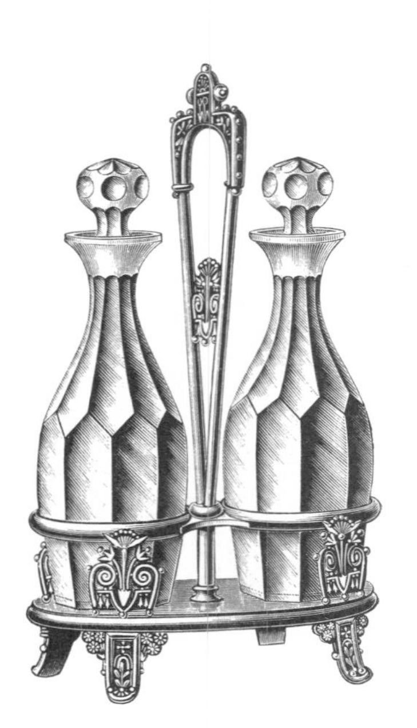

No. 12, . $12.00 (DAISY).

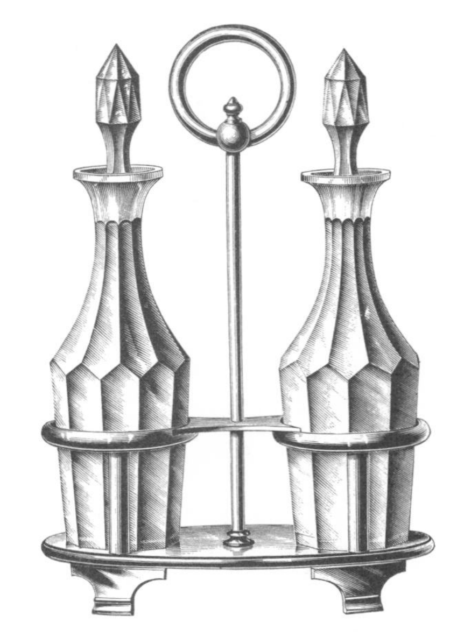

No. 13, . $13.50 (DAME).

No. 26, . $13.50 (PARODIST).

No. 14, . $16.50 (DANCER).

No. 28.

Assorted Colors, . $10.50 (PARTICIPATE).

COMMUNION WARE.

(One-Third Size.)

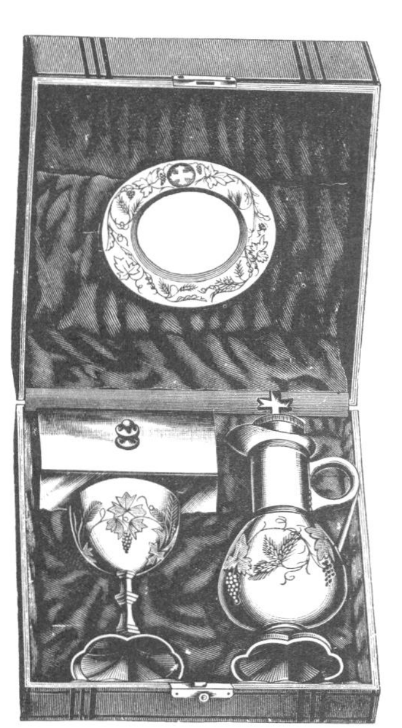

Flask. Goblet. Bowl.

Pocket Communion Set.

Four Pieces, Goblet Gold Lined, $13.50 (purity).

Morocco Case, $4.00 extra (purple).

Plate. Flagon. Cut showing Pieces put in Nest for carrying.

No. 22. Missionary Communion Set.

Set of Five Pieces.	Flagon.	Bowl.	Plate.	Goblet.	Flask.
$20.00 (race).	$7.50 (purl).	$4.00 (purline).	$3.00 (purview).	$2.75 (pussy).	$2.75 (putlog).

Goblet Gold Lined, $0.75 extra (ranger). Morocco Case, $6.00 extra (rack).

No. 19.

Set of Six Pieces.	Flagon.	Baptismal Bowl.	Plate.	Goblet, Gold Lined.	Paten.
$40.00 (protege).	2 Quarts, $14.00 (protest).	$8.00 (protract).	$5.00 (protrude).	$4.00 (proud).	$8.00 (prove).

Chased Plates, . $2.00 each, extra (provender).

TRADE MARK.
WHITE METAL.

GOLD AND SILVER PLATE.

TRADE MARK.
NICKEL SILVER.

No. 16. COMMUNION SET.

	Set of Six Pieces.	Flagon.	Baptismal Bowl.	Plate.	Goblet, Gold Lined.	Paten.
No. 16.	$40.00 (PROPHET).	2 Quarts, $14.00 (PROPITIATE).	$8.00 (PROPOSE).	$5.00 (PROPOUND).	$4.00 (PROSAIC).	$8.00 (PROSCRIBE).
No. 17.	44.00 (PROSE).	3 Quarts, 18.00 (PROSECUTE).	8.00 (PROSELYTE).	5.00 (PROSODY).	4.00 (PROSPECT).	8.00 (PROSPER).

No. 1389. GOBLET.
Gold Lined, $3.75 (PURITAN).

No. 1391. GOBLET.
Gold Lined, $3.75 (PURPOSE).

	Set of Six Pieces.	Flagon.	Baptismal Bowl.	Plate.	Goblet.	Paten.
* No. 1389.	$29.25 (PRUNELLA).	1 Quart, $8.50 (PRUSSIC).	$6.75 (PUBLIC).	$4.00 (PUBLICAN).	$3.00 (PUBLISH).	$6.50 (PUCKER).
* No. 1390.	31.25 (PUDDLE).	2 Quarts, 10.50 (PUERILE).	6.75 (PULLET).	4.00 (PULLEY).	3.00 (PULMONIC).	6.50 (PULP).
* No. 1391.	33.00 (PULPIT).	3 Quarts, 12.25 (PULSATE).	6.75 (PULSE).	4.00 (PULVERIZE).	3.00 (PUMICE).	6.50 (PUMP).

Goblets, Gold Lined, $0.75 each, extra (PUMPKIN).

* The Flagons for these numbers are the same style, the difference being only in size. No. 1391 is the largest, No. 1390 the medium, and No. 1389 the smallest. The remainder of the sets are the same, with the exception of the Goblets. No. 1389, same style as 1390, only smaller.

Patens furnished to match all styles of Sets, if desired.

WHITE METAL.

GOLD AND SILVER PLATE.

NICKEL SILVER.

No. 20. PATEN, $8.00 (PURIFY).

No. 20. COMMUNION SET.

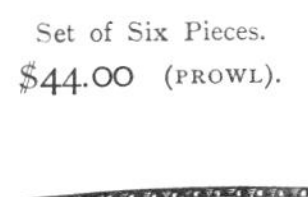

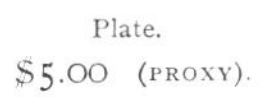

Set of Six Pieces.	Flagon.	Baptismal Bowl.	Plate.	Goblet, Gold Lined.
$44.00 (PROWL).	2 Quarts, $18.00 (PROXIMATE).	$8.00 (PROXIMO).	$5.00 (PROXY).	$4.00 (PRUDE).

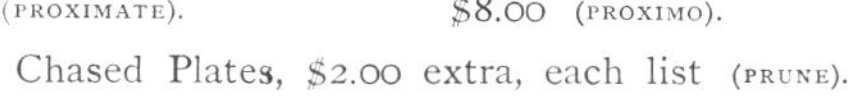

Chased Plates, $2.00 extra, each list (PRUNE).

No. 12. BOWL.
$7.25 (PROVISION).

No. 21. GOBLET.
Plain, $3.50 (RAMBLER).
Chased, 4.25 (RAISE).
Gold Lined.

No. 12. COMMUNION SET.

Set of Six Pieces.		Flagon.	Baptismal Bowl.	Plate.	Goblet.
$32.25 (PROVERB).	No. 12.	2 Quarts, $10.50 (PROVINCE).	$7.25 (PROVISION).	$4.00 (PROVISO).	$3.25 (PROVOKE).
31.00 (RADIX).	No. 11.	1 Quart, 9.25 (PROW).	7.25 (RAMBLER).	4.00 (RAGOUT).	3.25 (RAILER).

Goblets Gold Lined, $0.75 each, extra (PROWESS).

No. 21. LIBATION SET.

Candlestick.	Flagon.
$5.00 (RADIANT).	Plain, $10.50 (RADICATE).
	Chased, 12.00 (RAINBOW).

Trade Mark.
White Metal.

GOLD AND SILVER PLATE.

Trade Mark.
Nickel Silver.

No. 10. Paten, $6.75 (purport).

No. 10. Communion Set.

	Set of Six Pieces.	Flagon.	Baptismal Bowl.	Plate.	Goblet.
No. 9.	$31.00 (punish).	1 Quart, $9.25 (punster).	$7.25 (pupil).	$4.00 (puppet).	$3.25 (purchase).
No. 10.	32.25 (punch).	2 Quarts, 10.50 (puncheon).	7.25 (punctual).	4.00 (puncture).	3.25 (pungent).

Goblets, Gold Lined, $0.75 each, extra (purge).

No. 016. NICKEL SILVER, SILVER SOLDERED.

	Set of Six Pieces.	Flagon.	Baptismal Bowl.	Plate.	Goblet, Gold Lined.
No. 016.	$120.00 (purvey).	2 Quarts, . $51.00 (push).	$21.00 (putty).	$10.50 (puzzle).	$13.50 (pygmy).
No. 017.	133.00 (pyramid).	3 Quarts, . 64.00 (quadrant).	21.00 (quadrille).	10.50 (quaff).	13.50 (quagmire).

TRADE MARK.
WHITE METAL.

GOLD AND SILVER PLATE.

TRADE MARK.
NICKEL SILVER.

No. 04380. NICKEL SILVER, SILVER SOLDERED.

Set of Six Pieces.	Flagon.	Baptismal Bowl.	Plate.	Goblet, Gold Lined.	Paten.
$69.50 (PURSE).	2 Quarts, $24.00 (PURSER).	$11.00 (PURSUE).	$9.75 (PURSUIT).	$7.50 (PURSY).	$10.25 (PURVEYOR).

No. 0180. ENGRAVED.

	Set of Six Pieces.	Flagon.	Baptismal Bowl.	Plate.	Goblet, Gold Lined.	Paten.
Plain, .	$120.00 (QUARRY).	2 Quarts, $52.00 (QUARTER).	$19.50 (QUARTERN).	$12.25 (QUARTETTE).	$12.00 (QUARTO).	$19.00 (QUARTZ).
Engraved,	138.50 (QUAIL).	2 Quarts, 58.00 (QUAINT).	22.00 (QUAKE).	15.00 (QUAKER).	14.25 (QUALIFY).	21.00 (QUANDARY).

NICKEL SILVER, SILVER SOLDERED.

WHITE METAL CUPS

(FULL SIZE.)

No. 154.
Silver, ... $2.50 (LINEAGE).
Silver, Gold Lined, . 3.00 (LINEN).
Hammered, Gold Lined, 3.50 (LINGER).

No. 159.
Silver, ... $2.25 (LILAC).
Silver, Gold Lined, ... 2.75 (LIMB).
Silver, Gold Inlaid and Gold Lined, 3.75 (LIMBO).

No. 156.
Silver, ... $2.75 (LIGHTEN).
Silver, Gold Lined, ... 3.25 (LIGNITE).
Silver, Gold Inlaid and Gold Lined, 4.25 (LIKENESS).

No. 157.
Embossed, Chased, . . $3.00 (LIMIT).
Embossed, Chased, Gold Lined, 3.50 (LINDEN).

No. 169.
Satin, ... $2.75 (PATRIMONY).
Satin, Gold Lined, . . 3.25 (PATRIOT).
Satin, Engraved, Gold Lined, 3.75 (PEACE).

No. 160. CHASED D.
Plain, Gold Lined, ... $3.25 (LIME).
Brocade Chased, Gold Lined, . . . 3.75 (LIMEKILN).
Brocade Chased, Gold Inlaid and Gold Lined, 5.00 (LIMESTONE).
No. 158. Smaller (size of No. 159), . $0.50 less (PEACEFUL).

GOLD AND SILVER PLATE.

(HALF SIZE.)

No. 133.

Plain, ... $2.25 (FEET).
Plain, Gold Lined, 2.75 (FEIGN).
Chased, . . . 2.75 (FELICITY).
Chased, Gold Lined, 3.25 (FEIGNED).

No. 136.

Chased, . . . $3.00 (FIERY).
Chased, Gold Lined, 3.50 (FIFE).

No. 174.

Satin, ... $2.50 (PEACOCK).
Satin, Engraved, . . . 3.00 (PENDANT).
Satin, Engraved, Gold Lined, 3.50 (PENDING).

No. 108.

Embossed, Gold Lined, $3.50 (FILIAL).

No. 146.

Silver, Gold Lined, . . . $3.50 (FAIRY).
Gold Inlaid and Gold Lined, 4.50 (FAITH).
XX Gold Inlaid and Gold Lined, 5.50 (FAKIR).

No. 216. COMBINATION CASE.
Knife, Fork, Spoon, Napkin Ring, and
Chased, Gold Lined Cup, $11.50 (PENMAN).

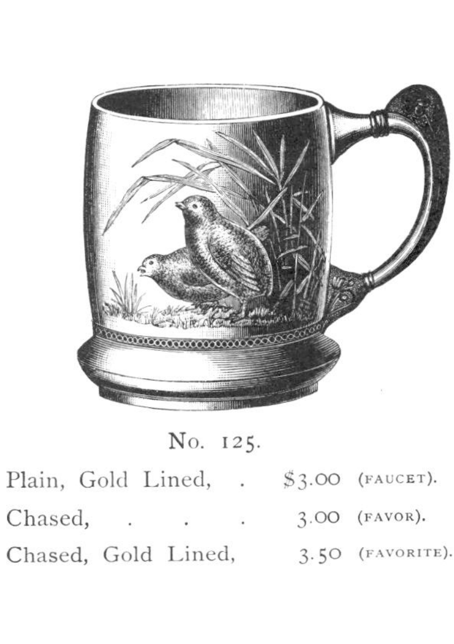

No. 125.

Plain, Gold Lined, . $3.00 (FAUCET).
Chased, ... 3.00 (FAVOR).
Chased, Gold Lined, 3.50 (FAVORITE).

CHASED, GOLD LINED.
No. 167 Cup in Plush Case, . $7.75 (PENDULUM).
Without Case, ... 3.75 (PENITENT).
(Also furnished Satin Chased at same price.)

No. 168.

Embossed, Gold Lined, . . $3.75 (PENNANT).
Embossed, Old Silver, Gold Lined, 4.75 (PENNON).
Embossed, Gold Inlaid, Gold Lined, 6.25 (PENSIVE).

SATIN, ENGRAVED, GOLD LINED.
No. 166 Cup in Plush Case, . $7.75 (PENETRATE).
Without Case, ... 3.75 (PENINSULA).

WHITE METAL.

GOLD AND SILVER PLATE.

NICKEL SILVER.

No. 150.
Plain, Gold Lined, . $2.25 (ANTIMONY).
Engraved, Gold Lined, 2.75 (ANTIPODE).

No. 151.
Satin, Gold Lined, . . $2.50 (ANNEAL).
Satin, Engraved, Gold Lined, 3.00 (ANNOTATE).

No. 152.
Satin, Gold Lined, . . $2.50 (ANTHEM).
Satin, Engraved, Gold Lined, 3.00 (ANTIDOTE).

No. 149.
Plain, Gold Lined, . $1.75 (ANNUAL).
Engraved, Gold Lined, 2.25 (ANNUL).

No. 135.
Plain, Gold Lined, $2.75 (FIELD).
Chased, . . 2.75 (FIEND).
Chased, Gold Lined, 3.25 (FIERCE).

No. 162.
Satin, ... $2.50 (PEONY).
Satin, Engraved, . . 3.00 (PEPSIN).
Satin, Engraved, Gold Lined, 3.50 (PENTAGON).

No. 147.
Gold Lined, . . . $3.50 (ANTIQUE).
Gold Inlaid and Gold Lined, 4.75 (ANTLER).

No. 144.
Plain, . . $2.00 (PEOPLE).
Plain, Gold Lined, 2.50 (FALCONER).
Chased, Gold Lined, 3.00 (FALLIBLE).

No. 172.
Satin, ... $3.00 (PERFORCE).
Satin, Engraved, . . 3.50 (PERFUSE).
Satin, Engraved, Gold Lined, 4.00 (PERCEIVE).

No. 142.
Plain, . . $2.50 (FLUTE).
Plain, Gold Lined, 3.00 (FLUTING).
Chased, . . 3.00 (FLYER).
Chased, Gold Lined, 3.50 (FOAM).

No. 138.
Silver, ... $3.00 (FARINA).
Gold Lined, . . . 3.50 (FARM).
Gold Inlaid and Gold Lined, 4.25 (FARMING).

No. 164.
Satin, ... $2.50 (PERFUMER).
Satin, Engraved, . . 3.00 (PERHAPS).
Satin, Engraved, Gold Lined, 3.50 (PERCUSSION).
No. 165. Larger, . $0.25 extra (PERISH).

No. 148.
Gold Lined, . $3.50 (ANIMATE).

No. 171.
Satin, Engraved, Gold Lined, $3.50 (PERIWIG).
No. 170. SMALLER.
Satin, Engraved, Gold Lined, $3.00 (PERPLEX).

No. 173.
Satin, ... $2.50 (PERMEATE).
Satin, Gold Lined, . 3.00 (PERPETUAL).
Satin, Engraved, Gold Lined, 3.50 (PERSEVERE).

No. 141.
Plain, . . $2.25 (FLUME).
Plain, Gold Lined, 2.75 (FLUNG).
Chased, . . 2.75 (FLURRY).
Chased, Gold Lined, 3.25 (PERSPIRE).

GOLD AND SILVER PLATE.

No. 132.

Plain, . . . $2.00 (FEBRUARY).
Chased, . . 2.50 (FEED).
Chased, Gold Lined, 3.00 (FEELING).

No. 133.

Hammered, Gold Lined, . $3.50 (FASHION).
Hammered, Chased, Gold Lined, 4.00 (FAST).

No. 116.

Plain, . . $2.50 (FINISH).
Plain, Gold Lined, 3.00 (FINITE).
Chased, . . 3.00 (FINNY).
Chased, Gold Lined, 3.50 (FIRE).

No. 137.

Silver, ... $2.50 (FARO).
Gold Lined, . . 3.00 (FARRIER).
Gold Inlaid and Gold Lined, 3.75 (FARROW).

No. 163.

Satin, ... $2.75 (PETARD).
Satin, Engraved, . . 3.25 (PETUNIA).
Satin, Engraved, Gold Lined, 3.75 (PERVERSE).

No. 102.

Satin, ... $2.00 (FLAIL).
Satin, Engraved, . . 2.50 (FLAKE).
Satin, Engraved, Gold Lined, 3.00 (FLAMBEAU).

No. 63.

Pearl, Chased, . . $2.75 (PETIT).
Pearl Chased, Gold Lined, 3.25 (FOCUS).

No. 176.

Satin, . . $2.50 (PHOENIX).
Chased, . . 3.00 (PHARMACIST).
Chased, Gold Lined, 3.50 (PHANTASM).

No. 116.

India Chased, Gold Lined, $4.00 (FOB).

No. 125.

Hammered, ... $3.00 (PHARISEE).
Hammered, Gold Lined, . 3.50 (FARTHER).
Hammered, Chased, Gold Lined, 4.00 (FARTHING).

No. 124.

Plain, . . $2.25 (FEND).
Chased, . 2.75 (FERMENT).
Chased, Gold Lined, 3.25 (FERRET).

No. 114.

Chased, . . $2.50 (FICTION).
Chased, Gold Lined, 3.00 (FIDDLE).

No 112.

Plain, . . $2.25 (FEUDAL).
Chased, . . 2.75 (FIBRE).
Chased, Gold Lined, 3.25 (FICKLE).

No. 126.

Plain, . . $2.25 (FINERY).
Chased, . . 2.75 (FINESSE).
Chased, Gold Lined, 3.25 (FINGER).

No. 139.

Silver, ... $3.00 (FARCE).
Gold Lined, . . . 3.50 (FARE).
Gold Inlaid and Gold Lined, 4.50 (FAREWELL).

TRADE MARK.
WHITE METAL.

GOLD AND SILVER PLATE.

TRADE MARK.
NICKEL SILVER.

No. 127.

Plain, . . . $2.00 (FERTILE).
Chased, . . 2.50 (FERULE).
Chased, Gold Lined, 3.00 (FERVENT).

No. 140.

Plain, . . . $2.00 (FLUE).
Chased, . . 2.50 (FLUENT).
Chased, Gold Lined, 3.00 (FLUID).

No. 127.

Plain, Gold Lined, . . $2.50 (FERVOR).
Feather Chased, . . 2.50 (FESTAL).
Feather Chased, Gold Lined, 3.00 (FESTIVAL).

No. 113.

Plain, . . . $1.75 (FETE).
Chased, . . 2.25 (FETTER).
Chased, Gold Lined, 2.75 (FEUD).

No. 134.

Plain, . . $2.50 (FEAT).
Plain, Gold Lined, 3.00 (FEATHER).

No. 121.

Plain, Gold Lined, $2.00 (FLASH).
Chased, . . 2.00 (FLAP).
Chased, Gold Lined, 2.50 (FLARE).

No. 5.

Chased, Gilt, . $1.25 (FLATTEN).
Satin Chased, Gilt, 1.25 (FLAUNT).

No. 7.

Chased, Gilt, . $1.25 (FLAX).

No. 6.

Chased, Gilt, . . $1.00 (FLASK).
Satin Chased, Gilt, 1.00 (FLAT).

No. 8.

Chased, Gilt, . $1.50 (FLECK).

No. 9.

Chased, Gilt, . $1.50 (FLAY).

No. 4.

Chased, Gilt, . $1.50 (FLAVOR).
Satin Chased, Gilt, 1.50 (FLAW).

Cups Nos. 4, 5, 6, 7, 8, and 9 are single plate, and do not bear our trade-mark.

Trade Mark.
WHITE METAL.

COLLAPSION CUPS.

Trade Mark
NICKEL SILVER.

(Half Size.)

No. 3. Closed.

No. 3. Open.

Plain, . $1.50 (flew).

No. 4. Closed.

No. 4. Open.

Plain, . $2.00 (fled).

No. 2. Open.

Plain, . $1.55 (fleece).

View showing Cup only.

View showing Cup complete, balanced to stand on end.

No. 5. Silver Egg Collapsion Cup, Full Size.

Satin, Gold Lined, . . $3.00 (litimus).

No. 1 Open.

Plain, . $1.30 (fleet).

Engine, . 1.65 (flesh).

SHAVING CUPS.

(Half Size.)

No. 143.

Plain, . . . $4.00 (flow).

Chased, . . . 4 50 (flower).

Chased, Gold Lined, 5.00 (physical).

No. 143.

Hammered, ... $4.50 (philander).

Hammered, Old Silver, . . 5.00 (philippic).

Hammered, Old Silver, Gold Lined, 5.50 (pianist).

No. 128.

Porcelain, with Plated Mountings, $3.75 (flown).

View showing Soap Box or top of No. 175 Cup.

No. 175. Moorish, Old Silver.

Combination Cup and Soap Box.

Satin, ... $5.50 (piano).

Satin, Engraved, . . 7.00 (picayune).

Moorish, Old Silver, . 7.50 (pickerel).

Trade Mark.
White Metal.

NICKEL SILVER CUPS.

Trade Mark.
Nickel Silver.

(Full Size.)

No. 024.
Satin, Gold Lined, . $3.50 (library).

No. 023.
Plain, Gold Lined, . . $5.00 (physics).
Engraved, Gold Lined, . 6.00 (physician).

No. 027.
Satin, Gold Lined, . . $6.00 (libretto).
Hammered, Gold Lined, . 7.00 (lichen).
Satin, Engraved, Gold Lined, 7.00 (lictor).

No. 026.
Satin, Gold Lined, . . $5.25 (liege).
Hammered, Gold Lined, . 6.25 (ligament).
Satin, Engraved, Gold Lined, 6.25 (ligature).

No. 022.
Plain, Gold Lined, . . $5.00 (levy).
Hammered, Gold Lined, . 6.00 (lewis).
Engraved, Gold Lined, . 6.00 (lexicon).

No. 025.
Satin, Gold Lined, . . $5.00 (liable).
Hammered, Gold Lined, . 6.00 (liberal.)
Engraved, Gold Lined, . 6.00 (liberty).

NICKEL SILVER, SILVER SOLDERED.

GOLD AND SILVER PLATE.

(ONE-HALF SIZE.)

No. 028. NICKEL SILVER.

Satin, Gold Lined, $4.00 (PICKING).

No. 020. NICKEL SILVER.

Plain,	$5.25	(RECORD).
Plain, Gold Lined,	5.75	(RECOUNT).
Chased,	6.50	(RECOURSE).
Chased, Gold Lined,	7.00	(RECOVER).

No. 017. NICKEL SILVER.

Plain,	$4.50	(RECUR).
Plain, Gold Lined,	5.00	(RECUSANT).
Chased,	5.50	(REDAN).
Chased, Gold Lined,	6.00	(REDEEM).

No. 018. NICKEL SILVER.

Plain,	$3.75	(RECOMMEND).
Plain, Gold Lined,	4.25	(RECOMPENSE).
Chased,	4.50	(RECONCILE).
Chased, Gold Lined,	5.00	(RECONSIDER).

CUPS AND SAUCERS.

(ONE-THIRD SIZE).

No. 5.

Satin,	$3.00	(PICKLOCK).
Satin Engraved,	4.25	(FOLD).
Satin Engraved, Gold Lined Cup,	4.75	(FOLDER).

No. 6.

Satin,	$4.25	(PICKWICK).
Satin Engraved,	5.25	(FOIL).
Satin Engraved, Gold Lined Cup,	5.75	(FOIST).

No. 2.

Plain,	$3.75	(FOMENT).
Chased,	5.00	(FOND).
Chased, Gold Lined Cup,	5.50	(FONTAL).

No. 1.

Plain,	$3.25	(FOOD).
Chased,	4.50	(FOOTING).
Chased, Gold Lined Cup,	5.00	(FORAGE).

No. 7. MOUSTACHE.

Plain,	$6.50	(FOLIAGE).
Plain, Gold Lined Cup,	7.25	(FOLIO).
Chased,	9.00	(FOLK).
Chased, Gold Lined Cup,	9.75	(FOLLOW).

No. 8. MOUSTACHE.

Satin, Gold Lined Cup,	$6.50	(PIGMENT).
Brocade Chased, Gold Lined Cup,	8.00	(PIGEON).

No. 9. MOUSTACHE.

Satin, Gold Lined Cup,	$7.00	(PILGRIM).
Satin Engraved, Gold Lined Cup,	8.50	(PILASTER).

PAP SETS.

(One-Third Size.)

No. 204.

Plate, Silver, ... $3.00 (FOGGY).
Plate, Silver, Gold Inlaid, . 4.00 (FOIBLE).
Bowl Gold Lined, ... 5.50 (FOE).
Bowl Gold Inlaid and Gold Lined, 6.50 (FORMAN).

No. 203.
INDIVIDUAL SOUP OR PAP BOWL.
Satin, . . . $4 50 (FLIGHTY).

No. 202.

Plate, . . . $2.75 (FLINT).
Bowl Gold Lined, 5.00 (FLIP).
With Case and Spoon, $6.00 extra.

No. 200. PLUSH OR MOROCCO CASE.

Set Complete, Bowl Gold Lined, $13.75 (FLICKER).
Plate, ... 2.75 (FLIGHT).
Bowl, Gold Lined, . . . 5.00 (FLIER).

No. 206. OATMEAL BOWL.

Satin, Plate, ... $3.00 (PILLAR).
Satin, Engraved, Plate, . . 3.50 (PILLORY).
Satin, Bowl Gold Lined, . . 5.00 (PILLOW).
Satin, Engraved, Bowl, Gold Lined, 6.00 (PILLAGE).
Without Gold Lining $1.00 less.

No. 201

Plate, . . . $2.75 (FLINCH).
Bowl Gold Lined, 4.50 (FLING).

No. 206. PLUSH OR MOROCCO CASE.

Satin, Set Complete, Bowl Gold Lined, $14.00 (PINION).
Satin, Engraved Set, Bowl Gold Lined, 15.50 (PILOT).

No 207.

Satin, Plate, ... $3.25 (PINAFORE).
Satin, Bowl Gold Lined, . 5.25 (PINNACLE).
With Case and Spoon, $6.00 extra.

No. 205. PLUSH OR MOROCCO CASE.

Satin, Set Complete, Bowl Gold Lined, $14.25 (PIPING).
Plate, Satin, ... 3.25 (PIQUANT).
Bowl Gold Lined, ... 5.00 (PLACIDLY).

For Gold Lined Plates add 75 cents. For Silver Lined Bowls deduct $1.00 each.

PRIZE CUPS.

(One-Third Size.)

No. 2000. Yacht Cup.

Chased, Gold Inlaid and Gold Lined, . $137.50 (abdication.)

No. 1900. Racing.

Hammered, Old Silver,

Gold Inlaid and Gold Lined, . $125.00 (adjustment).

GOLD AND SILVER PLATE.

No. 2200. Bicycle.

Brocade Chased, Old Silver, Gold Inlaid and Gold Lined, $87.50 (abridgment).

No. 1700. Bicycle.

Engraved, Gold Lined, ... $140.00 (lavatory).
Engraved, Gold Inlaid and Gold Lined, $150.00 (layman).

No. 2600. AGRICULTURAL.
Shell Hammered, Gold Lined, $16.50 (COMPANION).
Moorish, Gold Inlaid, . . 20.00 (COMPORT).

No. 1100. LACROSSE OR LAWN TENNIS.
Gold and Silver, Gold Lined, $13.50 (FLOAT).

No. 2400. LAWN TENNIS.
Satin Engraved, Gold Lined, . . $13.50 (CONCILIATE).
Satin Engraved, Gold Inlaid and Gold Lined, 15.50 (CONCORDANT).

No. 1200. SHOOTING.
Engraved, Gold Inlaid and Gold Lined, $30.00 (FLOCK).

No. 100. SHOOTING.
Satin Engraved, Gold Inlaid and Gold Lined, $136.00 (ACADEMIC).

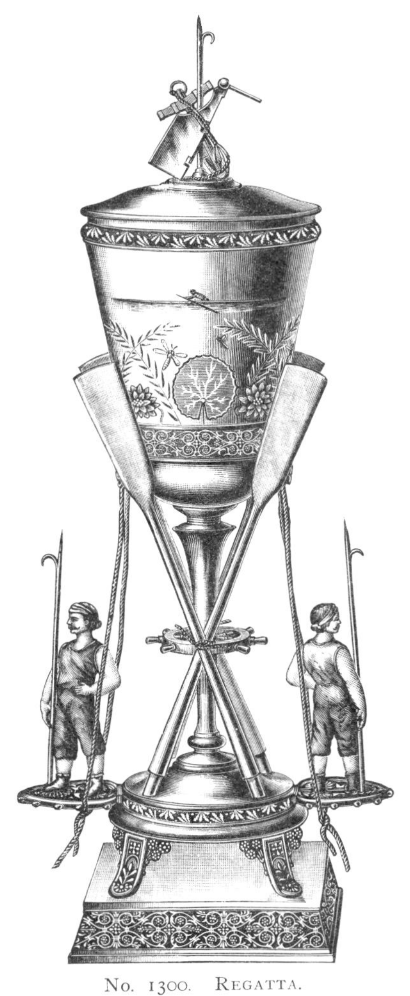

No. 1300. REGATTA.
Engraved, Gold Inlaid and Gold Lined, $35.00 (FLOOD).

TRADE MARK.
WHITE METAL.

GOLD AND SILVER PLATE.

TRADE MARK.
NICKEL SILVER.

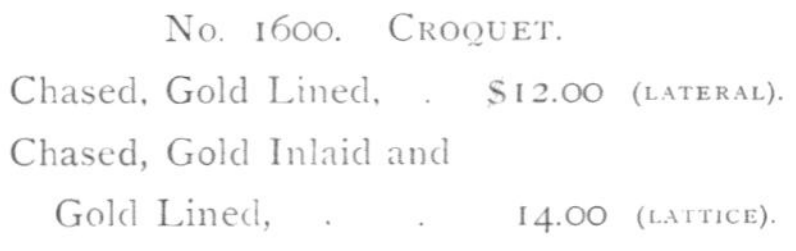

No. 1600. CROQUET.
Chased, Gold Lined, . $12.00 (LATERAL).
Chased, Gold Inlaid and
Gold Lined, . . 14.00 (LATTICE).

No 2900. BICYCLE.
Satin Engraved, Gold Lined, $10.50 (COMMAND).

No. 2300. POLO.
Chased, Gold Lined, . $11.50 (COMPLEXION).
Chased, Gold Inlaid and
Gold Lined, . . 13.50 (COMPLIANCE).

No. 2700. KENNEL.
Shell Hammered, Gold Lined, $16.50 (COMPENSATE).
Moorish, Gold Inlaid, . 20.00 (COMPETENCE).

No. 1800. REGATTA.
Hammered, Old Silver.
Gold Lined, . . $25.00 (ACCOMPLISH).

No. 2100. FOOT BALL.
Chased, Gold Inlaid and Gold Lined, . $40.00 (ACCLIMATE).

No. 800. BASE BALL.
Engraved, . . $25.00 (FLORA).

No. 1400. Bicycle.

Satin Engraved, Gold Lined, . . $25.00 (laudable).

Satin Engraved, Gold Inlaid and Gold Lined, 27.00 (laundry).

No. 2800. Roller Skating.

Satin Engraved, Gold Lined, . . $15.50 (comprehend).

Satin Engraved, Gold Inlaid and Gold Lined, 17.50 (concession).

No. 400. Racing.

Satin Engraved, Gold Lined, $16.50 (florid).

No. 3300. Polo.

Shell Hammered, Gold Lined, . $28.50 (commodious).

Moorish, Gold Inlaid and Gold Lined, 33.50 (commodore).

No. 3400. Knights Templar.

Chased, Gold Lined, . . . $30.00 (commons).

Chased, Gold Inlaid and Gold Lined, 35.00 (confederate).

No. 3200. Regatta.

Shell Hammered, Gold Lined, . $25.00 (comment).

Moorish, Gold Inlaid and Gold Lined, 30.00 (commerce).

Trade Mark
WHITE METAL.

GOLD AND SILVER PLATE.

Trade Mark.
NICKEL SILVER.

No. 3100. Lawn Tennis.
Old Silver, Hammered and Engraved.
Gold Lined, . . . $12.00 (committee).

No. 3500. Kennel.

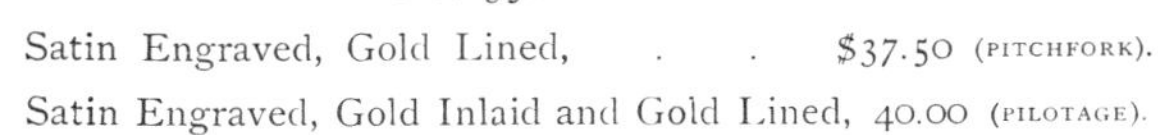

Satin Engraved, Gold Lined, . . $37.50 (pitchfork).
Satin Engraved, Gold Inlaid and Gold Lined, 40.00 (pilotage).

No. 1000. Regatta.
Niello and Gold, Gold Lined, $12.50 (floral).

No. 900. Regatta.
Satin Engraved, Gold Inlaid and Gold Lined, $12.50 (floor).

No. 3000. Baseball.
Satin Engraved, Gold Lined, $12.00 (commingle).

No. 300. Regatta.
Chased, Gold Lined, . $15.00 (accountant).

No. 700. Racing.
Plain, . . $30.00 (florist).
Engraved, . 36.00 (flotilla).

No. 2500. Curling.
Satin Engraved, Gold Lined, $13.50 (complot).
Satin Engraved, Gold Inlaid and Gold Lined, 16.50 (composure).

CIGAR BOXES.

(ONE-THIRD SIZE.)

No. 20. For 25 Cigars.
Brass, . . $12.00 (CONDIMENT).
Enameled Copper, 12.00 (CONDUCIVE).

No. 4. For 25 Cigars.
Nickel Plated, . $6.75 (PLOUGH).

No. 17. For 25 Cigars.
Old Silver, . $12.00 (PHAETON).

No. 24. For 25 Cigars.
Old Silver, . $12.00 (REAP).

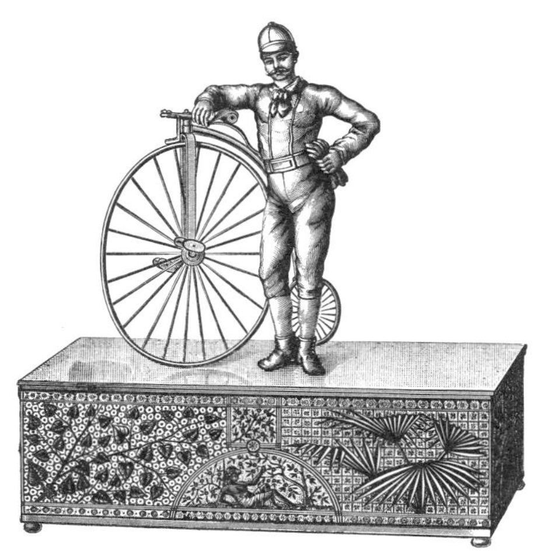

No. 23. For 50 Cigars.
Brass, . . $18.50 (CONDITION).
Enameled Copper, 18.50 (CONDUIT).

No. 18. For 50 Cigars.
Old Silver, . . $16.50 (PHALANX).
No. 21. (Border like No. 23.)
Enameled Copper, . $16.50 (REALISTIC).

No. 3. For 50 Cigars.
Nickel Plated, . $10.00 (PLUMBAGO).

No. 19. For 100 Cigars.
Old Silver, . . . $24.00 (PHARMACY).
No. 22. (Border like No. 23)
Enameled Copper, . . $24.00 (REAM).

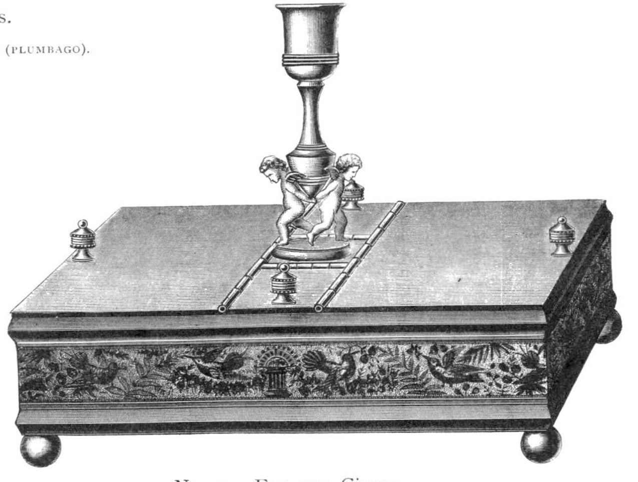

No. 2. For 100 Cigars.
Nickel Plated, . . . $18.00 (PLUMAGE).

CLOCKS.

(HALF SIZE.)

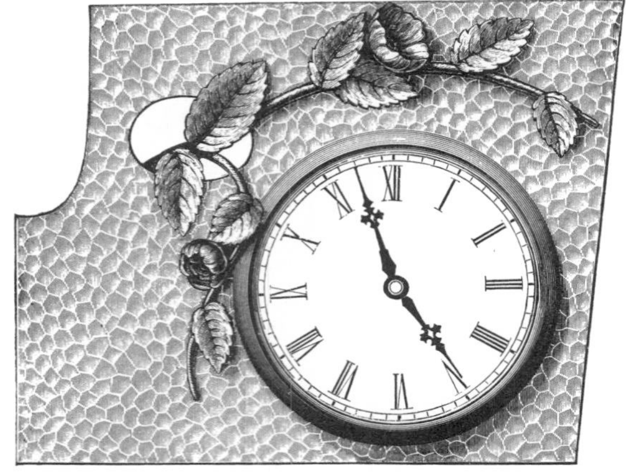

No. 300.
Old Silver, Gold Inlaid, . $12.00 (YARROW).

No. 400.
Old Silver, Gold Inlaid, . $13.50 (YELLOW).

No. 700.
Old Silver, . . . $18.50 (PLACATE).
Old Silver, XX Gold Inlaid, 21.00 (PLACEMAN).

No. 200.
Old Silver and Gold, . $11.00 (YARN)

No. 900.
Embossed Old Silver, . $13.50 (PITCHPINE).

GOLD AND SILVER PLATE.

No. 600. Enameled Copper.
Gold Inlaid Mountings, $10.50 (PLAINTIFF).

No. 500. Enameled Copper.
Gold Inlaid Mountings, $10.00 (PLANCHET).

No. 1000.
Old Silver, . . . $14.50 (RASCAL).
Old Silver, XX Gold Inlaid, 16.50 (RARE).

No. 800.
Old Silver, . . . $19.00 (RASURE).
Old Silver, XX Gold Inlaid, 21.50 (PLANISH).

No. 1100.
Old Silver, . . . $20.00 (RATE).
Old Silver, XX Gold Inlaid, 24.00 (PLANTER).

For material tipped into the original edition between pages 146 and 147, see page 451.

DESSERT SETS.

No. 20.

Cut Glass, . . . $24.00 (POLLARD).

No. 6.

Without Spoon, . . . $30.00 (DISOWN).

No. 19.

Complete, . $13.50 (HESITATE).

No. 17. DESSERT SET.

Silver, . . . $27.50 (HOMINY).

Silver, Gold Inlaid, . 30.00 (HONEY).

No. 19.

Cream, . $4.00 (HIDDEN).

Colored Glass.

No. 19.

Sugar, . . $5.00 (HIGHLY).

Colored Glass.

WHITE METAL.

GOLD AND SILVER PLATE.

NICKEL SILVER.

(ONE-THIRD SIZE.)

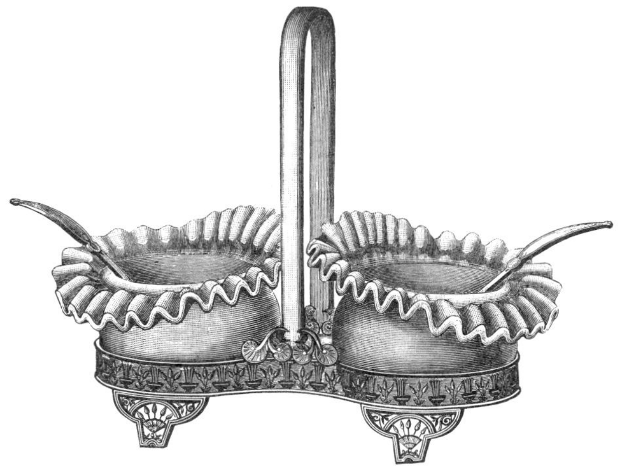

No. 22. SUGAR AND CREAM.
Including Cream Ladle and Sugar Spoon.
Ivory Glass, Assorted Colors.
Silver, ... $13.50 (PLUMPER).
Silver, Gold Inlaid, . 15.00 (PLUMP).

No. 18.
Complete, . $13.50 (HERSELF).

No. 24.
Decorated, . $15.00 (PLATEFUL).
Assorted Colors.

No. 12.
Crystal, . $18.75 (DISPATCH).

No. 23.
Silver, . . . $20.00 (PLAYTHING).
Silver, Gold Inlaid, . 22.50 (PLAYMATE).

GOLD AND SILVER PLATE.

No. 47. SUGAR.

Satin, . . . $6.00 (PLUME).

Satin, Engraved, . 7.00 (PLUMBING).

No. 21.

Cut Glass, . . . $30.00 (PLUMMET).

No. 47. CREAM.

Satin, Gold Lined, . . $6.00 (PLUG).

Satin, Engraved, Gold Lined, 7.00 (PLUCK).

No. 8, . . $36.00 (DISORDER).

Cut Glass.

No. 11, . . $22.00 (DISOBEY).

DESSERT SUGARS AND CREAMS.

(One-Third Size.)

No. 35. Cream.

Ruby or Crystal, $4.75 (distend).

No. 35. Sugar.

Ruby or Crystal, $7.00 (distant).

No. 43. Sugar.

Sugar, . . $6.50 (director).

No. 43. Cream.

Cream, . . $5.50 (directly).

No. 46. Sugar.

Cut Glass, . $8.50 (hobnail).

No. 46. Cream.

Cut Glass, . $8.50 (hobble).

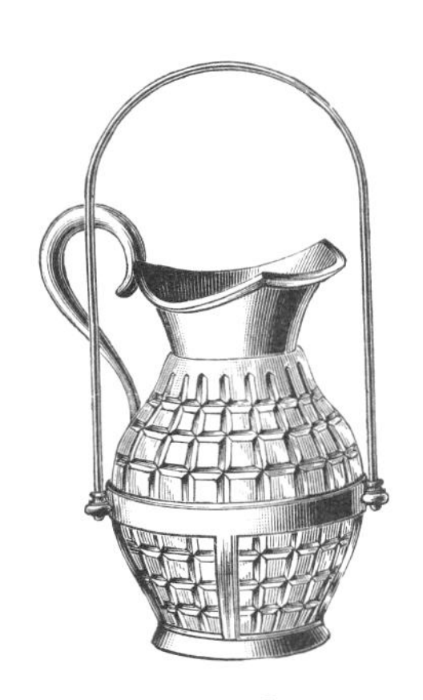

No. 32. Cream.

Cut Glass, . $7.25 (distaff).

No. 32. Sugar.

Cut Glass, . $7.50 (distance).

No. 33. Cream.

Crystal, . $5.50 (distich).

No. 33. Sugar.

Crystal, . $6.00 (distill).

No. 31. Cream.

Cut Glass, . $7.75 (distort).

No. 31. Sugar.

Cut Glass, . $8.00 (distinct).

WHITE METAL.

GOLD AND SILVER PLATE.

NICKEL SILVER.

No. 34. Spoon Holder.

Plain, Gold Lined, . $6.00 (dispel).
Chased, Gold Lined, . 7.00 (dispense).

No. 34. Sugar.

Plain, . . $6.00 (disperse).
Chased, . . 7.00 (displace).

No. 34. Cream.

Plain, Gold Lined, . $6.00 (display).
Chased, Gold Lined, . 7.00 (disport).

No. 39. Cream.

Assorted Colors, $6.50 (disturb).

No. 39. Sugar.

Assorted Colors, $7.50 (distrust).

No. 36. Sugar.

Engraved, $5.00 (disprove).

No. 36. Cream.

Engraved, Gold Lined, $5.00 (dispose).

No. 40. Cream.

Gold Lined, . $5.50 (disquiet).

No. 40. Sugar.

Plain, . . $6.00 (dispute).

No. 37. Sugar.

Engraved, . $7.00 (dissolve).

No. 37. Cream.

Engraved, Gold Lined, $7.00 (dissuade).

No. 44.

Cream, . $4.25 (hireling).

No. 44.

Sugar, . . $5.50 (hitherto).

No. 45. Cream.

Gold Lined, . $5.50 (hindoo).

No. 45. Sugar.

Plain, . . $6.25 (portal).

WHITE METAL DISH COVERS.

PLAIN OR SATIN FINISH.

(ONE-THIRD SIZE.)

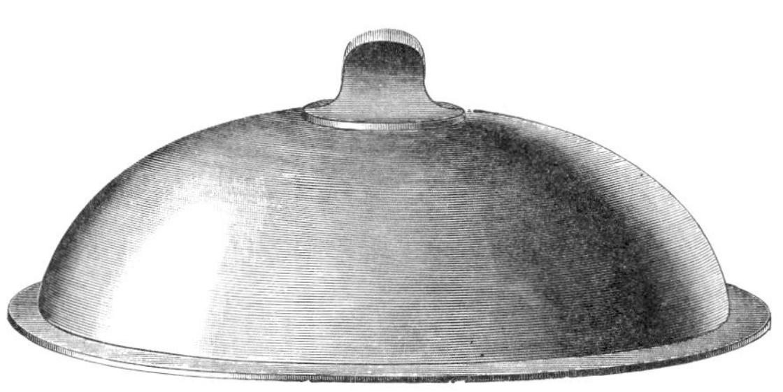

No. 50.

8 inch, $8.50 (PLOWER). 11 inch, $13.00 (PLOWMAN).
9 inch, 9.50 (PLIERS). 12 inch, 14.00 (PLIGHT).
10 inch, 11.00 (PLIABLE). 14 inch, 16.00 (PLENTEOUS).

No. 100. PERFORATED BUCKWHEAT CAKE DISH.
Plain or Satin, . $10.50 (PLUCKY).

No. 55. ROUND COVER.

6 inch, $4.50 (PLOVER). 9 inch, $8.25 (PLOT).
7 inch, 5.25 (PLIANT). 10 inch, 10.00 (PLOD).
8 inch, 7.00 (PLENTY).

No. 30. OVAL, FLUTED.

10 inch, $13.00 (PLEAD). 16 inch, $23.00 (PLANT).
12 inch, 15.50 (PLAIT). 18 inch, 29.00 (PIED).
14 inch, 18.00 (PEDAL). 20 inch, 39.00 (MYTHIC).

No. 20. OVAL.

10 inch, $12.00 (PLANTAIN). 16 inch, $21.00 (NEST).
11 inch, 13.00 (NEPOTISM). 18 inch, 27.00 (NESTLE).
12 inch, 14.00 (PLAINTIVE). 20 inch, 36.00 (NETTING).
14 inch, 16.00 (NERVINE).

Also furnished with Cross Bar Handles, if desired.

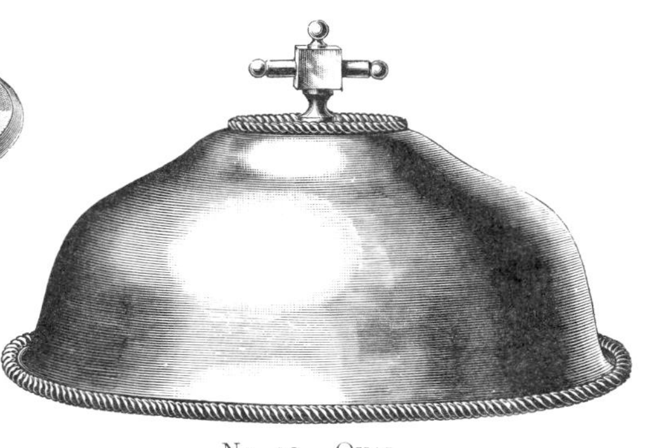

No. 10. OVAL.
Block Tin, Plated Mounts.

10 inch, $8.00 (NIBBLE). 16 inch, $15.00 (NIGHT).
12 inch, 11.00 (NICE). 18 inch, 19.00 (NIMBLE).
14 inch, 13.50 (NICK). 20 inch, 23.00 (NITRE).

No. 40.

10 inch, $12.00 (PLEDGE). 16 inch, $21.00 (PLEASURE).
12 inch, 14.00 (PLEASE). 18 inch, 27.00 (PLEASANT).
14 inch, 16.00 (PLEADER). 20 inch, 36.00 (PLEASING).

Plain Handles furnished on above Cover if desired.

NICKEL SILVER DISH COVERS.

PLAIN OR SATIN FINISH.

(ONE-THIRD SIZE.)

No. 01625. ROUND.

6 inch, $11.00 (PITTANCE). 9 inch, $14.00 (PLACABLE).
7 inch, 12.00 (PICADOR). 10 inch, 16.00 (PHOSPHORUS).
8 inch, 13.00 (PEARLASH). 12 inch, 20.00 (PEACEABLE).

No. 01625. ROUND, PERFORATED.

6 inch, $11.00 (PITHILY).
8 inch, 13.00 (PEDAGOGUE).

No. 01600. OVAL.

7 inch, $9.75 (MUSCADINE). 10 inch, $15.00 (MURIATIC).
8 inch, 10.75 (MUNICIPAL). 11 inch, 17.50 (MUNGO).
9 inch, 13.00 (MUMMY). 12 inch, 22.50 (MUMBLE).

No. 01630. OVAL.

7 inch, $13.50 (MULTIPLY). 10 inch, $18.50 (MULLEN).
8 inch, 15.00 (MULLET). 11 inch, 20.00 (MULBERRY).
9 inch, 16.00 (MUFFLER). 12 inch, 22.50 (MUDDY).

No. 01635. OVAL.

7 inch, $16.00 (MUDDLE). 14 inch, $31.50 (MOWER).
9 inch, 18.50 (MOVING). 16 inch, 41.50 (MOVEMENT).
10 inch, 21.00 (MOUSER). 18 inch, 52.00 (MOUNTING).
12 inch, 23.50 (MOTTLE). 20 inch, 67.50 (MOUNTAIN).

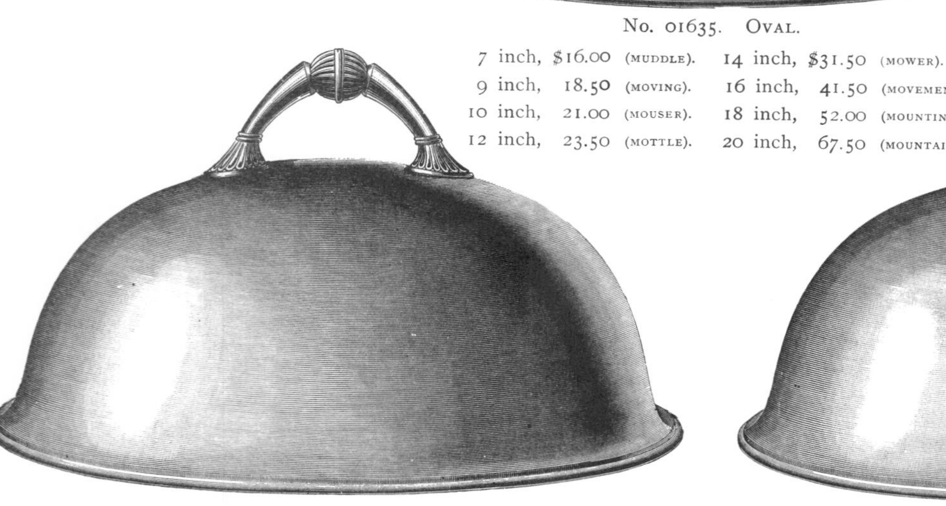

No. 01615.

7 inch, $15.00 (MYSTIC). 14 inch, $30.00 (MYSTICAL).
9 inch, 17.50 (MYOPE). 16 inch, 40.00 (MUTINOUS).
10 inch, 20.00 (MURMUR). 18 inch, 50.00 (MUTATION).
12 inch, 22.50 (MUSKRAT). 20 inch, 65.00 (MUSKETRY).

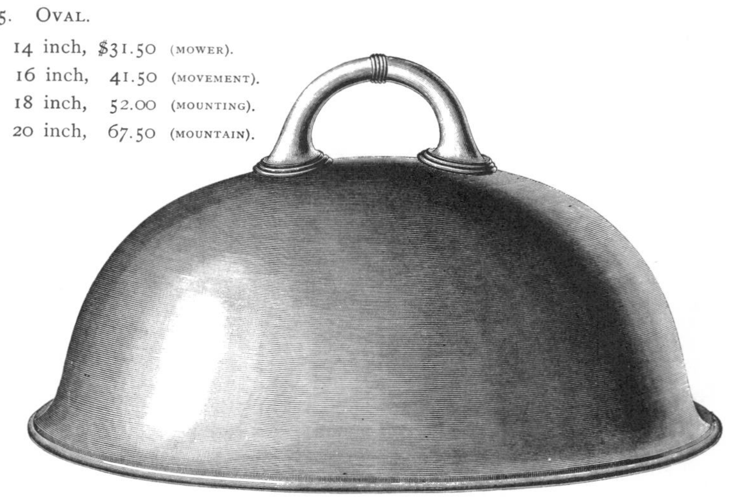

No. 01620.

7 inch, $15.00 (MYSTERIOUS). 14 inch, $30.00 (MYRMIDON).
9 inch, 17.50 (MUTILATE). 16 inch, 40.00 (MUTELY).
10 inch, 20.00 (MUTABLE). 18 inch, 50.00 (MUSTANG).
12 inch, 22.50 (MUSICAL). 20 inch, 65.00 (MUSHROOM).

NICKEL SILVER, SILVER SOLDERED.

DINNER SET.

(ONE-FIFTH SIZE.)

No. 0500. SOUP TUREEN.

4 Quarts, Engraved, complete, . $210.00 (SABRE).
Tureen, without stand, ... 125.00 (SABLE).

No. 0500. VEGETABLE DISH.

12 inch, Engraved, complete, . $150.00 (SACHEM).

No. 0500. GRAVY BOATS.

Gold Lined, Engraved, complete, each, $60.00 (SACK).
Without Waiter, . . . " 48.00 (SACRIFICE).

No. 0500. FISH DISH.

26 inch, Engraved, with Hot Water Dish,
Complete, $275.00 (SADDLE).

No. 0500. MEAT DISH.

22 inch, Engraved, with Hot Water Dish,
Complete, $275.00 (SADIRON).

NICKEL SILVER, SILVER SOLDERED.

GOLD AND SILVER PLATE.

PLAIN OR SATIN FINISH.

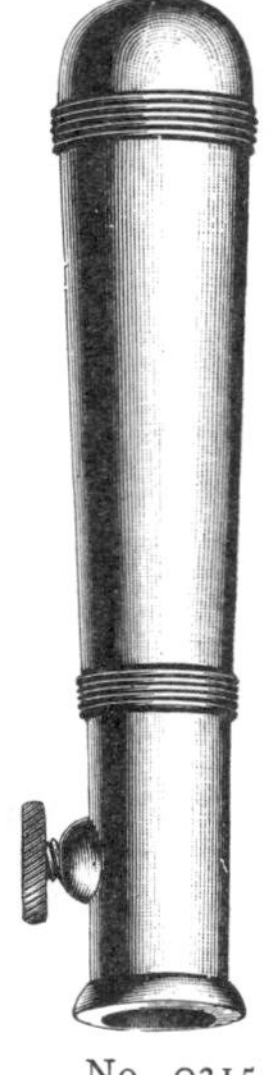

No. 06. GAME DISH.
13 inch, Plain or Satin, . . $32.50 (PORPOISE).

No. 0305.
MUTTON LEG HOLDER.
Plain or Satin, . $5.00 (POROUS).
(One-Half Size.)

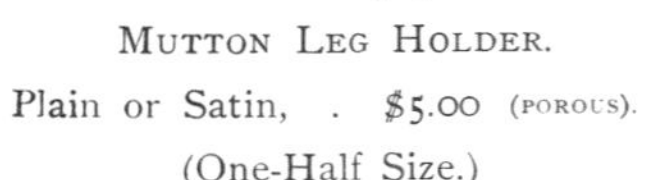

No. 0315.
MUTTON LEG HOLDER.
Plain or Satin, . $6.50 (PORTABLE).
(One-Half Size.)

No. 0810. MEAT DISH.

	Complete.	Cover.	Dish.
20 inch,	$104.00 (POMMEL).	$50.00 (POMATUM).	$54.00 (POLYGON).

For Prices of Smaller Sizes see page 158.

No. 0810. FISH DISH.

	Complete.	Cover.	Dish.
20 inch,	$110.00 (POMPOUS).	$60.00 (PORTE).	$50.00 (POPGUN).
22 inch,	117.50 (POPULATE).	63.50 (POPULAR).	54.00 (POPULACE).
24 inch,	130.00 (PORKER).	70.00 (PORCUPINE).	60.00 (PORCH).

NICKEL SILVER, SILVER SOLDERED.

GOLD AND SILVER PLATE.

No. 030. Terrapin Dish.
Plain or Satin, . $8.50 (mostly).

No. 020. Terrapin Dish.
Satin, . $7.00 (mossy).
Hammered, 8.50 (mortar).

No. 025. Terrapin Dish.
Silver, . $18.50 (mortmain).
Gold Inlaid, 22.50 (morrow).

No. 0300.
Mutton Leg Holder.
Plain or Satin, $4.50 (moose).

No. 0840. Meat Dish.

Complete.	Cover.	Dish.
20 inch, $104.00 (mormon).	$50.00 (russet).	$54.00 (rush).

(For smaller Sizes see page 158.)

No. 0310.
Mutton Leg Holder.
Plain, . $5.00 (morbid).
(Half Size.)

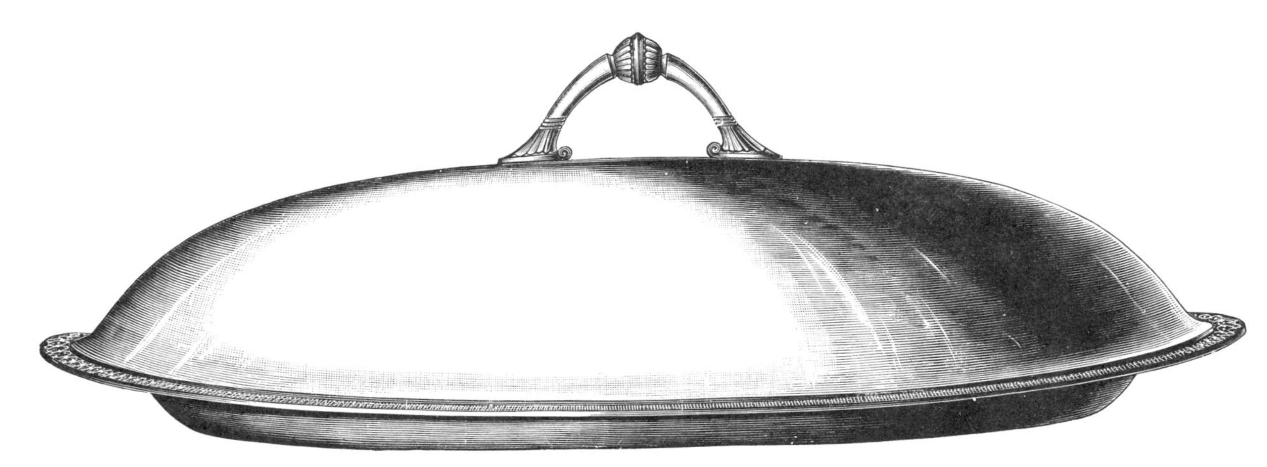

No. 0840. Fish Dish.

Complete.	Cover.	Dish.
20 inch, $105.00 (moonshine).	$55.00 (mopboard).	$50.00 (moralize).
22 inch, 112.50 (moody).	58.50 (moon).	54.00 (moonbeam).
24 inch, 125.00 (ruth).	65.00 (month).	60.00 (rustic).

NICKEL SILVER, SILVER SOLDERED.

NICKEL SILVER MEAT DISHES, ETC.

PLAIN OR SATIN FINISH.

(ONE-THIRD SIZE.)

No. 0800.

Dish.		Cover.		Complete.	
8 inch, $7.00	(ROSEWOOD).	$10.75	(MONTANIC).	$17.75	(MONSOON).
9 inch, 8.25	(ROSIN).	13.00	(MONOLITH).	21.25	(MONOGRAM).

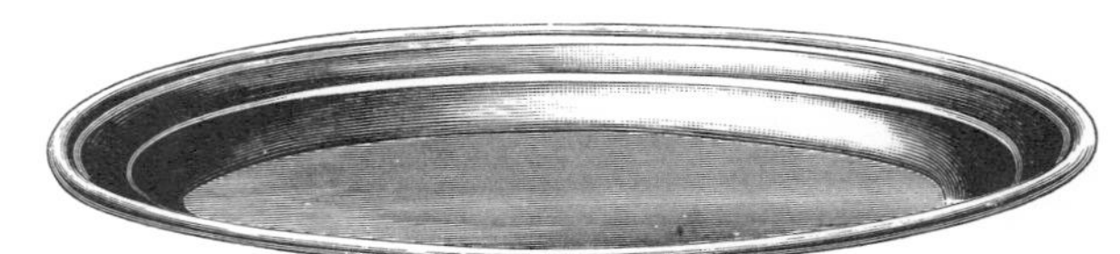

No. 0805.

Dish.		Cover.		Complete.	
9 inch, $8.25	(RUMINATE).	$13.00	(MONOTONE).	$21.25	(MONOPOLY).
11 inch, 13.50	(RULING).	15.00	(MONODY).	28.50	(MONODIST).
13 inch, 18.50	(RUMOR).	22.50	(MONK).	41.00	(MONKISH).

No. 020. GRATIN DISH.

6 inch, $6.00 (MONITOR).
7 inch, 7.00 (MONARCHY).
8 inch, 9.50 (MISHAP).
10 inch, $12.50 (MONGREL).
12 inch, 17.00 (MISGUIDE).

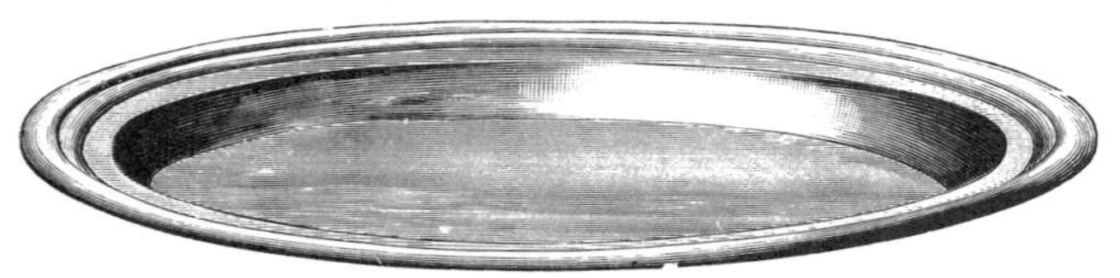

No. 0820.

10 inch, $11.50 (ROUTINE).
12 inch, 16.00 (ROWEL).
14 inch, 21.00 (RUBBER).
16 inch, $28.50 (RUBICUND).
18 inch, 39.00 (RUBY).
20 inch, 51.00 (RUDDER).

No. 0830.

8 inch, $8.50 (ROPE).
10 inch, 11.50 (ROSARY).
12 inch, 17.00 (ROSE).
14 inch, $23.00 (ROSETTE).
16 inch, 31.00 (MISGIVING).

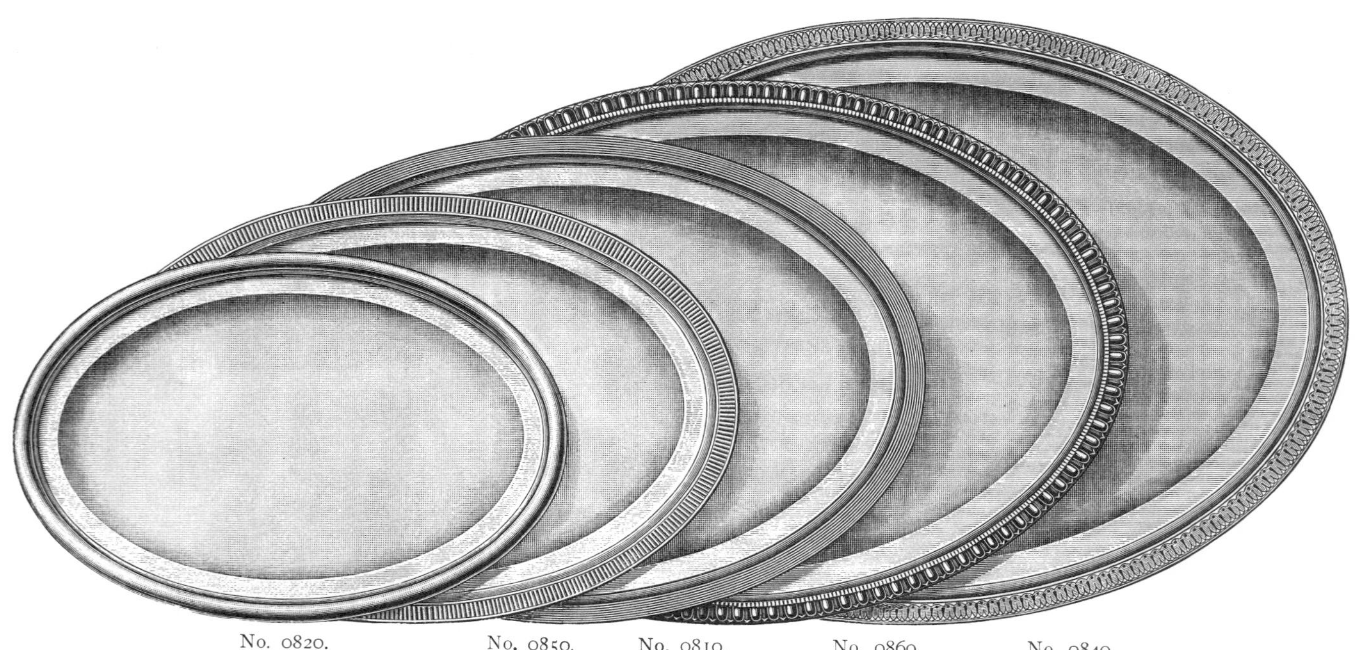

No. 0820. No. 0850. No. 0810. No. 0860. No. 0840.

	No. 0820.		No. 0850.		No. 0810.		No. 0860.		No. 0840.	
10 inch.	$11.50	(JUTTY).	$12.00	(MINTAGE).	$12.00	(MIRAGE).	$15.00	(MISDEEM.)	$12.00	(MISER).
12 inch.	16.00	(JUSTIFY).	17.50	(JUSTLY).	17.50	(MIRTHFUL).	21.00	(MISCALL).	17.50	(MISCHANCE).
14 inch.	21.00	(JULEP).	23.50	(JUMPER).	23.50	(JUNCTION).	28.25	(JUNTO).	23.50	(JURIST).
16 inch.	28.50	(JUDAISM).	31.50	(JUDGESHIP).	31.50	(JUDGMENT).	37.75	(JUDICIOUS).	31.50	(JUGGLE).
18 inch.	39.00	(JONQUIL).	42.00	(JOUNCE).	42.00	(JOURNALIST).	50.00	(JOURNEYMAN).	42.00	(JOYFUL).
20 inch.	51.00	(JIMMY).	54.00	(JOINT).	54.00	(JOINTLY).	65.00	(JOINTURE).	54.00	(JOKER).

Prices for Covers only.

9 inch.	$17.50	(JUTE).
10 inch.	20.00	(JURYMAN).
12 inch.	22 50	(JUJUBE).
14 inch.	30.00	(JUBILANT).
16 inch.	40.00	(JOLLY).
18 inch.	50.00	(JINGLE).

NICKEL SILVER, SILVER SOLDERED.

NICKEL SILVER ENTREE DISHES.

PLAIN OR SATIN FINISH.

(ONE-THIRD SIZE.)

No. 0555. ROUND.

Complete, with Hot Water Dish.

8 inch, $45.00 (BARRICADE).

10 inch, 52.00 (BAROUCHE).

No. 0600. ROUND.

	Complete.	Without Stand.
8 inch,	$25.00 (JIBBOOM).	$17.50 (JEWELER).
9 inch,	30.00 (JASMINE).	21.00 (JEOPARDY).
10 inch,	35.00 (JAUNTY).	24.50 (JAUNDICE).

No. 0520. OVAL, LOCK HANDLE.

	Complete, with Blazer.	Without Stand.
9 inch,	$48.50 (JARGON).	$32.50 (JAMB).
10 inch,	55.50 (JACOBITE).	37.50 (JACKDAW).
11 inch,	61.50 (JACKSCREW).	41.50 (JACKAL).
12 inch,	68.00 (BEADSMAN).	46.00 (BANDOLEER).

No. 0615. ROUND.

	Complete, with Hot Water Dish.	Without Stand.
8 inch,	$41.00 (BASSOON).	$28.00 (BARREL).
10 inch,	48.00 (BARRIER).	34.00 (BARLEY).

No. 0515. OBLONG, LOCK HANDLE.

	Complete, with Blazer in place of Hot Water Dish.	Complete, with Hot Water Dish.
10 inch,	$67.50 (JETTY).	$82.50 (JETSON).
11 inch,	75.00 (JENNET).	92.00 (JEALOUS).

No. 0525. OVAL, LOCK HANDLE.

Complete, with Blazer.

11 inch, $62.50 (JILT).

12 inch, 68.50 (JELLY).

NICKEL SILVER, SILVER SOLDERED.

NICKEL SILVER VEGETABLE DISHES.

PLAIN OR SATIN FINISH.

(ONE-THIRD SIZE.)

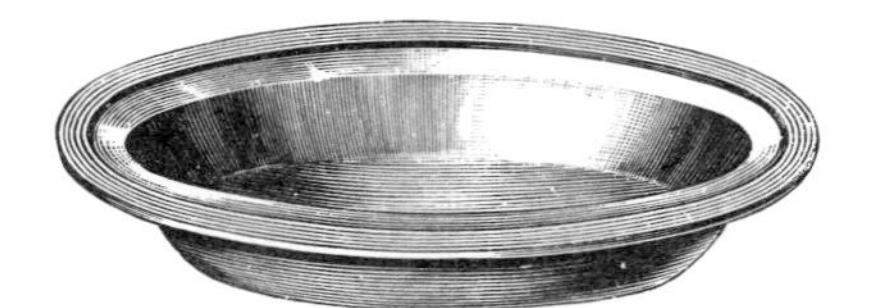

No. 0410.

5 inch, $5.50 (BASTE). 7½ inch, $9.00 (BARRACK).
6 inch, 6.75 (BASIS). 8 inch, 10.25 (BARONESS).
7 inch, 8.00 (BASEBALL).

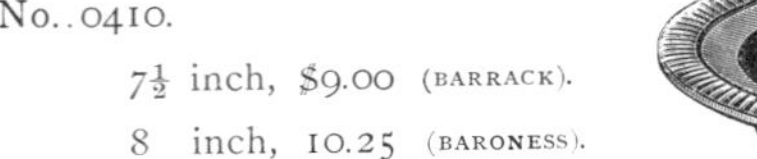

No. 0450.

No. 0420.

5 inch, $5.00 (PORTION). 7½ inch, $8.00 (ROOST).
6 inch, 6.00 (POSSESS). 8 inch, 9.25 (ROOT.)
7 inch, 7.00 (ROOM).

No. 0450.

	Complete.	Dish.	Cover.
5 inch,	$13.00 (POSSET).	$5.50 (POSSIBLY).	$7.50 (POSTER).
6 inch,	15.00 (POSTILION).	6.75 (POSTMARK).	8.25 (POSTOBIT).
7 inch,	17.00 (BEARDED).	8.00 (BAUBLE).	9.00 (BASTINADO).
7½ inch,	18.75 (BATTERY).	9.00 (BATTALION).	9.75 (BATOON).
8 inch,	21.00 (BATING).	10.25 (BATTER).	10.75 (BATHOS).

No. 0440.

	Complete.	Dish.	Cover.
5 inch,	$13.00 (BANJO).	$5.50 (BANDIT).	$7.50 (BANDBOX).
6 inch,	15.00 (BAMBOO).	6.75 (BALMY).	8.25 (BALLOON).
7 inch,	17.00 (BALLET).	8.00 (BALLAST).	9.00 (BALKY).
7½ inch,	18.75 (BALEFUL).	9.00 (BALDRIC).	9.75 (BAKERY).
8 inch,	21.00 (BEGONE).	10.25 (BEAKER).	10.75 (BEARING).

No. 0420.

	Complete.	Dish.	Cover.
5 inch,	$12.50 (BECOME).	$5.00 (BEDROP).	$7.50 (BEDTICK).
6 inch,	14.25 (BEFALL).	6.00 (BEGAN).	8.25 (BEGUILE).
7 inch,	16.00 (BEHAVE).	7.00 (BEHEAD).	9.00 (BELATE).
7½ inch,	17.75 (BELIEVE).	8.00 (BELOVED).	9.75 (BETROTH).
8 inch,	20.00 (BIGOTED).	9.25 (BILLION).	10.75 (BISTER).

No. 0510. LOCK HANDLE.

11 inch, $42.50 (RIGGING). 12 inch, $46.50 (RIGHT).

No. 0545. LOCK HANDLES.

10 inch, $37.50 (BANISTER). 12 inch, $46.50 (RINGLET).
11 inch, 42.50 (RING).

No. 0605. LOCK HANDLE.

10 inch, $44.50 (JABBER).
11 inch, 51.00 (BABBLE).
12 inch, 56.00 (BABOON).

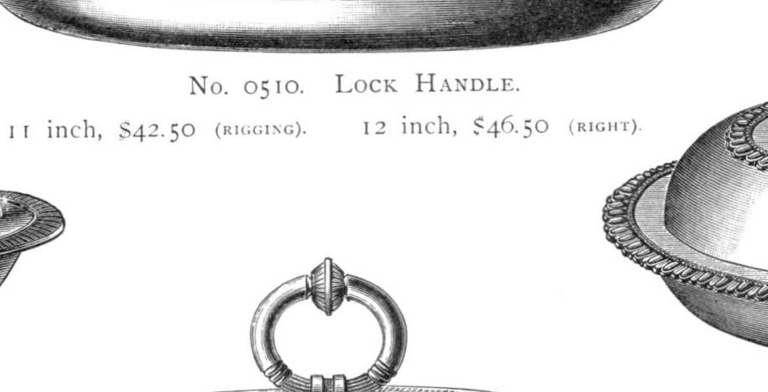

No. 0540. LOCK HANDLE.

9 inch, $32.00 (RIGHTFUL).
10 inch, 37.50 (RIGID).
11 inch, 42.50 (RIGOR).
12 inch, 46.50 (RIND).

No. 0610. LOCK HANDLE.

10 inch, . . . $55.00 (PORTEND).
11 inch, . . . 62.50 (PORTAGE).

No. 0515. LOCK HANDLE.

10 inch, . . . $46.00 (PORTFOLIO).
11 inch, . . . 52.00 (PORTICO).

NICKEL SILVER, SILVER SOLDERED.

WHITE METAL VEGETABLE DISHES.

PLAIN OR SATIN FINISH.

(ONE-THIRD SIZE.)

No. 7.

Plain, . . . $15.00 (NUNCIO).
Hammered, . . 17.50 (NURTURE).

No. 6.

Silver, . . . $16.50 (NUMB).
X Gold Inlaid, . . 22.50 (NUMERIC).

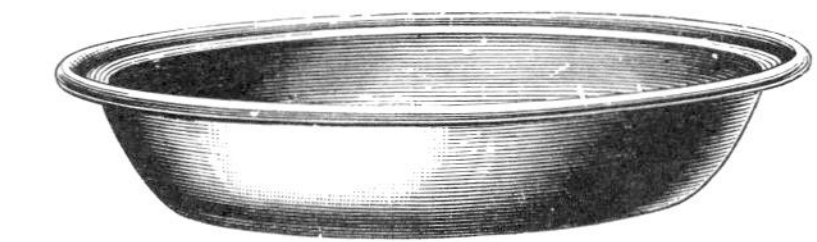

No. 50.

7 inch, $4.00 (NECK). 8 inch, $5.00 (NECKLACE).

No. 8. LOCK HANDLE.

11 inch, Satin, . . $22.00 (BAGPIPE).
11 inch, Hammered, . 25.00 (BAKER).

No. 4.

Plain, ... $22.00 (NEIGH).
Satin, Engraved, . . . 24.00 (NEIGHBOR).

No. 4½.

Plain, without Handles and Feet, $18.00 (NEPHEW).

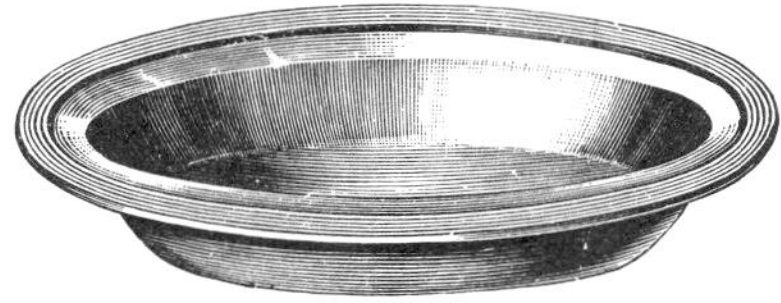

No. 60.

7 inch, $4.75 (NECTAR). 8 inch, $5.50 (NEEDLE).

No. 3. LOCK HANDLE.

Plain, . . $25.00 (NEGOTIATE).

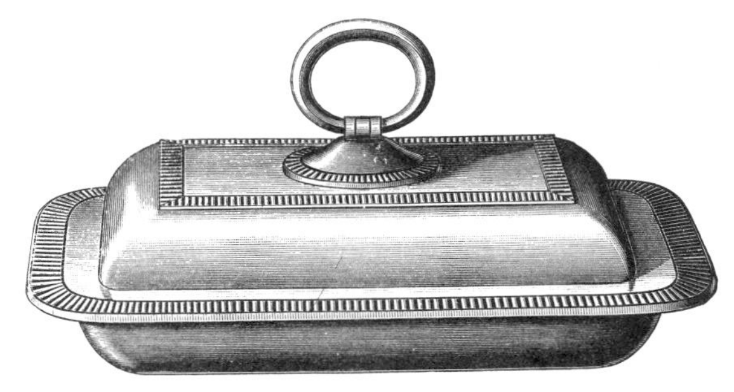

No. 9. LOCK HANDLE.

11 Inch, Satin, . . $25.00 (BAFFLE).
11 Inch, Hammered, . 28.00 (BAGGAGE).

Trade Mark.
WHITE METAL.

EGG STANDS, BOILERS, ETC.

Trade Mark.
NICKEL SILVER.

(One-Third Size.)

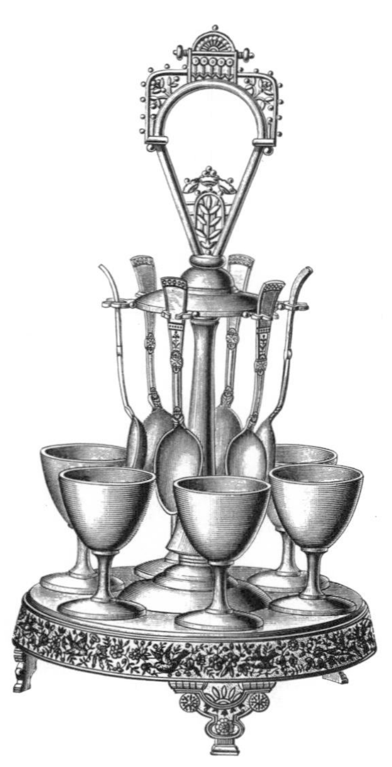

No. 52. Egg Stand with Spoons.
4 Gold Lined Cups, . $11.50 (bachelor).
No. 53. With Spoons.
6 Gold Lined Cups, . $15.75 (backslide).

No. 54. Egg Stand with Spoons.
4 Gold Lined Cups, . $13.50 (backward).
No. 55. With Spoons.
6 Gold Lined Cups, . $18.00 (badinage).

No. 5. Egg Boiler. Satin, Engraved.
For 6 Eggs, . $13.50 (platter).
For 12 Eggs, . 15.00 (platoon).

No 055. Fluted Egg Boiler. Nickel Silver.
For 4 Eggs, . $25.00 (badge).
For 6 Eggs, . 27.00 (badger).

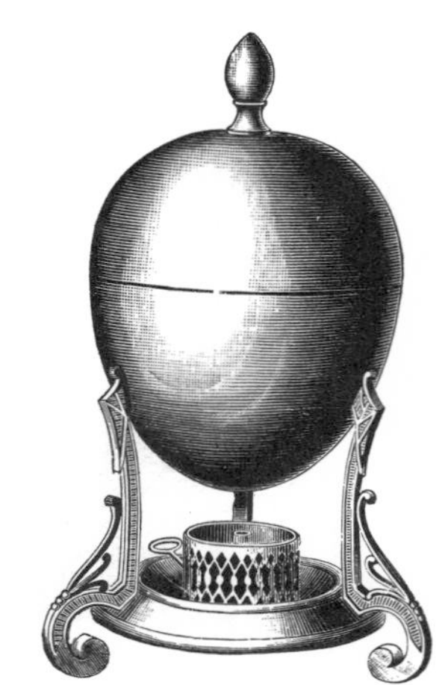

No. 050. Egg Boiler. Nickel Silver.
Plain or Satin Finish.
For 4 Eggs, . $20.00 (platform).
For 6 Eggs, . 26.00 (platinum).

No. 0100. Camp Set. Nickel Silver, Silver Soldered.
Complete, with Tea Kettle, Kettle, Stand, Egg Stand, and Ladle, . $34.50 (background).

No. 1612. Fruit or Nut Bowl.

Satin Engraved, - - - - - - $16.00 (chevron).

Satin Engraved, Gold Inlaid and Gold Lined, 19.00 (chicory).

No. 26. Nut Bowl.

Satin Quilted, Gold Lined, $22.50 (chicken).

No. 1047. Epergne.

Silver, Gold Lined, $110.00 (chirrup). Gold Inlaid and Gold Lined, $125.00 (chlorine).

Trade Mark.
WHITE METAL.

EPERGNES, FRUIT STANDS, ETC.

Trade Mark.
NICKEL SILVER.

(One-Third Size.)

No. 1038, ... $110.00 (pointer).
Silver, Gold Inlaid, . 125.00 (poignant).

No. 1024.

Damascene, Silver, Gold Inlaid, . . $162.00 (DECLINE).

No. 1039.

Silver, ... $125.00 (FOREARM).

Silver, Gold Inlaid, . . 150.00 (FORECAST).

GOLD AND SILVER PLATE.

No. 1014.

Silver, Gold Lined, ... $78.00 (DECOY).

Gold Inlaid and Gold Lined, . . . 84.00 (DECREASE).

No. 1001.

Engraved, Gold Lined, . . . $60.00 (DEEP).

GOLD AND SILVER PLATE.

No. 1027.

Gold Lined, ... $42.00 (DEDUCTION).
Gold Inlaid and Gold Lined, . 50.00 (DEED).

No. 1036. Fruit or Orange Bowl.

Silver, Gold Inlaid, . . $162.50 (DEVISEE).

GOLD AND SILVER PLATE.

No. 1044.

Gold Lined, . . $50.00. (BLACKFISH).

No. 1041.

Silver, ... $52.00 (FRANKNESS).
Silver, Gold Inlaid, . . 60.00 (FRAUGHT).

No. 1026.

Silver, ... $28.00 (DELIVER).
Gold Inlaid, . . . 30.00 (DELUDE).

GOLD AND SILVER PLATE.

No. 1030.

Silver, ... $42.50 (DELPHINE).

Silver, Gold Inlaid, . 45.00 (DELIVERER).

No. 1029.

Silver, ... $30.00 (DEVEST).

GOLD AND SILVER PLATE.

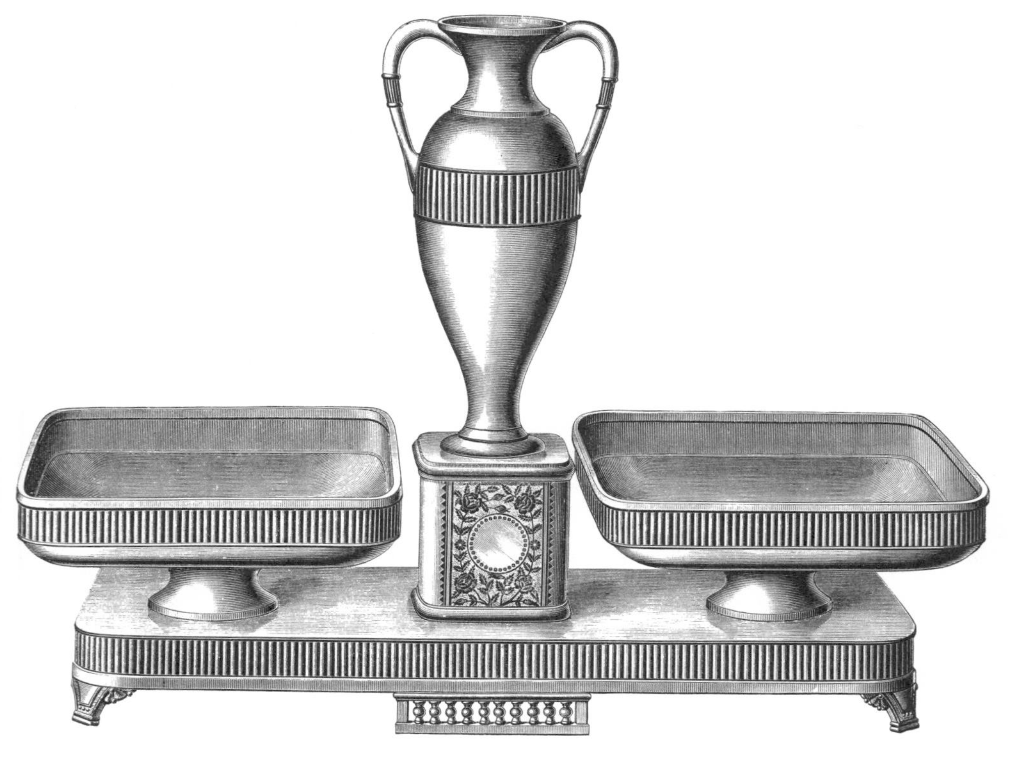

No. 1046.

Gold Lined, ... $48.00 (BILLIARDS).
Gold Inlaid and Gold Lined, 54.00 (BINDERY).

No. 1032.

Silver, ... $58.00 (DEVICE).
Silver, Gold Inlaid, . . 62.00 (DEVIOUS).

GOLD AND SILVER PLATE.

No. 1602.
Decorated Porcelain, . $25.00 (BARITONE).

No. 1610.
Silver, ... $23.00 (BANTAM).
Silver, Gold Inlaid, . 25.00 (BETRAY).
Rose and Gold Decorations.

No. 1608.
Silver, ... $22.00 (BITTERN).
Silver, Gold Inlaid, . 24.00 (BILLHOOK).
Canary, Ruby Lined.

No. 1050.
Silver, ... $80.00 (BOOKSTORE).
Silver, Gold Inlaid, . . 90.00 (BIOGRAPHER).

GOLD AND SILVER PLATE.

No. 1593.

Silver, ... $35.00 (BLACKBALL).

Silver, Gold Inlaid, . 37.50 (BLACKBIRD).

Decorated Porcelain.

No. 1586.

Silver, ... $28.00 (BLEAKLY).

Silver, Gold Inlaid, . 32.00 (BLEMISH).

Decorated Porcelain.

No. 1456.

Gold Inlaid and Gold Lined, . . . $90.00 (DEDICATE).

TRADE MARK.
WHITE METAL.

GOLD AND SILVER PLATE.

TRADE MARK.
NICKEL SILVER.

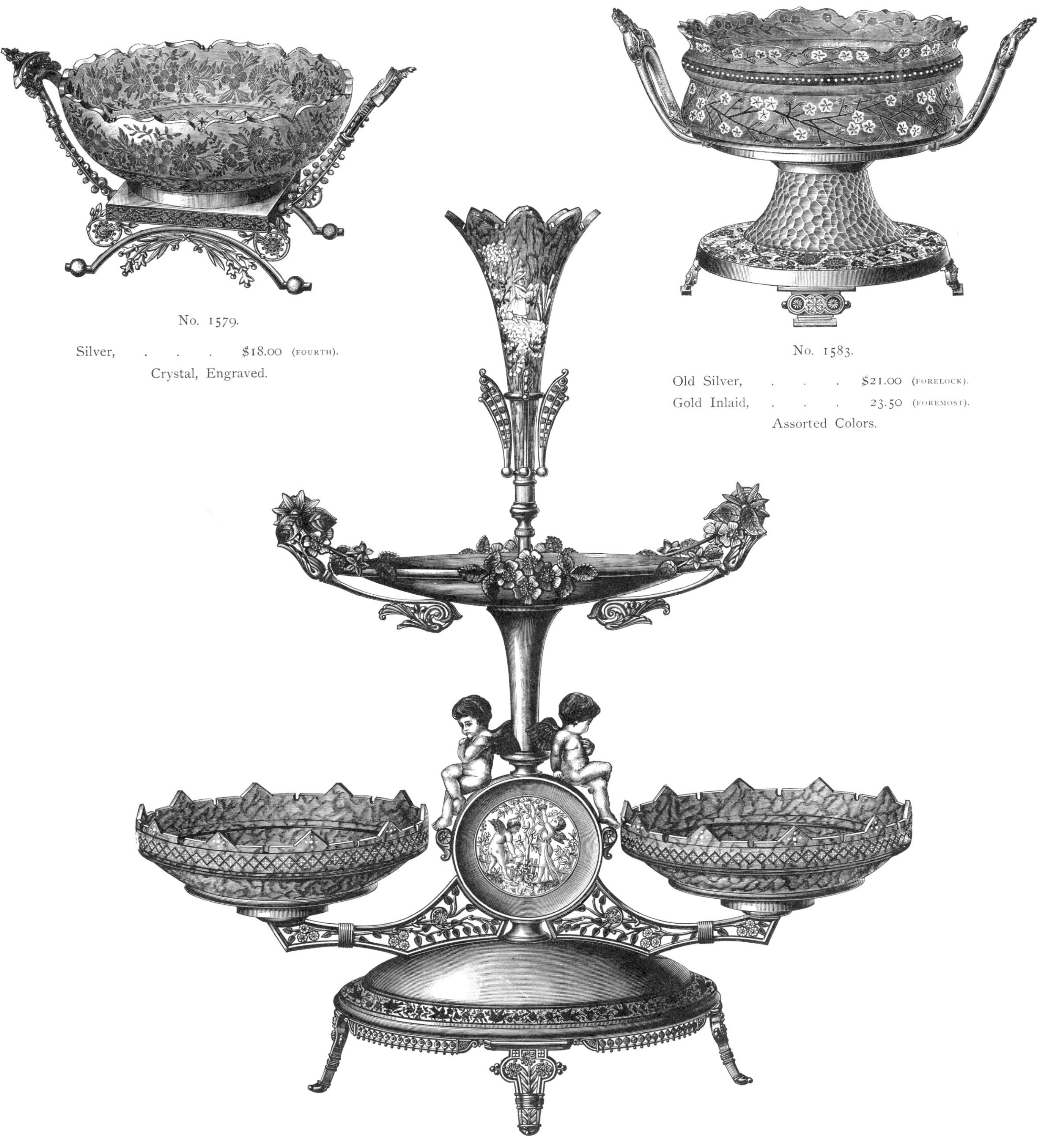

No. 1579.

Silver, . . . $18.00 (FOURTH).

Crystal, Engraved.

No. 1583.

Old Silver, . . . $21.00 (FORELOCK).

Gold Inlaid, . . . 23.50 (FOREMOST).

Assorted Colors.

No. 1034.

Silver, Gold Lined, . . . $62.50 (DETRACT).

Gold Inlaid and Gold Lined, . 72.50 (DEUCE).

GOLD AND SILVER PLATE.

No. 1040.

Silver, ... $60.00 (FORERUN).

Silver, Gold Inlaid, . 70.00 (FOREST).

Assorted Colors.

No. 1577. FRUIT OR ORANGE BOWL.

Old Silver, . . . $33.00 (FRITTER).

Gold Inlaid, . . . 36.00 (FROUNCE).

Assorted Colors.

No. 1033. ORANGE BOWL.

Silver, Gold Inlaid, . . $100.00 (DEVELOP).

Crystal Cut Glass.

No. 1585.

Silver, . . . $25.00 (FOREGO).

Silver, Gold Inlaid, . 28.00 (FOREIGN).

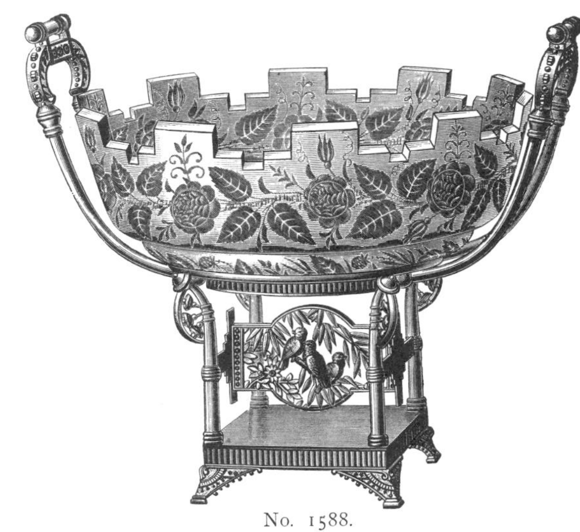

No. 1588.

Crystal Cut, . . $17.50 (BOLTER).

No. 1016.

Silver and Gold Lined, . . . $87.50 (DECLIVITY).

Gold Inlaid and Gold Lined, . . 95.00 (DECOCT).

GOLD AND SILVER PLATE.

No. 1578.
Silver, ... $26.00 (BLUBBER).
Silver, Gold Inlaid, . 28.00 (BLITHELY)
Rose Decorated.

No. 1503. FRUIT AND BON-BON DISH.
Silver, . . $22.00 (DEMEAN).
Gold Lined, . 26.00 (DEMEANOR).

No. 1020.
Gold Lined, . . $50.00 (DEFEND).
No. 1019. (Same Style as No. 1020, without Vase.)
Gold Lined, . . $45.00 (DEFENSIVE).

GOLD AND SILVER PLATE.

No. 1573.

Silver, ... $21.50 (HOOD).
Silver, Gold Inlaid, . 23.50 (HOOF).

No. 1574.

Silver, ... $25.00 (HABITUAL).
Silver, Gold Inlaid, . 28.00 (HAGGLE).

No. 1017.

Crystal, . . . $28.00 (DELF).
Ruby, ... 30.25 (DELICACY).

GOLD AND SILVER PLATE.

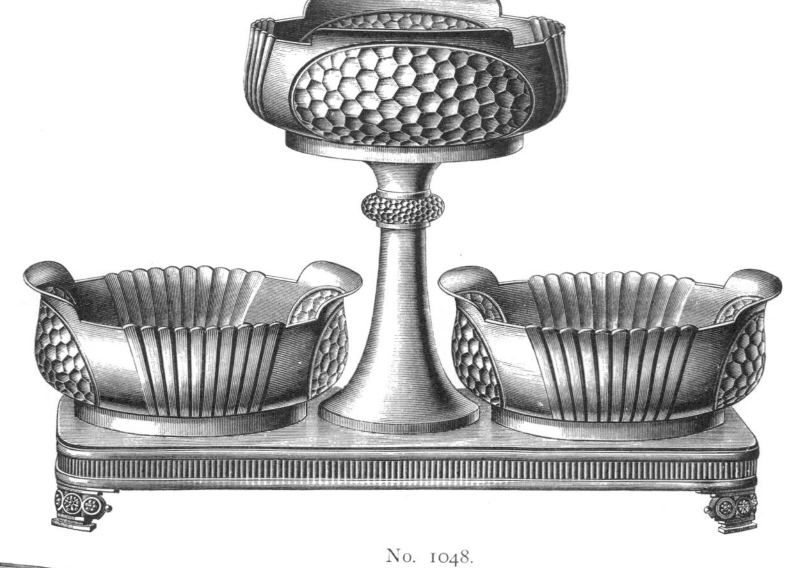

No. 1048.
Hammered, Gold Lined, . $37.50 (BLOWPIPE).

No. 1548.
Silver, ... $20.00 (DELHI).
Silver, Gold Inlaid, . 21.00 (DELAWARE).

No. 1607.
Ruby, . . $9.50 (BLOCKHOUSE).

No. 1051.
Old Silver, ... $38.00 (BLOOMER).
Silver, Gold Inlaid, . 42.00 (BLUDGEON).

GOLD AND SILVER PLATE.

No. 1018.

Gold Lined, . . . $36.00 (DEMENSE).
Gold Inlaid and Gold Lined, 40.00 (DEMAND).

No. 1022.

Damascene, Silver, Gold Inlaid, . $47.50 (DELVE).

No. 1000.

Engraved, Gold Lined, . $36.00 (DELUGE).

GOLD AND SILVER PLATE.

No. 1562.

Chased, Gold Lined, . . . $14.50 (DICKEY).
Chased, Gold Inlaid and Gold Lined, 17.50 (DICTATOR).

No. 1564.

Silver, ... $18.00 (DOESKIN).
Silver, Gold Inlaid, . 20.00 (DOFF).

No. 1576.

Silver, . . $20.00 (FORETOP).
Crystal, Engraved.

No. 1037.

Silver, ... $47.50 (FORFEIT).
Silver, Gold Inlaid, . 55.00 (FORM).

GOLD AND SILVER PLATE.

No. 1512.
Gold Lined, . . $18.00 (DELAY)

No. 1568.
Silver, . . $18.50 (FLUEBOOK).

No. 1467.
Gold Lined, . . $39.00 (DEJECT).

No. 1567.
Silver, . . $19.00 (BLUNTLY).

No. 1520.
Silver, ... $16.00 (DESPOILER).
Silver, Gold Inlaid, . 17.00 (DESPOIL).

GOLD AND SILVER PLATE.

No. 1499.

Gold Lined, . . . $37.50 (DEFRAY).

No. 1526.

Plain, Gold Lined, ... $16.50 (DERANGE).
Hammered, Gold Lined, ... 18.50 (DERIDE).
Hammered, Chased, Gold Lined, . 21.00 (DERIVE).
XX Gilt, Hammered, Chased, Gold Lined, 24.50 (DEROGATE).

No. 1529.

Gold Lined, ... $18.00 (DESERT).
Hammered, Gold Lined, ... 20.60 (DESERVE).
Hammered, Chased, Gold Lined, . . 22.50 (DESIGN).
XX Gilt, Hammered, Chased, Gold Lined, 26.00 (DESIRE).

No. 1021.

Gold Lined, ... $45.00 (DEFER).

No. 1515.

Gold Lined, . . . $17.00 (DEFINITE).

No. 1533.

Plain, ... $12.50 (DEPORT).
Chased, ... 13.50 (DEPOSE).
Chased, Gold Lined, 15.50 (DEPOSIT).

No. 1007.

Crystal, . . . $34.00 (DEFY).

GOLD AND SILVER PLATE.

No. 1531.

Silver, . . $24.00 (DELIGHT).
Silver, Gold Inlaid, 26.50 (DELINEATE).

No. 1575.

Silver, . . $15.00 (BOOKCASE).
Silver, Gold Inlaid, 16.50 (BOLTHEAD).

No. 1604.

Ruby, . . $15.00 (BOLDLY).

No. 1049.

Silver, . . . $35.00 (BLUELIGHT).

No. 1043.
Gold Lined, . . . $45.00 (FRIEZE).

No. 1571.
Old Silver, . . $40.00 (BOILING).

No. 1570.
Old Silver, . . . $27.00 (FRENCH).
Old Silver, Gold Inlaid, . 30.00 (FRIEND).

WHITE METAL.

GOLD AND SILVER PLATE.

NICKEL SILVER.

No. 1605.

Fruit or Salad Bowl.

Decorated Porcelain, . $24.00 (bluish).

No. 1611.

Silver, ... $24.00 (boldness).

Silver, Gold Inlaid, . 26.00 (bombic).

Rose and Gold Decorations.

No. 1606.

Silver, . $30.50 (blinkard).

Decorated Porcelain.

No. 1603.

Silver, ... $36.00 (bluster).

Silver, Gold Inlaid, . 39.00 (boastful).

Decorated Porcelain.

No. 1609.

Silver, ... $18.50 (boarder).

Silver, Gold Inlaid, . 19.50 (boathook).

Assorted Colors.

No. 1572.

Silver, . . . $19.00 (FOWLER).
Silver, Gold Inlaid, . 20.00 (FRAGILE).

No. 1592.

Silver, . . $18.00 (BOBOLINK).

No. 1545.

Silver, . . $20.00 (DELIVERANCE).
Silver, Gold Inlaid, 22.50 (DELL).

No. 1595.

Silver, ... $28.00 (BOMBASTIC).
Silver, Gold Inlaid, . 31.00 (BOATMAN).

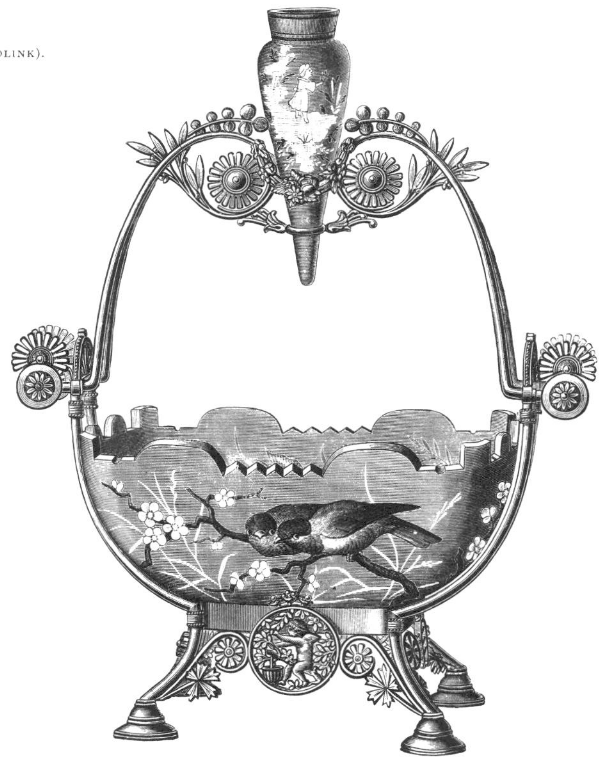

No. 1594.

Silver, ... $27.50 (BOATSWAIN).
Silver, Gold Inlaid, . 30.00 (BODDICE).

GOLD AND SILVER PLATE.

No. 1614.
Satin, Engraved, . . . $25.00 (BONDSMAN).
Satin, Engraved, Gold Inlaid, 27.50 (BORAGE).
Mother-of-Pearl Glass.

No. 1553.
Silver, ... $22.00 (DEVOTEE).
Silver, Gold Inlaid, . 24.00 (DEVOTION).

No. 1569.
Silver, ... $20.00 (DOCUMENT).
Silver, Gold Inlaid, . 22.50 (DODGE).

No. 1561.
Silver, ... $25.00 (DEXTROUS).
Silver, Gold Inlaid, . 27.50 (DIAGNOSIS).

No. 1613.
Silver, ... $30.00 (BOSCAGE).
Silver, Gold Inlaid, . 33.00 (BRAHMA).

No. 1549.
Silver, ... $24.50 (DIETARY).
Silver, Gold Inlaid, . 26.50 (DIFFIDENT).

TRADE MARK.
WHITE METAL.

GOLD AND SILVER PLATE.

TRADE MARK.
NICKEL SILVER.

No. 1563.

Silver, ... $16.00 (DOCK).
Silver, Gold Inlaid, . 17.50 (DOCKET).

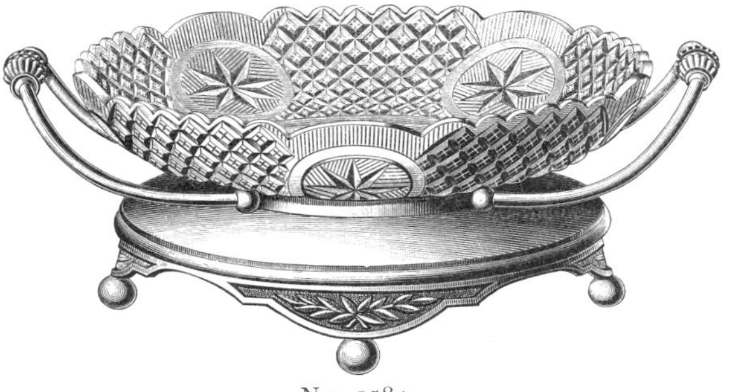

No. 1584.

Silver, . . $17.50 (HOLIDAY).
Fine Cut Glass.

No. 1591.

Silver, ... $28.00 (BROADCAST).
Silver, Gold Inlaid, 30.00 (BRUNETTE).

No. 1580.

Silver, . . $13.50 (BRITISH).
Assorted Colors.

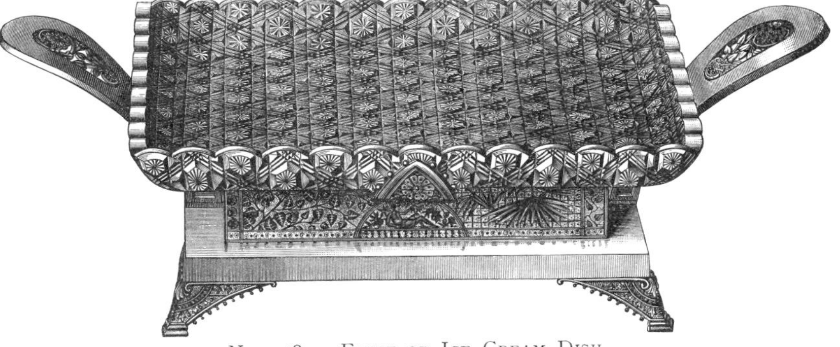

No. 1581. FRUIT OR ICE CREAM DISH.

Silver, ... $51.00 (HOMER).
Silver, Gold Inlaid, . 54.00 (HOMESPUN).
Fine Cut Glass.

No. 1597.

Moorish, Old Silver, . $26.50 (BROMINE).
Moorish, Gold Inlaid, . 31.50 (BRUSHWOOD).

WHITE METAL.

GOLD AND SILVER PLATE.

NICKEL SILVER.

No. 1587½.

Silver, ... $20.00 (BOVINE).

Silver, Gold Inlaid, . 22.50 (BOWSTRING).

Rose and Gold Decorated.

No. 1599.

Ruby, . . $10.50 (BOWLINE).

No. 1596.

Silver, . $25.00 (POKER).

Crystal, Engraved.

No. 1600. FRUIT OR ORANGE BOWL.

Silver, . $16.50 (BOYHOOD).

Assorted Colors.

No. 1554. FRUIT OR ICE CREAM DISH.

Silver, . $15.00 (DISAPPOINT).

GOLD AND SILVER PLATE.

No. 1023.

Silver, . . $24.00 (DEMUR).

No. 1525.

Chased, ... $20.00 (DENOTATE).

Niello and Gold, . 23.00 (DENOTEMENT).

No. 1511.

Plain, ... $14.00 (DEPICT).

Chased, ... 15.00 (DEPART).

Chased, Gold Lined, . 17.00 (DEPEND).

FINGER BOWLS.

(HALF SIZE.)

No. 208.

Per Dozen.

Satin, ... $42.00 (BUCKTHORN).

Satin, Engraved, . . 57.00 (BUFFO).

Satin, Engraved, Gold Lined, 69.00 (BUCCANEER).

No. 209.

Per Dozen.

Satin, ... $51.00 (BUCKWHEAT).

Satin, Engraved, . . 66.00 (BUGBEAR).

Satin, Engraved, Gold Lined, 78.00 (BUCKRAM).

FLASKS.

(One-Half Size.)

No. 1.

Hammered, ... $2.75 (bramble).
Hammered, Old Silver, . . 3.25 (brackish).
Hammered and Applied, Old Silver, 4.00 (bravery).

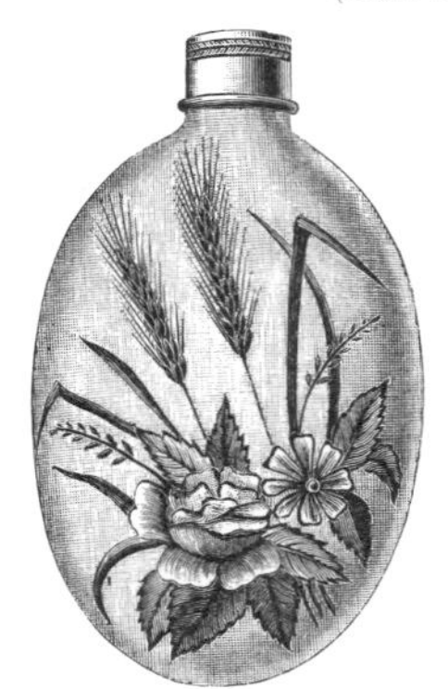

No. 1.

Satin, . $2.00 (borough).
Satin, Engraved, 2.75 (boyish).

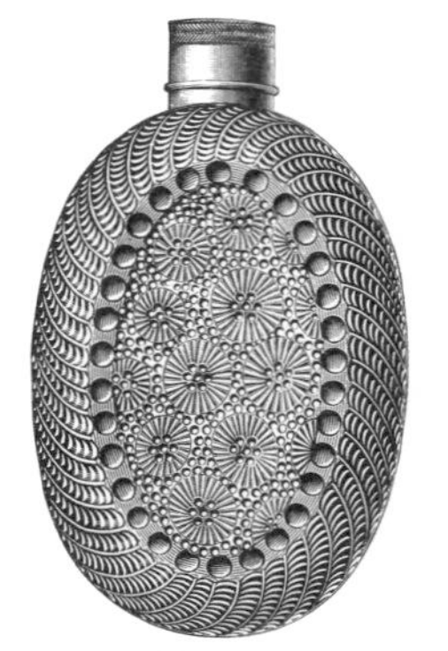

No. 1.

Moorish, Old Silver, $3.50 (brandy).
Moorish, Gold Inlaid, 4.75 (brakeman).

No. 3. (One-Third Size.)

Cut Glass, . $6.75 (pongee).
Morocco Case, $3.75 extra (poncho).

No. 6. With Collapsion Cup Cap.

Silver, . . . $5.50 (breakfast).
Old Silver, . . 6.50 (breastpin).
Old Silver, Gold Inlaid, 7.00 (brawny).
Hammered, $1.00 extra.

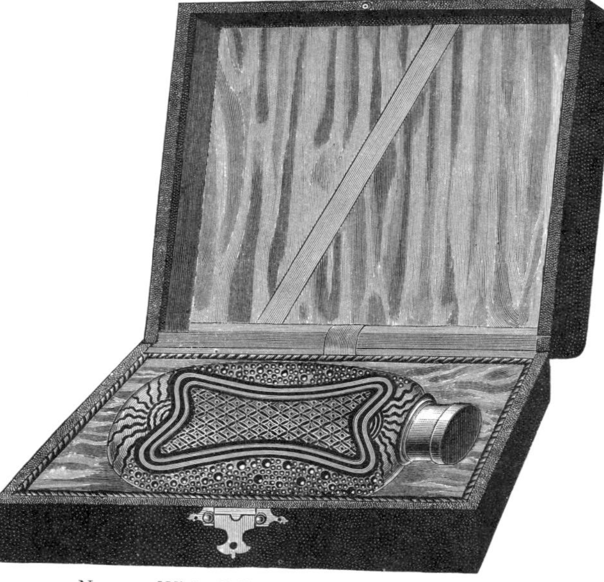

No. 9. With Collapsion Cup Cap.

Satin, ... $6.00 (bridle).
Moorish, Old Silver, . 8.00 (brewery).
Plush or Morocco Case, extra, 4.00 (briefly).

No. 7. Moorish.

Satin, . . . $4.50 (breeding).
Moorish, Old Silver, 6.00 (brevity).
Moorish, Gold Inlaid, 8.00 (breathing).

No. 4. Size of No. 7.

With Ornamentation like No. 6.

Silver, . . . $4.50 (clubhouse).
Silver, Gold Inlaid, 6.00 (clutter).

Collapsion Cup

Cap to Nos. 6, 8, and 9 Flask.

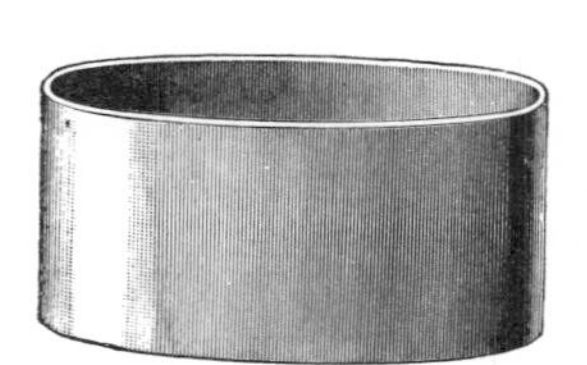

Cup to No. 5 Flask.

No. 5. With Cup.

Silver, . . . $7.00 (brigand).
Old Silver, . . 8.00 (brisket).
Hammered, . . 8.25 (brighten).
Hammered, Old Silver, 9.25 (by-law).

No. 050.

Nickel Silver, Silver Soldered.

Satin, . . $10.50 (polite).
Satin, Engraved, 12.50 (politic).

No. 8. With Collapsion Cup Cap.

Embossed, . . . $6.00 (bridoon).
Embossed, Old Silver, . 7.00 (brilliant).
Embossed, XX Gold Inlaid, 9.00 (polacca).

WHITE METAL.

FIREMAN'S TRUMPETS.

NICKEL SILVER.

(ONE-THIRD SIZE.)

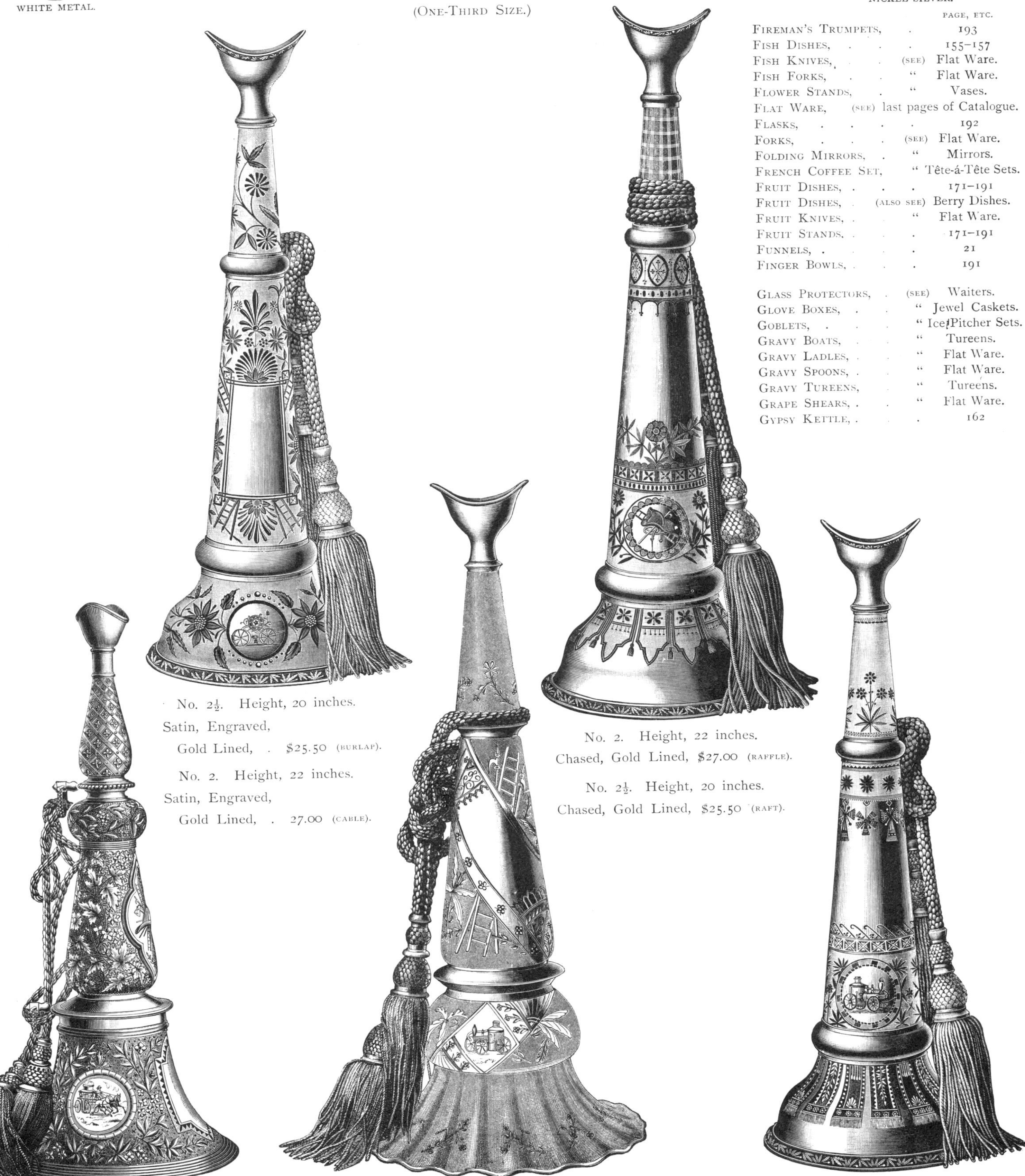

No. 2½. Height, 20 inches.
Satin, Engraved,
Gold Lined, . $25.50 (BURLAP).

No. 2. Height, 22 inches.
Satin, Engraved,
Gold Lined, . 27.00 (CABLE).

No. 2. Height, 22 inches.
Chased, Gold Lined, $27.00 (RAFFLE).

No. 2½. Height, 20 inches.
Chased, Gold Lined, $25.50 (RAFT).

No. 05. Height, 22 inches.
Nickel Silver, Silver Soldered.
Repoussé and Engraved, Silver and Gold Inlaid.
$150.00 (RAGE).

No. 4. Height, 22 inches.
Satin, Engraved, Gold Lined, $39.00 (RAFTER).

No. 3. Height, 19 inches.
Chased, ... $16.75 (RADISH).
Chased, Gold Lined, . 18.75 (RADIUS).

CORD AND TASSELS, $3.25, net, extra (RAGLAN).

HOTEL WARE.

(ONE-THIRD SIZE.)

No. 110 HOTEL SET.

CREAM.
Self-Adjusting Cover.
o. 110½, . $7.00 (BUOYANCY).
Three Fourth Pints.

SYRUP CUP.
Patent Cut-off.
No. 110, . $5.50 (BUSTLER).

SUGAR.
No. 110, . $7.50 (BUILDING).

SPOON HOLDER.
No. 110, . $6.00 (BULBOUS).

CREAM.
No. 110, . $6.75 (BULKHEAD).
Two Half Pints.

No. 7. COMPORT.
Plain or Satin, . $4.50 (BUTCHER).

No. 8. With High Standard.
Plain or Satin, . $5.00 (BYGONE).

No. 5001.
With Patent Crystal Drainer.
Plain, . . $7.00 (JOYOUS).

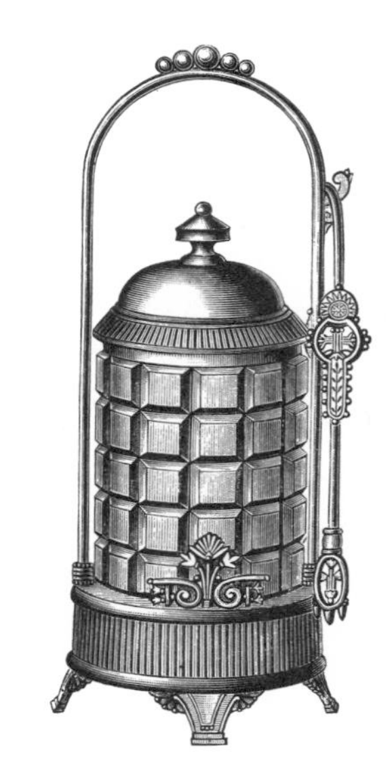

No. 213, . $4.00 (GOSSAMER).

No. 1885.
Plain, ... $6.50 (INUNDATE).
Plain, Gold Lined, . 8.50 (INVECTIVE).

No. 2164½.
5 No. 11 Bottles, . $7.75 (BANKER).
6 No. 11 Bottles, . 8.50 (BANNER).

No. 14, . $16.50 (DANCER).

Trade Mark.
WHITE METAL.

GOLD AND SILVER PLATE.

Trade Mark.
NICKEL SILVER.

PLAIN OR SATIN.

Spoon Holder. Oval.

No. 111, . $7.00 (polarize).

Sugar. Oval.

No. 111, . $8.50 (poetic).

Cream. Oval.

No. 111, . $7.25 (poacher).

Two Half Pints.

Cream.

Self-Adjusting Cover.

No. 109, . $6.25 (plutonic).

Two Half Pints.

Sugar.

No. 109, . $7.00 (carver).

Sugar.

No. 106, . $7.50 (plunder).

Cream.

No. 106, . $6.50 (plurality).

Two Half Pints.

Spoon Holder.

No. 109, . $5.25 (cartouch).

Spoon Holder.

No. 107, . $5.25 (cartage).

Sugar.

No. 107, . $7.00 (carrom).

Cream.

No. 107, . $6.25 (carouse).

Two Half Pints.

Spoon Holder.

No. 108, . $5.50 (carmine).

Butter Dish.

Patent Crystal Drainer.

No. 5016, . $7.50 (caress).

Sugar.

No. 108, . $7.25 (careen).

Cream.

No. 108, . $6.50 (capstan).

Two Half Pints.

WHITE METAL.

NICKEL SILVER.

CREAM.
No. 73, . $3.50 (ORDAIN).
One Half Pint.
No. 88½, . $4.00 (ORCHARD).
Two Half Pints.

SUGAR.
No. 88½, . $5.00 (ORCHESTRA).

SUGAR.
No. 92, . $5.50 (ORBIT).

CREAM.
Self-Adjusting Cover.
No. 92, . $5.50 (ORATORY).
Two Half Pints.

SPOON HOLDER.
No. 89, . $4.25 (OBSCURE).

CREAM.
Without Cover.
No. 89½, . $5.00 (OBLIVION).
Two Half Pints.

SUGAR.
No. 89, . $6.25 (OBLIQUE).

CREAM.
Self-Adjusting Cover.
No. 89, . $6.25 (OBLIGE).
Three Half Pints.

BUTTER DISH.
With Patent Crystal Drainer.
No. 1, . $8.00 (OBJECT).

SYRUP CUP.
No. 89, . $5.00 (OBTAIN).
With Plate, 6.25 (OBTRUDE).

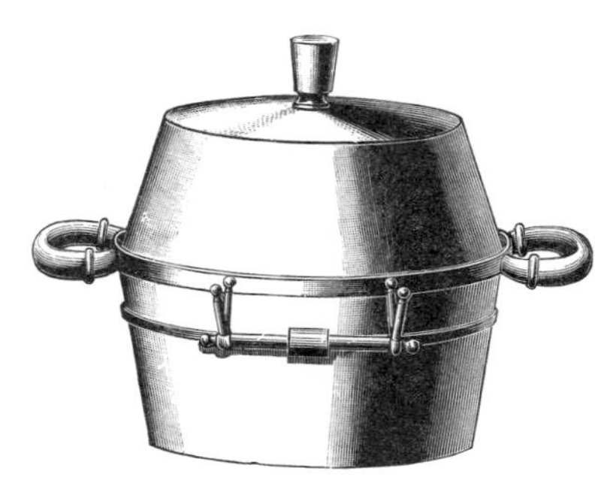

BUTTER DISH.
No. 89, . $5.75 (OBSERVE).

SYRUP CUP.
Patent Cut-off.
No. 1, . $5.00 (OBEDIENT).

SPOON HOLDER.
No. 1, . $6.00 (OBELISK).

SUGAR.
No. 1, . $7.00 (OBLIGATE).

CREAM.
No. 1, . $6.00 (OBEY).
Two Half Pints.

TRADE MARK.
WHITE METAL.

GOLD AND SILVER PLATE.

TRADE MARK.
NICKEL SILVER.

PLAIN OR SATIN FINISH.

BUTTER DISH.
No. 103, . $4.50 (BY-PATH).

SUGAR.
No. 103, . $5.50 (BY-WORD).

CREAM, Covered.
No. 103, . $5.00 (CABAL).
One Half Pint.

SUGAR.
No. 105, . $6.50 (CACHET).

CREAM, Covered.
No. 105, . $6.00 (CALENDS).
Three Fourth Pints.

SUGAR.
No. 104, . $5.50 (CALLOUS).

CREAM, Covered.
No. 104, . $5.00 (CALORIC).
One Half Pint.

SPOON HOLDER.
No. 99, . $4.75 (ORGAN).

SUGAR.
No. 97, . $5.00 (ORDEAL).

CREAM.
No. 97, . $4.25 (ORDINANCE).
One Half Pint.

SUGAR.
No. 98, . $6.00 (ORGANIST).

BUTTER DISH.
No. 98, . $5.00 (OASIS).

CREAM.
No. 98, . $5.00 (ORIENT).
Two Half Pints.

SYRUP CUP.
No. 188, . $5.00 (OAKUM).
Plain.

SUGAR.
No. 99, . $7.00 (OAR).

CREAM.
No. 99, . $6.00 (OBDURATE).
Three Half Pints.

GOLD AND SILVER PLATE.

Spoon Holder.
No. 102, . $5.50 (omelet).

Sugar.
No. 102, . $6.00 (omnibus).

Cream.
No. 102, . $5.00 (ogre).
Two Half Pints.

Syrup Cup.
No. 102, . $5.75 (offset).
With Plate, 7.00 (ogle).

Cream. Oval.
No. 88, . $5.25 (odeon).
Three Half Pints.

Sugar. Oval.
No. 88, . $6.50 (offing).

Sugar.
No. 86, . $5.75 (onset).

Cream.
No. 86, . $4.75 (onward).
Two Half Pints.

Spoon Holder.
No. 180, . $3.75 (opiate).

Sugar.
No. 180, . $4.25 (oppose).

Cream.
No. 180, . $3.75 (opinion).
Two Half Pints.

Spoon Holder.
No. 101, . $4.75 (option).

Patent Cut-off Syrup Cup.
No. 187, . $4.50 (oracle).

Butter Dish.
No. 101, . $7.00 (orange).

Sugar.
No. 101, . $5.50 (oration).

Cream.
No. 101, . $4.50 (oral).
Two Half Pints.

NICKEL SILVER HOTEL WARE.

PLAIN OR SATIN.

(ONE-THIRD SIZE.)

SYRUP CUP.
No. 01835, . $16.50 (RESUSCITATE).
With Plate, . 20.50 (CABALIST).

SUGAR.
No. 01835, . $16.50 (RETAIN).

CREAM.
No. 01835, . $15.00 (RETAIL).
Two Half Pints.

BUTTER DISH.
No. 0835, . $16.50 (RESUME).

CREAM.
No. 01855, . $16.50 (RETAKE).
Three Half Pints.

SUGAR.
No. 01855, . $18.50 (RETALIATE).

SYRUP CUP.
With Plate attached.
No. 01855, . $18.50 (RETENTION).

CREAM.
No. 01840, . $13.50 (RETICULE).
Two Half Pints.

SUGAR.
No. 01840, . $15.50 (RETINA).

SUGAR.
No. 01830, . $15.00 (RETIRE).

CREAM.
No. 01830, . $13.50 (RETORT).
Two Half Pints.

NICKEL SILVER, SILVER SOLDERED.

Trade Mark.
WHITE METAL.

GOLD AND SILVER PLATE.

Trade Mark.
NICKEL SILVER.

Individual Lump Sugar.
No. 055. For One Person, $6.00 (captious).
No. 056. For Two Persons, 8.00 (caramel).
(Half Size.)

Individual Lump Sugar.
No. 053. For One Person, $6.00 (captivity).
No. 054. For Two Persons, 8.00 (caraway).
(Half Size.)

Individual Lump Sugar.
No. 050. For One Person, $5.50 (revel).
No. 051. For Two Persons, 7.50 (carbine).
(Half Size.)

Cream.
No. 01847, . . $12.50 (camlet).
Three Fourth Pints.

Sugar.
No. 01847, . . $13.50 (camomile).

Syrup Cup.
No. 01847, . . $17.50 (campaign).
Without Plate, . 13.50 (carbonic).

Butter Dish.
No. 01847, . $16.00 (candidly).

Sugar.
No. 01860, . $16.00 (canonist).

Hot Milk.
Self-Adjusting Cover.
No. 01860, . $18.50 (capitalist).
Four Half Pints.

Butter Dish.
No. 0833, . $11.00 (trellis).

Syrup Cup.
No. 01850, . $13.50 (canebrake).
With Plate, . 17.50 (cajoler).

Sugar.
No. 01850, . . $13.50 (capsicum).

Cream.
No. 01850, . $12.50 (cabriolet).
Three Fourth Pints.

NICKEL SILVER, SILVER SOLDERED.

INK STANDS.

(HALF SIZE).

No. 43.

Old Copper, . $3.50 (CASEMATE).
Old Silver, . 4.00 (CASESHOT).

No. 31.

Silver, Gold Inlaid, . $6.25 (PISTON).

No. 44.

Old Copper, . $4.50 (CASTAWAY).
Old Silver, . 5.00 (CASTIGATE).

No. 47.

Enameled Copper, Old Silver Mountings, $4.75 (CHEST).

No. 49.

Old Silver, . $8.50 (CASSIMERE).
Gold Inlaid, . 10.00 (CASSINO).

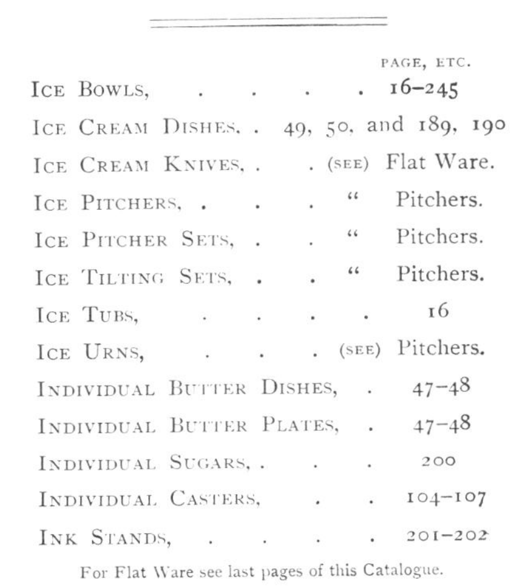

No. 37.

Old Silver, . $6.00 (PLATONIC).

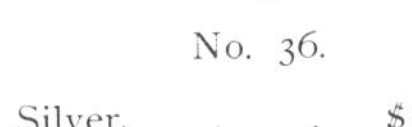

No. 36.

Old Silver, . . $5.50 (PLATINA).
Old Silver, Gold Inlaid, 6.50 (PLATING).

No. 50.

Old Silver, . $10.50 (CASHBOOK).
(Half Size.)

No. 35.

Old Silver, . . $4.50 (PLAT).
Old Silver, Gold Inlaid, 5.50 (PLATE).

GOLD AND SILVER PLATE.

(One-Third Size.)

No. 40.
Silver, . $4.50 (astute).
Gold Inlaid, 5.00 (athlete).

No. 41.
Hammered, . . $5.50 (ascribe).
Hammered, Gold Inlaid, 6.50 (aspen).

No. 29.
Gold and Silver, $3.50 (pitch).

No. 30.
Gold and Silver, $4.50 (pistol).

No. 45.
Old Copper and Gold, $8 50 (capote).
Old Silver and Gold, 9.00 (capable).

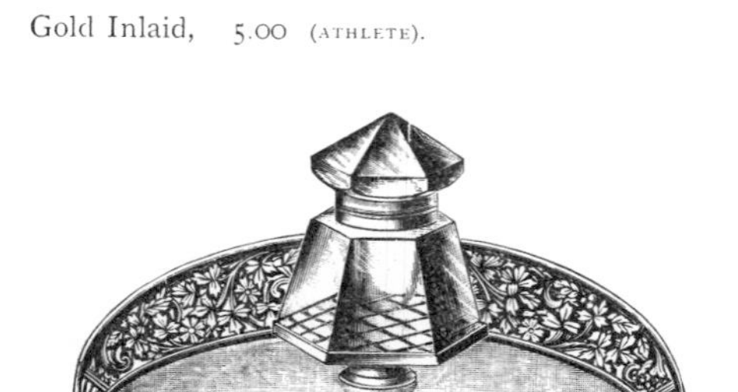

No. 32.
Silver, . . $8.00 (plaster).
Gilt, . . 9.00 (plastic).

No. 38. Old Silver.
Hammered, . . $9.00 (assume).
Hammered, Gold Inlaid, 10.50 (astonish).

No. 39.
Silver, . . $8.00 (asphalt).
Gold Lined, . 9.00 (assembly).

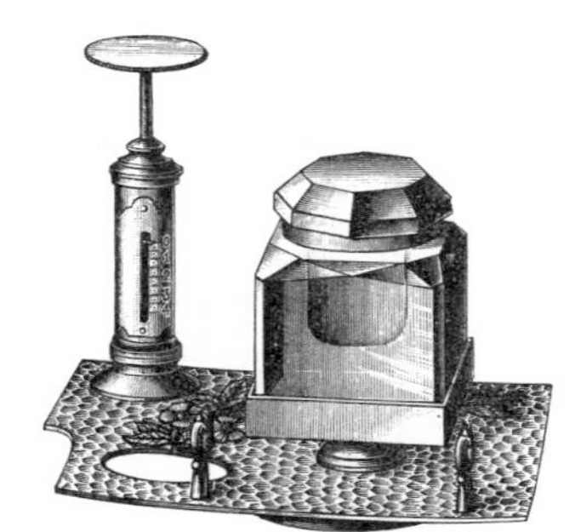

No. 46. With Letter Scale.
Hammered, Old Copper and Gold, $9.50 (capacity).
Hammered, Old Silver and Gold, 10.00 (calipers).

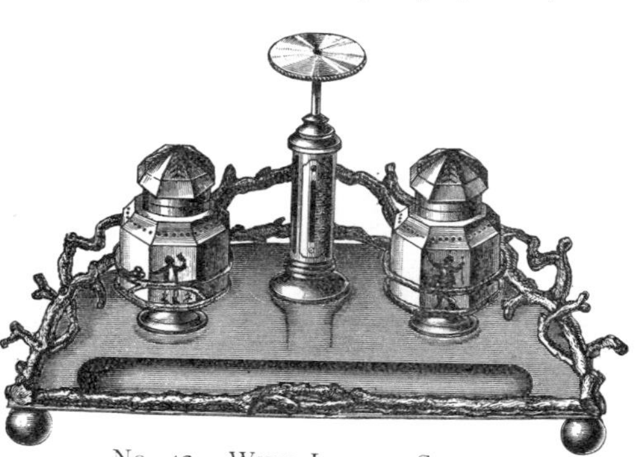

No. 42. With Letter Scale.
Silver, . . $10.00 (petition).
Old Silver, . 11.00 (petrel).

No. 48.
Enameled Copper, Old Silver Mountings, $7.50 (caprice).

No. 28.
Silver, . . $9.00 (planet).
Gold and Steel, 10.50 (plank).

No. 51.
Old Silver, . . $18.00 (caste).
Gold Inlaid, . . 20.00 (choicely).
(One-Third Size.)

No. 18.
Old Silver, . . $9.00 (placid).
Gold Inlaid, . . 10.00 (plaid).

TRADE MARK.
WHITE METAL.

JEWEL CASKETS, ETC.

TRADE MARK.
NICKEL SILVER.

(ONE-THIRD SIZE.)

No. 90.
Old Silver, . . $9.00 (CASUALLY).
Old Silver and Gold, 10.50 (CASUIST).

No. 05. BONBONNIERE. Nickel Silver.
Satin, Gold Lined, . . $2.00 (CATACOMB).
Satin, Engraved, Gold Lined, 2.50 (CATERER).
(Full Size, Top View.)

No. 05. BONBONNIERE. Nickel Silver.
Moorish, Old Silver, Gold Lined, $2.75 (CATAMOUNT).
(Full Size, Side View.)

No. 107.
Satin, Engraved, . . $13.50 (CAUTERIZE).
Satin, Engraved, Gold Inlaid, 16.00 (CELIBACY).
(PATENTED.)

No. 104.
Old Silver, . $8.00 (CATHEAD).
Gold Inlaid, . 9.50 (CATSPAW).
(PATENTED.)

No. 105.
Old Silver, . $8.00 (CAVALIER).
Gold Inlaid, . 9.50 (CENTIME).
(PATENTED.)

No. 52.
Chased, $11.50 (GLUE).
(PATENTED.)

No. 60.
Silver, . . $13.50 (GOBLIN).
Silver, Gold Inlaid, 15.00 (GOING).

No. 47. JEWEL TABLE. (Half Open.)
Satin, Chased, Silver, . . $14.50 (GONDOLA).
Chased, Silver, Gold Inlaid, . 16.00 (GONG).

No. 78.
Silver, . . . $10.50 (GRATIFY).
Silver, Gold Inlaid, 12.00 (GRATIS).

WHITE METAL.

GOLD AND SILVER PLATE.

NICKEL SILVER.

No. 103. BONBON BOX.
Satin, Engraved, . . . $11.50 (CHARTISM).
Satin, Engraved, XX Gold Inlaid, 13.50 (CHARY).

No. 72.
Old Silver, . $7.50 (GRATER).

No. 101. BONBON BOX.
Satin, Old Silver, . $10.50 (CHEAPLY).
Satin, Gold Inlaid, . 12.00 (CHARMING).

No. 106.
Old Silver, . $10.50 (CHALDRON).
Gold Inlaid, . 12.00 (CHALDER).
(PATENTED.)

No. 99. BONBON BOX.
Silver, . . $10.50 (CEREMENT).
Silver, Gold Inlaid, 11.50 (CERAMIC).

No. 100. BONBON BOX.
Old Silver, $15.00 (CEREMONY).
Gold Inlaid, 16.50 (CERTIFY).

No. 102. BONBON BOX.
Silver, . . $12.00 (CENTRAL).
Silver, Gold Inlaid, 13.50 (CHARACTER).

No. 92.
Old Silver, . $12.50 (CHERRY).
Gold Inlaid, . 15.00 (CHECKER).

No. 43.
Chased, . $9.00 (GOVERN).
With Mirror, 10.50 (GOVERNOR).
(PATENTED.)

No. 53.
Chased, . $12.50 (GOAT).
(PATENTED.)

No. 93.
Silver, . . $15.00 (CHEERFUL).
XX Gold Inlaid, 18.00 (CHEROOT).

No. 34.
Gold and Steel Finish, $13.50 (GNARL).

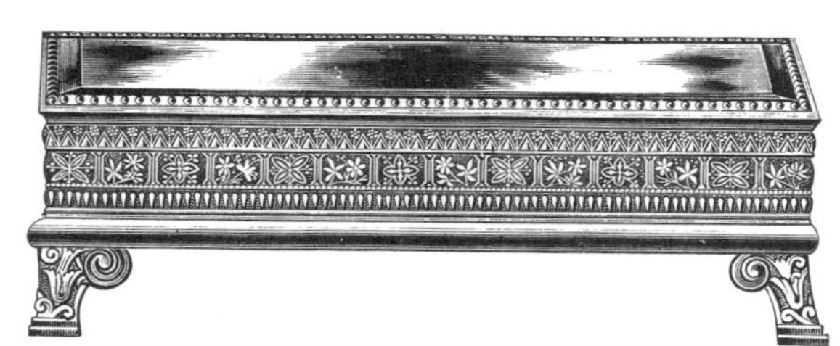

No. 48. GLOVE BOX.
Silver, Satin Lined, Crystal Cover, . . $13.50 (GOAD).
Silver, Gold Inlaid, Satin Lined, Crystal Cover, 15.00 (GOAL).

No. 35.
Gold and Steel Finish, $15.00 (GNARLED).

GOLD AND SILVER PLATE.

No. 50, . $7.50 (GRAND).

No. 40.
Old Silver, . $10.50 (GOTHIC).

No. 1½.
Porcelain, . . $3.00 (GOTH).

No. 59.
Old Silver, . . $10.50 (GLEN).
Silver, Gold Inlaid, 12.00 (GLIB).

No. 36, . . $8.50 (GRAFT).

No. 65.
Silver, . . $11.50 (GLEAM).

No. 71.
Silver, . . . $15.00 (GREATLY).
Silver, Gold Inlaid, 17.50 (GRECIAN).

No. 64.
Silver, . . . $23.00 (GLISTEN).
Silver, Gold Inlaid, 25.00 (GLITTER).

No. 67.
Silver, . . $23.00 (GROAN).
Silver, Gold Inlaid, 25.00 (GROG).

No. 88. Handkerchief Box.

Silver, ... $24.00 (logic).
Silver, Gold Inlaid, . 26.00 (logman).

No. 84.

Silver, ... $11.00 (mature).
Silver, Gold Inlaid, 12.50 (maxim).
Crystal, Plated Mountings.

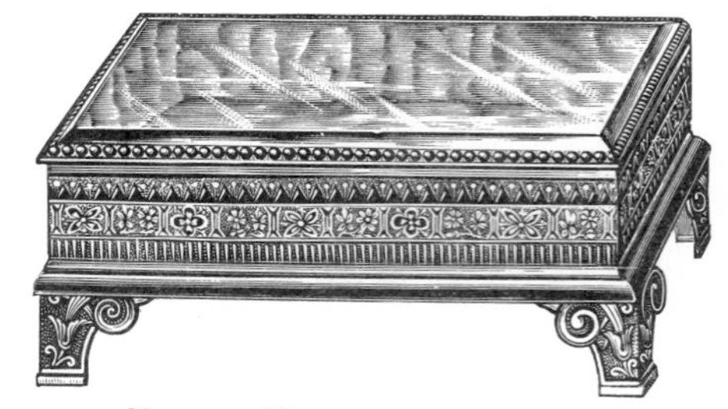

No. 55. Handkerchief Box.

Silver, Crystal Cover, . . $15.00 (gnash).
Silver, Gold Inlaid, Crystal Cover, 16.50 (gnat).

No. 85.

Old Silver, . . $9.00 (matin).
X Gold Inlaid, . 11.00 (matinee).
XX Gold Inlaid, . 13.00 (matron).

No. 81.

Silver, ... $30.00 (lounge).
Silver, Gold Inlaid, . 35.00 (louvre).

No. 87.

Silver, . . $15.00 (matting).

No. 63.

Silver, ... $19.00 (globe).
Silver, Gold Inlaid, . 20.50 (gloss).

No. 68.

Silver, ... $20.00 (gritty).
Silver, Gold Inlaid, . 22.00 (grizzle).

No. 61.

Silver, ... $15.50 (glebe).
Silver, Gold Inlaid, . 17.00 (glee).

GOLD AND SILVER PLATE.

No. 73.

Silver, . . . $20.50 (GRANTEE).
Silver, Gold Inlaid, 22.50 (GRANULATE).

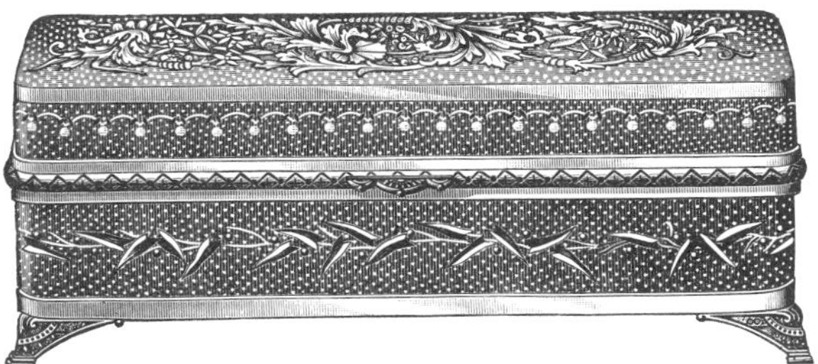

No. 89. HANDKERCHIEF BOX.

Silver, ... $24.00 (LOGWOOD).
Silver, Gold Inlaid, . 26.00 (LOITER).

No. 86.

Silver, . . $15.00 (LONELY).

No. 95.

Enameled Copper Base, Silver Mountings, $21.00 (EYESTONE).

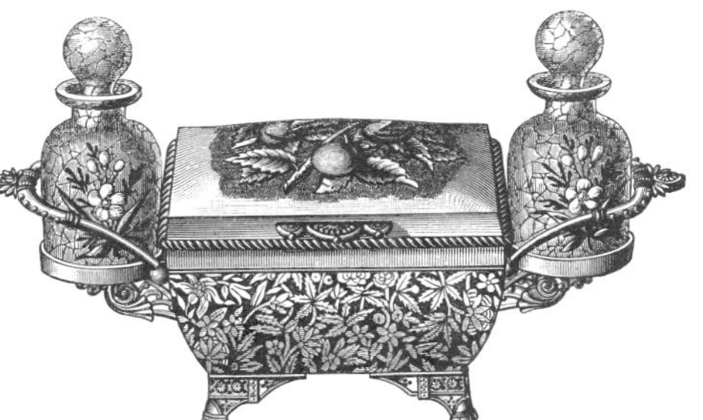

No. 91.

Old Silver, . . $12.00 (EYEBROW).
Gold Inlaid, . . 14.00 (EYEBALL).

No. 96.

Enameled Copper Base, Silver Mountings, $15.50 (EXULTANT).

No. 82.

Silver, . . . $25.00 (LOTION).
Silver, Gold Inlaid, 30.00 (LOTUS).

No. 62.

Silver, . . . $15.50 (GLIDE).
Silver, Gold Lined, 17.00 (GLIMPSE).

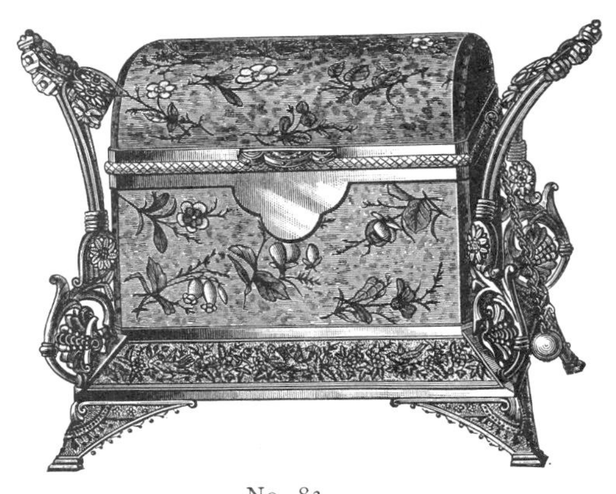

No. 83.

Silver, . . . $25.00 (LOOT).
Silver, Gold Inlaid, 30.00 (LOOSER).

WHITE METAL.

KNIFE RESTS.

NICKEL SILVER.

(FULL SIZE.)

No. 26.
Per dozen, . . $9.00 (DETECTOR).

No. 25.
Per dozen, . . $7.50 (DETERMINE).

No. 31.
Per dozen, . . $12.00 (DETRACTION).

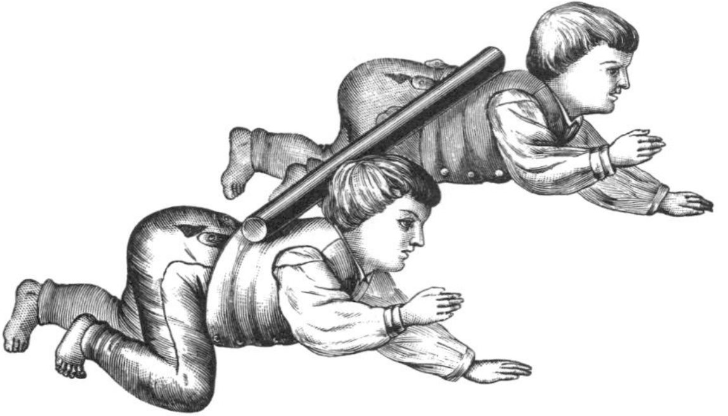

No. 32.
Per dozen, . . $13.50 (DETORT).

No. 30.
Per dozen, . . $9.00 (DEVASTATE).

No. 27.
Per dozen, . . $12.00 (ETCHING).

No. 28.
Per dozen, . . $13.50 (EXACTNESS).

No. 29.
Per dozen, . . $10.50 (EXECUTION).

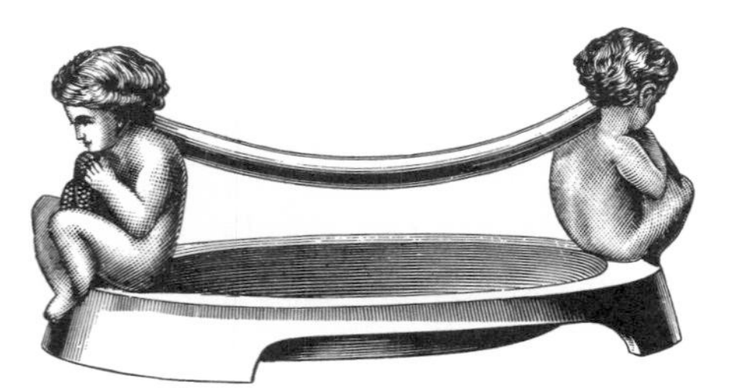

No. 15.
Per dozen, . . $12.00 (DISCUSS).

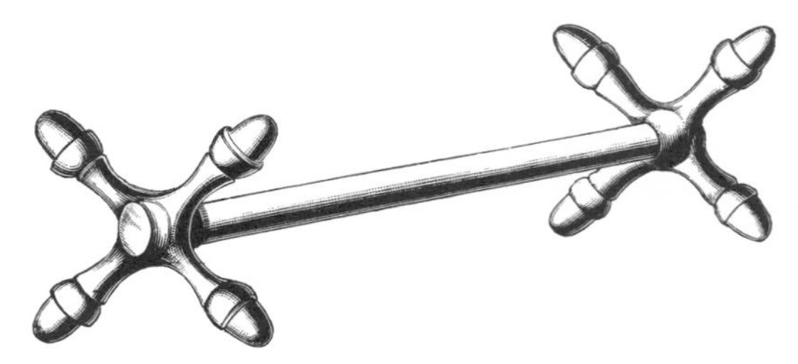

No. 2.
Per dozen, . . $7.50 (DISCREDIT).

TRADE MARK.
WHITE METAL.

LAVATORY SETS.

TRADE MARK.
NICKEL SILVER.

(ONE-THIRD SIZE.)

No. 510. CUP.

Satin, Engraved, Gold Lined, ... $3.50 (CURVE).
Satin, Engraved, Gold Inlaid and Gold Lined, 5.50 (CURVET).

No. 510. SPONGE DISH.

Gold Lined, . . . $7.50 (CONGRUITY).
Satin, Engraved, Gold Lined, 8.50 (CONVEYANCE).
Satin, Engraved, Gold Inlaid, 10.00 (CONVOCATE).
With Glass Drainer, $1.00 extra.

No. 510. POWDER BOX.

Satin, Engraved, . . $5.50 (CUTICLE).
Satin, Engraved, Gold Inlaid, 7.50 (COPIOUSLY).

No. 510. SOAP BOX.

Satin, Engraved, . . $11.50 (CORALLINE).
Satin, Engraved, Gold Inlaid, 15.50 (CONVENTION).

No. 510. BRUSH BOX.

Satin, Engraved, . . $12.50 (CORINTHIAN).
Satin, Engraved, Gold Inlaid, 16.50 (CORROSIVE).

No. 510. PUFF BOX.

Satin, Engraved, . . $8.50 (CORKSCREW).
Satin, Engraved, Gold Inlaid, 11.00 (CO-OPERATE).

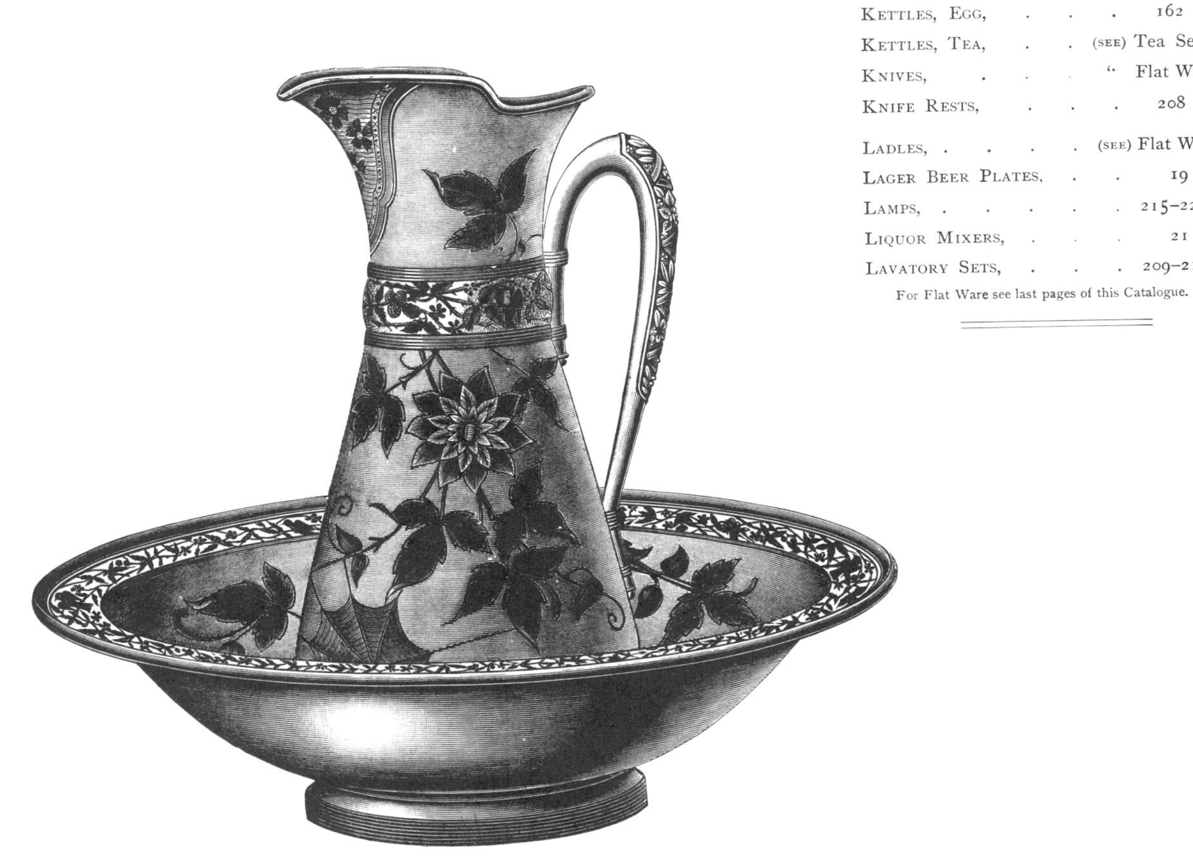

No. 510. EWER AND BASIN.

	Ewer.	Basin.
Satin, Engraved, ...	$35.00 (CURTLY).	$35.00 (CORONER).
Satin, Engraved, Gold Inlaid, .	55.00 (CUSHION).	55.00 (COOLER).

No. 506. BROCADE, ROSE EMBOSSED LAVATORY SET.

	Ewer.	Basin.	Brush Box.	Soap Box.	Puff Box.	Sponge Dish. Brocade, Gold Lined.	Cup. Gold Lined.
Brocade, Rose Embossed,	$35.00 (custody).	$35.00 (cuttle).	$10.50 (custom).	$10.00 (cutlass).	$5.50 (cutlef).	$7.50 (cutlet).	$3.00 (cutter).
XX Gold Inlaid, .	50.00 (cycle).	50.00 (cygnet).	14.50 (cylinder).	14.00 (cypress).	7.50 (choose).	9.00 (chopper).	5.00 (chorus).

Satin Lined Case, $50.00 extra (chopstick).

GOLD AND SILVER PLATE.

No. 508. Soap Box.

Satin, Chased, . $10.00 (conquest).
Russian, Gold Inlaid, 14.00 (contradict).

No. 508. Puff Box.

Satin, Chased, . . $5.50 (constancy).
Russian, Gold Inlaid, 8.50 (continent).

No. 508. Brush Box.

Satin, Chased, . . $10.50 (conjunct).
Russian, Gold Inlaid, 14.50 (consumer).

No. 508. Brush Cup.

Satin, Chased, . $6.00 (contrast).
Russian, Gold Inlaid, 10.00 (contusion).

No. 508. Sponge Dish.

Gold Lined, . . $6.50 (contrite).
With Glass Drainer, $1.00 extra.

No. 508. Cup.

Chased, Gold Lined, $3.50 (consider).
Russian, Gold Inlaid, 7.00 (contribute).

No. 506. Covered Jar.

Satin, Chased, . . . $48.00 (conjurer).
Satin, Chased, Gold Inlaid, . 68.00 (consul).
Gold Lined, $10.00 extra.

No. 506.
Complete Set furnished to match, price same as Brocade Rose Embossed.

No. 508. Ewer and Basin.

	Ewer.	Basin.
Satin, Chased, .	$35.00 (congest).	$35.00 (citizen).
Russian, Gold Inlaid,	55.00 (constraint).	55.00 (clapper).

TRADE MARK.
WHITE METAL.

GOLD AND SILVER PLATE.

TRADE MARK.
NICKEL SILVER.

BRUSH BOX.
No. 502, . $9.00 (RALLY).

PUFF BOX.
No. 502, . $2.75 (RAKING).

SOAP BOX.
No. 502, . $8.00 (RAKE).

No. 500.
Chased Ewer, . . . $18.00 (RAMROD).
Basin, ... 22.00 (RANCH).

No. 503. BRUSH BOX.
Chased, . . $10.50 (RAISIN).

No. 503. PUFF BOX.
Chased, . . $6.00 (CONJUNCTION).

No. 503. SOAP BOX.
Chased, . . $10.50 (RAILWAY).

No. 503.
Chased, Gold Lined, $3.50 (HAMMOCK).

No. 503.

	Ewer.	Basin.
Satin, ...	$17.00 (RAMPANT).	$16.50 (RAMPART).
Chased, ...	21.00 (RALLY).	20.50 (RAMPAGE).

No. 502.
Ewer, . . . $18.00 (RAMBLE).
Basin, . . . 21.00 (RAMIFY).

GOLD AND SILVER PLATE.

No. 511 Tooth-Powder Box.

Chased, . . $5.50 (splendent).
Chased, Gold Inlaid, 7.00 (stanchion).

No. 511 Soap Box.

Chased, . . $10.00 (statesman).
Chased, Gold Inlaid, 12.00 (statuesque).

No. 511 Puff Box.

Chased, . . $7.00 (sparse).
Chased, Gold Inlaid, 9.00 (speaker).

No. 511 Brush Cup.

Chased, Gold Lined, . . . $6.00 (somnolent).
Chased, Gold Inlaid and Gold Lined, 7.50 (spasmodic).

No. 511 Cup.

Chased, Gold Lined, . . . $3.50 (spearman).
Chased, Gold Inlaid and Gold Lined, 5.00 (spearment).

No. 511 Basin.

Chased, ... $35.00 (sombrous).
Chased, Gold Inlaid, . 45.00 (soliloquy).

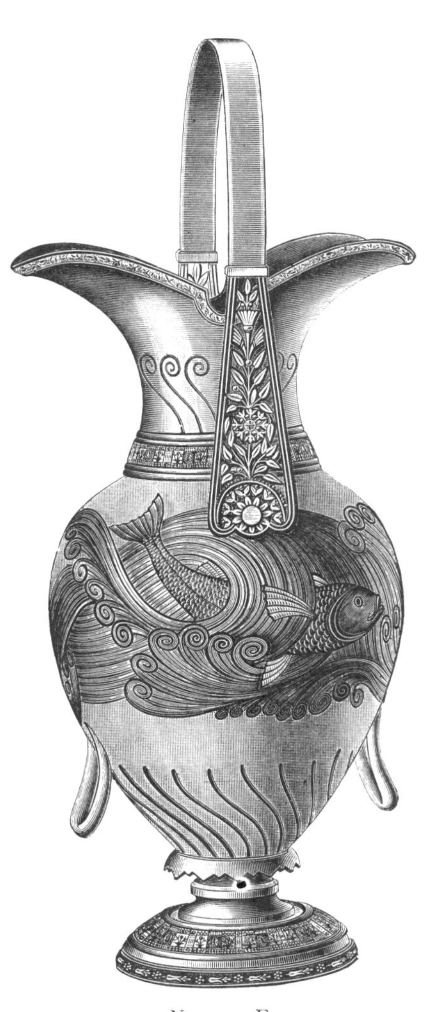

No. 511 Ewer.

Adjustable Handle.

Chased, ... $37.50 (solicitor).
Chased, Gold Inlaid, . 47.50 (solidify).

GOLD AND SILVER PLATE.

No. 100. Soap Box.

Hammered, ... $2.50 (solecist).

Hammered, Old Silver, . 2.75 (soluble).

Moorish, Old Silver, . . 3.25 (solvency).

(Half Size.)

No. 101. Shaving Box.

Satin, ... $1.50 (rapid).

Hammered, Old Silver, 2.50 (somehow).

(Half Size.)

No. 100. Soap Box.

Satin, . . . $1.50 (ranchero).

Satin, Engraved, . 2.50 (somnific).

No. 0200. Nickel Silver, Silver Soldered.

Satin, . . . $4.75 (songster).

Satin, Engraved, . 5.75 (soothsay).

Hammered, . . 5.75 (sophism).

(Half Size.)

No. 99. Tooth Brush Holder.

Silver, . . $0.75 (rank).

(Half Size.)

Soap Rack.

No. 104, . . $1.25 (rancid).

Soap Box.

No. 102, . . $6.00 (rapine).

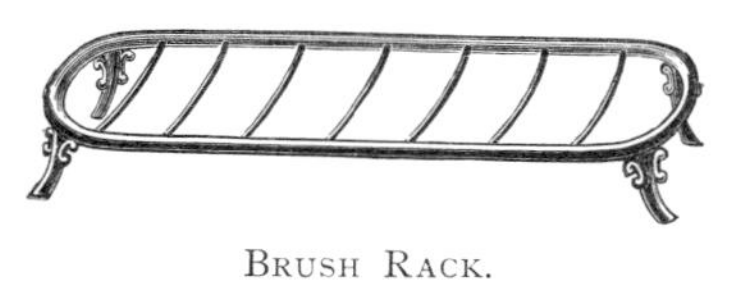

Brush Rack.

No. 105, . . $2.00 (rankle).

No. 1. Cuspadore.

Plain, . . $4.50 (ransom).

Engine, . . 5.25 (rant).

Brush Box.

No. 103, . . $7.00 (ransack).

Cuspadore.

No. 6, . . $5.50 (rancor).

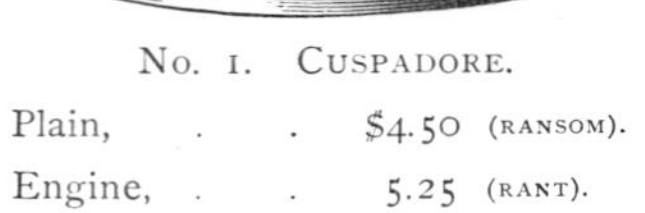

No. 5. Cuspadore.

Plain, . . . $6.75 (random).

Japanese, . . 7.50 (range).

Chamber.

No. 502, . . $12.00 (rapier).

(One-Third Size.)

Cuspadore.

No. 4, . . $8.00 (rapt).

WHITE METAL.

NICKEL SILVER.

LAMPS.

(One-Third Size, Excepting Extension Lamps.)

No. 600.

Enameled Copper, Old Silver Mountings,

$25.00 (SOPHOMORE).

No. 630.

Old Copper, . . $16.00 (SOUCHONG).

Old Silver, . . 18.00 (SOUNDING).

No. 635. FLUTED.

Old Copper, . . $18.00 (SPANDREL).

Old Silver, . . 20.00 (SPANKING).

SHADES OR GLOBES EXTRA.

No. 670. ROCHESTER BURNER.
Old Silver and Gold, . $27.50 (SPARING).
Shade extra.

No. 595.
Enameled Copper Old Silver Mountings, $22.50 (STRAIT).
Shade extra.

No. 675. ROCHESTER BURNER.
Old Silver, Gold Inlaid, $110.00 (SPARKISH).
Height, when extended, 69 inches.
Shade extra.

GOLD AND SILVER PLATE.

No. 660. Rochester Burner.
Old Copper, . . $25.00 (strangely).
Old Silver, . . 27.50 (stratify).
Shade extra.

No. 680. Rochester Burner.
Old Silver, . . $27.50 (streamer).
Shade extra.

No. 685. Extension Lamp.
Complete with No. 680 Lamp.
Old Silver, Gold Inlaid, . $125.00 (stratum).
Height, when extended, 75 inches.

No. 615.

Old Copper, . . . $15.00 (STREAMLET).

Old Copper and Old Silver, 17.00 (STRETCHER).

No. 610.

Enameled Copper, Old Silver Mountings, . $27.50 (STRICKEN).

Globe Extra.

No. 655.

Old Copper, Old Silver Mountings, . $100.00 (STRICTLY).

Height, when extended, 68 inches.

GOLD AND SILVER PLATE.

No. 485.

Old or Bright Copper, . . $35.00 (ADVANCE).
Old Silver, ... 40.00 (ADVANTAGE).
Old Silver, X Gold Inlaid, . 45.00 (ADVERSE).

No. 700. ROCHESTER BURNER.
Enameled Copper, Old Silver Mountings, $25.00 (STRINGENT).
Shade extra.

No. 665.
Complete with No. 700 Lamp.
Old Copper and Old Silver, . $85.00 (STRINGER).
Height, when extended, 75 inches.

No. 605.
Old Copper, . . $12.50 (STRONGLY).
Old Silver, . . 14.50 (STRUCTURE).
Globe extra.

No. 690.
Enameled Copper, Old Silver Mountings, $20.00 (STRUGGLE).
Shade extra.

No. 695. EXTENSION LAMP.
Old Copper, Old Silver Mountings, . $60.00 (STRIPLING).
Height, when extended, 65 inches.

No. 640. Duplex Burner.
Copper, . . $23.00 (citation).
Old Silver, . 25.00 (civilian).
Shade or Globe extra.

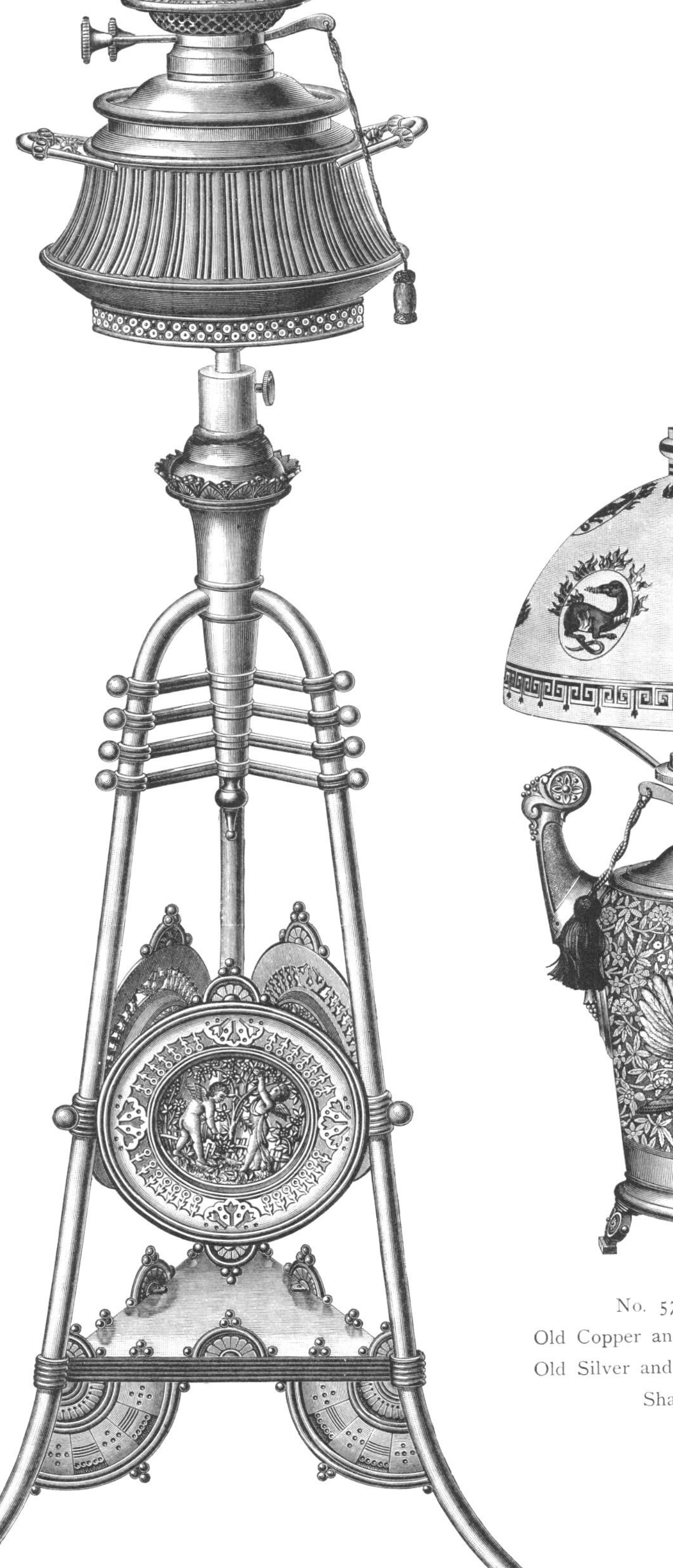

No. 645. Extension Lamp. Complete.
Old Copper, . . . $77.50 (clamorous).
Old Silver, ... 85.00 (claimant).
Height when extended, 65 inches.

No. 570. Duplex Burner.
Old Copper and Gold, . $27.50 (clanship).
Old Silver and Gold, . 30.00 (civilize).
Shade or Globe extra.

Trade Mark.
WHITE METAL.

GOLD AND SILVER PLATE.

Trade Mark.
NICKEL SILVER.

No. 430. Hammered and Applied.

Old Silver, $27.50 (agrarian).
XX Gold Inlaid, 30.00 (agreement).

No. 420. Hammered and Applied.

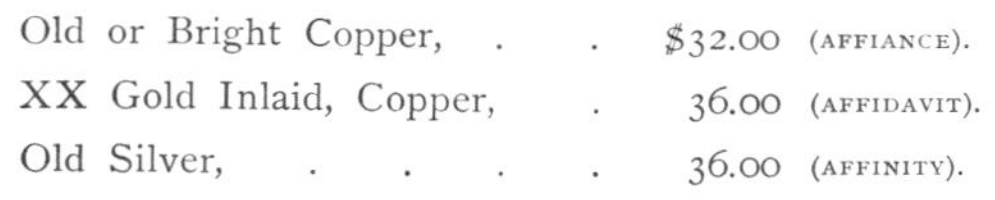

Old or Bright Copper, . . $32.00 (affiance).
XX Gold Inlaid, Copper, . 36.00 (affidavit).
Old Silver, ... 36.00 (affinity).
Old Silver, XX Gilt, Gold Inlaid, 40.00 (cinnabar).

No. 480.

Bright Copper, . . . $40.00 (abandon).
Old Silver, ... 45.00 (abash).
Old Silver, Gold Inlaid, . 50.00 (abbess).

Shades or Globes Extra.

GOLD AND SILVER PLATE.

No. 545.

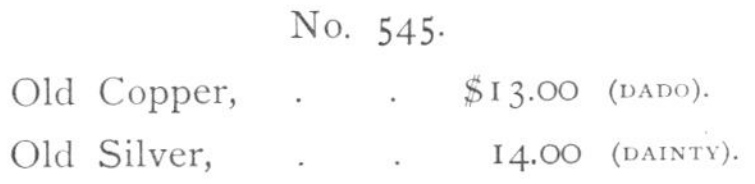

Old Copper, . . $13.00 (DADO).
Old Silver, . . 14.00 (DAINTY).

No. 505.

Old Copper, . . $13.00 (ANALYSIS).
Old Silver, . . 14.00 (ANARCH).

No. 530. Hammered and Applied.

Old Silver, . . $27.50 (ULTRA).
XX Gold Inlaid, . 30.00 (UMBER).

No. 410. Hammered and Applied.

Old Silver, . . $26.50 (AFFRAY).
XX Gilt, . . 30.00 (AFFRONT).

No. 555.

Old Copper, . . $15.00 (DABSTER).
Old Silver, . . 17.00 (DAGGER).

Shades or Globes Extra.

MIRRORS, PLACQUES, ETC.

(ONE-THIRD SIZE.)

NON-TARNISHABLE.

No. 9903. MIRROR.

Enameled Copper, . . $10.00 (CONGENER).

No. 9900. MIRROR.

Enameled Copper, . . $13.50 (CIRCULATE).

No. 9100. PATENT TRIPLICATE FOLDING MIRROR. (Closed.)

Hammered and Applied.

	Old Copper.	Old Silver.
Gold Inlaid Centre, . .	$43.00 (HANDFUL).	$45.00 (ZEAL).
XX Gold Inlaid Border and Centre,	48.00 (HAND).	50.00 (ZEALOT).

No. 9918. SCONCE.

Old Silver, . . $25.00 (HALFWAY).

XX Gold Inlaid, . 27.50 (CINCTURE).

No. 900. Clock.
Embossed Old Silver, $13.50 (patronage).

No. 1000. Clock.
Silver, $14.50 (peanut). Gold Inlaid, $16.50 (pedestal).

No. 9400. Triplicate Folding Mirror.
Moorish, Old Silver, $47.00 (pellucid). Moorish, Gold Inlaid, $53.00 (penchant.)

illustrations half size.

No. 9919. Enameled Copper.

Old Silver Mountings and Border, . . $24.00 (dentate).

XX Gold Inlaid Mountings, Old Silver Border, 27.50 (dentil).

No. 9920. Enameled Copper.

Old Silver Mountings and Border, . . $24.00 (deplete).

XX Gold Inlaid Mountings, Old Silver Border, 27.50 (detour).

No. 9300. Patent Triplicate Folding Mirror.

Old Copper Border, XX Gold Inlaid Centre, . . $42.00 (damage).

Old Silver Border, XX Gold Inlaid Centre, . . 44.00 (dasher).

X Gold Inlaid Border, XX Gold Inlaid Centre, . . 48.00 (dative).

No. 8000. Mirror.
Hammered, XX Gold Inlaid, $30.00 (letter).

No. 9910. Mirror.
Enameled Copper, Old Silver Trimmings, $16.50 (dome).

No. 9200. Patent Triplicate Folding Mirror. (Open).
Hammered and Applied, Old Silver, Gold Inlaid Centre, . . $65.00 (zebra).
XX Gilt, Hammered and Applied, Old Silver, Gold Inlaid Centre, 70.00 (zenith).

GOLD AND SILVER PLATE.

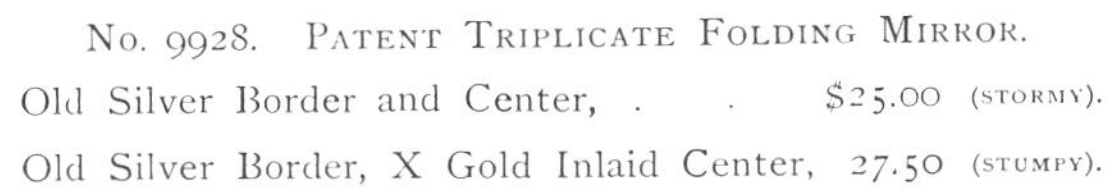

No. 9928. Patent Triplicate Folding Mirror.

Old Silver Border and Center, . . $25.00 (stormy).

Old Silver Border, X Gold Inlaid Center, 27.50 (stumpy).

No. 9932. Mirror.

Old Silver, . . $80.00 (strife).

Gold Plated, . . 90.00 (strike).

No. 9931. Mirror.

Old Silver and Copper, . $30.00 (stove-coal).

GOLD AND SILVER PLATE.

No. 9914. Mirror.
Old Silver, . . $9.50 (dethrone).
Old Silver, Gold Inlaid, 11.00 (detonate).

No. 8200. Mirror.
Hammered and Applied, Gold Inlaid, . $35.00 (incorrupt).

No. 8100. Smaller.
Hammered and Applied, Gold Inlaid, . $22.50 (increase).

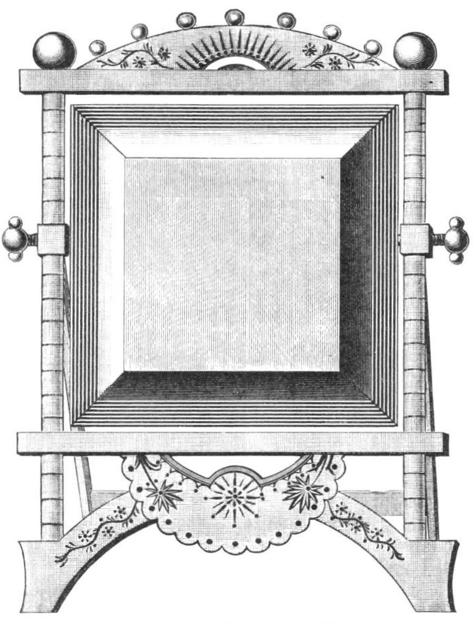

No. 9915. Shaving Mirror.
Old Silver, . . $21.00 (doleful).
Old Silver, Gold Inlaid, 24.00 (dolphin).

No. 9917. Patent Triplicate Folding Mirror.
Old Silver Border, XX Gold Inlaid Centre, . $35.00 (designate).
Gold Inlaid Border, XX Gold Inlaid Centre, . 40.00 (detention).

No. 9916. Patent Triplicate Folding Mirror.
Enameled Copper, X Gold Inlaid Centre, . $30.00 (detective).

WHITE METAL.

NICKEL SILVER.

No. 9929. Hand Mirror.

Satin, . . . $5.50 (stole).

Satin, Engraved, . 6.50 (stoop).

(Half Size.)

No. 9930. Hand Mirror.

Old Silver, . . . $8.50 (store).

Old Silver, Gold Inlaid, . 9.50 (stuff).

(Half Size.)

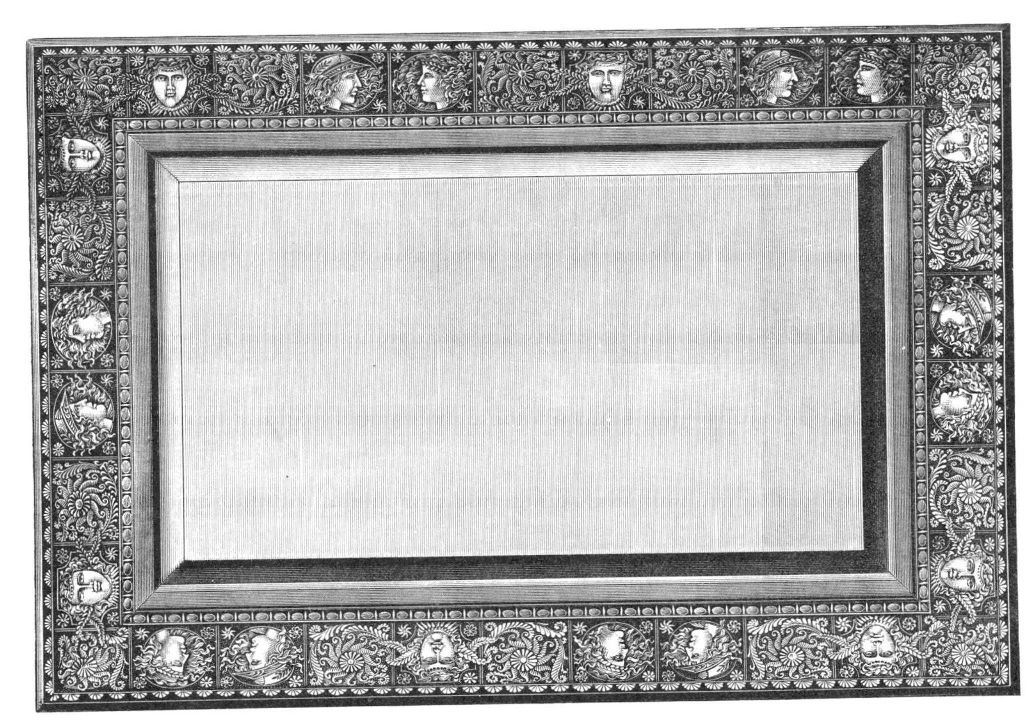

No. 9933. Mirror.

Old Silver, . . . $37.50 (straight).

(One-Third Size.)

GOLD AND SILVER PLATE.

No. 9924. SCONCE.

Old Silver, ... $32.50 (GURGLE).

Old Silver, XX Gold Inlaid, . 35.00 (GUTTER).

No. 9911. MIRROR. Without Candelabra.

Old Silver, ... $27.50 (GUSSET).

Old Silver, XX Gold Inlaid, . 30.00 (GUSTO).

No. 9908. MIRROR.

Enameled Copper, Old Silver Trimmings, $14.00 (HANDMAID).

No. 9909. MIRROR.

Enameled Copper, Old Silver Trimmings, $14.50 (HANDBILL).

No. 9800. MIRROR.

Old Copper, XX Gold Inlaid, . $27.50 (GYMNAST).

Old Silver, XX Gold Inlaid, . . 30.00 (HALF-PAY).

GOLD AND SILVER PLATE.

No. 9700. Mirror.

Old Copper,	$28.00	(domestic).
Old Silver,	30.00	(domicile).
Gold Inlaid,	34.00	(dominate).

No. 8500. Placque.
Moorish, Old Silver, X Gilt Mountings, $9.00 (domineer).
(Half Size.)

No. 9906. Mirror.
Enameled Copper, . $6.75 (dominion).

No. 8500. Placque.
Moorish, Old Silver, X Gilt Mountings, $9.00 (domino).
(Half Size.)

GOLD AND SILVER PLATE.

HAND MIRRORS.

(ONE-THIRD SIZE.)

No. 9913.

Old Silver, . $7.50 (CONJOINTLY).

No. 9912.

Enameled Copper,
Old Silver Handle, $7.50 (FUTILE).

No. 9922.

Old Silver, . $7.50 (GUNNING).

No. 9923.

Satin, ... $9.00 (FUMIGATE).
Hammered, Old Silver, 9.50 (FUTURE).
Moorish, Old Silver, . 10.00 (FUSTIN).

No. 9921.
Back View.

Moorish, Old Silver, $9.00 (FURNACE).
Moorish, Gold Inlaid, 11.00 (FUNCTION).

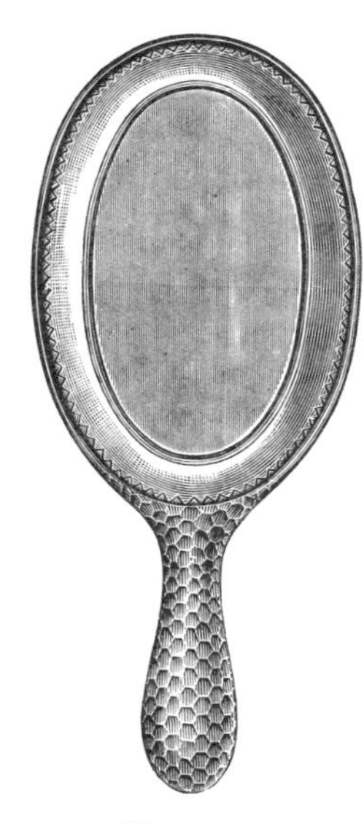

No. 9921.
Front View.

Hammered, Old Silver, $8.50 (FLITCH).

No. 9921.
Back View.

Satin, . . $7.50 (FORLORN).
Satin, Engraved, 8.50 (FURLONG).

No. 9921.
Back View.

Embossed, . . $12.00 (FORGIVE).
Embossed, Old Silver, 12.00 (FORGET).

No. 8300. PLACQUE.
Hammered, XX Gilt, . . $37.50 (LETTUCE).

No. 8700. PLACQUE.
Hammered, Old Copper, Gold Inlaid, . $45.00 (NIGH).
Hammered, Old Silver, Gold Inlaid, . 50.00 (NIGHTLY).

No. 8800. PLACQUE.
Hammered, Old Copper, Gold Inlaid, . $45.00 (NIHILISM).
Hammered, Old Silver, Gold Inlaid, . 50.00 (NICTATE).

No. 8400. PLACQUE.
Hammered, XX Gilt, Old Silver, . $40.00 (LETHE)
Assorted Decorations.

No. 9904. PLACQUE.
Enameled Copper.
Old Silver Centre, . $12.00 (FUSEE).
XX Gold Inlaid Centre, 13.50 (FURZE).
No. 9905. (Centre like No. 9901.)
Enameled Copper.
Old Silver Centre, . $12.00 (FUSION).
XX Gold Inlaid Centre, 13.50 (FUSIL).

No. 9901. PLACQUE.
Enameled Copper.
Old Silver Centre, . $12.00 (FURROW).
XX Gold Inlaid Centre, 13.50 (FURTIVE).
No. 9902. (Centre like No. 9904.)
Enameled Copper.
Old Silver Centre, $12.00 (GYRATE).
XX Gold Inlaid Centre, 13.50 (DOMAIN).

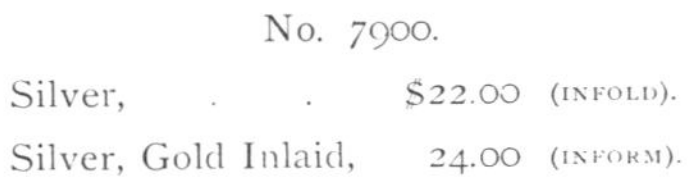

No. 7900.
Silver, . . $22.00 (INFOLD).
Silver, Gold Inlaid, 24.00 (INFORM).

No. 8600. PLACQUE.
Old Copper, . . $12.00 (NIPPLE).
Old Silver, . . 13.50 (NITRIC).

No. 9907. PLACQUE.
Enameled Copper, Old Silver Ferns, . $10.50 (GUNWALE).

WHITE METAL.

TOOTHPICK OR MATCH HOLDERS.

NICKEL SILVER.

(HALF SIZE.)

No. 28.

Silver, Gold Lined, . . $3.00 (POTTER).
Gold Inlaid and Gold Lined, 3.50 (POUND).

No. 33.

Silver, . . $2.50 (FUNDAMENT).
Old, Silver, . 3.00 (FOREVER).

No. 23.

Silver and Gold, . $3.25 (POSTURE).

No. 1. PORCUPINE.

Silver, . . $1,12 (POSTAL).

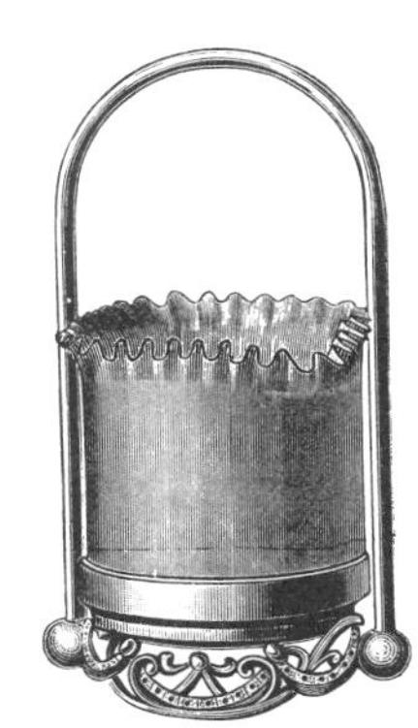

No. 32.

Silver. . . $2.75 (FURIOUS).

No. 24.

Silver and Gold, . $3.50 (POTASH).

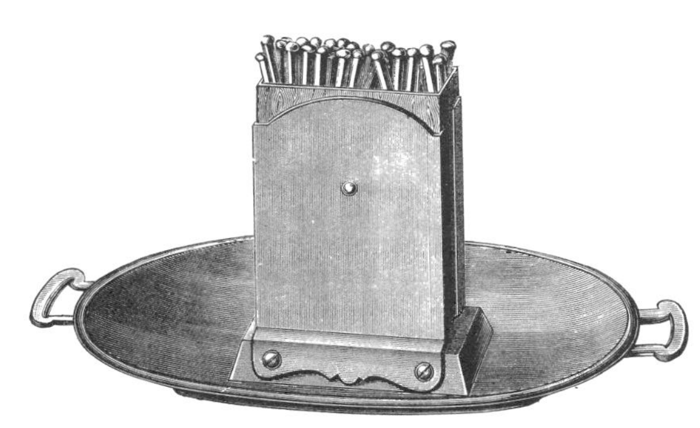

No. 34. SAFETY MATCH BOX HOLDER.

Enameled Copper, . . $4.50 (FURBISH).

No. 22.

Gold Lined, . $3.00 (POTATO).

No. 25.

Old Silver, Gold Lined, $3.75 (POSITIVE).

No. 26, . . $3.00 (POTENT).

No. 29.

Silver, Gold Lined, . $5.00 (POTION).
Gold Inlaid and Gold Lined, 6.00 (POUNCE).

NICKEL SILVER MATCH BOXES.

(FULL SIZE.)

No. 020.

Old Silver, $2.00 (DOOR).

No. 021.

Old Silver, . $2.50 (DORIC).

No. 022.

Old Silver, . $1.75 (DOTAGE).

No. 016.

Plain or Satin, . . $1.50 (PRACTICE).
Engraved, . . . 2.00 (PRAISE).
Hammered, Old Silver, . 2.50 (FRANCE).

No. 019. MOORISH.

Hammered, Old Silver, . $3.00 (DOUBTFUL).
Moorish, Old Silver, . 3.25 (DRAGOMAN).
Moorish, Gold Inlaid. . 3.75 (DOZE).

No. 019.

Plain or Satin, . . $1.75 (FRANK).
Satin, Engraved, . 2.25 (PRATE).

WHITE METAL MATCH SAFES.

(HALF SIZE.)

No. 12.

Old Silver, . $3.00 (PRECLUDE).

No. 21.

Oxidized and Gilt, $5.00 (PRECISE).

No. 11.

Old Silver and Gold, $2.75 (PRECIPICE).

No. 13.

Old Silver, . . $2.50 (PRECEDE).
Old Silver and Gold, 3.00 (HAILSTONE).

No. 20.

Oxidized and Gold, $4.50 (PREDICT).

TRADE MARK.
WHITE METAL.

TRADE MARK.
NICKEL SILVER.

NAPKIN RINGS.

(FULL SIZE.)

GOLD LINED, $3.00 PER DOZEN EXTRA.

No. 270.
Chased, per dozen, $10.00 (DONATE).

No. 247.
Chased, . per dozen, $15.00 (APPROVE).

No. 242.
Chased, per dozen, $13.50 (LOCATION).

No. 227.
Chased, . per dozen, $15.00 (FUGITIVE).

No. 267.
Satin, Engraved, per dozen, $13.50 (DORMANT).

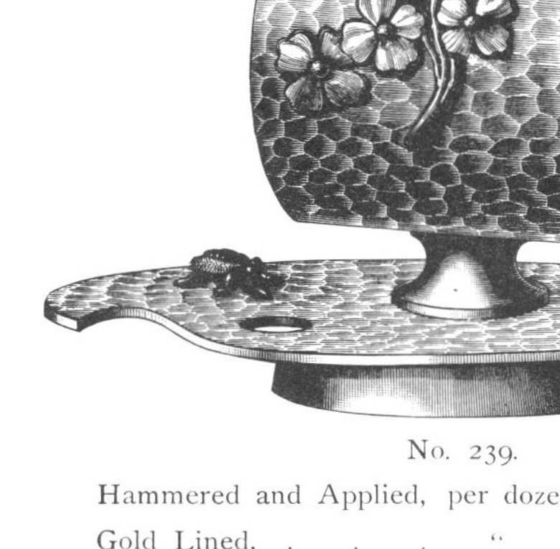

No. 239.

Hammered and Applied,	per dozen, $24.00	(ANXIOUS).
Gold Lined, . . .	" 27.00	(APERTURE).
Gold Inlaid and Gold Lined,	" 30.00	(APEX).

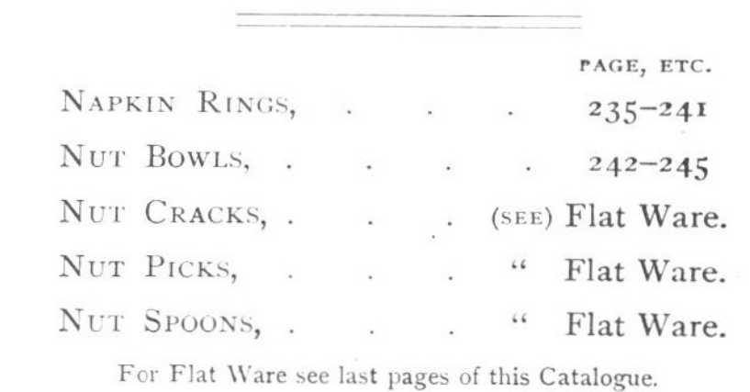

No. 268.
Chased, . per dozen, $13.50 (DONATION).

No 243.
Chased, per dozen, $15.00 (APPRAISE).

No. 222.

	Per dozen.	
Chased, ...	$21.00	(FREQUENT).
Chased, Gold Lined, . . .	24.00	(FRESCO).
Chased, Gold Inlaid and Gold Lined,	27.00	(FRESH).

No. 246.
Hammered, Chased, per dozen, $21.00 (LOCKET).

GOLD AND SILVER PLATE.

No. 226.
Chased, . per dozen, $12.00 (FRUITAGE).

No. 238.
Chased, . per dozen, $18.00 (APIECE).

No. 244.
Chased, . per dozen, $18.00 (APRICOT).

No. 269.
Satin, Engraved, per dozen, $18.00 (DOOM).

No. 245.
Chased, . per dozen, $18.00 (LOCK).

No. 266.
Chased, . per dozen, $10.50 (DORMER).

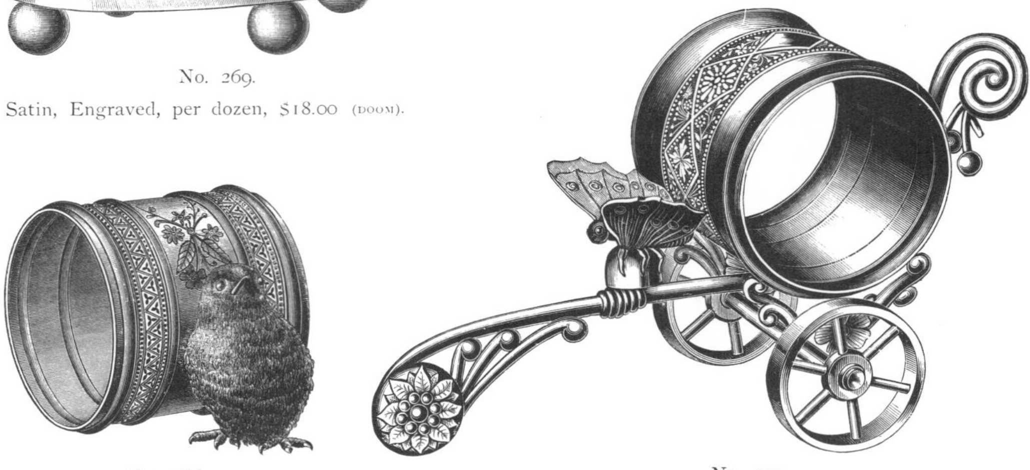

No. 211.
Chased, . per dozen, $18.00 (FRISK).

No. 234.
Chased, . per dozen, $18.00 (APPAREL).

No. 209.
Chased, . per dozen, $24.00 (FREEHOLD).

No. 155.
Silver, Chased, per dozen, $18.00 (FREEDOM).

GOLD AND SILVER PLATE.

No. 250.
Chased, . per dozen, $30.00 (LOBBY).

No. 235.
Chased, . per dozen, $24.00 (APPEAL).

No. 251.
Chased, . per dozen, $30.00 (LOBE).

No. 212.
Chased, . per dozen, $18.00 (FRISKY).

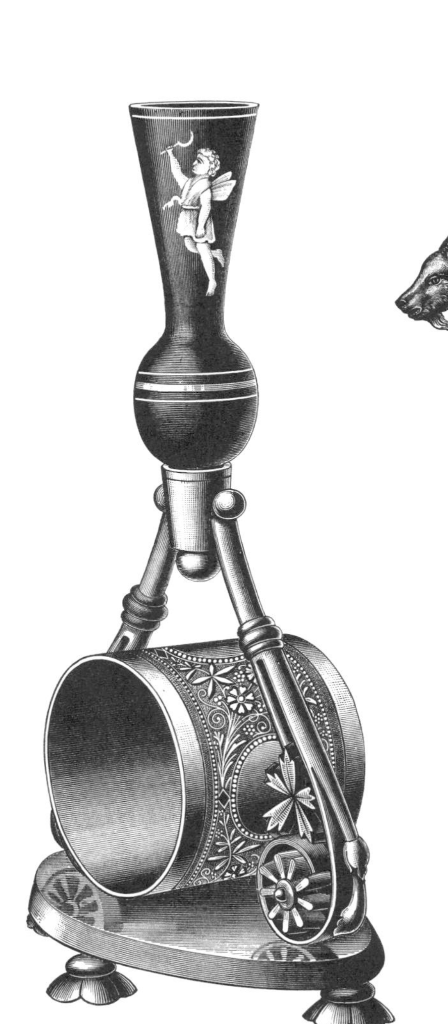

No. 219.
Chased, . per dozen, $33.00 (FRONTAL).

No. 248.
Chased, . per dozen, $16.50 (APPOINT).

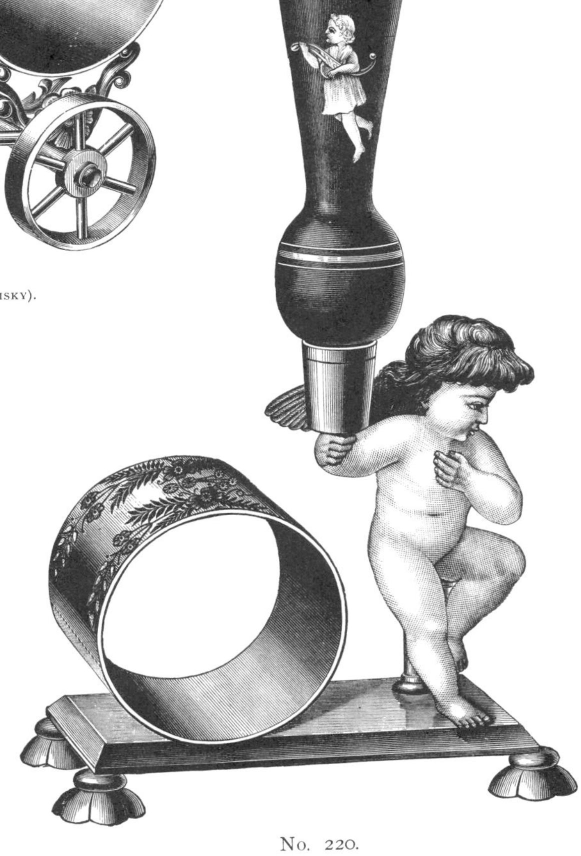

No. 220.
Chased, . per dozen, $33.00 (FRAY).

GOLD AND SILVER PLATE.

No. 168.

Chased, . per dozen, $16.00 (FRIGATE).

No. 231.

	Per dozen.	
Hammered and Applied, .	$15.00	(FULLER).
Hammered and Applied, Gilt,	18.00	(FULMINATE).
Hammered and Applied, XX Gilt,	21.00	(FUMBLE).

No. 194.

Chased, . per dozen, $21.00 (FROCK).

No. 146.

Chased, . per dozen, $12.00 (FRONTAGE).

No. 202.

Chased, . per dozen, $15.00 (FRONT).

No. 161.

Silver, Chased, per dozen, $15.00 (FROZE).

No. 214.

Chased, . . per dozen, $18.00 (FRETWORK).

Chased, Gold Lined, per dozen, 21.00 (FRIAR).

No. 208.

Chased, . per dozen, $18.00 (FREE).

No. 199.

Chased, . per dozen, $18.00 (FROWN).

GOLD AND SILVER PLATE.

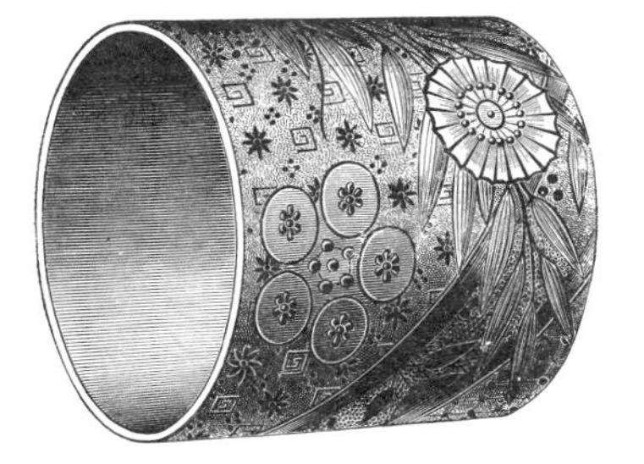

No. 225.
Chased A, per dozen, $8.00 (FRUGAL).

No. 218.
Chased, per dozen, $8.50 (FORTRESS).

No. 225.
Chased, B, per dozen, $8.00 (FRUSTRATE).
Chased B, XX Gold Inlaid, per dozen, 14.00 (FOREWARN).

No. 262.
Satin, Engraved, per dozen, $8.00 (FORESEE).

No. 216.
Chased . per dozen, $8.00 (FUDGE).

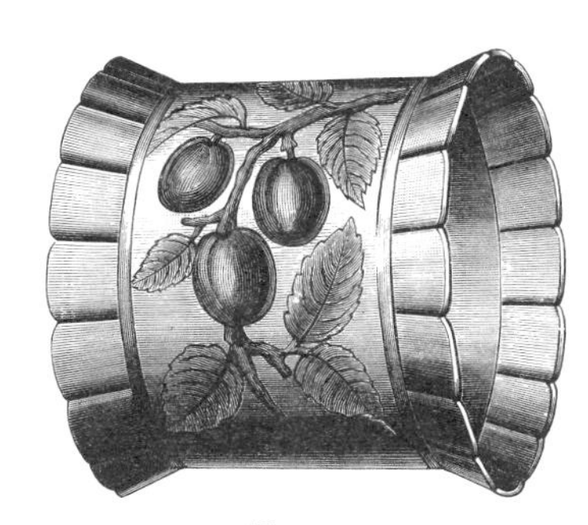

No. 252.
Chased, . per dozen, $9.00 (LIVELY).
Chased, Gold Lined, " 12.00 (LIVING).
Chased, XX Gold Inlaid and Gold Lined, " 15.00 (LOAM).

No. 257. Oval Initial Ring.
Assorted Letters.
Per dozen, . . $15.00 (FLORIN).
Gold Inlaid and Gold Lined, . per dozen, 24.00 (FORESIGHT).
No. 258, Round, $1.50 per dozen less.

No. 237.
Chased, per dozen, $9.00 (APPLICANT).

No. 259.
Chased, . per dozen, $8.50 (FORESTER).
Satin, Chased, per dozen, 8.50 (FORGETFUL).

No. 216.
XX Gold Inlaid, per dozen, $15.00 (FLEECY).

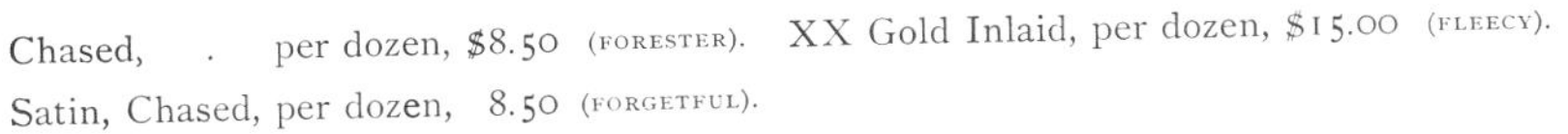

No. 253.
Silver, . per dozen, $8.00 (FLOTSAM).
Gold Lined, per dozen, 11.00 (FLEXION).

No. 260.
Chased, . per dozen, $8.00 (FORETELL).
Satin, Chased, per dozen, 8.00 (FLOSS).

No. 216. Assorted Engravings.
XX Gold Inlaid, . per dozen, $15.00 (FORESTALL).

GOLD AND SILVER PLATE.

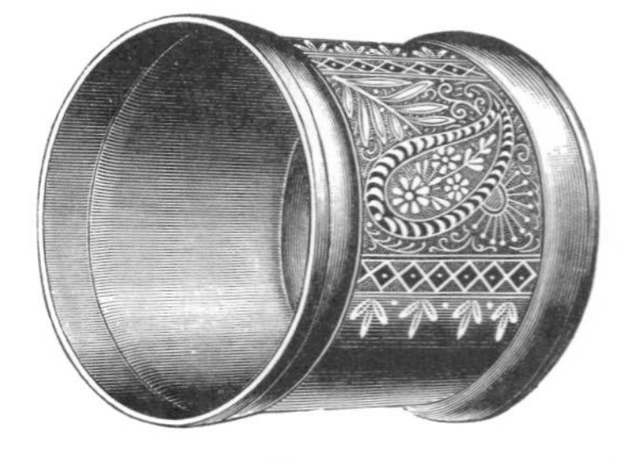

No. 215.

Chased, per dozen, $8.00 (FORUM).

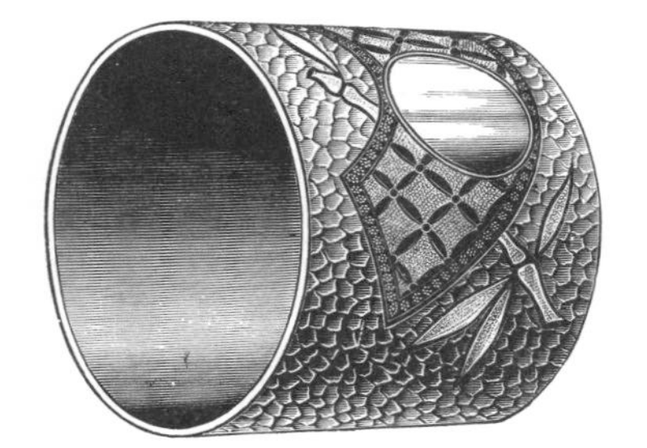

No. 179.

Hammered, Chased, per dozen, $10.50 (FORTUNE).

No. 198.

Chased, per dozen, $9.50 (FORSWEAR).

No. 197.

Chased, per dozen, $9.50 (FORSOOTH).

No. 175.

Plain, . per dozen, $5.50 (FORTIFY).

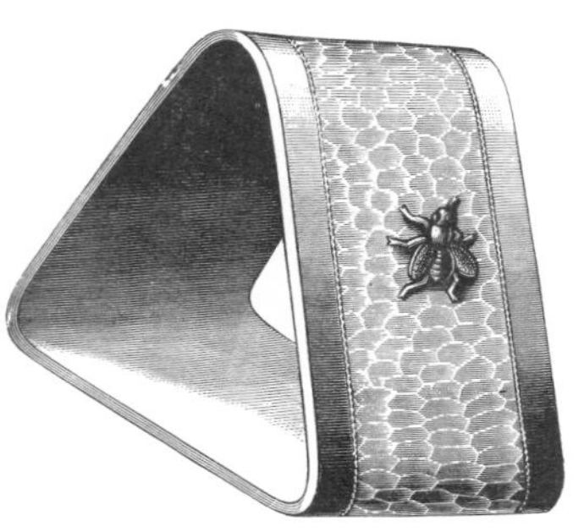

No. 241.

Hammered and Applied.

Per dozen, . $12.00 (APPEASE).

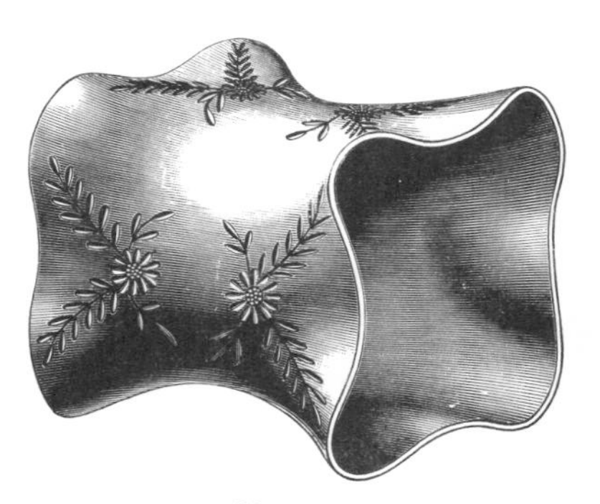

No. 236.

Chased, per dozen, $10.50 (APOGEE).

No. 255.

Old Silver, . . per dozen, $9.00 (FLINDERS).
Old Silver, Gold Lined, per dozen, 12.00 (FLEETING).
Gold Inlaid and Gold Lined, . . per dozen, 18.00 (FIXEDLY).

No. 256.

Fluted, per dozen, $7.00 (FLAXEN).

No. 184.

Chased, per dozen, $9.50 (FORT).

No. 207.

Chased, per dozen, $8.00 (FORTH).

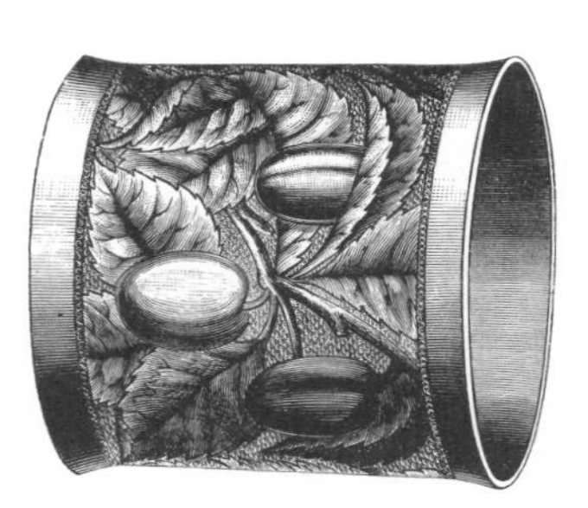

No. 254.

Old Silver, per dozen, . $9.00 (FLOATING).
XX Gold Inlaid, per dozen, 18.00 (FLAMEN).

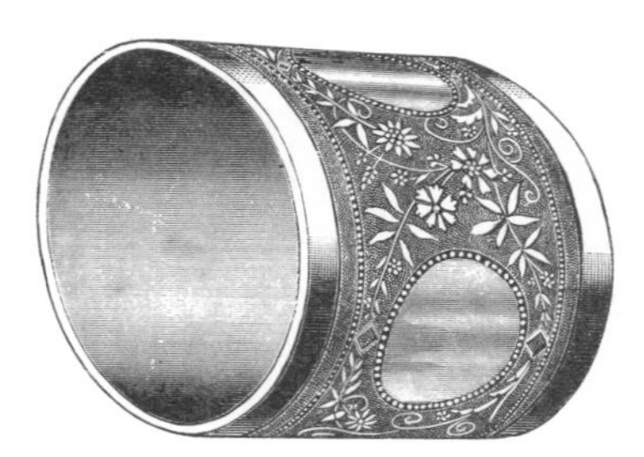

No. 178. Oval.

Chased B., per dozen, $9.00 (FRACAS).
Also furnished Chased A (FRACTION).

No. 179. Round.

Chased, per dozen, $7.50 (FOX).

No. 175.

Chased, per dozen, $8.50 (FORTUNATE).

No. 179. Round.

Chased A., per dozen, $7.50 (FOUNTAIN).
Also furnished Chased B (FOWL).

GOLD LINED, $3.00 PER DOZEN EXTRA; GOLD INLAID AND GOLD LINED, $6.00 PER DOZEN EXTRA.

GOLD AND SILVER PLATE.

No. 271.
Chased, . per dozen, $5.50 (FICTITIOUS).
Satin, Chased, per dozen, 5.50 (FIERCELY).

No. 261.
Satin, Engraved, per dozen, $8.50 (FIDGETY).

No. 240.
Chased, . per dozen, $6.50 (APPLAUD).

No. 173.
Chased, . per dozen, $4.00 (FOSTER).

No. 192.
Chased, . per dozen, $6.00 (FOUGHT).
No. 191. OVAL.
Chased, . per dozen, $6.50 (FOUND).

No. 172.
Chased, . per dozen, $3.50 (FOSSIL).

No. 221.
Per dozen, $2.50 (FOSSE).

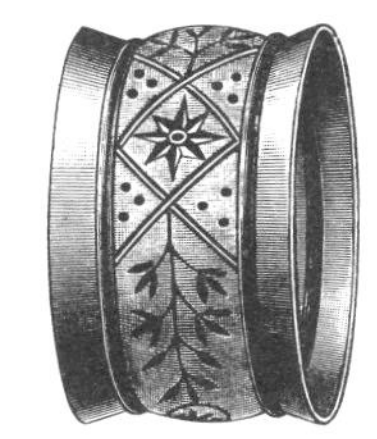

No. 263.
Chased, . per dozen, $3.75 (DRASTIC).
Satin, Chased, per dozen, 3.75 (DROSKY).

No. 264.
Chased, . per dozen, $3.75 (DRAUGHT).
Satin, Chased, per dozen, 3.75 (DROWSY).

No. 265.
Chased, . per dozen, $4.00 (DRILLING).
Satin, Chased, per dozen, 4.00 (FIBRINE).

NICKEL SILVER NAPKIN RINGS.

No. 055.
Plain or Satin, . per dozen, $12.00 (FRANCHISE).

No. 065.
Plain or Satin, . per dozen, $13.50 (FRANK).

No. 060.
Plain or Satin, . per dozen, $13.50 (FRATERNAL).

No. 069.
Satin, . . per doz., $12.00 (FIGURATE).
Satin, Engraved, per doz., 15.00 (FILTRATE).

No. 067.
Satin, . . per doz., $10.50 (FISTIC).
Satin, Engraved, per doz., 13.50 (FINDING).

No. 066.
Satin, . . per doz., $10.00 (FILLIP).
Satin, Engraved, per doz., 13.00 (FINICAL).

No. 068.
Satin, . . per doz., $12.00 (FILMY).
Satin, Engraved, per doz., 15.00 (FIRMLY).

NICKEL SILVER, SILVER SOLDERED.

NUT BOWLS, ETC.

(ONE-THIRD SIZE.)

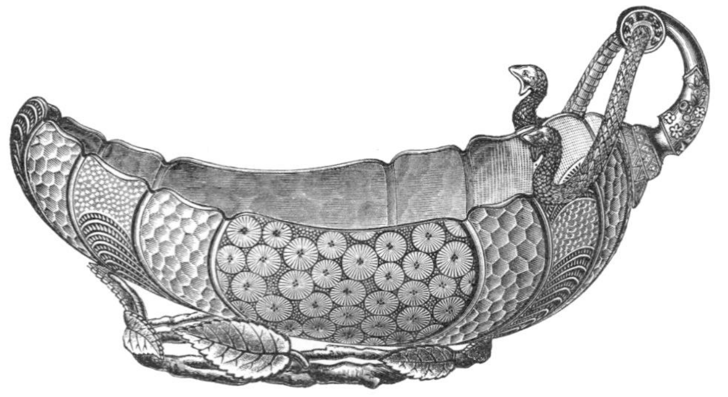

No. 31.

Moorish, Old Silver, Gold Lined, . $22.50 (FLOWERET).
Moorish, Gold Inlaid and Gold Lined, 28.50 (FOREFOOT).

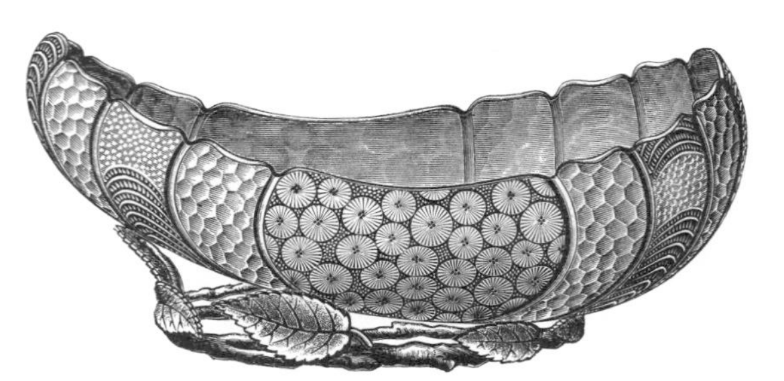

No. 24.

Moorish, Old Silver, Gold Lined, . $20.00 (FORECASTLE).
Moorish, Gold Inlaid and Gold Lined, 26.00 (FOREHEAD).

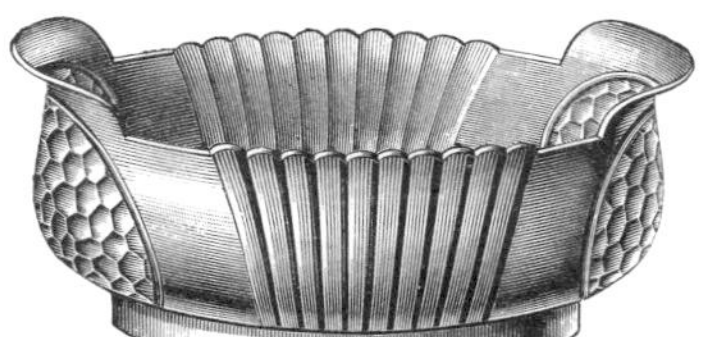

No. 22. HAMMERED.
Gold Lined, . $10.00 (FLATIRON).

No. 28.
Gold Lined, Satin Quilted, $22.50 (FORESAIL).

No. 25.
Gold Lined, Satin Fluted, $21.00 (FISHHOOK).

No. 23. PERSIAN CHASED.
Gold Lined, . . $11.00 (FORENOON).
Gold Inlaid, . 13.00 (FORETASTE).

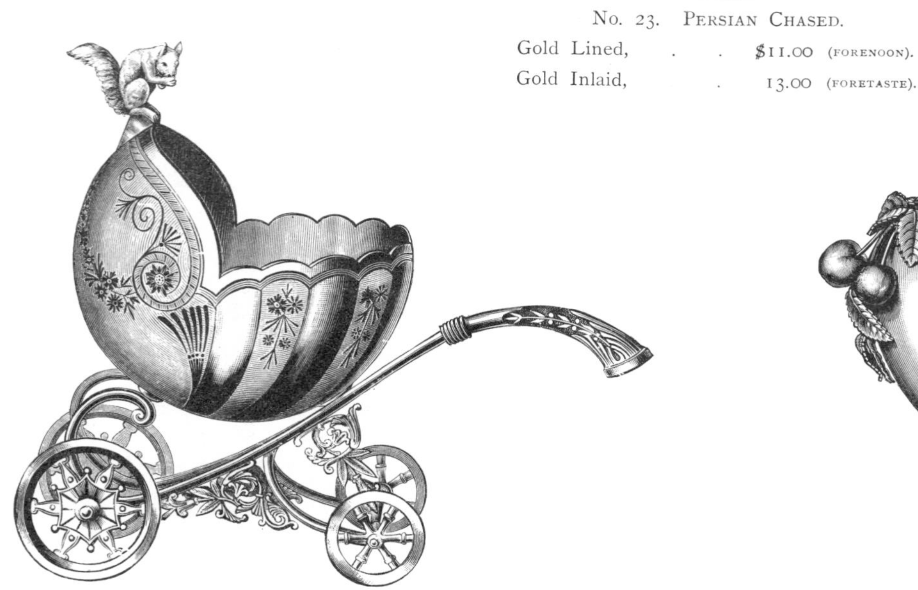

No. 6.
Engraved, Gold Lined, . $21.00 (DISINHERIT).

No. 17.
Gold Lined, . . . $22.50 (HEMPEN).
Gold Inlaid and Gold Lined, 27.50 (HENCHMAN).

GOLD AND SILVER PLATE.

No. 7.
Damascene, Silver, Gold Inlaid, $12.50 (DISMANTLE).

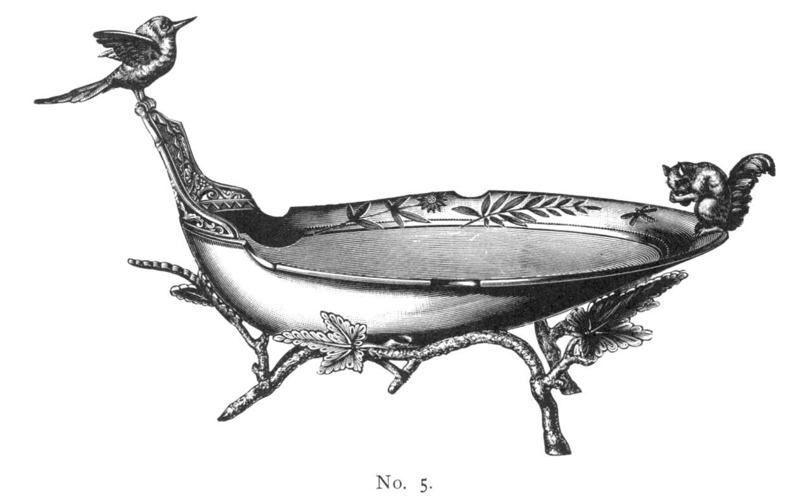

No. 5.
Plain, Gold Lined, . . $13.50 (DISK).
Chased, Gold Lined, . . 14.50 (DISLODGE).

No. 13. Gold Lined.
Hammered and Applied, . . $16.00 (HAMES).
Hammered and Applied, Old Silver, 18.00 (HAMSTRING).

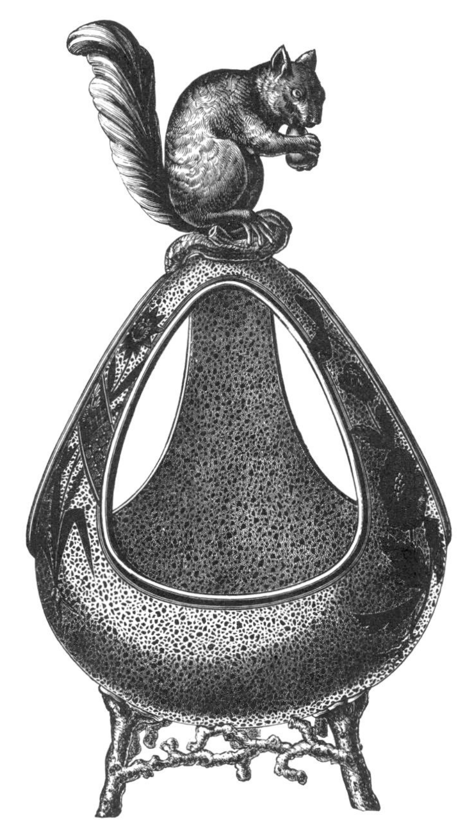

No. 8.
Damascene, Chased, Gold Lined, $20.00 (DISH).
Russian Gold, Inlaid, . . 24.00 (DISHEVEL).

No. 12. Gold Lined.
Satin, ... $13.50 (DIVAN).
Hammered and Applied, Old Silver, 16.00 (DIVERSE).

No. 1.
Satin, Gold Lined, . . $18.00 (DISINFECT).

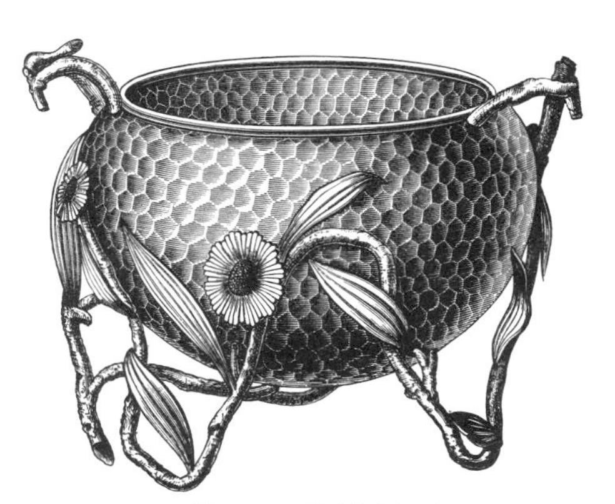

No. 10. Gold Lined.
Hammered, Old Silver, . $22.00 (DIAPASON).
Hammered, Old Silver, XX Gilt, 25.00 (DIARY).

GOLD AND SILVER PLATE.

SALAD OR FRUIT BOWL.

		Hammered, Gold Lined.	Hammered and Applied, Gold Lined.
No. 15.	Eight Half Pints,	$15.00 (HANKER).	$16.00 (HAPPEN).
No. 16.	Twelve Half Pints,	17.50 (HARBINGER).	18.50 (HARDEN).

No. 20. NUT OR SALAD BOWL.

Satin, Gold Lined, . . . $16.00 (FIRESIDE).
Satin, Engraved, Gold Lined, . 17.00 (FISHWIFE).

No. 19.

Satin, Gold Lined, . . $13.00 (FISHERY).

No. 27.

Old Silver, Gold Lined, . $14.00 (FIREPROOF).

No. 9.

Damascene, Chased, . . $16.00 (DISJOIN).
Damascene, Chased, Gold Lined, 18.00 (DISJOINTED).
Damascene, Chased, Gold Inlaid, 20.00 (DISJOINT).

No. 11.

Satin, Gold Lined, . . . 13.00 (DISUNITE).
Hammered, Old Silver, Gold Lined, 15.00 (DISUSE).

No. 4.

Satin, Gold Lined, . $15.00 (DISGUISE).

No. 2. ACORN.

Plain or Satin, Gold Lined, . $23.00 (DISGORGE).

GOLD AND SILVER PLATE.

SATIN C, SALAD, NUT OR FRUIT BOWL, Gold Lined.

	Diameter.	Capacity.	Old Silver.	X Gold Inlaid.
No. 4.	8½ inches.	10 Half Pints.	$12.50 (HEAD).	$15.50 (HEADWAY).
No. 6.	9½ inches.	13 Half Pints.	15.00 (HEAP).	18.00 (HEARKEN).
No. 5.	10 inches.	17 Half Pints.	16.50 (HEEDFUL).	19.50 (HEELTAP).

No. 3. SALAD BOWL. Gold Lined.

Hammered, ... $26.00 (DESPOND).
Hammered, Chased, . . . 31.00 (DESPOT).
XX Gilt, Hammered, Chased, . 36.00 (DESSERT).

SALAD BOWL.

No. 1, ... $45.00 (DESTINATION).

No. 29. NUT BOWL.

Satin, Gold Lined, ... $20.00 (PLUMB).
Moorish, Old Silver, Gold Lined, . 24.00 (PLENITUDE).

NICKEL SILVER, SILVER SOLDERED.

No. 0600. ICE OR SALAD BOWL.

Satin, Eight Half Pints, . $24.00 (PLEBEIAN).

No. 0610. FRUIT OR ICE BOWL.

Satin, ... $30.00 (PLIANCY).
Satin, Gold Lined, . . 33.00 (PIQUANCY).
Chased, Gold Lined, . 37.50 (PINEAPPLE).

No. 0620. ICE BOWL.

Satin, Eight Half Pints, . $25.00 (PLENARY).

PAPER WEIGHTS, ETC.

(HALF SIZE.)

No. 15. PAPER KNIFE.

Satin, Engraved, Old Silver, . . $2.25 (PIRATE).
Satin, Engraved, Old Silver, Gold Inlaid, 2.75 (PIQUE).

No. 14. PAPER KNIFE.

Old Silver, ... $2.50 (PINCHERS).
Old Silver, Gold Inlaid, . 3.00 (PINCH).

No. 6.

Silver, . . $1.00 (PATTER).
Old Silver, . 1.25 (PICKED).

No. 2. DOGS FIGHTING.

Silver, . . $2.25 (PATRIOTIC).
Old Silver, . 2.50 (PINK).

No. 7.

Silver, . . $1.75 (PEBBLY).
Old Silver, . 2.25 (PHIZ).

No. 9. SPHINX.

Old Silver, $3.50 (PIGMY).

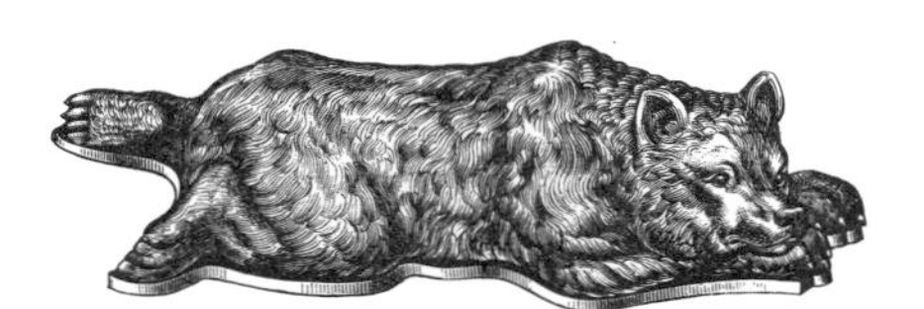

No. 12. BEAR.

Old Silver, . $4.25 (PICK).

No. 11. BULL.

Old Silver, . $3.75 (PIKE).

No. 3160. DOG AND BIRD.

Old Silver, ... $5.00 (WORMWOOD).
Old Silver, Gold Inlaid, . 6.00 (WORKBOX).

No. 13.

Old Silver, . . $6.00 (PAUCITY).

No. 10. HORSE.

Old Silver, . . $4.00 (PAVER).

PUFF BOXES, ETC.

(HALF SIZE).

PRICES INCLUDE PUFFS.

No. 8. Hammered Cover.

Silver, . . $3.50 (FIRSTLY).
Old Silver, . 4.00 (FLATLY).
Gold Inlaid, . 5.00 (FIRMNESS).
Gold Lined, $0.75 extra.

No. 10. Satin, Engraved.

Satin, . . . $4.50 (PEDANTIC).
Satin, Engraved, . 6.00 (PENITENCE).
Hammered, . . 5.50 (PENNATE).
Hammered, Old Silver, 6.00 (PENSILE).
Gold Lined, $1.00 extra.

No. 9.

Silver, . . $5.00 (PEDLER).
Old Silver, . 6.00 (PEEK).
Gold Inlaid, . 7.50 (PEEL).
Gold Lined, $1.00 extra.

No. 13.

Satin, . . . $5.00 (FILAMENT).
Satin, Engraved, . 5.50 (FIREARM).
Gold Lined. $1.00 extra.

No. 6.

Hammered, Old Silver, $4.00 (PERFECT).
Gold Lined, $0.75 extra.

No. 10.

Moorish, Old Silver, $6.50 (PERFIDY).
Moorish, Gold Inlaid, 8.00 (PERIODIC).
Gold Lined, $1.00 extra.

No. 11.

Embossed, . . . $6.50 (PERIGEE).
Embossed, Old Silver, . 8.00 (PERJURE).
Embossed, XX Gold Inlaid, 10.00 (PERMANENT).
Gold Lined, $1.00 extra.

No. 7.

Hammered, Old Silver, $5.00 (PEER).
Gold Lined, $0.75 extra.

PEN-WIPERS.

(HALF SIZE.)

No. 202.

Old Silver, . $2.75 (PERQUISITE).

No. 200.

Old Silver, . $2.00 (PERSECUTE).

No. 204.

Old Silver, . $3.00 (PERSONATE).

MUSTARD STANDS.

GLASS LINED.

(HALF SIZE.)

No. 17, . $3.75 (COXCOMB).

No. 31. With Spoon.

Satin, . . . $4.00 (PAGANIZE).

Moorish, Old Silver, 4.75 (PAINFUL).

No. 29. WEDGEWOOD.

With Spoon, . $3.75 (PACT).

No. 28.

With Spoon, . $4.00 (PETRIFY).

No. 32.

With Spoon, . $4.25 (PAINLESS).

No. 0205.

Nickel Silver, Silver Soldered.

Satin, . $5.50 (PERTLY).

No. 2, . $7.50 (CRACK).

No. 0210. Nickel Silver, Silver Soldered.

Satin, . $10.50 (PERSUASION).

No. 0200.

Nickel Silver, Silver Soldered.

Satin, . $4.75 (PERVIOUS).

No. 30, . $4.25 (COWHIDE).

No. 21, . $4.50 (COWL).

No. 15, . $4.50 (COWLICK).

No. 20, . $4.00 (COWSLIP).

TRADE MARK.
WHITE METAL.

INDIVIDUAL PEPPERS.

TRADE MARK
NICKEL SILVER.

(FULL SIZE.)

No. 70.

Silver, . . $1.00 (CURB).
X Gilt, . . 1.25 (CURDLE).

No. 67.

Silver, . . $1.00 (COUNTERPLOT).
Silver, Gilt Cap, 1.25 (COUNTERSIGN).

No. 68.

Silver, . . . $1.00 (COUNTRYSEAT).
Oxidized and Gilt, 1.25 (COUNTERSCARP).
Gilt, ... 1.50 (COUNTERVAIL).

No. 71.

Silver, . . $2.00 (CURRY).
X Gilt, . . 2.25 (CURTAIL).

No. 69.

Silver, . . $2.00 (CURRICLE).
X Gilt, . . 2.50 (CURRIER).

No. 04. PEPPER OR SALT.
Nickel Silver.

Silver Top, . . $1.25 (COUNTLESS).
Gilt Top, . . . 1.50 (COURAGEOUS).

No. 72.

Old Silver, . $2.25 (CURE).
X Gilt, . . 2.75 (CURFEW).
X Gilt, Oxidized, 3.00 (CURIOUS).

No. 65.

Silver, . $2.00 (COUNTERPOISE).
Gilt, . 2.50 (COUNTERPART).

No. 66.

Silver, . $2.00 (COUNSEL).
Gilt, . 2.50 (COUNTENANCE).

No. 73.

Old Silver, . . $2.25 (CURL).
X Gilt, . . . 2.75 (CURLEW).
X Gilt, Oxidized, . 3.00 (CURRANT).

GOLD AND SILVER PLATE.

(HALF SIZE.)

No. 5½, . $1.50 (COURIER).

No. 1. OWL.

Silver, . $2.00 (COURSER).
Gilt, . 2.25 (COURTSHIP).

No. 9. BEAR.

Silver, . $2.00 (COURSE).

No. 59.

Silver, . . $2.50 (CRAFTILY).
Silver, Gold Inlaid, 3.00 (CRAFTSMAN).

No. 54.

Silver, . . $2.25 (COW).
Silver, Gold Inlaid, 2.50 (COWRY).

No. 77.

Satin, $2.00 (PAPAL).

No. 76.

Satin, $2.00 (PANE).

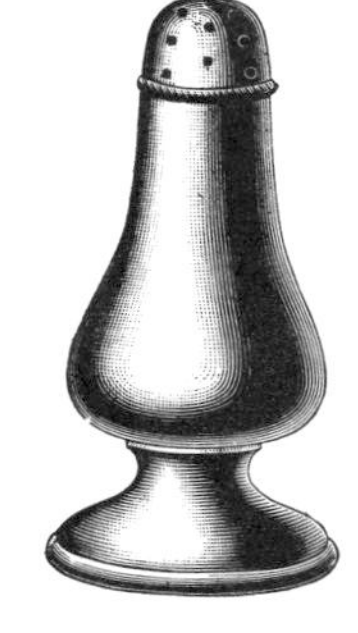

No. 15.

Plain, $1.75 (COURTESY).

No. 16.

Plain, $1.75 (COURTIER).

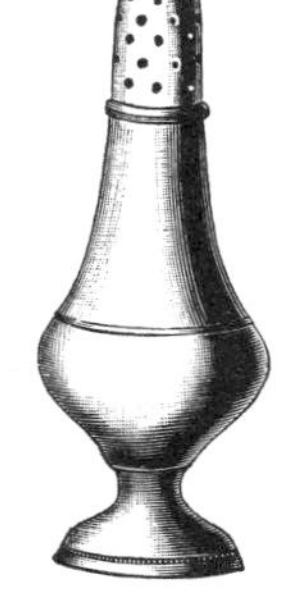

No. 01.

Nickel Silver.

Plain, . $5.00 (SANGAREE).
Engraved, 6.25 (SANGFROID).

No. 02.

Nickel Silver.

Plain, . $5.00 (SANDWICH).
Engraved, 6.25 (SANG).

No. 3.

Plain, . $2.75 (COVER).

No. 6.

Plain, . $3.00 (COVEY).
No. 5. Smaller.
Plain, . $2.75 (COURTLY).

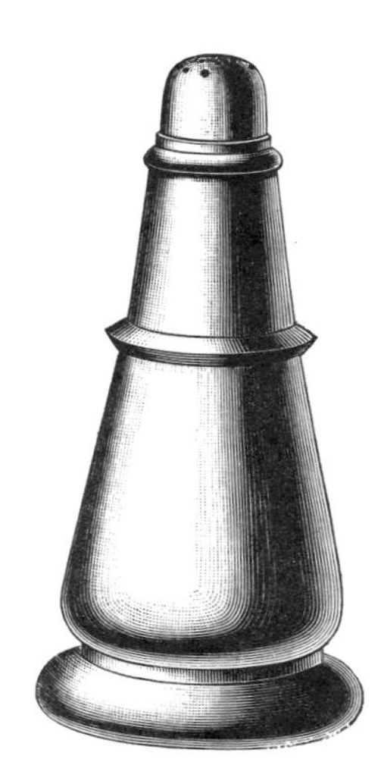

No. 4.

Plain, . $3.25 (COVERLET).
Engraved, 4.00 (COVERT).

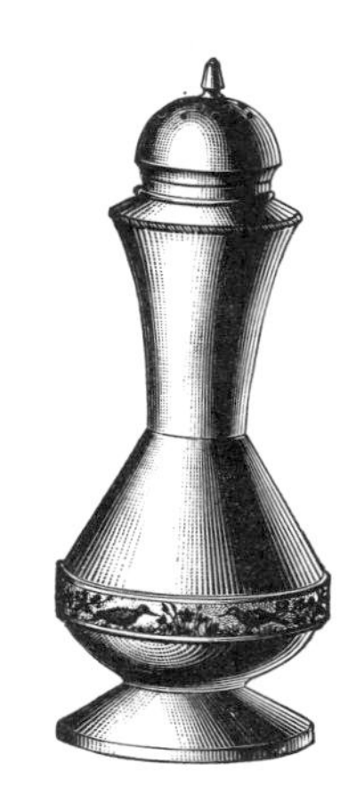

No. 7.

Plain, . $2.50 (COVET).

No. 3.

Engraved, . $3.00 (COWER).

TRADE MARK.
WHITE METAL.

GOLD AND SILVER PLATE.

TRADE MARK.
NICKEL SILVER.

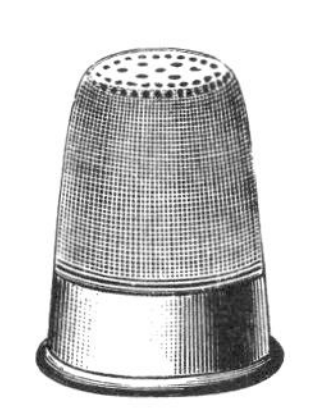

No. 8.
Thimble, . $2.00 (COURT).

No. 18.
Satin Engraved, $2.00 (COUSINLY).

No. 18.
Plain, . $1.75 (COUSIN).
Satin, . 1.75 (COWELL).

No. 17.
Satin, . $1.75 (COVE).
Satin, Engraved, 2.00 (COWLES).

No. 1½.
Plain, . $1.25 (COURTEOUS).
Satin, . 1.25 (COURTING).

No. 50.
Gold Inlaid, $2.00 (COURTEOUSLY).

No. 51.
Gold Inlaid, $2.50 (COURTYARD).

No. 74. MOORISH.
Old Silver, $3.50 (PITCHY).
No. 75. Smaller.
Moorish, Old Silver, $2.50 (PLIANT).

No. 53.
Silver, . . $2.25 (COVERTLY).
Silver, Gold Inlaid, 2.75 (COVETOUS).

No. 57.
Silver, . $4.00 (CRAGGY).
Gold Inlaid, 4.50 (CREAMY).

TABLE SALTS.

No. 10, . $3.00 (CRANE).
(One-Third Size.)

No. 11. Gilt, . $3.00 (CRANIUM).
Ruby Lining.
(One-Third Size.)

No. 9, . $2.25 (CRANBERRY).
(One-Third Size.)

No. 151.
With Spoons, . . $3.50 (PINCASE).
(Half Size.)

No. 153. Cut Glass.
With Spoons, . . $6.00 (PINNATE).
(Half Size.)

No. 152.
With Spoons, . . $4.50 (PHEASANT).
(Half Size.)

SALTS.

No. 35.

Gold Lined, . per dozen, $10.00 (CRACKER).
Plush Case, for ½ dozen, $4.00 extra (STAGER).
Plush Case, for 1 dozen, 5.25 extra (STAIR).
(Full Size.)

No. 020. Nickel Silver.

Satin, Gold Lined, . per dozen, $12.25 (CRAGGED).
(Full Size.)

No. 32. Cut Glass.

PER DOZEN.
Mounted on Gold Lined Stand, $10.00 (COY).
Case for ½ dozen, . . $4.00 extra (COWHERD).
Case for 1 dozen, . . 5.25 extra (COZEN).
(Full Size.)

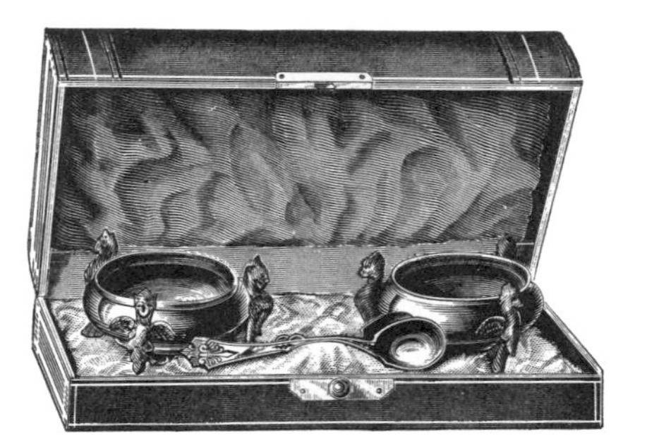

No. 18.

PER PAIR.
Gold Lined, . . $4.50 (CRAVEN).
With Case and Spoons, 8.50 (CRAW).
(One-Third Size.)

No. 31.

Gold Lined, . per dozen, $9.00 (CRAB).
Plush Case for ½ dozen, $4.00 extra (SURCHARGE).
Plush Case for 1 dozen, 5.25 extra (SUPREMELY).
(Full Size.)

No. 28.

PER PAIR.
Gold Lined, . . . $6.00 (LEAFAGE).
With Case and Spoons, 10.50 (CRAWL).
(One-Third Size.)

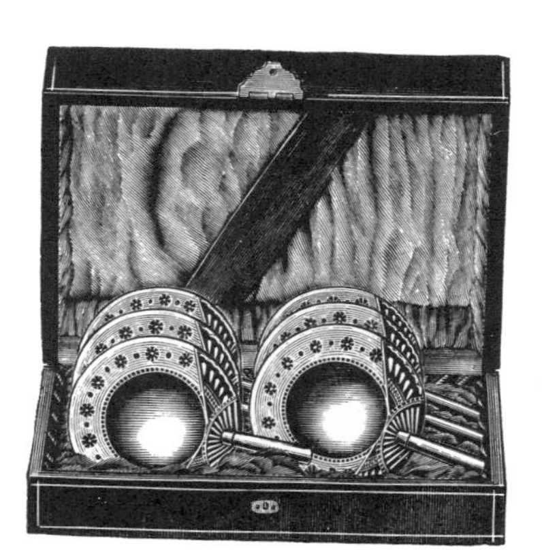

No. 46. INDIVIDUAL SALTS.

X Gold Lined, . per dozen, $18.00 (CRAFT).
Case for ½ dozen, . $4.50 extra (CRAM).
Case for 1 dozen, . 6.00 extra (CRAG).
(One-Third Size.)

No. 29.

PER PAIR.
Gold Lined, ... $6.50 (CRAZY).
With Morocco Case and Spoons, 11.00 (CREAK).
(One-Third Size.)

GOLD AND SILVER PLATE.

No. 148. Hammered.

Gold Lined, . per dozen, $12.00 (PAREGORIC).

No. 1480. PLUSH CASE.

Containing one-half dozen 148 Salts, Gold Lined ;
one-half dozen Individual Salt Spoons, Gold Lined, $13.50 (PANT)

(Full Size.)

No. 040. Nickel Silver.

Gold Lined, per dozen, $12.00 (PALATINE).

(Full Size.)

No. 149. Satin.

Gold Lined, . per dozen, $10.00 (PALENESS).

No. 1490. PLUSH CASE.

Containing one-half dozen 149 Salts, Gold Lined ;
one-half dozen Individual Salt Spoons, Gold Lined, $12.50 (PALLID).

(Full Size.)

No. 1470. PLUSH CASE.

Containing one-half dozen 147 Salts, Moorish, Gold Lined ;
one-half dozen Individual Salt Spoons, Gold Lined, $13.00 (PARRY).

No. 147. SALTS.

Moorish, Gold Lined, . per dozen, $11.00 (PANG).

No. 040. Nickel Silver.

Gold Lined, per dozen, $12.00 (COURANT).
Half dozen in Plush Case, 9.75 (COVERTURE).
One dozen in Plush Case, 16.75 (CRANIAL).

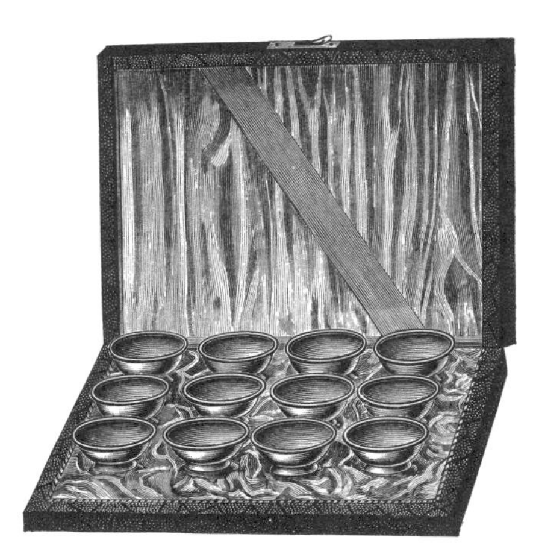

No. 020. Nickel Silver.

Gold Lined, per dozen, $12.25 (PARSE).
Half dozen in Plush Case, 9.50 (PARDONER).
One dozen in Plush Case, 16.50 (PARENTAL).

No. 1500. PLUSH CASE.

Containing one-half dozen 150 Salts, Satin, Gold Lined ;
one-half dozen Individual Salt Spoons, Gold Lined, $15.00 (PARASOL).

No. 150. SALTS.

Satin, Gold Lined, . per dozen, $13.50 (PALESTRA).

No. 0400. PLUSH CASE.

Containing one-sixth dozen 04 Peppers ; one-half dozen 040 Salts, Gold Lined ;
and one-half dozen Individual Salt Spoons, Gold Lined, $16.75 (PALPABLY).
Nickel Silver.

(One-Third Size.)

STAR SALTS AND PEPPERS.

(HALF SIZE.)

PRICES PER DOZEN. DISCOUNT SAME AS HOLLOW WARE.

No. 337, . $7.50.

No. 341, . $11.00.

No. 335, . $16.00.

No. 343, . $9.50.

No. 342, . $11.00.

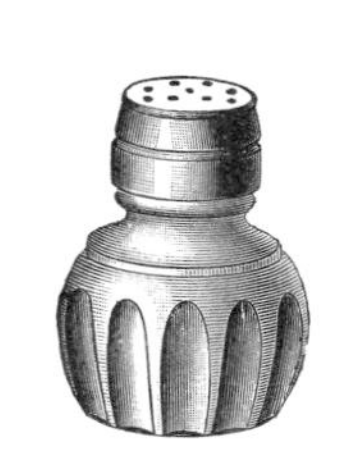
No. 336, . $7.50.

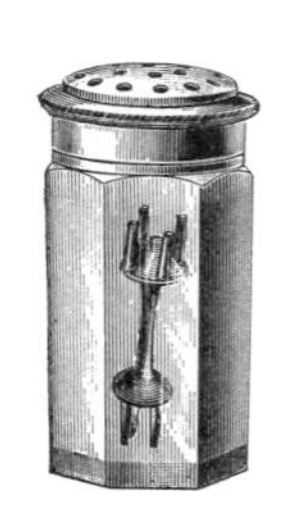
No. 345, . $10.50.

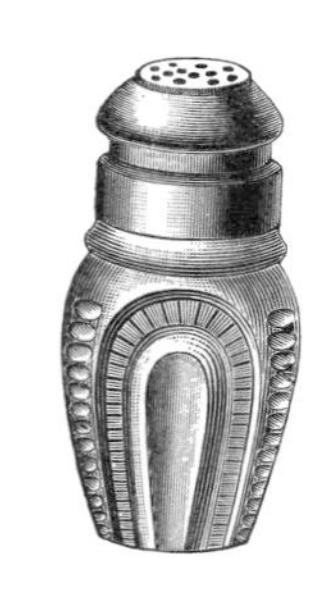
No. 344, . $12.00.

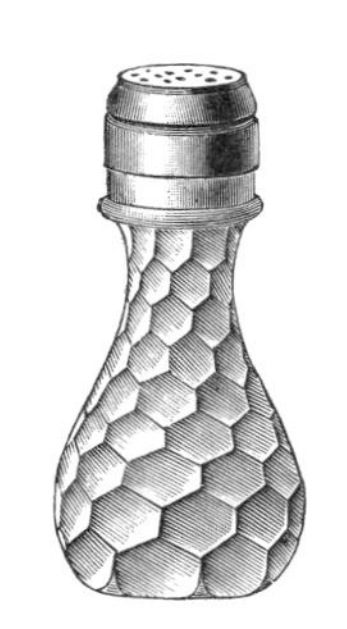
No. 339, . $10.00.

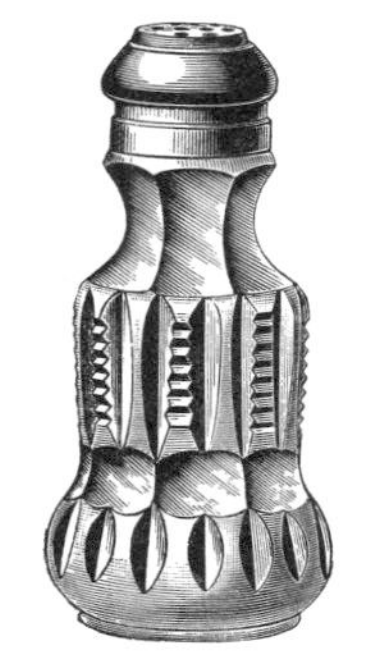
No. 320, . $10.00.

No. 334, . $12.00.

No. 273, . $4.75.

No. 270, . $5.00.

No. 269, . $4.75.

No. 261, Assorted, $5.00.

No. 265, . $6.00.

No. 267, . $4.75.

No. 268, . $4.75.

No. 257, Ruby, $8.00.

No. 262, Assorted, $5.00.

No. 255, . $6.00.

No. 264, . $5.00.

No. 272, . $6.00.

No. 271, . $5.00.

TRADE MARK.
WHITE METAL.

GOLD AND SILVER PLATE.

TRADE MARK.
NICKEL SILVER.

No. 311.

Per dozen, . $9.00.

No. 317. Saloon.

Per dozen, . $10.00.

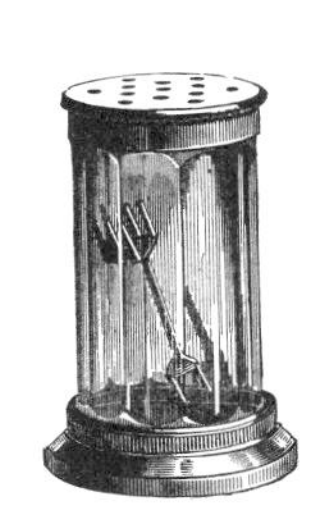

No. 313.

Per dozen, . $10.00.

No. 305.

Per dozen, . $11.00.

No. 306.

Per dozen, . $13.50.

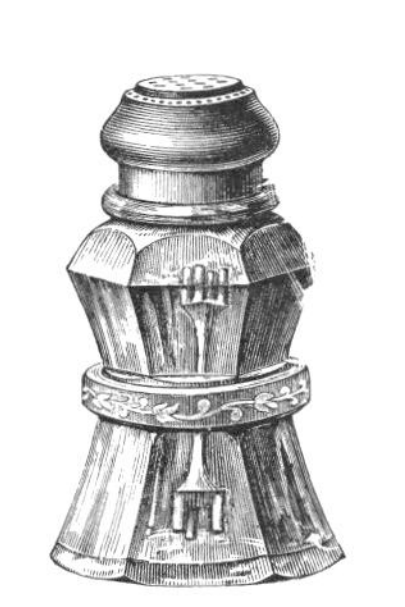

No. 315.

Per dozen, . $12.00.

No. 302.

Per dozen, . $30.00.

(Three-Quarter Size.)

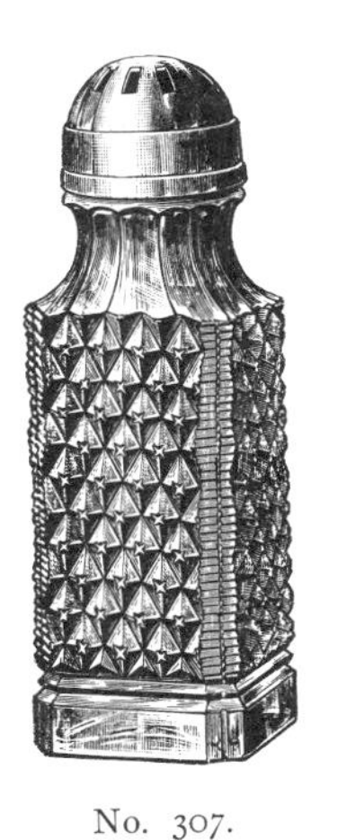

No. 307.

Per dozen, . $24.00.

(Three-Quarter Size.)

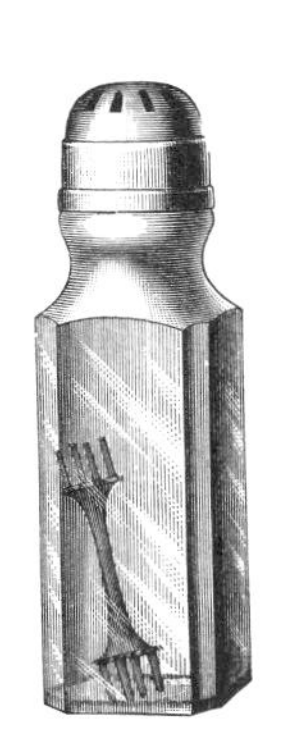

No. 308.

Per dozen, . $10.00.

No. 309.

Per dozen, . $30.00.

No. 4. Plain Individual.

	Per Gross.
Metal Caps, .	$18.00.
Plated Caps, .	21.00.

No. 3. Plain Saloon.

	Per Gross.
Metal Caps, .	$27.00.
Plated Caps, .	33.00.

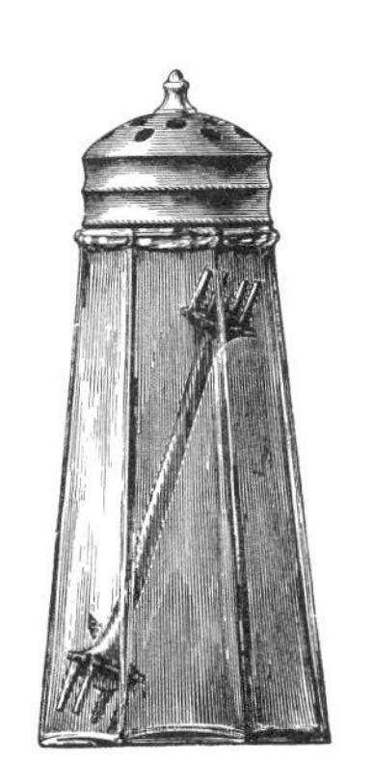

No. 1. Fluted Saloon.

	Per Gross.
Metal Caps, .	$27.00.
Plated Caps, .	33.00.

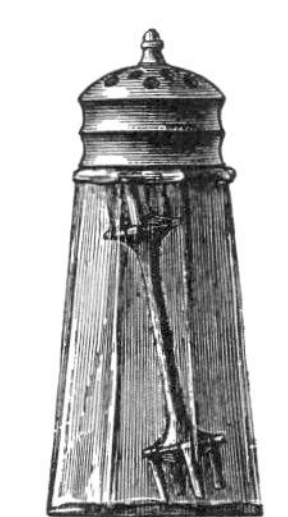

No. 6. Fluted Individual.

	Per Gross.
Metal Caps, .	$18.00.
Plated Caps, .	21.00.

DISCOUNT SAME AS HOLLOW WARE.

PORCELAIN LINED ICE URNS.

(ONE-THIRD SIZE.)

No. 1871. CHASED.

2½ gallons, .	$90.00 (CADET).	6 gallons, .	$150.00 (CAKE).
3 gallons, .	100.00 (CAGE).	8 gallons, .	180.00 (CALASH).
4 gallons, .	120.00 (CAJOLE).	10 gallons, .	250.00 (CALICO).

The above Urn, Metal Lined, only in 10-gallon size.

No. 1870. CHASED.

3 quarts, .	$36.00 (CALL).	3 gallons, .	$112.00 (CAME).
5 quarts, .	58.00 (CALM).	4 gallons, .	135.00 (CAMEO).
8 quarts, .	80.00 (CALVE).	6 gallons, .	160.00 (CAMP).
10 quarts, .	96.00 (CAM).	8 gallons, .	190.00 (CAMPHOR).

PORCELAIN LINED.

GOLD AND SILVER PLATE.

For Flat Ware see last pages of this Catalogue.

No. 62. Five Gallons. Chased, . $325.00 (enrobe). Chased, Gold Inlaid, $375.00 (enthrall).

PORCELAIN LINED.

No. 1872.

	Plain or Satin.	Hammered.
2 gallons, .	$50.00 (PALLMALL).	$56.00 (PALMARY).
3 gallons, .	65.00 (PALMATE).	74.00 (PANCAKE).
4 gallons, .	80.00 (PATRICIAN).	92.00 (PASTORAL).

No. 1873.

	Plain or Satin.	Hammered.
2 gallons, .	$70.00 (PASSIVELY).	$78.00 (PARTAKER).
3 gallons, .	90.00 (PLURALIST).	102.00 (PLUMY).
4 gallons, .	110.00 (PLUMPLY).	126.00 (PLUM-PIE).

PORCELAIN LINED.

No. 59.

Chased, ... $62.50 (WORSTED).
Chased, Gold Inlaid, . 75.00 (WORTH).

Goblets Gold Lined,

No. 54. CHASED.

Chased, ... $80.00 (CLUE).
Chased, Gold Inlaid, . 100.00 (CLUMP).

Goblets and Slop Bowl Gold Lined.

PORCELAIN LINED

ICE PITCHER AND TILTING SETS.

(One-Third Size.)

The following Pitchers have PATENT PORCELAIN LININGS, which are enameled on Hard Metal, and cannot be cracked or broken by rough usage. This specialty is valued for retaining purity and coolness as well as for its chemical qualities, the water not coming in contact with any metal surface whatever. The simplicity, cleanliness, and durability of the interior construction of these Pitchers render it unnecessary ever to remove the lining, thus saving no little trouble to the purchaser.

All excepting Single Plate Ice Pitchers furnished with Metal Linings, if desired, at a reduction in price of $3.00 each.

No. 66. Tilting Pitcher Set.

Goblets and Slop Bowl Gold Lined.

Brocade, Embossed, Chased, ... $125.00 (gaffer).

Brocade, Embossed, Chased, XX Gold Inlaid, . . 150.00 (gage).

No. 238.

Satin, ... $17.00 (PROPOSE).
Satin, Old Silver Borders, 18.00 (PROPEL).

No. 220.

Hammered, ... $18.00 (PRECLUSIVE).
Embossed, Chased, . 19.00 (PREDICTION).

No. 15. Repousse Tilting Pitcher Set.
Goblets and Slop Bowl, Gold Lined, . $60.00 (CAST).

No. 65. Brocade, Embossed Tilting Pitcher Set.
Goblets and Slop Bowl, Gold Lined, . $75.00 (PRAGMATIC).

GOLD AND SILVER PLATE.

No. 233. Satin Engraved Ice Pitcher Set.

Set complete, . $54.50 (polisher).

Pitcher, ... $19.00 (preface).

Goblets, Gold Lined, each, . 4.75 (polarity).

Slop Bowl, Gold Lined, . 7.50 (political).

No. 85—16 inch Waiter, . 18.50 (politely).

Patent Plate Glass Protector, $2.50 extra (pomp).

No. 73. Satin Engraved Band Tilting Pitcher Set.

Goblets and Slop Bowl Gold Lined, . . . $42.50 (pomace).

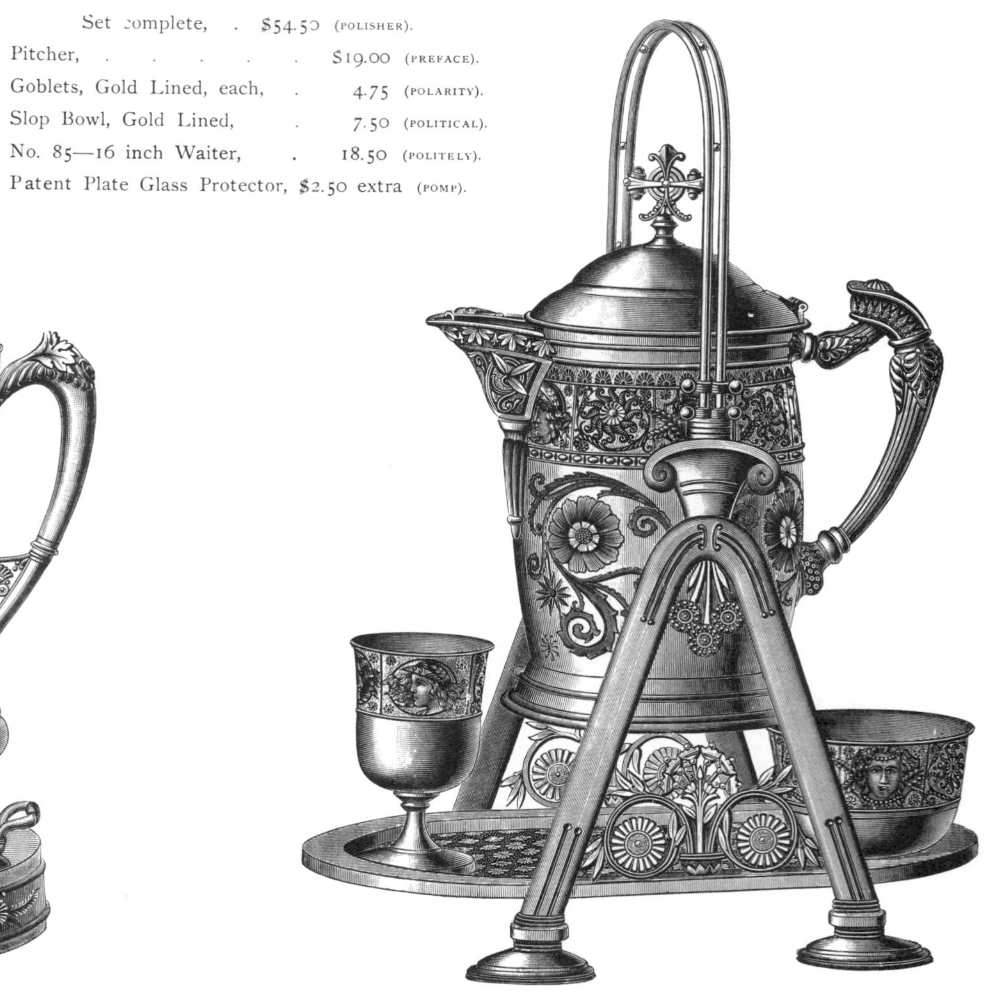

No. 74. Chased Tilting Pitcher Set.

Goblets and Slop Bowl Gold Lined.

Satin, Old Silver Border, . . $47.00 (pluvious).

Chased, Old Silver Border, . . 49.50 (polity).

No. 232. Chased Ice Pitcher Set.

Set complete, . $54.00 (prairie).

Pitcher, ... $20.00 (precursive). Goblets, Gold Lined, each, $4.75 (precocious).

No. 105—16 inch Waiter, 17.00 (precocity). Slop Bowl, Gold Lined, . 7.50 (predatory).

Satin Engraved, Price Same as Chased.

Patent Plate Glass Protector, . $2.50 extra (predicate).

No. 63. Tilting Pitcher Set.

Goblet and Slop Bowl Gold Lined.

Satin, $34.50 (gaffer). Hammered, $37.50 (gage).

No. 68. Satin, Engraved Tilting Pitcher Set.

Goblet and Slop Bowl Gold Lined.

Satin, $40.00 (pare). Satin, Engraved, $42.50 (pasty). Chased, $42.50 (pate).

GOLD AND SILVER PLATE.

No. 223. Brocade Chased.

Set complete, . $53.75 (ethic).
Pitcher, ... $19.00 (epistle).
Goblets, Gold Lined, each, 5.00 (equerry).
Slop Bowl, Gold Lined, . 7.75 (esteem).
No. 89—17 inch Waiter, . 17.00 (estrange).

No. 219. Chased Ice Pitcher Set.

Set complete, $53.00 (evade).
Pitcher, ... $20.00 (exaction).
Goblets, Gold Lined, each, . . 4.00 (exception).
Slop Bowl, Gold Lined, . . 6.50 (excision).
No. 88—16 inch Waiter, . . 18.50 (exclusive).
Patent Plate Glass Protector, $2.50 extra (exigence).

No. 56. Chased Tilting Pitcher Set.

Goblets and Slop Bowl Gold Lined.
Plain, $39.50 (excoriate). Chased, $42.50 (exculpate).

No. 61. Chased Tilting Pitcher Set.

Goblets and Slop Bowl Gold Lined.
Satin, $42.00 (excusable). Chased, $45.00 (executrix). Hammered, $45.00 (exemption).
(For style Hammered, see Ice Pitcher Set No. 221, page 265.)

Trade Mark.
White Metal.

GOLD AND SILVER PLATE.

Trade Mark.
Nickel Silver.

No. 58. Chased Tilting Pitcher Set.
Goblets and Slop Bowl Gold Lined.
Satin, $43.00 (gaiety). Chased, $45.00 (gainer).

No. 75. Satin Tilting Pitcher Set.
Goblets and Slop Bowl Gold Lined.
Silver, $39.00 (patois). Old Silver Borders, $41.50 (peal).

No. 221. Hammered Ice Pitcher Set.

	Satin.	Hammered.
Pitcher, ...	$19.00 (fancy).	$21.00 (fandango).
Goblets, Gold Lined, each,	4.00 (fantasm).	4.50 (fisher).
Slop Bowl, Gold Lined,	6.50 (fixity).	7.00 (flagging).

	Satin.	Hammered.
No. 93—16 inch Waiter,	$14.00 (flageolet).	$16.00 (gabardine).
Set of Five Pieces, complete,	47.50 (gabion).	53.00 (gable).
Patent Plate Glass Protector,	2.50 extra (gadfly).	

No. 221. Chased Ice Pitcher Set, price same as Hammered (see No. 61 Tilter, page 264).

No. 218. SATIN C. ICE PITCHER SET.

	Silver.		X Gold Inlaid.	
Set complete,	$50.00	(FAMILY).	$62.00	(FAMINE).
Pitcher,	18.00	(EXTERIOR).	22.00	(EXTERNAL).
Goblets, Gold Lined, each,	4.50	(EXTINGUISH).	5.50	(EXTOL).
Slop Bowl, Gold Lined,	6.50	(EXTRACT).	8.00	(EXTRACTION).
No. 85—16 inch Waiter,	16.50	(FALTER).	21.00	(FAME).

Patent Plate Glass Protector, $2.50 extra (FANCIER).

No. 26. CHASED TILTING PITCHER SET.

Goblet and Slop Bowl Gold Lined, . $42.00 (POLICE).

No. 55. CHASED TILTING PITCHER SET.

Goblet and Slop Bowl Gold Lined.

Plain, $30.00 (CLUNG). Chased, $33.00 (CLUSTER).

GOLD AND SILVER PLATE.

No. 194. CHASED.

Set complete, . . $46.50 (CATNIP).
Pitcher, ... 18.00 (CATTLE).
Goblets, Gold Lined, each, 3.75 (CAUGHT).
Slop Bowl, Gold Lined, 5.50 (CAUSE).
No. 47—16 inch Waiter, 15.50 (CAUDLE).

No. 194. CHASED D, ICE PITCHER SET.

Set complete, . $49.00 (CASTLE).
Pitcher, ... $19.00 (CASUAL).
No. 47—16 inch Waiter, 16.00 (CATCH).
Goblets, Gold Lined, each, $4.00 (CAT).
Slop Bowl, Gold Lined, . 6.00 (CATSUP).
Patent Plate Glass Protector, $2.50 extra (CATER).

No. 223.

Satin, . . $17.00 (POND).
Hammered, . 19.00 (POOL).

No. 216. CHASED PITCHER SET.

Set complete, . $52.00 (GAINSAY).
Pitcher, ... $19.00 (GAIN).
No. 82—16 inch Waiter, 17.00 (GAITER).
Goblets, Gold Lined, each, $4.50 (GALA).
Slop Bowl, Gold Lined, . 7.00 (GALAXY).
Patent Plate Glass Protector, $2.50 extra (GALE).

No. 236. Swing Pitcher.
Satin, Applied, . $21.00 (paynim).
Crystal, Chased, . 23.00 (pear).

No. 236. Goblet, Gold Lined.
Satin, Applied, . $4.00 (pointed).
Crystal, Chased, . 4.75 (poetize).

No. 235. Swing Pitcher.
Satin Shield, . . $20.00 (peaked).
Brocade, Chased, . 22.00 (polemic).

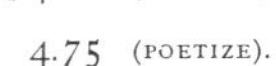

No. 241. Fountain Pitcher.
Porcelain Lined.
Satin, $28.00 (poet). Satin, Engraved, $30.00 (polar). Hammered, $30.00 (pole).
Metal Lined, $3.00 less.

PATENT FOUNTAIN PITCHER.

Patented April 28, 1885.

New, durable, simple in construction, works easily, will not get out of order, and keep ice longer than any other Ice Pitcher manufactured.

No. 240. Fountain Pitcher.
Porcelain Lined.
Satin, $28.00 (genesis). Chased, $30.00 (genet).
Metal Lined, $3.00 less.

Trade Mark.
WHITE METAL.

GOLD AND SILVER PLATE.

Trade Mark.
NICKEL SILVER.

No. 207.
Chased E, . $21.00 (CANONRY).

No. 70. Satin, Engraved Tilting Pitcher Set.
Goblet and Slop Bowl Gold Lined.
Satin, . $30.00 (PREFER). Satin, Engraved, . $32.50 (POUCH).

No. 234. Satin, Engraved Band Ice Pitcher Set.
Set complete, . $49.25 (POWDER).

Pitcher, . . . $17.50 (POULTICE). Goblets, Gold Lined, each, . $4.50 (POUNDAGE).
No. 108—17 inch Waiter, 16.00 (POULTRY). Slop Bowl, Gold Lined, . . 6.75 (POWERFUL).

Patent Plate Glass Protector, $3.00 extra (POWDERY).

No. 213. CHASED ICE PITCHER SET.

Set Complete, . $43.00 (CLASP).

Pitcher, ... $15.00 (CLASPER).

Goblets, Gold Lined, each, . . 4.00 (CLASSIC).

Slop Bowl, Gold Lined, . . 6.00 (CLASSIFY).

No. 75—12 inch Waiter, . . 14.00 (CLASS).

Patent Plate Glass Protector, . $2.00 extra (CLASSMATE).

No. 198. CHASED E, ICE PITCHER SET.

Set Four Pieces, complete, $29.75 (CHAMBER).

Pitcher, ... $15.00 (CHAMOIS).

Goblet, Gold Lined, . . . 3.25 (CHANCE).

Slop Bowl, Plain, Gold Lined, . 3.00 (CHANGE).

No. 303—12 inch Waiter, . 8.50 (CHANCEL).

Patent Plate Glass Protector, $2.00 extra (CHANNEL).

No. 208. CHASED ICE PITCHER SET.

Set complete, $57.75 (CAPER).

Pitcher, ... 22.00 (CAPITAL).

No. 69—18 inch Waiter, . . 20.00 (CAPSIZE).

Goblets, Gold Lined, each, . $4.50 (CAPON).

Slop Bowl, Gold Lined, . . 6.75 (CAPTAIN).

Patent Plate Glass Protector, $3.75 extra (CAPTIVE).

No. 227.

Plain, . . $14.00 (WORLD).
Hammered, . 15.50 (WORLDLY).

No. 226.

Plain, . $13.00 (WONDROUS). Hammered, . $14.50 (WOODBINE).

No. 229. Larger.

Satin, . $17.00 (PONDEROUS). Satin, Engraved, $19.00 (POODLE).

No. 41. CHASED TILTING PITCHER SET.

Goblet and Slop Bowl Gold Lined.

Satin, $34.00 (PORT). Chased, $37.00 (POST). Satin, Chased, $37.00 (POPPY).

No. 32. CHASED D, TILTING PITCHER SET.

Goblets and Slop Bowl Gold Lined, . $48.00 (CASTING).
Also furnished CHASED A, at same price.

No. 209.

Satin, . . $17.50 (CANNONADE).

Chased, . . 19.00 (CANNONIER).

No. 237. Metal Lined.

Satin, ... $12.00 (PORCELAIN).

Satin, Engraved, . 13.50 (POPULOUS).

No. 71. SATIN ENGRAVED TILTING PITCHER SET.

Goblet and Slop Bowl Gold Lined.

Metal Lined, ... $25.00 (PREDISPOSE).

No. 31. CHASED TILTING PITCHER SET.

Goblets and Slop Bowl Gold Lined, . $37.00 (CELLAR).

GOLD AND SILVER PLATE.

No. 224. Hammered.

	Satin.		Hammered.	
Set of Five Pieces, complete,	$45.00	(extensive).	$51.00	(extenuate).
Pitcher,	17.00	(export).	19.00	(exporter).
Goblets, Gold Lined, each,	3.50	(expose).	4.00	(expound).
Slop Bowl, Gold Lined,	6.00	(expugn).	7.00	(exquisite).
No. 89—17 inch Waiter,	15.00	(extant).	17.00	(extempore).

No. 214.

Plain,	$15.75	(climax).
Chased,	17.25	(clime).
Satin, Chased,	17.25	(pour).

No. 43. Chased Tilting Pitcher Set.

Goblet and Slop Bowl, Gold Lined, . . . $34.00 (click).

Plain, $32.00 (nautical). Satin, Chased, 34.00 (cliff).

No. 60. Hammered Tilting Pitcher Set.

Goblets and Slop Bowl Gold Lined.

Satin, $35.00 (galena). Hammered, $39.00 (galiot).

Trade Mark.
WHITE METAL.

GOLD AND SILVER PLATE.

Trade Mark.
NICKEL SILVER.

No. 210. Satin Engraved Ice Pitcher Set.

Set Complete, $52.50 (clinch).

Pitcher, ... $17.00 (clincher).
No. 72—17 inch Waiter, 19.00 (clinic).
Goblets, Gold Lined, each, . $4.50 (cling).
Slop Bowl, Gold Lined, . 7.50 (clink).

Patent Plate Glass Protector, $2.50 extra (clinker).

No. 69. Satin Shield Tilting Pitcher Set.

Cup Gold Lined.

Metal Lined, . . $24.00 (porcine).

No. 197. Chased D, Ice Pitcher Set.

Set complete, . $45.75 (cavil).

Pitcher, ... $17.00 (cavity).
No. 53—16 inch Waiter, 15.00 (cedar).
Goblets, Gold Lined, each, $4.00 (cease).
Slop Bowl, Gold Lined, 5.75 (celery).

Patent Plate Glass Protector, $3.00 extra (cell).

Also furnished Chased at same price (see Tilting Set No. 31, page 272) (ceil).

No. 187. Chased Ice Pitcher Set.

Set complete, . $40.00 (CHECKMATE).

No. 187 Pitcher, . $14.00 (CHEER).
No. 3—16 inch Waiter, 14.00 (CHERISH).
No. 1528 Goblets, Gold Lined, each, $3.50 (CHEMIST).
No. 49 Slop Bowl, Gold Lined, . 5.00 (CHERUF).

Patent Plate Glass Protector, $3.00 extra (PORTHOLE).

No. 181. Ice Pitcher.

Chased, . . $14.00 (CHEAP).
Chased D, . . 14.00 (CHECK).

No. 179. Ice Pitcher.

Satin, . . $12.00 (CHIEFTAIN).
Chased D, . 14.00 (CHICK).
Chased, . . 14.00 (CHIDE).

No. 179. Chased Ice Pitcher Set.

Set complete, . $41.00 (CHIEF).

No. 179 Chased Pitcher, $14.00 (CHILD).
No. 3—16 inch Waiter, 14.00 (CHIME).
No. 1523 Goblets, Gold Lined, each, $4.00 (CHILL).
No. 47 Slop Bowl, Gold Lined, . 5.00 (CHIN).

Patent Plate Glass Protector, $3.00 extra (POSTAGE).

GOLD AND SILVER PLATE.

No. 188. Ice Pitcher.

Chased, Single Wall, . $8.00 (choler).

No. 195.

Chased, Double Wall, . $9.50 (chop).

No. 231.

Chased, . . $10.50 (potable).

Satin, Chased, . 10.50 (potation).

No. 230.

Chased, . . $10.50 (poteen).

Satin, Chased, . 10.50 (potency).

No. 72. Chased Tilting Pitcher Set.

Cup Gold Lined.

Single Wall, . $16.50 (potently). Porcelain Lined, . $19.50 (pothook).

Pitchers on this page are Single Plate, and do not bear our Trade-Mark.

No. 404. EMBOSSED XX GOLD INLAID PITCHER.

Embossed Old Silver, -	$24.50	(TINFOIL).
Embossed XX Gold Inlaid,	34.50	(TINGLE).

No. 405. MOORISH GOLD INLAID PITCHER SET.

	Moorish, Old Silver.		Moorish, Gold Inlaid.	
Set complete, - -	$53.50	(STEALTHY).	$70.00	(STEADILY).
Pitcher, - - -	28.50	(STEER).	37.50	(STEERSMAN).
Goblet, Gold Lined, -	5.00	(STEPSON).	6.50	(STERNLY).
Slop Bowl, Gold Lined,	5.50	(STICKLE).	7.00	(STIFFLY).
No. 315, 13 inch Waiter,	14.50	(STIMULANT).	19.00	(STILLNESS).

No. 405. PERSIAN CHASED XX GOLD INLAID PITCHER SET.

Set complete, $77.50 (STOICAL).

Pitcher, $37.50 (STOICISM). No. 106, 12 inch Waiter, $26.50 (STONER). Goblet, $6.50 (STOOD). Slop Bowl, $7.00 (STOPGAP).

Patent Plate Glass Protector, $2.00 extra, (STOVER).

WATER PITCHERS.

(ONE-THIRD SIZE.)

No. 400. HAMMERED AND APPLIED.

	Hammered, Old Silver.	Hammered and Applied, Old Silver.	Hammered and Applied, Old Silver, XX Gold Inlaid.
Pitcher, . . .	$16.50 (GELID).	$19.50 (GERAMITE).	$23.00 (GENERAL).
Goblet, Gold Lined,	4.25 (GENDARME).	5.00 (GESTIC).	6.00 (GENERATE).
Slop Bowl, Gold Lined,	5.25 (GENDER).	6.00 (GESTURE).	7.00 (GENERIC).

No. 397. SATIN C, PITCHER SET.

	Old Silver.	X Gold Islaid.	XX Gold Inlaid.
Set complete, . .	$31.25 (GATHRING).	$38.25 (GAUGER).	$45.25 (GAUNT).
Pitcher, Eleven Half Pints,	13.50 (GAMBOGE).	16.50 (GAMESTER).	19.50 (GASCONADE).
Goblet, Gold Lined, .	4.25 (GASP).	5.25 (GASTRIC).	6.25 (GASTHRINGE).
No. 84—12 inch Waiter,	13.50 (GASEOUS).	16.50 (GASH).	19.50 (GASKET).

Patent Plate Glass Protector, . $2.00 extra (GAVEL).

No. 396. PITCHER.

	Old Silver.	X Gold Inlaid.	XX Gold Inlaid.
Six Half Pints, . .	10.00 (GAZE).	12.50 (GAZELLE).	15.00 (GAZETTE).

No. 401. HAMMERED PITCHER SET, IN CASE.

	Hammered.	Hammered, Old Silver.	Hammered, Old Silver, XX Gold Inlaid.
Set complete, . . .	$24.75 (GEOLOGY).	$26.75 (GEOMETRY).	$36.75 (GERM).
Pitcher, Nine Half Pints,	14.50 (GENEVA).	15.50 (GENIAL).	23.00 (GENIUS).
Goblet, Gold Lined, .	4.50 (GENTEEL).	5.00 (GENTIAN).	6.00 (GENTLE).
Slop Bowl, Gold Lined,	5.75 (GENTRY).	6.25 (GENUINE).	7.75 (GENUINELY).

Morocco Case, . $24.00 extra (GERMAN).

No. 408. SATIN ENGRAVED PITCHER SET.

	Satin.	Satin, Engraved.
Set complete, . . .	$33.75 (PREFIX).	$39.75 (PREJUDGE).
Pitcher, Eight Half Pints,	16.00 (PREPAY).	19.00 (PRIMAL).
Goblet, Gold Lined, .	3.50 (PRIMER).	4.25 (PRIMING).
Slop Bowl, Gold Lined,	4.25 (PRIMLY).	5.00 (PRIMNESS).
No. 102—11 inch Waiter,	10.00 (PRINCE).	11.50 (PRIMACY).

Patent Plate Glass Protector, . . $2.00 extra (PRIMAGE).

No. 402. Satin Embossed Chased Pitcher Set.

	Satin.	Satin Embossed, Chased.	Satin Embossed, XX Gold Inlaid.
Set of Four Pieces, . .	$28.50 (wrench).	$36.25 (wrestle).	$48.25 (weight).
Pitcher, Nine Half Pints, .	11.00 (wring).	14.00 (wrinkle).	20.00 (wrist).
Goblet, Gold Lined, . .	3.00 (write).	4.00 (yacht).	5.25 (yard).
Slop Bowl, Gold Lined, . .	5.00 (yawl).	6.25 (yeast).	8.00 (yeoman).
No. 96—13 inch Waiter, .	9.50 (yield).	12.00 (yonder).	15.00 (young).

Patent Plate Glass Protector, $2.50 extra (youth).

No. 405. Satin Engraved Pitcher Set.

	Satin.	Satin, Engraved.
Set complete, . .	$34.75 (prudish).	$42.75 (prudence).
Pitcher, Ten Half Pints,	17.00 (publicist).	21.00 (pugilist).
Goblet, Gold Lined, .	3.50 (pummel).	4.25 (pumpion).
Slop Bowl, Gold Lined,	4.25 (punctilio).	5.00 (punctuate).
No. 106—12 inch Waiter,	10.00 (pullback).	12.50 (publicly).

Patent Plate Glass Protector, $2.00 extra (proverbial).

No. 393. Hammered, XX Gold Inlaid Pitcher Set.

	Hammered.	Hammered and Applied.	Hammered and Applied, XX Gold Inlaid.
Set complete, . .	$29.50 (chord).	$37.00 (chore).	$45.50 (chose).
Pitcher, Ten Half Pints,	14.50 (chronic).	18.50 (chub).	22.50 (chum).
Goblet, Gold Lined,	4.50 (cicatrice).	6.00 (cider).	7.50 (cinnamon).
No. 64—11 inch waiter,	10.50 (chunk).	12.50 (churl).	15.50 (churn).

Patent Plate Glass Protector, $1.75 extra (pundit).

GOLD AND SILVER PLATE.

No. 86. Eight Half Pints.

Embossed, ... $10.00 (choral).

No. 409. Ten Half Pints.

Embossed, ... $15.00 (rarefy).
Embossed, Old Silver, . 17.50 (rarely).
Embossed, Old Silver,
XX Gold Inlaid, . 24.50 (ramp).

No. 394. Eight Half Pints.

Plain, ... $11.00 (wrap).
Hammered, ... 13.50 (wrapper).
Hammered and Applied, . 16.00 (wrath).

No. 406. Six Half Pints.

Moorish, ... $17.50 (rankness).
Moorish, Old Silver, . 20.00 (propitious).
Moorish, Gold Inlaid, . 26.00 (prophecy).

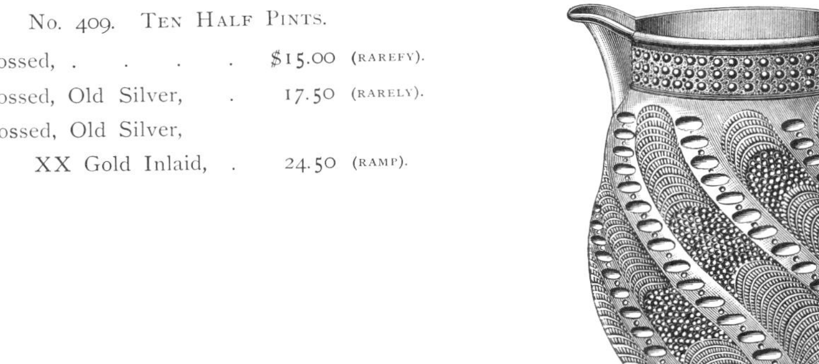

No. 407. Ten Half Pints.

Moorish, ... $19.00 (raiment).
Moorish, Old Silver, . 21.50 (prorogue).
Moorish, Gold Inlaid, . 27.50 (protean).

No. 87. Seven Half Pints.

Chased, . . . $10.50 (cistern).

No. 395. Fourteen Half Pints.

Plain, ... $12.50 (wreath).
Hammered, ... 15.00 (wreck).
Hammered and Applied, . 18.50 (wrecker).
Hammered and Applied, XX Gilt, 22.00 (wren).

No. 404. Eleven Half Pints.

Embossed, Silver, . . $23.00 (protocol).
Embossed, Old Silver, . 24.50 (provisory).
Embossed, XX Gold Inlaid, 34.50 (proximity).

GOLD AND SILVER PLATE.

No. 73. One Half Pint, . $3.50 (CLAD).
No. 88½. Two Half Pints, . 4.00 (CLAM).
No. 88. Three Half Pints, 5.25 (CLAMOR).
No. 390. Five Half Pints, . 7.50 (CLAMP).

NICKEL SILVER, SILVER SOLDERED.

No. 0880. One Half Pint, . $10.00 (REVISIT).
No. 0881. Two Half Pints, . 13.50 (REVIVE).
No. 0882. Three Half Pints, 16.50 (REVOKE).
No. 0883. Five Half Pints, . 20.00 (REVOLT).
No. 0884. Nine Half Pints, . 25.00 (REVOLVE).
No. 0885. Twelve Half Pints, 32.00 (REWARD).

No. 388. ELEVEN HALF PINTS.
Plain, . . . $11.00 (PREFERENCE).
Engraved, . . 13.50 (CIGAR).

No. 83. TEN HALF PINTS.
Plain, ... $10.00 (CITE).
No. 82. FOURTEEN HALF PINTS.
Plain, ... $11.00 (CIRCUIT).
With Ice Fender, . 11.75 (CIRCUS).

No. 392. NINE HALF PINTS.
Plain, ... $9.00 (CLAN).
No. 391. TWELVE HALF PINTS.
Plain, ... $10.00 (CLANK).
Ice Fender, $0.75 extra.

No. 85. NINE HALF PINTS.
Without Ice Fender, . $9.00 (CIVIC).
With Ice Fender, . 9.75 (CITY).
No. 77. TWELVE HALF PINTS.
Without Ice Fender, . $10.00 (CLAMBER).
With Ice Fender, . 10.75 (CLACK).

NICKEL SILVER, SILVER SOLDERED.

No. 0886. Eleven Half Pints, $30.00 (PREJUDICE).
No. 0887. Thirteen Half Pints, 36.00 (PRESERVER).

No. 389. TWELVE HALF PINTS.
Plain, . . . $11.50 (CIPHER).
Chased, . . 14.00 (CIRCLE).

SARDINE BOXES.

(ONE-THIRD SIZE.)

No. 05.

Nickel Silver, Silver Soldered, $13.50 (PHANTOM).

No. 1876, . . $10.00 (PHENIX).

No. 1867.

Satin, ...	$5.00	(PHIAL).
Engraved, . . .	6.00	(PHILTER).
Hammered, . . .	6.00	(PHRASE).
Hammered, and Applied,	6.50	(PHYSIC).

No. 1878, . . $10.00 (PERTAIN).

No. 1880, . . $10.50 (PERTINENT).

No. 1881, . . $11.50 (PERUKE).

No. 1874, Satin, Engraved, $10.50 (PICA).

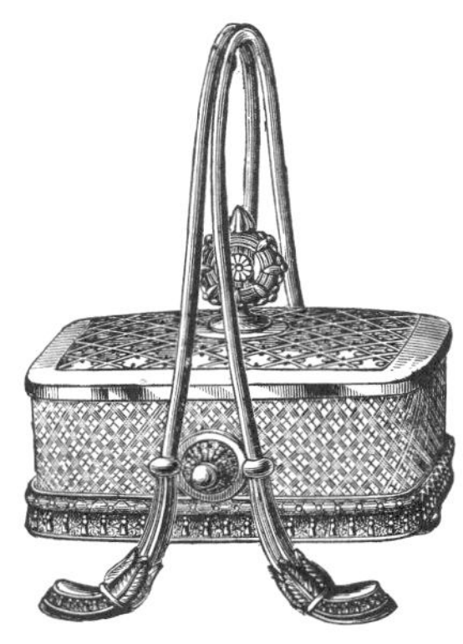

No. 1877, . . $12.00 (PICTURE).

No. 1875, . . $10.50 (PICKET).

SARDINE TONGS, $1.50 each (see Flat Ware) (PICNIC).

SPOON HOLDERS.

FOR ADDITIONAL PATTERNS SEE TEA SETS.

(ONE-THIRD SIZE.)

No. 1440.

Satin, Chased, . . $4.50 (PREMATURE).
Satin, Chased, Gold Lined, 5.25 (PRESENTLY).

No. 1425.

Chased, . . $6.00 (EVIDENCE).
Chased, Gold Lined, 7.00 (EVINCE).

No. 1434.

Gold Lined, . . . $6.50 (KINDLE).
Gold Inlaid and Gold Lined, 8.00 (KINGDOM).

No. 1432.

Gold Lined, . . . $6.50 (KINSHIP).
Gold Inlaid and Gold Lined, 7.50 (KIRTLE).

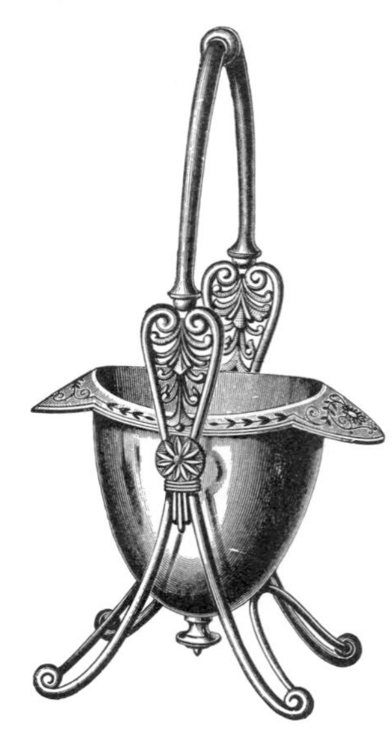

No. 1411.

Chased, Gold Lined, . $8.00 (EXECUTIVE).

No. 1430.

Gold Lined, . . . $6.50 (EXPEDITE).
Gold Inlaid and Gold Lined, 8.00 (EXPEL).

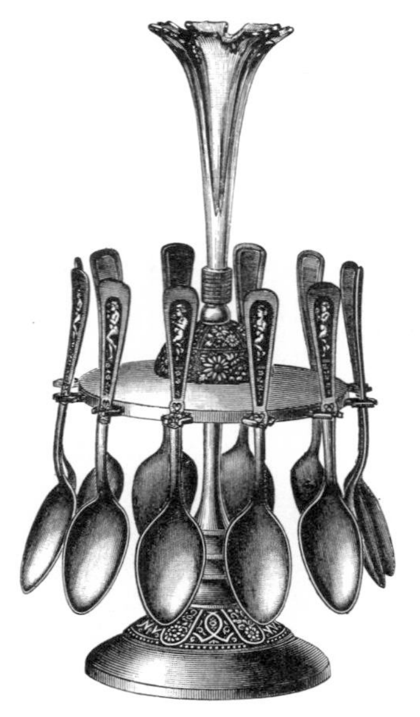

No. 1443. SPOON STAND.

With Vase, . . $6.75 (PRESIDENCY).
Price does not include Spoons.

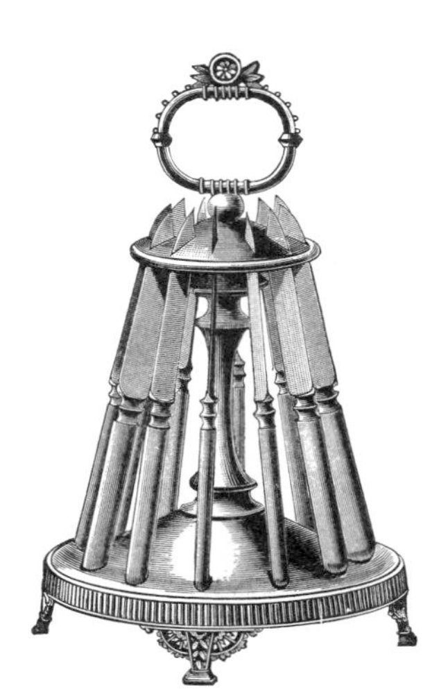

No. 1445. FRUIT KNIFE STAND.

Plain, . . . $5.50 (PRESSMAN).
Price does not include Knives.

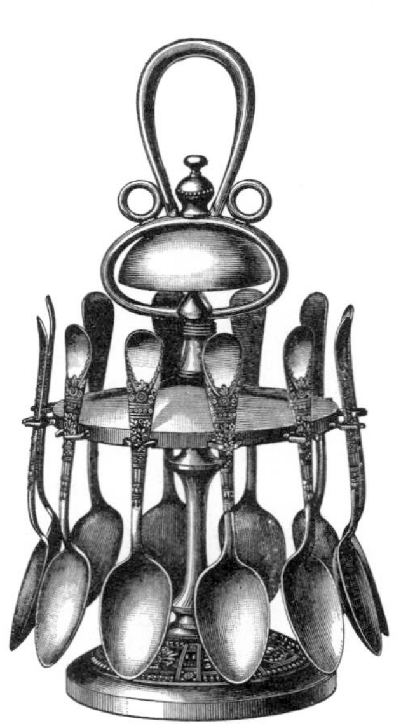

No. 1444. SPOON STAND.

With Bell, . . $8.25 (PRETENDER).
Price does not include Spoons.

GOLD AND SILVER PLATE.

No. 1441.

Chased, Gold Lined, . $5.75 (PROCREATE).
Satin, Chased, Gold Lined, 5.75 (PRODIGY).

No. 1433.

Gold Lined, . . $6.50 (LACQUER).
Old Silver, Gold Lined, 7.00 (PRODUCTION).

No. 1431.

Plain, Gold Lined, $6.75 (EXPECT).
Chased, Gold Lined, 7.50 (EXPEDIENT).

No. 1439.

Satin, Engraved, Gold Lined, $6.50 (PROBABLY).

No. 1422.

Plain, Gold Lined, $5.75 (EXCEED).
Chased, . . 5.75 (EXCEL).
Chased, Gold Lined, 6.50 (EXCEPT).

No. 1435. SPOON TRAY.

Satin, Gold Lined, . $8.50 (KNAPSACK).
Hammered, Gold Lined, 10.00 (LACERATE).

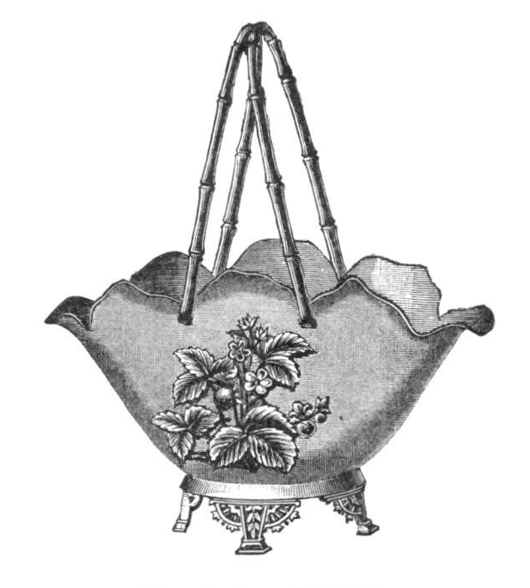

No. 1442. DOUBLE.

Satin, Applied, Gold Lined, $7.50 (PRONG).
Satin, Engraved, Gold Lined, 8.50 (PROBATE).

No. 1437.

Satin, Engraved, . . $6.25 (PRIVET).
Satin, Engraved, Gold Lined, 7.00 (PRIZE).

No. 1426.

Plain, Gold Lined, $8.50 (EXACT).
Chased, . . 8.00 (EXALT).
Chased, Gold Lined, 9.50 (EXALTED).

No. 1406.

Embossed, Gold Lined, $8.50 (EXECUTE).

No. 1404.

Chased, Gold Lined, $8.50 (EXECUTOR).

GOLD AND SILVER PLATE.

No. 1436.

Satin, Engraved, . . . $4.75 (PROMISER).
Satin, Engraved, Gold Lined, 5.50 (PREVENTIVE).

No. 1420.

Plain, Gold Lined, $4.75 (EVENTFUL).
Chased, . . 4.75 (EVER).
Chased, Gold Lined, 5.50 (EVERGREEN).

No. 1438.

Chased, ... $5.00 (PROPENSE).
Satin, Chased, . . 5.00 (PREVIOUSLY).
Satin, Chased, Gold Lined, 5.75 (PROJECTION).

No. 1421.

Plain, Gold Lined, $4.75 (EVOKE).
Chased, . . 4.75 (EVOLVE).
Chased, Gold Lined, 5.50 (EWE).

No. 1416.

Plain, Gold Lined, $4.25 (EVERMORE).
Chased, . . 4.25 (EVERY).
Chased, Gold Lined, 5.00 (EVICT).

No. 1423.

Plain, Gold Lined, $5.25 (EVEN).
Chased, . . 5.25 (EVENING).
Chased, Gold Lined, 6.00 (EVENT).

No. 1424.

Plain, Gold Lined, $5.00 (EVAPORATE).
Chased, . . 4.75 (EVASION).
Chased, Gold Lined, 5.50 (EVE).

No. 1410.

Chased, Gold Lined, . $7.50 (EXAMINE).

No. 1408.

Chased, Gold Lined, . $6.75 (EXCLAIM).

No. 1409.

Chased, Gold Lined, . $7.50 (EWER).

GOLD AND SILVER PLATE.

No. 1402.

Satin, Engraved, Gold Lined, $5.50 (EXHIBIT).

No. 1414.

Plain, . . $4.00 (EXIST).
Gold Lined, . 4.75 (EXIT).

No. 1412.

Satin, . . $3.25 (EXODUS).
Satin, Gold Lined, 4.00 (EXONERATE).
Chased, . . 3.75 (EXOTIC).
Chased, Gold Lined, 4.50 (EXPAND).

No. 1396.

Plain, . . $3.50 (EXERT).
Gold Lined, . 4.25 (EXHALE).

No. 1398.

Plain, . . $3.75 (EXEMPT).
Gold Lined, . 4.50 (EXERCISE).

No. 1405.

Satin, Chased, Gold Lined, $5.00 (EXILE).

No. 1401.

Gold Lined, . $4.00 (EXHAUST).

No. 1380.

Plain, . . $3.00 (EXEMPLAR).
Plain, Gold Lined, 3.75 (EXEMPLARY).

No. 1413.

Chased, . . $4.50 (EXCESS).
Chased, Gold Lined, 5.25 (EXCHANGE).

No. 1415.

Chased, . . $4.50 (EXAMPLE).
Chased, Gold Lined, 5.25 (EXCAVATE).

No. 1417.

Plain, Gold Lined, $5.25 (EXCLUDE).
Chased, . . 5.25 (EXCURSION).
Chased, Gold Lined, 6.00 (EXCUSE).

No. 1418.

Plain, Gold Lined, $5.25 (EXCISE).
Chased, . . 5.25 (EXCITE).
Chased, Gold Lined, 6.00 (EXCITED).

GOLD AND SILVER PLATE.

No. 190.

Satin, . $3.75 (LARGELY).
Hammered, 4.25 (LARIAT).

No. 195.

Engraved, Glass, . $6.50 (QUOIT).

No. 194.

Cut Glass, . $7.50 (LANDMARK).

No. 0197.

Cut Glass, . $12.00 (PROCEEDING).
Nickel Silver Mountings.

No. 189.

Plain, . $3.75 (LAMENT).

No. 192.

Satin, . $5.25 (LAMPOON).
Hammered, 6.00 (LANDING).

No. 191.

Plain, . $5.00 (LANGUOR).
Chased, . 5.75 (LAPSTONE).

No. 196.

Satin, . $5.50 (PROBATIVE).

No. 188.

Plain, . $5.00 (FABULOUS).
Chased, . 6.00 (FACADE).

No. 36.

Plain, with Plate, $7.25 (EXPLOIT).
Chased, with Plate, 8.00 (EXPLORE).

No. 38.

Satin, with Plate, . $7.50 (PRINCEDOM).
Satin, Engraved, with Plate, 8.50 (PROCONSUL).

No. 37.

Plain, with Plate, $7.50 (EXPLODE).

SYRUP CUPS.

FOR ADDITIONAL PATTERNS SEE TEA SETS.

(ONE-THIRD SIZE.)

No. 198.

Decorated Porcelain, . $5.00 (PUNK).

No. 180.

Plain, . $4.50 (FABRICATION).
Engine, . 5.50 (FABRICATE).
Chased, . 5.50 (FABULIST).

No. 1.

Satin, . $5.00 (FACETIOUS).

No. 187.

Plain, . $4.50 (FACE).

No. 193.

Decorated Porcelain, . $5.00 (LASCAR).

No 184.

Plain, . $5.00 (FACILE).
Silver Chased, 6.00 (FACING).

No. 186.

Plain, . $5.00 (FACTOR).
Chased, . 6.00 (FACTORY).

No. $2\frac{1}{2}$.

Plain, . $5.00 (FACT).
Chased, . 6.00 (FACTION).

No. 1.

Chased, . $6.00 (FACTOTUM).

For Flat Ware, see last pages of this Catalogue.

GOLD AND SILVER PLATE.

No. 32.

Chased, with Plate, . $6.75 (EYELASH).

No. 28.

Chased, with Plate, . $6.00 (FABLE).

No. 29.

Chased, with Plate, . $7.00 (EYESIGHT).

No. 27.

Satin, Engraved, with Plate, $6.75 (EXTREME).

No. 26.

Embossed, with Plate, $6.50 (FABRIC).

No. 33.

Plain, with Plate, $7.25 (EXUDE).
Chased, with Plate, 8.00 (EXULT).

No. 30.

Chased, with Plate, $6.75 (EYE).

No. 31.

Hammered, with Plate, . $7.50 (EXTRINSIC).
Hammered, Chased, with Plate, 8.50 (EXTREMIST).

No. 34.

Silver, with Plate, . $7.00 (EXPEND).
X Gold Inlaid, with Plate, 8.50 (EXPERT).
XX Gold Inlaid, with Plate, 10.00 (EXPIATE).

No. 35.

Satin, with Plate, $7.00 (EXPLETIVE).
Chased, with Plate, 7.75 (EXPLICIT).

No. 31.

Chased, with Plate, $7.00 (EYELET).

TRADE MARK.
WHITE METAL.

SKEWERS, SCALLOPS, AND SCOOPS.

(HALF SIZE).

TRADE MARK.
NICKEL SILVER.

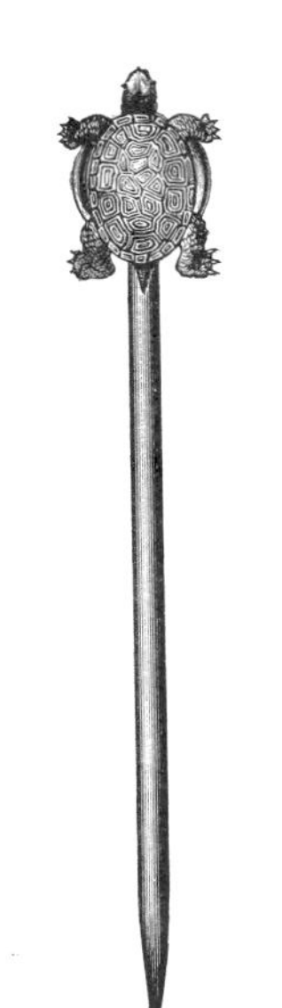

No. 06.
Per dozen, $18.00 (PURELY).

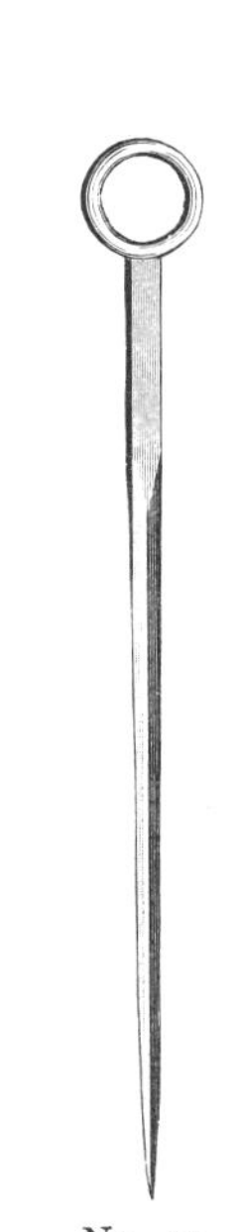

No. 02.
Per dozen, $13.50 (SAILOR).

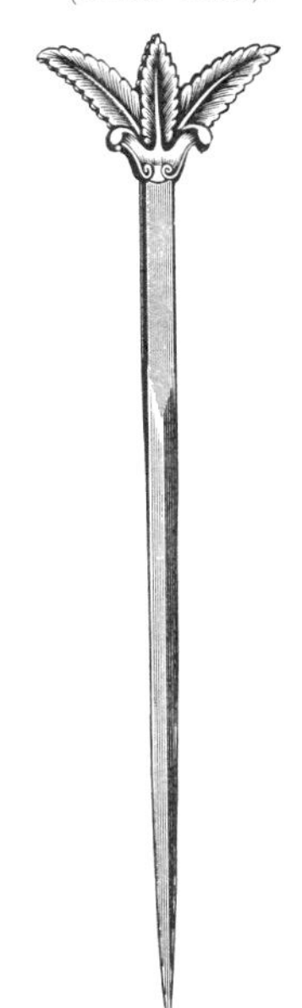

No. 03.
Per dozen, $15.00 (SALERATUS).

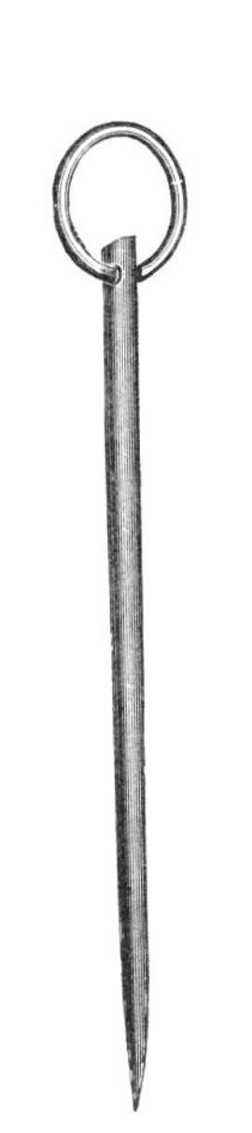

No. 01.
Per dozen, $12.00 (SAINT).

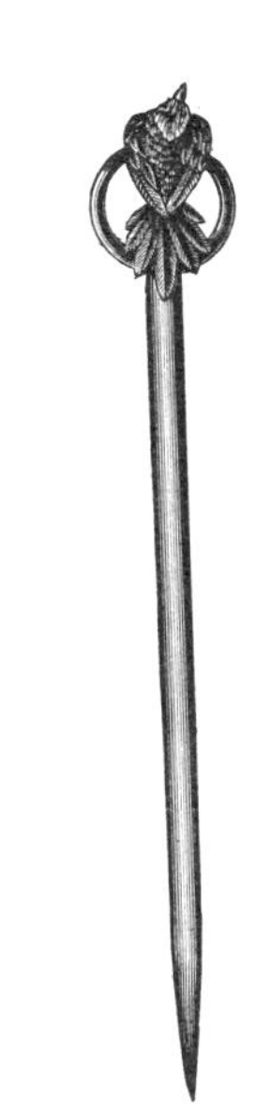

No. 07.
Per dozen, $18.00 (PURIST).

No. 04. Per dozen, $12.00 (SALARY).
(Half Size.)

No. 05. Per dozen, $10.50 (SALAD).
(Full Size.)

SCALLOPS.

(ONE-THIRD SIZE.)

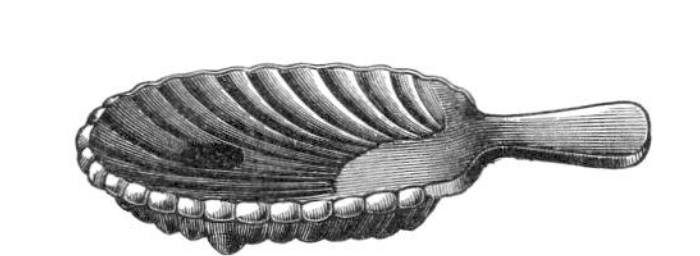

No. 070.
Satin, . $2.25 (PURPOSELY).

No. 060.
Silver, . . $3.75 (SALIENT).
Gold Lined, . 4.50 (SALINE).

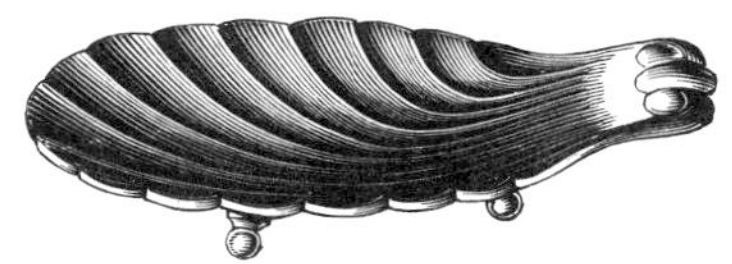

No. 065.
Silver, . . $4.75 (SALIVA).
Gold Lined, . 5.75 (SALLOW).

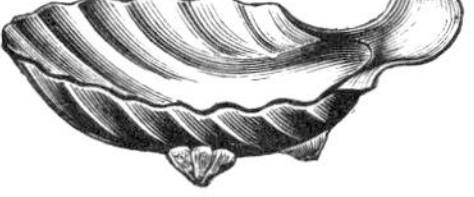

No. 055.
Silver, . . $4.25 (SALT).
Gold Lined, . 5.00 (SALMON).

No. 050. Smaller.
Satin, . . $3.75 (PYRITES).
Gold Lined, . 4.50 (PYTHIAN).

SCOOPS.

(ONE-THIRD SIZE.)

No. 09. Satin, . $6.50 (PURSUANCE).

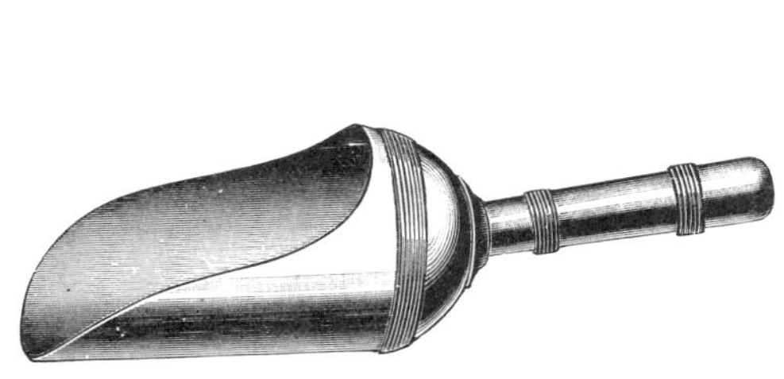

No. 04, . $10.00 (SAPLING).

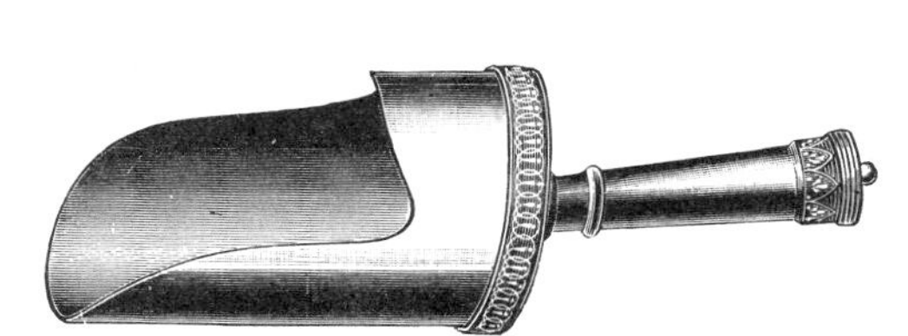

No. 03, . $11.00 (SAPPHIRE).

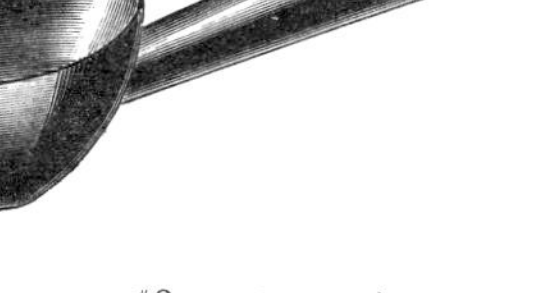

No. 01, ... $8.00 (SAPIENT).
No. 05. Smaller, . 5.50 (PYRAMIDIC).

NICKEL SILVER, SILVER SOLDERED.

GOLD AND SILVER PLATE.

MERIDEN B COMPANY
TRADE MARK
NICKEL SILVER.

(ONE-THIRD SIZE.)

No. 7500. SMOKING TABLE.

Hammered, Old Copper, . . $65.00 (RATCHET).
Hammered, Old Silver, . . 70.00 (RATIFY).

No. 9925. EXTENSION SHAVING TABLE.

Old Copper, . . . $27.50 (RAGGED).
Height, extended, 66 inches.

MERIDEN B. COMPANY
TRADE MARK.
WHITE METAL.

SMOKING SETS.

NICKEL SILVER.

No. 1.

Satin, Gold Lined, . . . $10.00 (REMIT).
Moorish, Old Silver, Gold Lined, 12.00 (REGRASS).

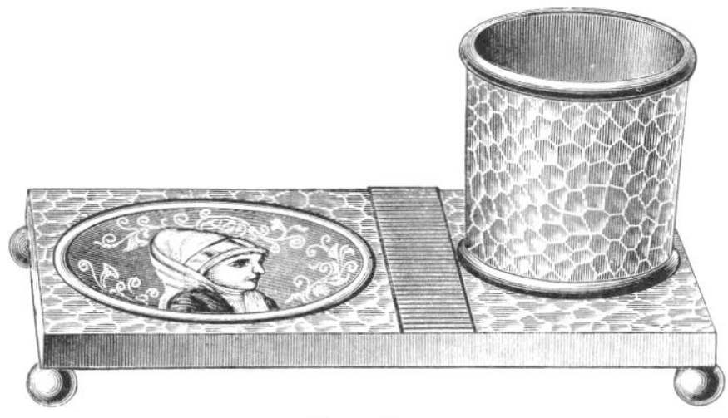

No. 8.

Hammered, Old Silver, . . $6.50 (PHOSPHATE).
Hammered, Old Silver, X Gilt, . 7.50 (PROFESS).
(Half Size.)

No. 15. HAMMERED, CUPS GOLD LINED.

Hammered, Old Copper, . . $27.50 (PROFOUND).
Hammered, Old Silver, . . 30.00 (PROFILE).
(One-Third Size.)

No. 18. ENAMELED COPPER.

Set of Five Pieces, Cigar Holder Gold Lined, $12.00 (QUICKEN).
No. 10—8½ inch Waiter, $3.50 (QUESTOR). No. 18 Ash Holder, $1.75 (QUAKERISM).
No. 18 Cigar Holder, 2.50 (QUERIST). No. 18½ Match Holder, 1.50 (QUARTERLY).
No. 18 Cigar Lamp, $2.75 (QUALIFIED).
(Half Size.)

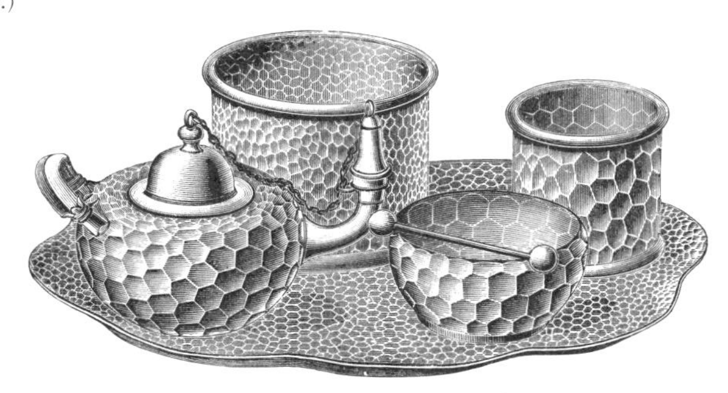

No. 17. HAMMERED OLD SILVER.

Set of Five Pieces, Cups Gold Lined, . $17.75 (QUIBBLE).
No. 10—8½ inch Waiter, $5.00 (QUENCH). No. 16 Ash Holder, $2.25 (QUEER).
No. 17 Cigar Holder, . 3.50 (QUANTUM). No. 31 Match Holder, 2.00 (QUAVER).
No. 15 Cigar Lamp, $5.00 (RAINY).
(Half Size.)

No. 16.

Hammered, Old Copper, Gold Lined, . $11.50 (PHAROS).
Hammered, Old Silver, Gold Lined, . 12.00 (PHILOPENA).
(Half Size.)

No. 9.

Hammered, Old Silver, . . $14.50 (PROFESSOR).
Hammered, Old Silver, X Gilt, . 16.50 (PROFFER).
(Half Size.)

TRADE MARK.
WHITE METAL.

GOLD AND SILVER PLATE.

TRADE MARK.
NICKEL SILVER.

(HALF SIZE.)

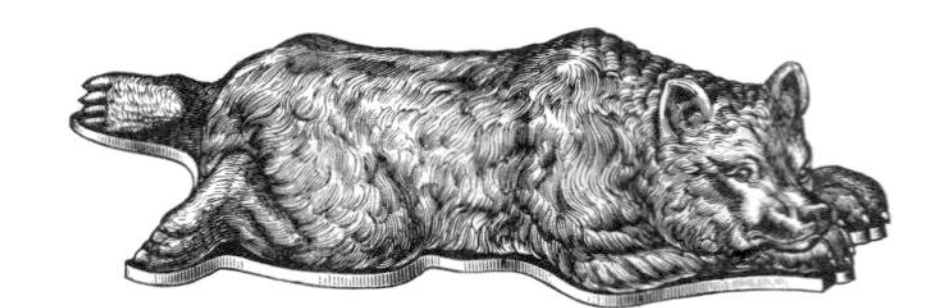

No. 200. STAMP BOX.
Old Silver, Gold Lined, . $4.75 (QUIETLY).

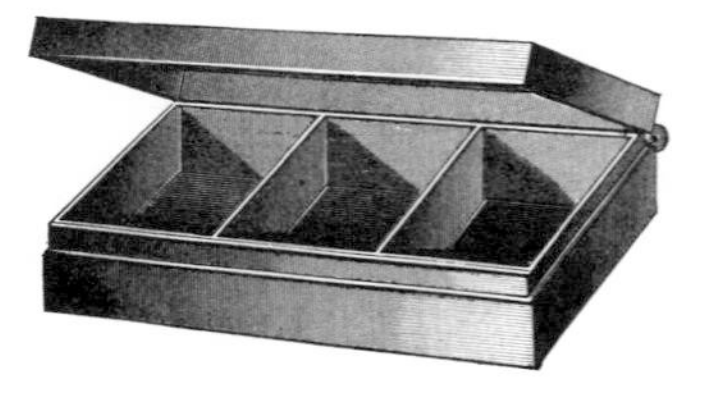

No. 202. STAMP BOX.
Satin, . . . $3.00 (QUICKSET).
Hammered, Old Silver, 3.75 (QUIESCENT).

No. 201. STAMP BOX.
Satin, . . $3.75 (QUIETUS)

No. 106. SHAVING-STICK BOX.
Satin, . . $2.25 (QUINTAL).
Satin, Engraved, 2.75 (QUITTANCE).

No. 106. SHAVING-STICK BOX.
Hammered, Old Silver, $3.00 (QUITE).
Moorish, Old Silver, . 3.50 (RAIL).

No. 15 CIGAR LAMP.
Hammered, Old Copper, . $4.50 (PRONE).
Hammered, Old Silver, . 5.00 (PRONOUN).

No. 46. CIGAR LAMP.
Old Copper, . $5.00 (PROMOTE).
Old Silver, . 5.50 (PROMOTER).

No. 2. SHAVING SET.
With Drawer for Razor, . $13.50 (INCLUDE).
(One-Third Size.)

No. 01. LIQUOR LABEL.
Per dozen, . . $6.00 (PEDIGREE).
(Full Size.)

No. 02. LIQUOR LABEL.
Per dozen, . . $12.00 (PEDIMENT).
(Full Size.)

Nos. 01 and 02 Labels furnished with Assorted Names if desired.

CIGAR ASH RECEIVERS.

(HALF SIZE.)

No. 19.

Fine Decorated, Porcelain Lining, . $3.25 (ROAMER).

No. 20.

Fine Decorated, Porcelain Lining, $3.25 (REDDISH).

No. 01.

Nickel Silver, Silver Soldered.

Satin, Gold Lined, . $4.50 (REDUCER).

No. 6, . . $4.50 (POPLAR).

No. 31. MATCH HOLDER.

Hammered, Old Copper, Gold Lined, $1.75 (UPSIDE).

Hammered, Old Silver, Gold Lined, 2.00 (UPSHOT).

No. 16.

Hammered, Old Copper, Gold Lined, $2.00 (PROJECT).

Hammered, Old Silver, Gold Lined, 2.25 (PROLIFIC).

No. 1. FROG.

Silver, Gold Lined, . . $3.00 (CRAVAT).

Gold Inlaid and Gold Lined, 3.50 (CRAVE).

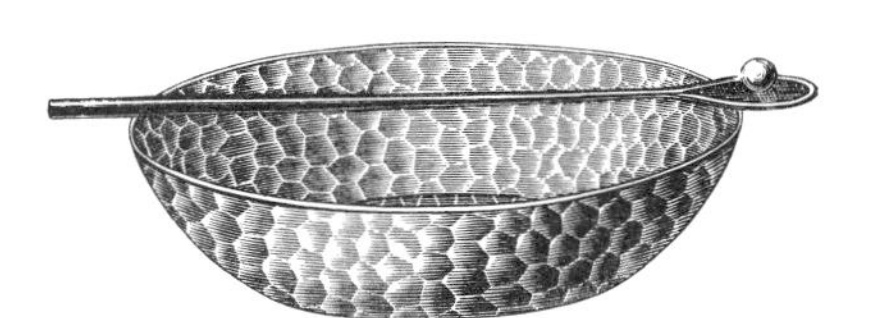

No. 15.

Hammered, Old Copper, Gold Lined, $3.50 (PROMINENT).

Hammered, Old Silver, Gold Lined, 4.00 (PROMISE).

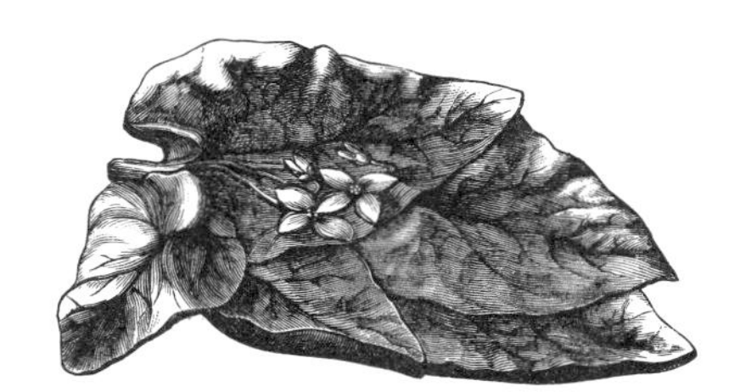

No. 13.

Old Silver, . . $2.00 (PROLIX).

Old Silver, Gold Inlaid, 2.50 (PROLIXITY).

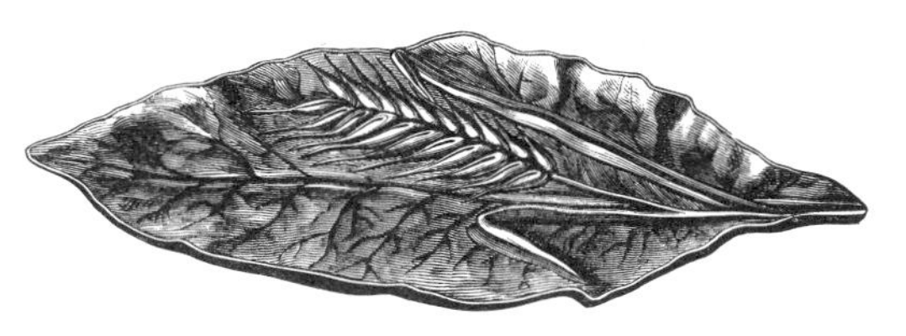

No. 12.

Old Silver, . . $1.50 (PROFUSE).

Old Silver, Gold Inlaid, $2.00 (PROGRESS).

TOBACCO BOXES.

(FULL SIZE.)

No. 010. CIGARETTE CASE.
Nickel Silver, Silver Soldered.
Satin, . . . $8.00 (RETROACT).
Satin, Engraved, . 9.00 (RIVULET).

No. 03. Nickel Silver, Silver Soldered.
Chased, Gold Lined, . . $6.00 (PREVENT).

No. 08.
Nickel Silver, Silver Soldered.
Old Silver, Gold Lined, $6.00 (PENSENT).
No. 09. CIGARETTE CASE.
Same Style as above.
Old Silver, . . $7.00 (RITUAL).

No. 4.
Silver, Satin, Gold Lined, $3.50 (PRETEXT).
Chased, Gold Lined, . 3.50 (PREVAIL).

No. 05. TOBACCO OR SNUFF BOX.
Nickel Silver, Silver Soldered.
Chased U, Gold Lined, per dozen, $13.50 (PRESUME).

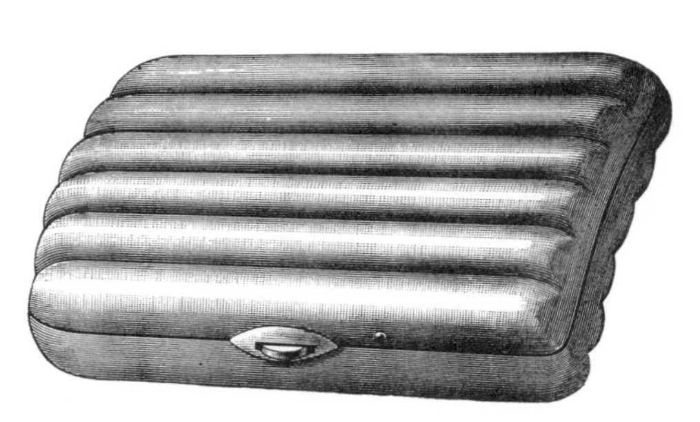

No. 011. CIGARETTE CASE.
Satin, Fluted, . . $6.50 (RIMPLE)
Nickel Silver, Silver Soldered.

No. 6. TOBACCO OR SNUFF BOX.
Chased, . . . $2.75 (PRESENT).
Chased, Gold Lined, 3.25 (PRESERVE).

No. 7.
Chased, . . . $2.50 (PRESIDE).
Chased, Gold Lined, 3.25 (PRESS).

No. 1972. SATIN ENGRAVED TEA SET.

Style.	Set of Six Pieces.	Coffee.	Tea, Six Half Pints.	Water, Five Half Pints.	Sugar.	Cream, Gold Lined.	Slop, Gold Lined.
Satin Engraved, -	$60.00 (VAIN.)	$14.25	$11.75	$10.75	$7.50	$8.25	$7.50
Embossed, Chased,	60.00 (VALLATION).	14.25	11.75	10.75	7.50	8.25	7.50

No. 71 — 26 Inch Waiter, Satin Engraved, $58.00 (VALVE). Patent Plate Glass Protector, $7.50 extra (VANITY).

	No. 1972. Swing Kettle. Seven Half Pints.	No. 1972. Butter Dish. With Patent Crystal Drainer.	No. 1972. Syrup Cup. With Plate.	No. 1972. Spoon Holder. Gold Lined.
Satin Engraved, -	$24.00 (VAPORABLE).	$8.00 (VILLAIN).	$8.50 (WAITER).	$8.00 (WATCHWORD).
Embossed, Chased,	24.00 (VENOMOUS).	8.00 (VIRTUE).	8.50 (WARMTH).	8.00 (WAXCANDLE).

TRADE MARK.
WHITE METAL.

TEA SETS.

TRADE MARK.
NICKEL SILVER.

(ONE-THIRD SIZE.)

No. 1961. SATIN, EMBOSSED, CHASED TEA SET.

Style.	Set of Six Pieces.	Coffee.	Tea, Six Half Pints.	Water, Five Half Pints.	Sugar.	Cream, Gold Lined.	Slop, Gold Lined.
Satin, ...	$60.00 (BUTTE).	$14.25	$11.75	$10.75	$7.50	$8.25	$7.50
Satin, Embossed, Chased, ...	70.00 (BEFORE).	16.25	13.75	12.50	9.00	9.75	8.75
Satin, Embossed Chased, XX Gold Inlaid,	100.00 (BEFRIEND).	22.50	19.75	17.75	13.50	14.00	12.50

No. 86½—26 inch WAITER. Satin, Rose Chased, . $60.00 (ELK). Satin, Rose Chased, XX Gold Inlaid, . $85.00 (ELLIPSE).

Patent Plate Glass Protector, . $7.50 extra (BAD).

	No. 1961 SWING KETTLE. Six Half Pints.	No. 1961 BUTTER DISH.	No. 1961 SYRUP CUP. With Plate.	No. 1961 SPOON HOLDER. Gold Lined.
Satin, ...	$26.00 (CADENCE).	$9.00 (BUXOM).	$8.00 (CACKLE).	$7.50 (CABIN).
Satin, Embossed, Chased, ...	29.00 (CAISSON).	10.25 (BUZZARD).	9.25 (CACTUS).	8.75 (CABINET).
Satin, Embossed, Chased, XX Gold Inlaid,	34.50 (CAIQUE).	14.50 (BYZANT).	13.50 (CADDY).	13.00 (CABOOSE).

EMBOSSED, CHASED, same price as Satin, Embossed Chased.

GOLD AND SILVER PLATE.

No. 1964 BUTTER DISH.

With Patent Crystal Drainer.

Satin, ... $7.75 (READY).
Satin, Engraved, . 8.75 (REAL).

No. 1964 SPOON HOLDER.

Gold Lined.

Satin, ... $6.75 (RE-ADJUST).
Satin, Engraved, . 7.75 (RE-ADMIT).

No. 1964 SYRUP CUP.

With Plate.

Satin, ... $7.25 (REALISM).
Satin, Engraved, . 8.25 (RE-APPEAR).

No. 1964. SATIN, ENGRAVED TEA SET.

Style.	Set of Six Pieces.	Coffee.	Tea, Six Half Pints.	Water, Five Half Pints.	Sugar.	Cream, Gold Lined.	Slop, Gold Lined.
Satin, ...	$52.00 (RASP).	$12.00	$10.00	$9.25	$6.25	$7.75	$6.75
Satin, Engraved, .	62.00 (RATION).	14.50	12.50	11.00	7.50	8.75	7.75

No. 1964 SWING KETTLE. Nine Half Pints. Satin, . $26.00 (RARELY). Satin, Engraved, . $28.00 (REACTIVE).

No. 105—24 inch WAITER. Satin, . $40.00 (RAZE). Satin, Engraved, . $48.00 (RAZURE).

Patent Plate Glass Protector, . $6.00 extra (READILY).

GOLD AND SILVER PLATE.

No. 11. Wine Cooler.

Satin, . . $15.00 (whiffle).

Satin, Engraved, 17.00 (whether).

No. 30. Ice Tub.

Silver, . $8.50 (rife).

No. 227, . $5.00 (parable).

Pomona Art Glass.

No. 68. Satin, Engraved Tilting Pitcher Set.

Goblet and Slop Bowl Gold Lined.

Satin, $40.00 (pare). Satin, Engraved, $42.50 (pasty). Chased, $42.50 (refer).

No. 1907.

Plain, . . $7.50 (unseen).

Gold Lined, . 9.50 (unseat).

No. 111. Satin, 8 inch, Six Half Pints, . . $13.50 (wardrobe).

No. 111. Satin, Engraved, 8 inch, Six Half Pints, 14.50 (reedy).

No. 112. Satin, 9 inch, Seven Half Pints, . . 15.00 (wakeful).

No. 112. Satin, Engraved, 9 inch, Seven Half Pints, 16.50 (renard).

No. 1877. Tureen.

	Satin.	Satin, Engraved.	Plate Extra.
Two Quarts, .	$16.00 (refine).	$18.00 (reflect).	$6.00 (refrain).
Three Quarts, .	18.00 (ride).	20.50 (rite).	7.00 (ripely).
Four Quarts, .	20.00 (rider).	23.00 (retract).	8.00 (retouch).

GOLD AND SILVER PLATE.

No. 1957 Spoon Holder.

Gold Lined.

Plain,	$7.00	(BECKON).
Satin,	7.00	(BEDECK).
Chased,	8.00	(BEDEW).

No. 1957 Butter Dish.

With Patent Chased Crystal Drainer.

Plain,	$7.50	(BEDOUIN).
Satin,	7.50	(BEECHEN).
Chased,	8.50	(BEECH).

No. 1957 Syrup Cup.

With Plate.

Plain,	$7.50	(BEDSIDE).
Satin,	7.50	(BEDIM).
Chased,	8.50	(BECOMING).

No. 1957. CHASED TEA SET.

Style.	Set of Six Pieces.	Coffee.	Tea, Six Half Pints.	Water, Five Half Pints.	Sugar.	Cream, Gold Lined.	Slop, Gold Lined.
Plain,	$52.00 (BATEAU).	$12.00	$10.00	$9.25	$6.25	$7.75	$6.75
Satin,	52.00 (BATHE).	12.00	10.00	9.25	6.25	7.75	6.75
Chased,	62.00 (BAYONET).	14.50	12.50	11.00	7.50	8.75	7.75

No. 1957 Urn. Thirteen Half Pints. Satin, . $28.50 (BEAGLE). Chased, . $33.50 (BEARER).

No. 92—24 inch Waiter. Satin, . $42.00 (BEACON). No. 1957, Chased, . 50.00 (BEADLE).

Patent Plate Glass Protector, . $6.75 extra (BECAME).

TRADE MARK.
WHITE METAL.

GOLD AND SILVER PLATE.

TRADE MARK.
NICKEL SILVER.

No. 1951. TEA SET.

Style.	Set of Six Pieces.	Coffee.	Tea, Six Half Pints.	Water, Five Half Pints.	Sugar.	Cream, Gold Lined.	Slop, Gold Lined.
Old Silver, . .	$57.00 (BLUING).	$13.00	$11.00	$9.75	$7.50	$8.25	$7.50
X Gold Inlaid, .	70.00 (BOULDER).	16.50	13.75	12.25	9.25	9.50	8.75

No. 86—26 inch WAITER. Chased, . $50.00 (BOWLDER). Chased, X Gold Inlaid, . $70.00 (BOWSPRIT).

Patent Plate Glass Protector, $7.50 extra (BRANDISH).

No. 1951 BUTTER DISH.

Old Silver, . . . $9.00 (BRASIER).

X Gold Inlaid, . . 11.75 (BRAVADO).

No. 1951 SPOON HOLDER.
Gold Lined.

Old Silver, . . . $8.00 (BROADSIDE).

X Gold Inlaid, . 9.50 (BROCHURE).

No. 1951 SYRUP CUP.
With Plate.

Old Silver, . . $8.50 (BROKEN).

X Gold Inlaid, . 10.00 (BROMA).

No. 1951 SWING KETTLE.
Six Half Pints.

Old Silver, . . $27.50 (BROTHER).

X Gold Inlaid, . 30.00 (BUCKSKIN).

GOLD AND SILVER PLATE.

No. 1967. SATIN, ENGRAVED TEA SET.

Style.	Set of Six Pieces.	Coffee.	Tea, Six Half Pints.	Water, Five Half Pints.	Sugar.	Cream, Gold Lined.	Slop, Gold Lined.
Plain or Satin,	$58.00 (RECEPTIVE).	$13.00	$11.25	$10.75	$7.25	$8.25	$7.50
Satin, Engraved,	68.00 (RECHARGE).	16.50	13.25	12.25	8.50	9.25	8.25

No. 105—24 inch WAITER. Satin, . $40.00 (RECITATION). Satin, Engraved, $48.00 (RECKONER).

Patent Plate Glass Protector, . $6.00 extra (RECOVERY).

No. 1967 BUTTER DISH.

With Patent Crystal Drainer.

Satin, . . . $8.50 (REASONING).

Satin, Engraved, . 9.50 (REBATEMENT).

No. 1967 SPOON HOLDER.

Gold Lined.

Satin, . . . $7.00 (REBUILD).

Satin, Engraved, . 8.00 (RECENCY).

No. 1967 SYRUP CUP.

With Plate.

Satin, . . . $7.75 (REBUT).

Satin, Engraved, . 8.75 (RECOIN).

No. 1967 SWING KETTLE.

Nine Half Pints.

Satin, . . . $27.50 (RECAST).

Satin, Engraved, . 30.00 (RECORDER).

GOLD AND SILVER PLATE.

No. 1969 SPOON HOLDER.
Gold Lined.

Chased, . . . $8.50 (SYLPH).
Satin, Engraved, . 8.50 (SYMBOLIC).

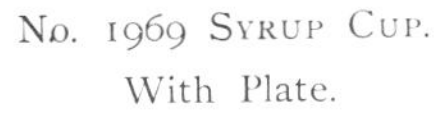

No. 1969 SYRUP CUP.
With Plate.

Chased, . . . $9.50 (SYLLABLE).
Satin, Engraved, . 9.50 (SYLLABUB).

No. 1969 BUTTER DISH.
With Patent Crystal Drainer.

Chased, . . . $10.00 (SYMPTOM).
Satin, Engraved, . 10.00 (SYNDAC).

No. 1969. SATIN, ENGRAVED TEA SET.

Style.	Set of Six Pieces.	Coffee.	Tea, Six Half Pints.	Water, Five Half Pints.	Sugar.	Cream, Gold Lined.	Slop, Gold Lined.
Chased, . .	$68.00 (SYMPATHY).	$16.50	$13.25	$12.25	$8.50	$9.25	$8.25
Satin, Engraved, .	68.00 (TALISMANIC).	16.50	13.25	12.25	8.50	9.25	8.25

No. 1969 URN. Twelve Half Pints. Chased, . $37.00 (TACTION). Satin, Engraved, . $37.00 (TALLNESS).

No. 107—26 inch WAITER. Chased, . 60.00 (TAPSTER). Satin, Engraved, . 60.00 (TARGUM).

Patent Plate Glass Protector, . $7.00 extra (TARDINESS).

GOLD AND SILVER PLATE.

No. 1947½. FLUTED TEA SET.

Style.	Set of Six Pieces.	Coffee.	Tea, Six Half Pints.	Water, Five Half Pints.	Sugar.	Cream, Gold Lined.	Slop, Gold Lined.
Fluted, . .	$68.00 (STUPENDOUS).	$15.50	$13.25	$12.25	$9.00	$9.50	$8.50

No. 1947½ KETTLE. Nine Half Pints. Fluted, . . . $30.00 (STUPEFY).

No. 105—24 inch WAITER. Satin, Shield, . $40.00 (STURGEON). Satin, Engraved, . $48.00 (SUBDUCT).

Patent Plate Glass Protector, . $6.00 extra (SUBDUER).

No. 1947½ BUTTER DISH.
With Patent Crystal Drainer.
Fluted, . . . $10.00 (SUBLIMATE).

No. 1947½ SPOON HOLDER.
Gold Lined.
Fluted, . . . $8.50 (SUBLATION).

No. 1947½ SYRUP CUP.
With Plate.
Fluted, . . . $9.00 (SYBARITE).

FLUTED, PLAIN, AND SATIN FINISH SAME PRICE.

Trade Mark.
WHITE METAL

GOLD AND SILVER PLATE.

Trade Mark.
NICKEL SILVER.

No. 1963 Butter Dish.
With Patent Crystal Drainer.
Embossed, . . $9.00 (sulphuric).

No. 1963 Spoon Holder.
Gold Lined.
Embossed, . . $7.50 (suggestion).

No. 1963 Syrup Cup.
With Plate.
Embossed, . . $8.00 (summons).

No. 1963. EMBOSSED TEA SET.

Style.	Set of Six Pieces.	Coffee.	Tea. Six Half Pints.	Water, Five Half Pints.	Sugar.	Cream, Gold Lined.	Slop, Gold Lined.
Embossed, . .	$62.00 (tenacious).	$14.50	$12.50	$11.00	$7.50	$8.75	$7.75

No. 1963 Urn. Thirteen Half Pints. Embossed, . $34.00 (tendency).

No. 26—28 inch Chased Waiter, . $65.00 (suddenly). Patent Plate Glass Protector, . $8.00 extra (suffix).

No. 1953. CHASED TEA SET.

Style.	Set of Six Pieces.	Coffee.	Tea, Six Half Pints.	Water, Five Half Pints.	Sugar.	Cream, Gold Lined.	Slop, Gold Lined.
Chased, . . .	$80.00 (BEETLE).	$18.75	$15.75	$14.00	$10.75	$11.00	$9.75
Chased, Gold Inlaid, .	125.00 (TRANSMIT).	28.00	24.25	23.25	17.50	16.50	15.50

No. 1953 URN. Ten Half Pints. Chased, . $37.50 (TRANSLATE). Chased, Gold Inlaid, . $45.00 (BEGIRD).

No. 80—26 inch WAITER. 1953 Chased, . 60.00 (BEHALF). Chased, Gold Inlaid, . 90.00 (BEHEST).

Patent Plate Glass Protector, . $7.50 extra (BEHOLD).

No. 1953 BUTTER DISH.
With Patent Crystal Drainer.
Chased, . . $11.00 (BELFRY).
Chased, Gold Inlaid, 16.50 (BELIKE).

No. 1953 SPOON HOLDER.
Gold Lined.
Chased, . . $9.50 (BEHOOF).
Chased, Gold Inlaid, 13.50 (BELAY).

No. 1953 SYRUP CUP.
With Plate.
Chased, . . . $10.00 (BELONG).
Chased, Gold Inlaid, 14.00 (BINOCLE).

GOLD AND SILVER PLATE

No. 1970. EMBOSSED TEA SET.

Style.	Set of Six Pieces.	Coffee.	Tea, Six Half Pints.	Water, Five Half Pints.	Sugar.	Cream, Gold Lined.	Slop, Gold Lined.
Embossed, . . .	$56.00 (TARTARUS).	$13.50	$11.00	$10.00	$6.75	$7.75	$7.00
Embossed, Old Silver,	60.00 (TASKER).	14.25	11.75	10.75	7.50	8.25	7.50

No. 1970 SWING KETTLE. Nine Half Pints. Embossed, . . $27.50 (TASTEFUL). Embossed, Old Silver, . . $28.50 (TAUTOG).

No. 109—24 inch WAITER. Satin, . $42.00 (TAXATION). Chased, . $50.00 (TEAMSTER). With Old Silver Border, $3.00 extra.

Patent Plate Glass Protector, . $6.00 extra (TELEPHONE).

No. 1970 BUTTER DISH.
With Patent Crystal Drainer.
Embossed, . . $7.00 (TEDIUM).
Embossed, Old Silver, 7.50 (TEARLESS).

No. 1970 SPOON HOLDER.
Gold Lined.
Embossed, . . $6.50 (TENDERLY).
Embossed, Old Silver, 7.00 (TEGUMENT).

No. 1970 SYRUP CUP.
With Plate.
Embossed, . . $7.00 (TEMPERATE).
Embossed, Old Silver, 7.50 (TEMPORIZE).

TRADE MARK.
WHITE METAL.

GOLD AND SILVER PLATE.

TRADE MARK.
NICKEL SILVER.

No. 1965. SATIN, ENGRAVED TEA SET.

Style.	Set of Six Pieces.	Coffee.	Tea, Six Half Pints.	Water, Five Half Pints.	Sugar.	Cream, Gold Lined.	Slop, Gold Lined.
Satin, ...	$50.00 (SUMPTUOUS).	$11.50	$9.75	$8.75	$6.25	$7.25	$6.50
Satin, Engraved, .	60.00 (SUPERVENE).	14.25	11.75	10.75	7.50	8.25	7.50

No. 1965 SWING KETTLE.

Nine Half Pints.

Satin, . . . $25.00 (SUITOR).
Satin, Engraved, 27.00 (SULCATE).

No. 1965 SPOON HOLDER.

Gold Lined.

Satin, . . . $6.50 (SUMAC).
Satin, Engraved, 7.50 (SUN-DIAL).

No. 1965 BUTTER DISH.

With Patent Crystal Drainer.

Satin, . . . $7.50 (SUNRISE).
Satin, Engraved, 8.50 (SUNDOWN).

No. 1965 SYRUP CUP.

With Plate.

Satin, . . . $7.00 (SWIRL).
Satin, Engraved, 8.00 (SWOOP).

No. 105—24 inch WAITER. Satin, Shield, . $40.00 (TENUITY). Satin, Engraved, . $48.00 (TERMER).
Patent Plate Glass Protector, $6.00 extra (TERMITE).

No. 1947. EMBOSSED A TEA SET IN CASE.

Style.	Set of Six Pieces.	Coffee.	Tea, Six Half Pints.	Water, Five Half Pints.	Sugar.	Cream, Gold Lined.	Slop, Gold Lined.
Embossed A, .	$140.00 (SURROGATE).	$31.50	$28.00	$26.00	$18.75	$18.75	$17.00

No. 1947 SWING KETTLE. Ten Half Pints. Embossed, $55.00 (SUPERVISE). No. 114—24 inch WAITER. 1947 Engraved A, $60.00 (SUPINELY).

Satin Lined CASE for Seven Pieces, . . . $62.50 extra (SURCOAT) Patent Plate Glass Protector, . . . $6.00 extra (SUPPLICANT).

Trade Mark.
WHITE METAL.

GOLD AND SILVER PLATE.

Trade Mark.
NICKEL SILVER.

No. 1973. CHASED TEA SET. Oval.

Style.	Set of Six Pieces.	Coffee.	Tea, Six Half Pints.	Water, Five Half Pints.	Sugar.	Cream, Gold Lined.	Slop, Gold Lined.
Plain, .	$58.00 (suspicion).	$12.00	$ 10.75	$10.00	$8.50	$9.25	$7.50
Chased, .	68.00 (surveying).	15.00	13.00	12.00	9.50	10.25	8.25

No. 1973 Swing Kettle. Seven Half Pints. Plain, . $25.00 (swagger). Chased, . $28.00 (swarth).

No. 113—26 inch Waiter. Satin, . $46.00 (sustainer). Satin, Engraved, . 56.00 (sweeper).

Patent Plate Glass Protector, . $7.50 extra (swelter).

No. 1973 Butter Dish.
With Patent Crystal Drainer.

Plain, . . $9.00 (technical).
Chased, . . 10.00 (templet).

No. 1973 Spoon Holder.
Gold Lined.

Plain, . . $8.00 (swerve).
Chased, . . 9.00 (swept).

No. 1973 Syrup Cup.
With Plate.

Plain, . . $8.50 (tenancy).
Chased, . . 9.50 (tenant).

GOLD AND SILVER PLATE.

No. 1945. CHASED TEA SET.

Style.	Set of Six Pieces.	Coffee.	Tea, Six Half Pints.	Water, Five Half Pints.	Sugar.	Cream, Gold Lined.	Slop, Gold Lined.
Chased, ...	$64.00 (BESOM).	$15.50	$12.50	$11.50	$8.00	$8.75	$7.75
Chased, Gold Inlaid, .	91.00 (RE-EMBARK).	21.00	17.75	16.75	12.00	12.25	11.25

No. 1945 URN. Sixteen Half Pints. Chased, . $36.00 (NEPTUNE). Gold Inlaid, . $48.00 (REFECTIVE).

No. 77—26 inch WAITER. 1945 Chased, . $60.00 (BESPEAK). Chased, Gold Inlaid, . $72.00 (REMOVAL).

Patent Plate Glass Protector, . $7.00 extra (BEST). No. 1946 Chased TEA SET (WITH FEET), $4.00 extra (REFORMER).

No. 1945 SPOON HOLDER.
Gold Lined.
Chased, . . . $8.00 (BESTIR).
Chased, Gold Inlaid, 12.00 (REFUGEE).

No. 1945 BUTTER DISH.
With Patent Crystal Drainer.
Chased, . . . $9.50 (BESTOW).
Chased, Gold Inlaid, 14.50 (BETAKE).

No. 1945 SYRUP CUP.
With Plate.
Chased, . . . $9.50 (BETHEL).
Chased, Gold Inlaid, 13.50 (REFUSE).

GOLD AND SILVER PLATE.

No. 1968 BUTTER DISH.

With Patent Crystal Drainer.

Plain or Satin, ... $7.50 (REMISE).
Plain or Satin, Old Silver Border, 8.00 (REND).

No. 1968 SPOON HOLDER.

Gold Lined.

Plain or Satin, ... $6.75 (RELIEF).
Plain or Satin, Old Silver Border, 7.25 (RELIEVE).

No. 1968 SYRUP CUP.

With Plate.

Plain or Satin, ... $7.50 (REPEAL).
Plain or Satin, Old Silver Border, 8.00 (REPENT).

No. 1968. PLAIN TEA SET.

Style.	Set of Six Pieces.	Coffee.	Tea, Six Half Pints.	Water, Five Half Pints.	Sugar.	Cream, Gold Lined.	Slop, Gold Lined.
Plain or Satin, ...	$50.00 (REPENTANT).	$11.50	$9.75	$8.75	$6.25	$7.25	$6.50
Plain or Satin, Old Silver Border,	54.00 (REPLANT).	12.50	10.50	9.50	6.75	7.75	7.00

No. 1968 URN. 10 Half Pints. Satin, . $28.00 (REPOSIT). Satin, Old Silver Border, $29.00 (REPREHEND).
No. 107½—26 inch Waiter. Satin, . 50.00 (REPRESS). 1968 Chased, . . 60 00 (REPRIMAND).

Patent Plate Glass Protector, . $7.00 extra (REPROACH).

TRADE MARK.
WHITE METAL.

GOLD AND SILVER PLATE.

TRADE MARK.
NICKEL SILVER.

No. 1958. EMBOSSED, CHASED TEA SET.

Style.	Set of Six Pieces.	Coffee.	Tea, Six Half Pints.	Water, Five Half Pints.	Sugar.	Cream, Gold Lined.	Slop, Gold Lined.
Satin, . . .	$50.00 (WALK).	$11.50	$9.75	$8.75	$6.25	$7.25	$6.50
Embossed, Chased,	64.00 (WALTZ).	15.25	12.75	11.50	8.00	8.75	7.75

No. 94—25 inch WAITER. Satin, $48.00 (WAMPUM). 1958 Chased, $55.00 (WARBLE). Patent Plate Glass Protector, $7.50 extra (WARD).

No. 1958 URN.
Thirteen Half Pints.
Satin, ... $28.50 (WARDEN).
Embossed, Chased, . 33.00 (WEATHER).

No. 1958 BUTTER DISH.
With Patent Crystal Drainer.
$8.00 (WARP).
9.50 (WEAVE).

No. 1958 SPOON HOLDER.
Gold Lined.
$6.50 (WARREN).
8.00 (WEAVER).

No. 1958 SYRUP CUP.
With Plate.
$7.00 (WASP).
8.50 (WEDGE).

GOLD AND SILVER PLATE.

No. 1919. EMBOSSED, CHASED TEA SET.

Set of Six Pieces.	Coffee.	Tea, Six Half Pints.	Water, Five Half Pints.	Sugar.	Cream, Gold Lined.	Slop, Gold Lined.
$68.00 (ABHOR).	$16.50	$13.25	$12.25	$8.50	$9.25	$8.25

No. 45—26 inch WAITER. Chased, . . $60.00 (ABIDE). Patent Plate Glass Protector, $7.50 extra (ABJECT).

No. 1919 BUTTER DISH.
With Patent Crystal Drainer.
Chased, . $10.00 (ABOARD).

No. 1919 URN.
Chased, Sixteen Half Pints, . $37.00 (ABLE).

No. 1919 SPOON HOLDER.
Chased, Gold Lined, . $8.00 (ABOUND).

No. 1919 SYRUP CUP.
Chased, with Plate, . $8.00 (ABROAD).

GOLD AND SILVER PLATE.

No. 1960. PLAIN TEA SET.

Style.	Set of Six Pieces.	Coffee.	Tea, Six Half Pints.	Water, Five Half Pints.	Sugar.	Cream, Gold Lined.	Slop, Gold Lined.
Plain, ...	$50.00 (WHOM).	$11.50	$9.75	$8.75	$6.25	$7.25	$6.50
Hammered, . .	58.00 (WIDGEON).	13.50	11.25	10.25	7.25	8.25	7.50

No. 76—22 inch WAITER. Satin, $35.00 (WIGHT). Hammered, $41.00 (WILDER). Patent Plate Glass Protector, $5.25 extra (WILT).

No. 76—24 inch WAITER. Satin, 42.50 (WIMPLE). Hammered, 50.00 (WINDER). Patent Plate Glass Protector, 6.00 extra (WISELY).

No. 1960 BUTTER DISH.
With Patent Crystal Drainer.

Plain, ... $7.50 (WISHFUL).
Hammered, . . . 8.50 (WITHAL).

No. 1960 KETTLE.
Nine Half Pints.

Plain, . . $26.00 (WHIST).
Hammered, . 28.00 (WHISTLE).

No. 1960 SPOON HOLDER.
Gold Lined.

Plain, . . $6.50 (WORDY).
Hammered, . 7.50 (WORM).

No. 1960 SYRUP CUP.
With Plate.

Plain, . . $7.00 (WHISKER).
Hammered, . 8.00 (WHISPER).

TRADE MARK.
WHITE METAL.

GOLD AND SILVER PLATE.

TRADE MARK.
NICKEL SILVER.

No. 1944. SATIN TEA SET.

Style.	Set of Six Pieces.	Coffee.	Tea, Six Half Pints.	Water, Five Half Pints.	Sugar.	Cream, Gold Lined.	Slop, Gold Lined.
Plain or Satin, .	$50.00 (BEND).	$11.75	$9.75	$8.75	$6.25	$7.00	$6.50
Hammered, .	62.00 (VAINLY).	14.50	12.50	11.00	7.50	8.75	7.75

No. 76—22 inch Satin WAITER, . $35.00 (BENEATH). Hammered, . . $41.00 (WILDER).

Patent Plate Glass Protector, . $5.25 extra (BENEFICE).

No. 1944 BUTTER DISH.

With Patent Crystal Drainer.

Plain or Satin, . $7.50 (BENIGN).
Hammered, . . 8.25 (TARE).

No. 1944 SPOON HOLDER.

Gold Lined.

Plain or Satin, . $6.50 (BEQUEST).
Hammered, . 8.00 (TARRY).

No. 1944 SYRUP CUP.

With Plate.

Plain or Satin, . $7.25 (BERTH).
Hammered, . 8.50 (TARTARIC).

No. 1944 KETTLE.

Nine Half Pints.

Plain or Satin, . $25.00 (BESIDE).
Hammered, . 28.00 (TARTLY).

GOLD AND SILVER PLATE.

No. 1924 BUTTER DISH.
With Patent Crystal Drainer.
Plain, . . $8.00 (ADJOIN).
Chased A, . 9.50 (ADJUST).

No. 1924 SPOON HOLDER.
Gold Lined.
Plain, . . $6.75 (ADHERE).
Chased A, . 7.50 (ADIEU).

No. 1924 SYRUP CUP.
With Plate.
Plain, . . $7.00 (ADO).
Chased A, . 7.50 (ADOPT).

No. 1924. CHASED A TEA SET.

Style.	Set of Six Pieces.	Coffee.	Tea, Six Half Pints.	Water, Five Half Pints.	Sugar.	Cream, Gold Lined.	Slop, Gold Lined.
Plain, . . .	$55.00 (ADD).	$13.00	$10.75	$9.75	$6.75	$7.75	$7.00
Chased A, . .	64.00 (ADAPT).	15.50	12.50	11.50	8.00	8.75	7.75

No. 1924 URN. Fifteen Half Pints. Plain, . $30.00 (ADMIRE). Chased A, . $34.00 (ADMIT).

No. 52—26 inch Chased A WAITER, . $60.00 (ADDICT). Patent Plate Glass Protector, . $7.50 extra (ADDLE).

Trade Mark.
WHITE METAL.

Trade Mark.
NICKEL SILVER.

No. 1956. HAMMERED AND APPLIED TEA SET.

Style.	Set of Six Pieces.	Coffee.	Tea, Six Half Pints.	Water, Five Half Pints.	Sugar.	Cream, Gold Lined.	Slop, Gold Lined.
Plain, ...	$50.00 (weigh).	$11.50	$9.75	$8.75	$6.25	$7.25	$6.50
Hammered, ...	58.00 (welcome).	13.00	11.25	10.75	7.25	8.25	7.50
Hammered and Applied, .	62.00 (welfare).	14.25	12.25	11.50	7.50	8.75	7.75

No. 92—24 inch Waiter. Satin, . $42.00 (welsh). Hammered, . $50.00 (welter). Patent Plate Glass Protector, . $6.75 extra (west).

No. 1956 Kettle. Plain, . . 24.00 (western). Hammered, . 27.00 (whale). Hammered and Applied, . . . $29.00 (wharf).

No. 1956 Butter Dish.
With Patent Crystal Drainer.

Plain, . . . $7.50 (whip).
Hammered, . . 8.50 (whirl).
Hammered and Applied, 9.50 (whisk).

No. 1956 Spoon Holder.
Gold Lined.

Plain, . . . $7.00 (whence).
Hammered, . . 8.00 (where).
Hammered and Applied, 8.75 (whiff).

No. 1956 Syrup Cup.
With Plate.

Plain, . . . $7.50 (whither).
Hammered, . . 8.50 (whiting).
Hammered and Applied, 9.25 (whitlow).

GOLD AND SILVER PLATE.

No. 1935 Spoon Holder.
Gold Lined.
Chased, . $8.00 (ABBOT).

No. 1935 Butter Dish.
With Patent Crystal Drainer.
Chased, . $9.00 (ABDUCT).

No. 1935 Syrup Cup.
With Plate.
Chased, . $8.50 (ABED).

No. 1935. CHASED TEA SET.

Style.	Set of Six Pieces.	Coffee.	Tea, Six Half Pints.	Water, Five Half Pints.	Sugar.	Cream, Gold Lined.	Slop, Gold Lined.
Chased, . .	$64.00 (ABACK).	$15.50	$12.50	$11.50	$8.00	$8.75	$7.75

No. 59—26 inch Waiter. 1935 Chased, . $60.00 (ABAFT).

Patent Plate Glass Protector, $7.00 extra (ABASE).

No. 1935 Kettle. Chased, Seven Half Pints, 27.00 (ABATE).

No. 1935 Urn. Chased, Fourteen Half Pints, $34.00 (ABBE).

GOLD AND SILVER PLATE.

No. 1940. CHASED D, TEA SET.

Style.	Set of Six Pieces.	Coffee.	Tea, Six Half Pints.	Water, Five Half Pints.	Sugar.	Cream, Gold Lined.	Slop, Gold Lined.
No. 1940 Chased D (with Feet),	$61.00 (ABROGATE).	$14.00	$11.75	$10.75	$7.75	$8.75	$8.00
No. 1938 Chased (without Feet),	58.00 (ABSOLUTE).	13.50	11.25	10.25	7.25	8.25	7.50

No. 70—26 inch Chased WAITER, . $60.00 (ABSOLVE). Patent Plate Glass Protector, . $7.00 extra (ABSTRACT).

No. 1938 BUTTER DISH.
With Patent Crystal Drainer.
Chased, . . $9.00 (ABSTINENCE).
No. 1940. With Feet.
Chased D, . $9.50 (ABUNDANCE).

No. 1938 URN.
Fifteen Half Pints.
Chased, . . $33.00 (ABRASION).
No. 1940.
Chased D, . . $33.00 (ABOVE).

No. 1938 SPOON HOLDER.
Gold Lined.
Chased, . . $7.50 (ABJURE).
No. 1940. With Feet.
Chased D, . $8.00 (ABILITY).

No. 1938 SYRUP CUP.
With Plate.
Chased, . . $8.00 (ABOLISH).
No. 1940. With Feet.
Chased D, . . $8.50 (ABLUTION).

GOLD AND SILVER PLATE

No. 1926. CHASED TEA SET.

Style.	Set of Six Pieces.	Coffee.	Tea, Six Half Pints.	Water, Five Half Pints.	Sugar.	Cream, Gold Lined.	Slop, Gold Lined.
Plain, ...	$46.00 (AUGUST).	$10.50	$8.50	$7.50	$6.00	$7.00	$6.50
Chased, ...	53.00 (AUGER).	12.00	9.75	8.75	7.00	8.00	7.50

No. 1926½. TEA SET, with Border around centre (see Swing Kettle), same price as 1926, Plain (AUNT).

No. 56—24 inch Chased WAITER, $42.50 (AUTHOR). Patent Plate Glass Protector, $7.00 extra (AVAIL).

No. 1926 BUTTER DISH.
With Patent Crystal Drainer.

No. 1926. Plain, . . $7.25 (AVAST).
No. 1926. Chased, . 8.25 (AVERT).
No. 1926½. Plain, . . 7.25 (AVOID).

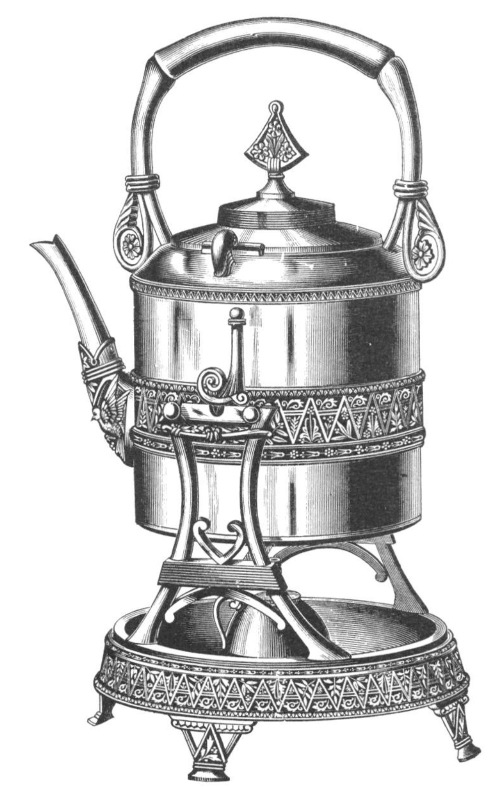

No. 1926½ SYRUP CUP.
With Plate.

No. 1926½. Plain, . $6.00 (AWARD).
No. 1926. Chased, . 6.75 (AWAIT).

No. 1926½ SPOON HOLDER.
Gold Lined.

No. 1926½. Plain, . $5.75 (AWL).
No. 1926. Chased, . 6.50 (AXE).

No. 1926½ SWING KETTLE.
Eleven Half Pints.

No. 1926½. Plain, . $22.00 (AXIS).
No. 1926. Chased, . 24.00 (AXLE).

No. 1926 URN. Fifteen Half Pints. Similar to 1927, only round, Plain, $28.00 (AWAKE). Chased, $30.00 (AWAY).

GOLD AND SILVER PLATE.

No. 1925. CHASED TEA SET.

Style.	Set of Six Pieces.	Coffee.	Tea, Six Half Pints.	Water, Five Half Pints.	Sugar.	Cream, Gold Lined.	Slop, Gold Lined.
Chased, . .	$60.00 (AMBER).	$13.50	$11.75	$11.25	$7.50	$8.50	$7.50

No. 1925 Butter Dish.
With Patent Crystal Drainer.
Chased, . . $6.75 (AMBLE).

No. 1925 Urn.
Thirteen Half Pints.
Chased, . . $33.00 (AMBUSH).

No. 1925 Spoon Holder.
Gold Lined.
Chased, . . $7.00 (AMEND).

No. 1925 Syrup Cup.
With Plate.
Chased, . . $7.00 (AMID).

WHITE METAL.

GOLD AND SILVER PLATE.

NICKEL SILVER.

No. 1939. CHASED TEA SET.

	Style.	Set of Six Pieces.	Coffee.	Tea, Six Half Pints.	Water, Five Half Pints.	Sugar.	Cream, Gold Lined.	Slop, Gold Lined.
No. 1939.	Plain (without Feet),	$46.00 (ABUTTAL).	$10.50	$8.50	$7.50	$6.00	$7.00	$6.50
No. 1939.	Chased (without Feet),	54.00 (ABUTMENT).	12.50	10.50	9.25	7.00	7.75	7.00
No. 1941.	Chased D (with Feet),	57.00 (ABUNDANT).	13.00	11.00	9.75	7.50	8.25	7.50

No. 62—24 inch Chased WAITER, . $42.50 (ABSTRACTED). Patent Plate Glass Protector, . $7.00 extra (ABSOLUTELY).

No. 1941 BUTTER DISH.

No. 1941. Chased D (with Feet), $9.00 (ABERDEEN).
No. 1939. Plain (without Feet), 7.50 (ABERNETHY).
No. 1939. Chased (without Feet), 8.50 (ABINGDON).

No. 1941 SYRUP CUP.
With Plate.
Chased D, . $8.00 (ABNORMAL).

No. 1939. Without Feet. With Plate.
Plain, . . $7.00 (ABOMINATE).
Chased, . . 7.75 (ABREAST).

No. 1941 SPOON HOLDER.
Gold Lined.
Chased D, . $7.50 (ABET).

No. 1939. Without Feet. Gold Lined.
Plain, . . $6.25 (ABETTOR).
Chased, . . 7.00 (ABEYANCE).

No. 1941 URN.
Twelve Half Pints.
Chased D, . $31.00 (ABROACH).

No. 1939.
Plain, . . $27.00 (ABRUZZO).
Chased, . 31.00 (ABORIGINAL).

GOLD AND SILVER PLATE.

No. 1927. PLAIN TEA SET—OVAL.

Style.	Set of Six Pieces.	Coffee.	Tea, Six Half Pints.	Water, Five Half Pints.	Sugar.	Cream, Gold Lined.	Slop, Gold Lined.
Plain, . .	$54.00 (BACKBONE).	$12.50	$10.50	$9.25	$6.75	$8.00	$7.00
Chased, . .	62.00 (BACK).	14.50	12.50	11.00	7.50	8.75	7.75

No. 56—26 inch Chased WAITER, . $50.00 (BACON). Patent Plate Glass Protector, . $7.50 extra (BAD).

No. 1927 KETTLE, Plain, Nine Half Pints, . $24.00 (BAG). Chased, . $26.00 (BAIL).

No. 1927 BUTTER DISH.
With Patent Crystal Drainer.
Plain, . . . $8.25 (BALL).
Chased, . . 9.00 (BAND).

No. 1927 URN.
Twelve Half Pints.
Plain, . . $31.00 (BAIT).
Chased, . . 34.00 (BAKE).

No. 1927 SPOON HOLDER.
Gold Lined.
Plain, . . $6.75 (BALD).
Chased, . . 7.50 (BALE).

No. 1927 SYRUP CUP.
With Plate.
Plain, . . $7.00 (BANE).
Chased, . . 7.75 (BANG).

Trade Mark.
WHITE METAL.

GOLD AND SILVER PLATE.

Trade Mark.
NICKEL SILVER.

No. 1962. SATIN TEA SET.

Style.	Set of Six Pieces.	Coffee.	Tea, Six Half Pints.	Water, Five Half Pints.	Sugar.	Cream, Gold Lined.	Slop, Gold Lined.
Satin, . . .	$45.00 (REPUGNANCE).	$10.25	$8.25	$7.25	$6.00	6.75	$6.50
Satin, Engraved, .	55.00 (RESIDUARY).	12.50	10.50	9.50	7.25	7.75	7.50

No. 1962 Butter Dish.

With Patent Crystal Drainer.

Satin, . . . $7.50 (RELUCTANT).

Satin, Engraved, . 8.50 (RENOVATION).

No. 1962 Urn.

Fifteen Half Pints.

Satin, . . . $26.50 (RETRACTION).

Satin, Engraved, . 29.50 (REMAINDER).

No. 1962 Spoon Holder.

Gold Lined.

Satin, . . . $6.00 (RESOLUTELY).

Satin, Engraved, . 7.00 (RETREAT).

No. 1962 Syrup Cup.

With Plate.

Satin, . . . $6.50 (RESOLVENT).

Satin, Engraved, . 7.50 (REPAYMENT).

GOLD AND SILVER PLATE.

No. 1931. PLAIN TEA SET.

Style.	Set of Six Pieces.	Coffee.	Tea, Six Half Pints.	Water, Five Half Pints.	Sugar.	Cream, Gold Lined.	Slop, Gold Lined.
Plain, . . .	$43.00 (BEER).	$10.00	$8.00	$7.00	$5.50	$6.50	$6.00

No. 1931 Butter Dish.
With Patent Crystal Drainer.
Plain, . $7.00 (BEET).

No. 1931 Urn.
Fifteen Half Pints.
Plain, . $25.00 (BEG).

No. 1931 Spoon Holder.
Gold Lined.
Plain, . $5.50 (BEING).

No. 1931 Syrup Cup.
With Plate.
Plain, . $6.00 (BELIE).

GOLD AND SILVER PLATE.

No. 1800. CHASED TEA SET.

Style.	Set of Six Pieces.	Coffee.	Tea, Six Half Pints.	Water, Five Half Pints.	Sugar.	Cream, Gold Lined.	Slop, Gold Lined.	Spoon Holder, Gold Lined.
Plain, . .	$36.00 (BELOW).	$7.75	$6.75	$6.25	$4.25	$5.75	$5.25	$4.25
Chased, . .	42.50 (BELL).	9.25	8.25	7.50	5.00	6.50	6.00	5.00

No. 117. CHASED TEA SET.

Style.	Set of Six Pieces.	Coffee.	Tea, Six Half Pints.	Water, Five Half Pints.	Sugar.	Cream, Gold Lined.	Slop, Gold Lined.
Plain, . .	$36.00 (BELT).	$8.00	$6.50	$6.00	$4.25	$5.75	$5.50
Chased, . .	42.50 (BENCH).	9.25	8.25	7.50	5.00	6.50	6.00

TRADE MARK.
WHITE METAL.

GOLD AND SILVER PLATE.

TRADE MARK.
NICKEL SILVER.

No. 1971. SATIN, ENGRAVED TEA SET.

Style.	Set of Six Pieces.	Coffee.	Tea, Six Half Pints.	Water, Five Half Pints.	Sugar.	Cream, Gold Lined.	Slop, Gold Lined.
Satin, ...	$40.00 (REGARDER).	$9.25	$7.50	$6.75	$5.00	$6.00	$5.50
Satin, Engraved, .	47.50 (REGENCY).	10.75	9.25	8.25	6.00	7.00	6.25

No. 1971 SPOON HOLDER. Gold Lined. Satin, . $6.00 (REGRATE). Satin, Engraved, . $7.00 (REGULATOR).

No. 95—24 inch WAITER. Satin Shield, . $37.50 (REGULUS). Patent Plate Glass Protector, . $7.00 extra (REHEAR).

No. 050. TEA STRAINER. Nickel Silver.
Plain or Satin, . $1.50 (ROUNCE).
(Full Size.)

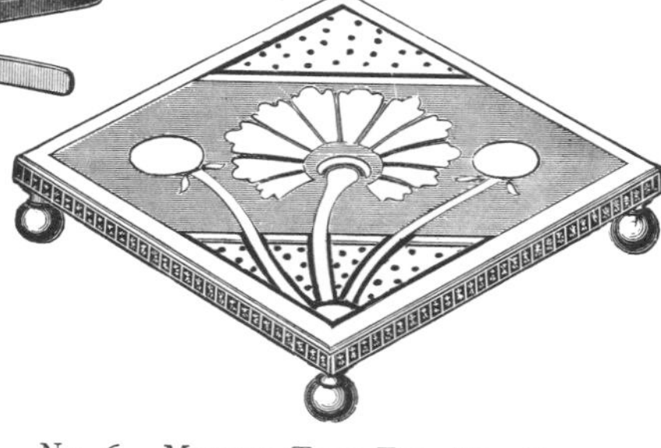

No. 6. MINTON TILE TEA POT STAND.
Silver, . $2.25 (PRIVATE).

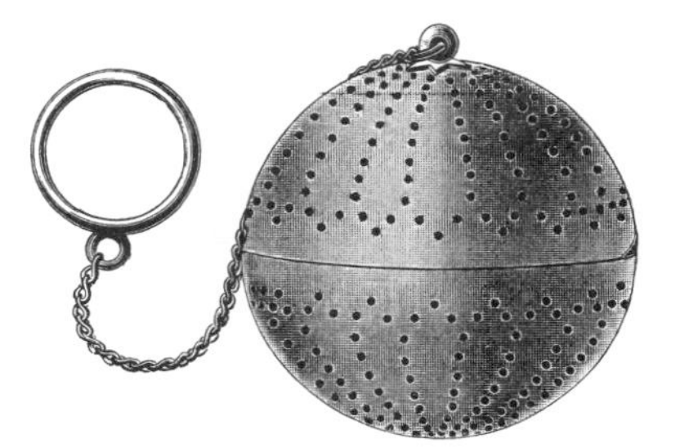

No. 060. TEA BALL. Nickel Silver.
Plain or Satin, . $3.00 (ROVER).
(Full Size.)

No. 7. MINTON TILE TEA POT STAND.
Silver, . $3.75 (PRISTINE).

No. 100. SATIN C, CHOCOLATE POT.
Six Half Pints.
Old Silver, . . . $13.50 (REITERATE).
Silver, Gold Inlaid, . 16.00 (REJECTION).

No. 8. LONGWY TEA POT STAND.
Silver, ... $5.00 (PRIORY).
Silver, Gold Inlaid, . . 6.00 (PRISON).

No. 101. SATIN C, CHOCOLATE POT.
Six Half Pints.
Old Silver, ... $13.50 (RELIABLE).
Silver, Gold Inlaid, . 16.00 (REMOTELY).

SWING KETTLES.

(ONE-THIRD SIZE.)

No. 2700.

Five Half Pints.

Satin, . . . $19.00 (VOCABLE).
Satin, Engraved, . 21.00 (VOLCANIC).

No. 2947.

Five Half Pints.

Fluted, . $23.00 (VIVIDLY).

No. 2964.

Five Half Pints.

Satin, . . . $19.00 (VOGUE).
Satin, Engraved, . 21.00 (VOCALIC).

No. 2965.

Five Half Pints.

Satin, . . . $18.50 (VIXEN).
Satin, Engraved, . 20.50 (VIXENLY).

No. 2500.

Seven Half Pints.

Plain, . . . $21.00 (VOLATILE).
Satin, . . . 21.00 (VOIDABLE).
Satin, Engraved, . 23.00 (VOID).

No. 2970.

Five Half Pints.

Embossed, . . $20.00 (VOCATIVE).
Embossed Old Silver, 21.00 (VOCALIZE).

NICKEL SILVER TEA SETS.

(ONE-THIRD SIZE.)

No. 01820. ENGRAVED TEA SET.

Style.	Set of Six Pieces.	Coffee.	Tea, Six Half Pints.	Water, Five Half Pints.	Sugar.	Cream, Gold Lined.	Slop, Gold Lined.
Plain, ...	$162.25 (RE-ASSURE).	$36.75	$33.75	$32.25	$22.00	$19.00	$18.50
Engraved, . . .	186.75 (REBATE).	41.25	38.25	36.75	25.75	22.00	22.75

No. 06030—26 inch Engraved Waiter, $140.00 (REBEL).

No. 01820 URN.

Fifteen Half Pints.

Plain, . . $85.00 (REBOUND).
Engraved, . 95.00 (REBUFF).

No. 01820 BUTTER DISH.

Plain, . . $21.00 (REBUKE).
Engraved, . 25.00 (REBUS).

No. 01820 SPOON HOLDER.

Gold Lined.

Plain, . . $16.50 (RECALL).
Engraved, . 19.50 (RECANT).

No. 01820 SYRUP CUP.

With Plate.

Plain, . . $21.50 (RECEDE).
Engraved, . 25.50 (RECEIPT).

NICKEL SILVER, SILVER SOLDERED.

TRADE MARK.
WHITE METAL.

GOLD AND SILVER PLATE.

TRADE MARK.
NICKEL SILVER.

No. 01848 SPOON HOLDER.
Gold Lined.
Plain, . . $14.50 (REPEALER).
Satin, . . 14.50 (ROGATION).

No. 01848 BUTTER DISH.
Plain, . . $16.50 (ROCKY).
Satin, . . 16.50 (ROGUISH).

No. 01848 SYRUP CUP.
With Plate.
Plain, . . $19.00 (ROLLER).
Satin, . . 19.00 (ROMANIC).

No. 01848. SATIN TEA SET.

Style.	Set of Five Pieces.	Coffee.	Tea.	Sugar.	Cream, Gold Lined.	Slop, Gold Lined.
Plain, . .	$106.00 (ROMPISH).	$29.50	$27.25	$17.50	$16.50	$15.25
Satin, . .	106.00 (ROOMY).	29.50	27.25	17.50	16.50	15.25

No. 01848 SWING KETTLE. Ten Half Pints. Satin, . . $80.00 (ROPERY).

NICKEL SILVER, SILVER SOLDERED.

GOLD AND SILVER PLATE.

No. 01810. ENGRAVED TEA SET.

Style.	Set of Five Pieces.	Coffee.	Tea, Six Half Pints.	Sugar.	Cream, Gold Lined.	Slop, Gold Lined.	Spoon Holder, Gold Lined.
Plain, ...	$130.00 (RECEIVE).	$36.75	$33.75	$22.00	$19.00	$18.50	$16.50
Engraved, . . .	150.00 (RECENT).	41.25	38.25	25.75	22.00	22.75	19.50

No. 06020—26 inch Engraved Waiter, . $140.00 (RECEPTACLE).

No. 01810 SYRUP CUP.

With Plate.

Plain, . . $21.50 (RECEIVER).
Chased, . . 25.50 (RECENTLY).

No. 01810 BUTTER DISH.

Plain, . . . $21.00 (RECESS).
Engraved, . . 25.00 (RECEPTION).

No. 01810 KETTLE.

Plain, . . . $85.00 (RECIPROCAL).
Engraved, . . 95.00 (RECIPIENT).

NICKEL SILVER, SILVER SOLDERED.

GOLD AND SILVER PLATE.

BUTTER DISH.

No. 01847, . . $16.00 (CANDIDLY).

No. 01847 SWING KETTLE.

Eight Half Pints.

Satin, . . $72.00 (ROSINY).

SYRUP CUP.

No. 01847, . . $17.50 (CAMPAIGN).
Without Plate, . 13.50 (CARBON).

No. 01847. SATIN TEA SET.

Set of Five Pieces.	Coffee.	Tea.	Sugar.	Cream, Gold Lined.	Slop, Gold Lined.	Spoon Holder, Gold Lined.
$80.00 (WHITEN).	$22.00	$20.00	$13.50	$14.50	$10.00	$13.50

NICKEL SILVER, SILVER SOLDERED.

TRADE MARK.
WHITE METAL.

NICKEL SILVER TÊTE-À-TÊTE SETS.

TRADE MARK.
NICKEL SILVER.

(ONE-THIRD SIZE.)

No. 0111. SUGAR.
Plain or Satin, . $12.25 (ROSEATE).

No. 0111. CREAM—Covered.
Plain or Satin, . $10.25 (ROUNDHEAD).
One-Half Pint.

No. 0108. TÊTE-À-TÊTE SET.

Style.	Set of Three Pieces.	Coffee, Two Half Pints.	Sugar.	Cream, One Half Pint.
Plain or Satin, . .	$46.50 (ROTARY).	$22.50	$12.50	$11.50

No. 0109. TÊTE-À-TÊTE SET.

Style.	Set of Four Pieces.	Coffee, Two Half Pints.	Tea, Two Half Pints.	Sugar.	Cream, One Fourth Pint.
Plain or Satin,	$59.00 (ROUSER).	$20.00	$16.50	$12.25	$10.25

No. 0110. HOTEL SET. PLAIN OR SATIN.

CHOCOLATE.
Two Half Pints, $20.00 (RUMBLER).
Four Half Pints, 24.00 (RUMINATOR).

TEA, Two Half Pints, . $19.00 (RUMPUS).
COFFEE, Two Half Pints, 20.00 (RUNIC).
COFFEE, Four Half Pints, 24.00 (RUPTION).

SUGAR.
For Two Persons, $12.50 (RUSHER).
For Four Persons, 17.50 (SACKFUL).

CREAM.
One-Fourth Pint, $7.50 (SADDEN).
One-Third Pint, 9.00 (VITRIFY).
Two Half Pints, 15.00 (VIVACITY).

HOT MILK—Covered.—Four Half Pints, 17.50 (VOLTAIC).

NICKEL SILVER, SILVER SOLDERED.

GOLD AND SILVER PLATE.

No. 0106. TÊTE-À-TÊTE SET.

Set of Four Pieces.
For One Person, $56.00 (REPRINT).
For Two Persons, 74.50 (REPROOF).

Coffee.
Two Half Pints, $19.00
Three Half Pints, 24.00

Tea.
Three Fourth Pints, $16.50
Two Half Pints, . 20.50

Sugar.
$11.00
16.00

Cream.
One Half Pint, $9.50
Three Fourth Pints, 14.00

No. 0104. TÊTE-À-TÊTE SET.

Set of Four Pieces.
$57.00 (REQUITE).

Coffee, Two Half Pints.
$20.00

Tea, Three Fourth Pints.
$16.50

Sugar.
$11.00

Cream, One Half Pint.
$9.50

(Cream, One Fourth Pint.
$6.50)

No. 0101. TÊTE-À-TÊTE SET.

TEA OR COFFEE.

One Half Pint, . .	$15.00	(RESONANT).
Two Half Pints, . .	16.50	(RESORT).
Three Half Pints, . .	19.00	(RESOUND).
Four Half Pints, . .	21.00	(RESOURCE).

SUGAR.

For One Person, . .	$10.00	(RESPITE).
For Two Persons, . .	11.50	(RESPOND).
For Three Persons, . .	13.50	(REST).
For Four Persons, . .	15.50	(RESTIVE).

CREAM.

One Third Pint, . .	$9.00	(RESTORE).
One Half Pint, . .	10.50	(RESTRAIN).
Three Fourth Pints, .	12.50	(RESTRICT).
Two Half Pints, . .	14.50	(RESULT).

NICKEL SILVER, SILVER SOLDERED.

TRADE MARK.
WHITE METAL.

GOLD AND SILVER PLATE.

TRADE MARK.
NICKEL SILVER.

No. 0103. TÊTE-À-TÊTE SET.

Style.	Set of Three Pieces.	Tea or Coffee, Two Half Pints.	Sugar.	Cream, One Half Pint.
Plain or Satin, . .	$39.00 (RULABLE).	$16.50	$12.00	$10.50

No. 0105. TÊTE-À-TÊTE SET.

Style.	Set of Four Pieces	Coffee, Three Half Pints.	Tea, Three Fourth Pints.	Sugar.	Cream, Two Half Pints.
Plain or Satin, . .	$57.00 (RESERVE).	$20.00	$16.50	$11.00	$9.50

No. 011. FRENCH COFFEE POT.

Plain or Satin.

Two Half Pints, . .	$20.00 (VERSER).
Four Half Pints, . .	24.00 (VERNACULAR).
Six Half Pints, . .	27.00 (VERSIFY).
Eight Half Pints, . .	32.00 (VERTEX).

No. 012. FRENCH COFFEE POT.

Plain or Satin.

Two Half Pints, . .	$21.00 (VERMIFUGE).
Four Half Pints, .	25.00 (VERSATILE).
Six Half Pints, . .	28.00 (VERST).
Eight Half Pints, . .	33.00 (VERT).

NICKEL SILVER, SILVER SOLDERED.

NICKEL SILVER TOAST RACKS.

(One-Third Size.)

NICKEL SILVER, SILVER SOLDERED.

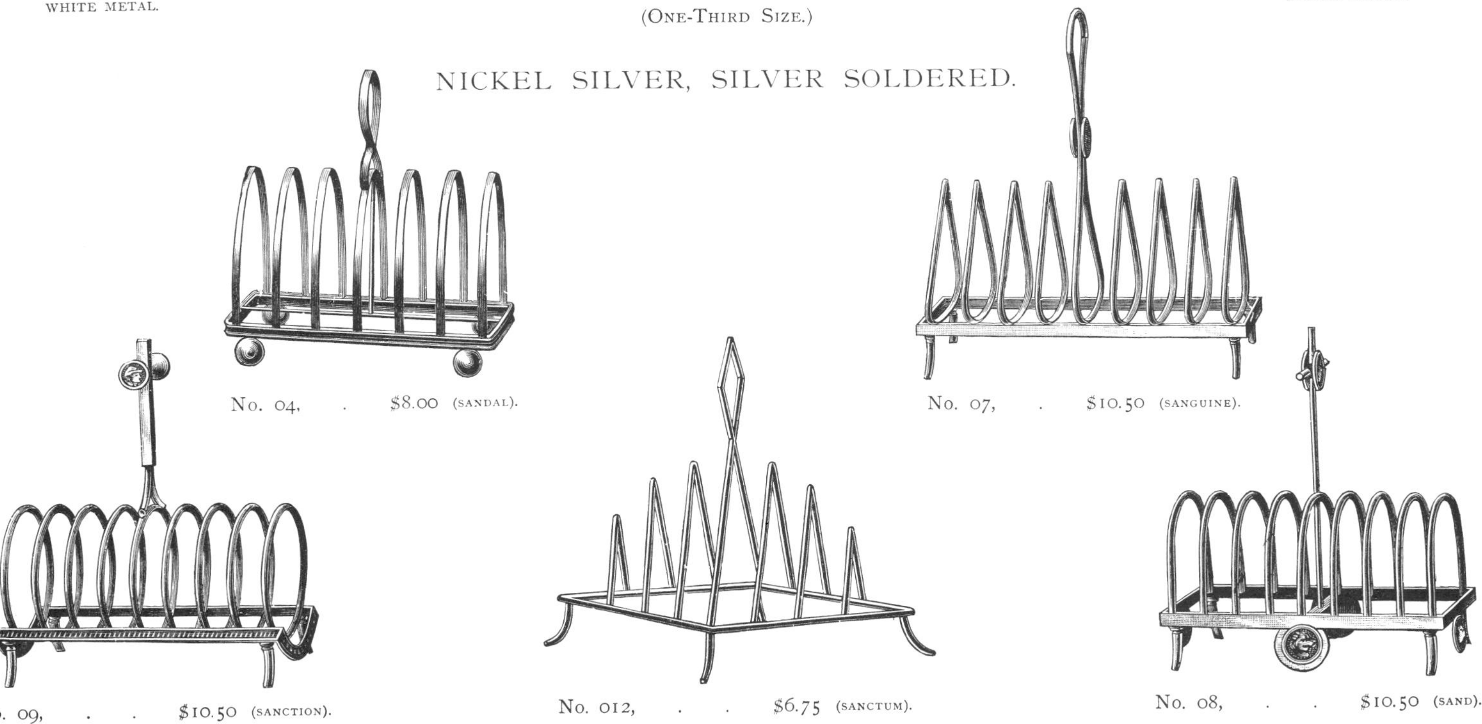

No. 04, . $8.00 (sandal).

No. 07, . $10.50 (sanguine).

No. 09, . . $10.50 (sanction).

No. 012, . . $6.75 (sanctum).

No. 08, . . $10.50 (sand).

TEA CADDIES.

(Half Size.)

No. 8. Brocade.

Brocade, . . $5.50 (waft).
Brocade, Old Silver, 6.00 (vote).
Brocade, Gold Inlaid, 7.50 (voluntary).

No. 8. Embossed.

Embossed, . $15.00 (wady).
Gold Inlaid, . 18.00 (voracity).

No. 8. Moorish.

Hammered, Old Silver, $6.50 (wader).
Moorish, Old Silver, 7.00 (voracious).
Gold Inlaid, . . 9.00 (voluble).

No. 8. Satin Engraved.

Satin, . . $5.00 (vulgate).
Satin, Engraved, 6.00 (volute).
Gold Inlaid, . 8.00 (voltaism).

No. 9.

Silver, . . $5.50 (ventricle).
Old Silver, . 6.25 (zealous).

No. 10.

Silver, . . $8.00 (vengeful).
Old Silver, . 9.00 (roughen).

No. 11.

Satin, . . $8.00 (wrestler).
Satin, Engraved, 9.00 (rotundity).

COFFEE SETS.

(ONE-THIRD SIZE.)

No. 864. SATIN, ENGRAVED COFFEE SET.

Style.	Set of Three Pieces.	Coffee, Six Half Pints.	Sugar.	Cream, Gold Lined.
Satin, ...	$28.50 (CARRIER).	$14.50	$7.00	$7.00
Satin, Engraved, ...	35.00 (CATAPULT).	17.00	9.00	9.00
Satin, Engraved, XX Gold Inlaid,	56.00 (CATARACT).	25.00	15.50	15.50

No. 870. SATIN, ENGRAVED COFFEE SET.

Style.	Set of Three Pieces.	Coffee, Four Half Pints.	Sugar.	Cream, Gold Lined.
Satin, . .	$30.00 (VESSEL).	$13.50	$8.50	$8.00
Satin, Engraved,	37.50 (VESTED).	16.50	10.75	10.25

No. 102—11 inch WAITER. Satin, . . $10.00 (VEST).
Satin, Engraved, 11.50 (VERVAIN).

Patent Plate Glass Protector, $2.00 extra (VERTICALLY).

No. 867. COFFEE SET.

Set of Three Pieces.	Coffee, Five Half Pints.	Sugar.	Cream, Gold Lined.
$27.50 (WHITTLE).	$14.00	$7.00	$6.50

No. 866. TÊTE-À-TÊTE SET. SMALLER.

Set of Three Pieces.	Coffee, Three Half Pints.	Sugar.	Cream, Gold Lined.
$19.50 (WICK).	$9.00	$5.50	$5.00

No. 314—12 inch WAITER. Satin, . $6.50 (WICKER).
Patent Plate Glass Protector, . $2.00 extra (WICKING).

No. 869. TÊTE-À-TÊTE SET.

LOUIS XV, SATIN ENGRAVED, XX GOLD INLAID.

Set of Four Pieces.	Coffee, Two Half Pints.	Tea, Three Fourth Pints.	Sugar.	Cream, Gold Lined, One Half Pint.
$40.00 (TWIRL).	$12.50	$11.50	$8.00	$8.00

No. 72 — 17 Inch WAITER, Satin Engraved, XX Gold Inlaid, $24.00 (TWITCH).

Patent Plate Glass Protector, $2.50 extra (BULGE).

No. 875. COFFEE SET.

SATIN ENGRAVED, XX GOLD INLAID.

Set of Three Pieces.	Coffee, Seven Half Pints.	Sugar.	Cream, Gold Lined, Two Half Pints.
$53.00 (TWOPLY).	$23.00	$15.00	$15.00

No. 107 — 16 Inch WAITER, Satin Engraved, XX Gold Inlaid. $30.00 (TYRANNY).

Patent Plate Glass Protector, $2.50 extra (PREDICATE).

GOLD AND SILVER PLATE.

No. 863. COFFEE SET.

Style.	Set of Three Pieces.	Coffee, Six Half Pints.	Sugar.	Cream, Gold Lined.
Silver, ...	$27.50 (CONNECTION).	$14.00	$7.00	$6.50
X Gold Inlaid, . .	33.50 (CONSEQUENT).	17.00	8.50	8.00
XX Gold Inlaid, .	39.50 (CONSTABLE).	20.00	10.00	9.50

No. 865. CHASED COFFEE SET.

Style.	Set of Three Pieces.	Coffee, Five Half Pints.	Sugar.	Cream, Gold Lined.
Satin,	$24.50 (WIDELY).	$12.00	$6.50	$6.00
Hammered,	28.00 (WIDEN).	13.50	7.50	7.00
Chased,	30.50 (WIDTH).	15.00	8.00	7.50

No. 97 WAITER.		
	Satin, . .	$9.50 (WIGWAM).
	Hammered, .	11.00 (WILLOW).
	Chased, . .	11.00 (WINCE).

Patent Plate Glass Protector, . $2.75 extra (WINDING).

No. 871. MOORISH COFFEE SET.

Style.	Set of Three Pieces.	Coffee, Four Half Pints.	Sugar.	Cream, Gold Lined.
Moorish, Old Silver,	$42.50 (VERTIGO).	$19.00	$12.00	$11.50
Moorish, Gold Inlaid,	56.00 (VESTING).	25.00	16.00	15.00

No. 103—12 inch WAITER.		
	Moorish, Old Silver, .	$13.50 (VESTRY).
	Moorish, Gold Inlaid, .	19.50 (VETCH).

Patent Plate Glass Protector, . $2.00 extra (VEXATION).

Trade Mark.
WHITE METAL.

GOLD AND SILVER PLATE.

Trade Mark.
NICKEL SILVER.

No. 1851 M. PLAIN TEA SET.

(For Two or Three Persons.)

Style.	Set of Five Pieces.	Coffee, Four Half Pints.	Tea, Three Half Pints.	Sugar.	Cream, Three Fourth Pints, Gold Lined.	Slop, Gold Lined.
Plain, . .	$29.25 (between).	$7.25	$6.50	$5.75	$5.25	$4.50
Satin, . .	29.25 (beverage).	7.25	6.50	5.75	5.25	4.50

No. 79—17 inch Waiter. Satin, . $17.00 (bewilder).

Patent Plate Glass Protector, . $3.25 extra (vintager).

TÊTE-À-TÊTE SETS.

(One-Third Size.)

No. 1851. PLAIN TÊTE-À-TÊTE SET.

Style.	Set of Four Pieces.	Coffee, Two Half Pints.	Tea, Three Fourth Pints.	Sugar.	Cream, One Half Pint, Gold Lined.
Plain, .	$18.00 (bisect).	$5.75	$4.75	$4.00	$3.50

No. 861. TÊTE-À-TÊTE SET.

Style.	Set of Four Pieces.	Coffee, Three Half Pints.	Tea, Two Half Pints.	Sugar.	Cream, One Fourth Pint, Covered.
Plain, . .	$25.00 (cestus).	$8.00	$7.00	$5.50	$4.50
Satin, . .	25.00 (chagrin).	8.00	7.00	5.50	4.50
Hammered, .	30.00 (chowder).	9.75	8.50	6.50	5.25

GOLD AND SILVER PLATE.

No. 1857. CHASED TÊTE-À-TÊTE SET.

Style.	Set of Four Pieces.	Coffee, Two Half Pints.	Tea, Three Fourth Pints.	Sugar.	Cream, One Half Pint, Gold Lined.
Chased, ...	$20.00 (BLANCH).	$6.25	$5.50	$4.25	$4.00
Chased, Gold Inlaid, .	23.00 (BLAND).	7.00	6.25	5.00	4.75

No. 873. SATIN TÊTE-À-TÊTE SET.

Style.	Set of Four Pieces.	Coffee, Two Half Pints.	Tea, Three Fourth Pints.	Sugar.	Cream, One Half Pint, Gold Lined.
Satin, ...	$18.50 (VIOLENT).	$5.75	$5.25	$3.75	$3.75
Satin, Engraved,	22.50 (VENTURER).	7.00	6.50	4.50	4.50

No. 876. FLUTED TÊTE-À-TÊTE SET.

Style.	Set of Four Pieces.	Coffee, Two Half Pints.	Tea, Three Fourth Pints.	Sugar.	Cream, One Half Pint, Gold Lined.
Fluted, .	$24.00 (VISOR).	$7.75	$6.50	$5.00	$4.75

No. 105—14 inch WAITER. Satin, . . . $12.00 (VISIONARY).
Satin, Engraved, 14.00 (VITREOUS).

Patent Plate Glass Protector, . . . $2.00 extra (VIRAGO).

No. 869. SATIN, ENGRAVED TÊTE-À-TÊTE SET.

Style.	Set of Four Pieces.	Coffee, Two Half Pints.	Tea, Three Fourth Pints.	Sugar.	Cream, One Half Pint, Gold Lined.
Satin, . .	$18.00 (VITAL).	$5.50	$5.00	$3.75	$3.75
Satin, Engraved,	22.50 (VISIT).	7.00	6.50	4.50	4.50

No. 101—10 inch WAITER. Satin, . . . $8.50 (VISABLE).
Satin, Engraved, 10.00 (VIRUS).

Patent Plate Glass Protector, . . . $1.75 extra (VIOLENCE).

TRADE MARK.
WHITE METAL.

GOLD AND SILVER PLATE.

TRADE MARK.
NICKEL SILVER.

No. 872. SATIN, ENGRAVED TÊTE-À-TÊTE SET.

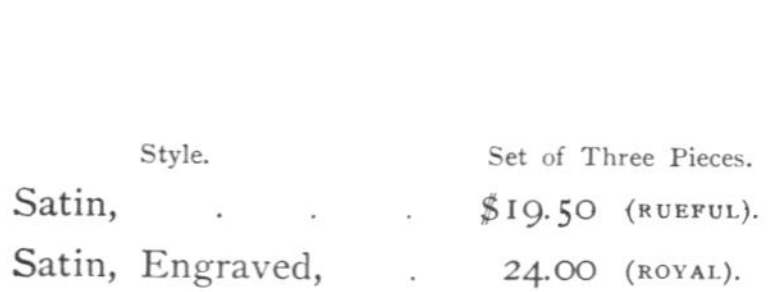

Style.	Set of Three Pieces.	Coffee, Two Half Pints.	Sugar.	Cream, One-Half Pint, Gold Lined.
Satin, . . .	$19.50 (RUEFUL).	$9.00	$5.50	$5.00
Satin, Engraved, .	24.00 (ROYAL).	11.00	6.75	6.25

No. 859. TÊTE-À-TÊTE SET.

Style.	Set of Three Pieces.	Coffee, Three Half Pints.	Sugar.	Cream One Half Pint, Gold Lined.
Satin, ...	$18.00 (CEREAL).	$8.50	$4.75	$4.75

No. 860. TÊTE-À-TÊTE SET.

Style.	Set of Three Pieces.	Coffee, Three Half Pints.	Sugar.	Cream, One Half Pint, Gold Lined.
Silver, . .	$19.50 (CALABASH).	$9.00	$5.50	$5.00
X Gold Inlaid,	23.50 (CALCIUM).	11.00	6.50	6.00
XX Gold Inlaid,	27.50 (CALDRON).	13.00	7.50	7.00

No. 311—12 inch WAITER. Satin C, Silver, . $6.50 (CANVASSER).
X Gold Inlaid, . 9.00 (CANZONET).
XX Gold Inlaid, . 11.50 (CARNATION).

Patent Plate Glass Protector, . $2.00 extra (CARPENTER).

No. 874. EMBOSSED TÊTE-À-TÊTE SET.

Style.	Set of Four Pieces.	Coffee, Two Half Pints.	Tea, Three Fourth Pints.	Sugar.	Cream, One Half Pint, Gold Lined.
Embossed, . . .	$19.00 (VETO).	$6.25	$5.25	$3.75	$3.75
Embossed, Old Silver,	21.00 (VENT).	6.75	5.75	4.25	4.25

No. 110—15 inch WAITER. Satin, . . . $16.00 (VEXINGLY).
Satin, Old Silver, 17.00 (VITALITY).

Patent Plate Glass Protector, . $2.25 extra (VISITANT).

GOLD AND SILVER PLATE.

No. 1851. ENGRAVED TÊTE-À-TÊTE SET.

Style.	Set of Four Pieces.	Coffee, Two Half Pints.	Tea, Three Fourth Pints.	Sugar.	Cream, One Half Pint, Gold Lined.
Engraved, .	$23.50 (BILLET).	$7.75	$6.00	$5.00	$4.75

No. 1855. ENGRAVED TÊTE-À-TÊTE SET.

Style.	Set of Four Pieces.	Coffee, Two Half Pints.	Tea, Three Fourth Pints.	Sugar.	Cream, One Half Pint, Gold Lined.
Plain, . .	$18.00 (BILK).	$5.50	$4.75	$4.00	$3.75
Engraved, .	22.50 (BILL).	6.75	6.25	4.75	4.75

No. 1846. SILVER, CHASED B TÊTE-À-TÊTE SET.

Style.	Set of Four Pieces.	Coffee, Three Half Pints.	Tea, Two Half Pints.	Sugar.	Cream, One Half Pint, Gold Lined.
Plain, . .	$20.00 (BIPED).	$6.50	$5.25	$4.50	$4.25
Silver, Chased B,	24.00 (BINDER).	8.00	6.25	5.00	4.75

GOLD AND SILVER PLATE.

No. 1858. PLAIN TÊTE-À-TÊTE SET.

Style.	Set of Four Pieces.	Coffee, Two Half Pints.	Tea, Three Fourth Pints.	Sugar.	Cream, One Half Pint, Gold Lined.
Plain or Satin, .	$18.50 (BLANKET).	$5.75	$5.25	$3.75	$3.75
Hammered, . .	22.50 (STAMPEDE).	7.00	6.50	4.50	4.50

No. 1856. TÊTE-À-TÊTE SET.

Style.	Set of Four Pieces.	Coffee, Two Half Pints.	Tea, Three Fourth Pints.	Sugar.	Cream, One Half Pint, Silver Lined.
Plain, . .	$17.00 (ORIGIN).	$5.75	$4.75	$3.75	$2.75
Chased, . .	20.00 (ORIOLE).	6.75	5.50	4.50	3.25

No. 868. TÊTE-À-TÊTE SET.

Style.	Set of Four Pieces.	Coffee, Two Half Pints.	Tea, Three Fourth Pints.	Sugar.	Cream, One Half Pint, Gold Lined.
Satin, . .	$18.50 (MASTERLY).	$5.75	$5.25	$3.75	$3.75
Hammered, .	22.50 (MASTIC).	7.00	6.50	4.50	4.50

No. 1852. PLAIN TÊTE-À-TÊTE SET.

Style.	Set of Four Pieces.	Coffee, Two Half Pints.	Tea, Three Fourth Pints.	Sugar.	Cream, One Fourth Pint, Silver Lined.
For One Person, . .	$19.00 (BITE).	$6.25	$5.50	$4.25	$3.00
		Six Gills.	Five Gills.		One Half Pint.
For Two Persons, . .	25.00 (BIVALVE).	8.00	7.00	5.50	4.50

Cream, Gold Lined, $1.00 extra.

TRADE MARK.
WHITE METAL.

GOLD AND SILVER PLATE.

TRADE MARK.
NICKEL SILVER.

No. 1848. TÊTE-À-TÊTE SET.

Set of Four Pieces.	Coffee, Three Fourth Pints.	Tea, One Half Pint.	Sugar.	Cream, Silver Lined.
$12.00 (BITING).	$4.25	$3.75	$2.25	$1.75

No. 1850. PLAIN TÊTE-À-TÊTE SET.

Set of Four Pieces.	Coffee, Two Half Pints.	Tea, Three Fourth Pints.	Sugar.	Cream, Gold Lined.
$16.50 (BIND).	$5.00	$4.50	$3.50	$3.50

No. 1843. PLAIN TÊTE-À-TÊTE SET.

Set of Four Pieces.	Coffee, Three Half Pints.	Tea, Three Fourth Pints.	Sugar.	Cream, Silver Lined.
$14.50 (BLADE).	$5.00	$4.00	$3.00	$2.50

No. 1837 COFFEE.

No. 1836 TEA.

No. 1837 SUGAR.

No. 1837 CREAM.

Nos. 1836 AND 1837. PLAIN TÊTE-À-TÊTE SET.

Style.	Set of Four Pieces.	Coffee, Three Half Pints.	Tea, Two Half Pints.	Sugar.	Cream, Silver Lined.
No. 1836, . .	$14.50 (BITTER).	$5.00	$4.00	$3.00	$2.50
No. 1837, . .	14.50 (BLACK).	5.00	4.00	3.00	2.50

TRADE MARK.
WHITE METAL.

SOUP TUREENS.

(ONE-THIRD SIZE.)

TRADE MARK.
NICKEL SILVER.

No. 1875. OVAL.

	Plain.
Two Quarts, . .	$16.00 (MUSTER).
Three Quarts, . .	20.00 (MUTTON).
Four Quarts, . .	23.00 (MUZZLE).

No. 1949.

	Silver.	X Gold Inlaid.	XX Gold Inlaid.
Two Quarts, .	$17.50 (PALMETTO).	$23.50 (PALMISTRY).	$29.50 (PALPABLE).
Three Quarts, .	20.50 (PALPITATE).	26.50 (PERSIST).	32.50 (PERSON).
Four Quarts, .	24.00 (PERSONAL).	30.00 (PERSONIFY).	36.00 (PERSUADE).

No. 1970. EMBOSSED OLD SILVER.

		Plate Extra.
Two Quarts, . .	$18.00 (VENUE).	$6.00 (VERACIOUS).
Three Quarts, . .	20.50 (VERBALLY).	7.00 (VENTILATOR).
Four Quarts, . .	23.00 (VERBIAGE).	8.00 (VERDANCY).

No. 1877.

	Satin.	Satin, Engraved.	Plate Extra.
Two Quarts, .	$16.00 (REFINE).	$18.00 (REFLECT).	$5.00 (REFRAIN).
Three Quarts, .	18.00 (RIDE).	20.50 (RITE).	6.00 (RIPELY).
Four Quarts, .	20.00 (RIDER).	23.00 (RETRACT).	7.00 (RETOUCH).

No. 1960.

	Plain.	Hammered.
Two Quarts, .	$17.50 (VERDANT).	$19.50 (VERGER).
Three Quarts, .	20.50 (VERDIGRIS).	23.00 (VERILY).
Four Quarts, .	24.00 (VERDURE).	27.50 (VERJUICE).

No. 1956.

	Plain.	Chased.	Hammered.	Plate Extra. Plain.	Plate Extra. Hammered.
Three Quarts,	$20.00 (PAINT).	$24.00 (PAINTING).	$24.00 (PALATE).	$6.00 (PALETTE).	$7.00 (PALFREY).
Four Quarts,	23.00 (PALING).	27.00 (PALISADE).	27.00 (PALLET).	7.00 (PALM).	8.00 (PALMER).

TRADE MARK.
WHITE METAL.

GOLD AND SILVER PLATE.

TRADE MARK.
NICKEL SILVER.

No. 1879.

	Satin.		Satin, Engraved.		Plate Extra.	
Two Quarts, .	$17.50	(MAYDAY).	$20.00	(MAYORESS).	$6.00	(MEAL-TIME).
Three Quarts, .	20.00	(MEDICATE).	23.50	(MEEKNESS).	7.00	(MEGRIM).
Four Quarts, .	24.00	(MELODIST).	28.00	(MERCIFUL).	8.00	(MERMAN).

No. 1880. OLD SILVER BORDER.

	Without Plate.		Plate Extra.	
Two Quarts, .	$17.50	(MEANING).	$5.00	(MEDALEST).
Three Quarts, .	20.00	(MELANGE).	6.00	(MELODEON).
Four Quarts, .	24.00	(METALLIC).	7.00	(MESSUAGE).

No. 1944.

	Plain or Satin.		Hammered.		Plate Extra. Plain.		Plate Extra. Hammered.	
Two Quarts,	$13.00	(NARROW).	$15.00	(NATTY).	$5.00	(MASTICATE).	$6.00	(MASTODON).
Three Quarts,	15.50	(NATION).	19.00	(NAVAL).	6.00	(MATADORE).	7.50	(MATCHLESS).
Four Quarts,	18.50	(NATIVE).	22.50	(NAVIGATE).	7.00	(MATERIAL).	8.50	(MATURELY).

No. 1947½. FLUTED.

	Without Plate.		Plate Extra.	
Two Quarts, .	$20.00	(METALLIST).	$5.00	(MACAW).
Three Quarts, .	22.50	(METEORIC).	6.00	(MACCABOY).
Four Quarts, .	25.00	(MACARONIC).	7.00	(MADCAP).

No. 1957.

	Plain.		Hammered.		Hammered and Applied.		Plate Extra. Plain.		Plate Extra. Hammered.	
Three Quarts,	$18.00	(NUTMEG).	$22.00	(PABULUM).	$24.00	(PACE).	$6.00	(PACER).	$7.50	(PACHA).
Four Quarts,	20.00	(PACIFY).	23.00	(PAD).	25.00	(PADDING).	7.00	(PAIL).	8.50	(PAINIM).

No. 1905.

Embossed, Four Quarts, . $30.00 (MYTH).

GOLD AND SILVER PLATE.

No. 1873. Chased.

Three Quarts, .	$22.00	(MYSTIFY).
Four Quarts, .	24.00	(MYTHOLOGY).

No. 1867.

	Plain.		Chased.		Satin, Chased.	
One Quart, .	$9.75	(MOUND).	$12.75	(MOUSE).	$12.75	(MOVE).
Two Quarts, .	12.75	(MUCILAGE).	17.25	(MUFFIN).	17.25	(MUFFLE).
Three Quarts,	15.75	(MULLION).	21.00	(MULTIPLE).	21.00	(MULTITUDE).
Four Quarts, .	19.00	(MUFTI).	25.00	(MUGGY).	25.00	(MULATTO).
Six Quarts, .	25.00	(MULCT).	32.25	(MULE).	32.25	(MULETEER).

No. 1874.

	Plain or Satin.		Hammered.		Plate Extra. Plain or Satin.		Hammered.	
Two Quarts, .	$13.50	(MUSIC).	$15.50	(VINE).	$5.00	(VIAL).	$6.00	(VILIFIER).
Three Quarts, .	16.50	(MUSK).	18.50	(VIAND).	6.00	(VIATIC).	7.50	(VICTIM).
Four Quarts, .	20.00	(MUSKET).	24.00	(VILLA).	7.00	(VIGOR).	8.50	(VILIFY).

No. 1919. Oval.

Chased, Four Quarts, . $34.00 (NABOB).

No. 1924. Oval.

Chased A, Four Quarts, .	$30.00	(NANKEEN).
Chased B, Four Quarts, .	32.00	(NARCOTIC).

WHITE METAL.

GOLD AND SILVER PLATE.

NICKEL SILVER.

No. 1947½. GRAVY TUREEN.
Three Half Pints.

	Without Plate.	With Plate.
Fluted, .	$10.50 (MADAM).	$13.50 (MADDER).

No. 103. SATIN.
Two Half Pints, . $5.00 (MACHINATE).

No. 1877. GRAVY TUREEN.
Three Half Pints.

	Without Plate.	With Plate.
Satin, . .	$8.00 (MAGICIAN).	$11.00 (MACHINIST).
Satin, Engraved,	9.50 (MAGICAL).	12.50 (MASCULINE).

No. 104. SATIN.
Four Half Pints, . $7.50 (MACHINERY).

No. 3.
Three Half Pints, . $6.00 (MOTION).
Four Half Pints, . 8.00 (MOTIVE).

No. 1852.
Three Half Pints, . $6.00 (MOTLEY).
Four Half Pints, . 8.00 (MOTTO).

No. 1876.

	Without Plate.	With Plate.
Two Half Pints,	$6.00 (MYRIAD).	$8.00 (MYSTERY).
Four Half Pints,	8.00 (MYRTLE).	10.75 (MYRRH).

No. 1851.
Three Half Pints, . $6.00 (MUSCLE).
Four Half Pints, . 8.00 (MUSCULAR).
Eight Half Pints, . 12.75 (MUSEUM).

No. 42. GRAVY BOAT.
Plain, . $7.50 (MANDAMUS).
Satin, . 7.50 (MANDRAKE).

No. 1853.
Two Half Pints, . $7.00 (MUNCH).
Four Half Pints, . 9.00 (MUNDANE).
Eight Half Pints, . 14.50 (MUNITION).
Twelve Half Pints, . 17.50 (MURAL).

NICKEL SILVER TUREENS.

(ONE-THIRD SIZE.)

No. 0200. GRAVY BOAT.
Without Plate, . $17.50 (WAFTER).
With Plate, . . 25.00 (WAGES).

No. 0575. FIVE QUARTS.
Plain, . . $125.00 (VIATICUM).
Satin, . . 125.00 (VIBRATORY).

No. 0205. GRAVY BOAT.
Plain, . $13.00 (VIEW).

No. 0210. Larger.
Plain, . $15.50 (VICARAGE).

No. 40. White Metal.
Plain, . $6.75 (VICIOUS).

No. 0215. GRAVY BOAT.
Without Plate, . $14.00 (SAFFRON).
With Plate, . . 21.50 (SAGACIOUS).

No. 0220. GRAVY BOAT.
Without Plate, . $15.00 (VICTUAL).
With Plate, . . 22.50 (VICTUALLER).

No. 0510. Plate Extra.
Three Quarts, . $75.00 (ROMP). $25.00 (VIEWLESS).
Four Quarts, . 90.00 (ROOD). 30.00 (VIEWER).

No. 0500. PLAIN OR SATIN.
Two Quarts, . $50.00 (VICTIMIZE).
Three Quarts, . 60.00 (VIGILANTLY).
Four Quarts, . 75.00 (VINDICATION).
Five Quarts, . 90.00 (VINDICATOR).
Six Quarts, . 110.00 (VIGOROUSLY).

NICKEL SILVER, SILVER SOLDERED.

TRADE MARK.
WHITE METAL.

GOLD AND SILVER PLATE.

TRADE MARK.
NICKEL SILVER.

No. 0410.

Two Half Pints,	$15.50	(MAGISTRATE).
Four Half Pints,	18.00	(MAGNATE).
Six Half Pints,	22.50	(MAGNESIA).
Eight Half Pints,	27.50	(MAGNETIC).

No. 0480.

	Without Plate.		Plate Extra.	
Two Half Pints,	$13.50	(ROAST).	$7.00	(ROARING).
Three Half Pints,	15.75	(MAST).	8.00	(MANIA).
Four Half Pints,	17.00	(ROBE).	9.00	(ROASTER).
Five Half Pints,	20.00	(ROBIN).	10.00	(ROAD).
Six Half Pints,	22.00	(ROAR).	11.00	(ROADSTER).
Eight Half Pints,	26.00	(MASK).	13.00	(MANAGER).

No. 0485.

	Without Plate.		Plate Extra.	
Two Half Pints,	$17.00	(ROACH).	$7.00	(RIVET).
Four Half Pints,	19.50	(ROAM).	9.00	(RIVAL).
Six Half Pints,	23.00	(RIVER).	11.00	(RIVALRY).
Eight Half Pints,	28.50	(MALIGN).	14.00	(MALLARD).

No. 0490. OVAL.

	Without Plate.		Plate Extra.	
Two Half Pints,	$20.00	(MAINMAST).	$9.00	(MAINDECK).
Four Half Pints,	23.00	(MASSIVE).	11.00	(MAINLAND).
Six Half Pints,	27.50	(MASKER).	13.00	(MASONRY).

No. 0495.

	Without Plate.		Plate Extra.	
Two Half Pints,	$21.00	(MAINLY).	$9.00	(MAINSAIL).
Four Half Pints,	31.50	(MAINTOP).	11.00	(MAINSTAY).
Six Half Pints,	37.50	(ROCKET).	13.00	(MAJESTIC).
Eight Half Pints,	42.50	(MAKER).	16.00	(MAJORITY).

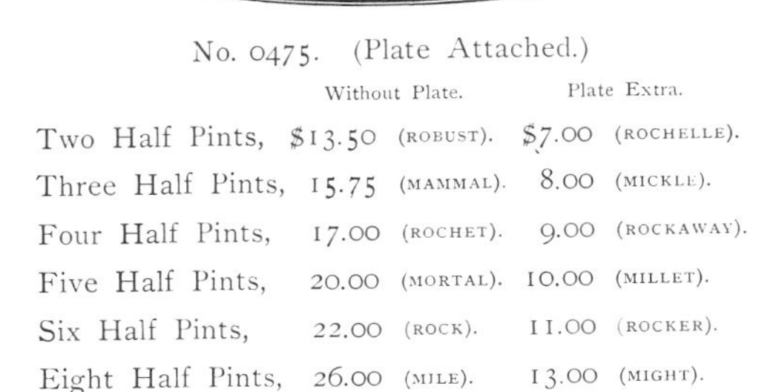

No. 0475. (Plate Attached.)

	Without Plate.		Plate Extra.	
Two Half Pints,	$13.50	(ROBUST).	$7.00	(ROCHELLE).
Three Half Pints,	15.75	(MAMMAL).	8.00	(MICKLE).
Four Half Pints,	17.00	(ROCHET).	9.00	(ROCKAWAY).
Five Half Pints,	20.00	(MORTAL).	10.00	(MILLET).
Six Half Pints,	22.00	(ROCK).	11.00	(ROCKER).
Eight Half Pints,	26.00	(MILE).	13.00	(MIGHT).

No 0505.

	Without Plate.		Plate Extra.	
Two Half Pints,	$20.00	(MALICE).	$7.00	(MALTMAN).
Four Half Pints,	27.00	(RODENT).	9.00	(MALTSTER).
Six Half Pints,	32.50	(ROLL).	11.00	(MALMSEY).
Eight Half Pints,	39.00	(ROMANCE).	14.00	(MALADY).

No. 0400.

	Without Plate.		Plate Extra.	
Two Half Pints,	$15.50	(MASONIC).	$7.00	(MARQUIS).
Four Half Pints,	18.00	(MASTER).	9.00	(MARTYR).
Six Half Pints,	22.50	(MARTIAL).	11.00	(MARTINET).
Eight Half Pints,	27.50	(MARMOT).	14.00	(MARPLOT).

NICKEL SILVER, SILVER SOLDERED.

TOILET SETS.

(ONE-THIRD SIZE.)

TRADE MARK.
NICKEL SILVER.

No. 200. TOILET.

Silver, . . $60.00 (INCOGNITO).

Silver, Gold Inlaid, 75.00 (INCOME).

No. 152. With Jewel Drawer.

Silver, ... $20.00 (HOUND).

Silver, Gold Inlaid, . 22.00 (HOUSE).

No. 211.

Silver, ... $30.00 (MORTISE).

Silver, Gold Inlaid, . 35.00 (MOSLEM).

No. 205.

Old Silver, ... $18.00 (NICKNACK).
Old Silver, Gold Inlaid, . 20.00 (NIMBUS).

No. 176.

Silver, ... $15.00 (HUSTINGS).
Silver, Gold Inlaid, . 17.00 (HUSTLE).

No. 172½. With Jewel Drawer.

Silver, ... $31.50 (HORNPIPE).
Silver, Gold Inlaid, . 34.50 (HORSE).

No. 206.

Silver, ... $35.00 (NEATNESS).
Silver, Gold Inlaid, . 40.00 (NEBULAR).

GOLD AND SILVER PLATE.

No. 144.

Silver, ... $14.00 (HYDROGEN).

Silver, Gold Inlaid, . 15.00 (HYPHEN).

No. 196.

Silver, ... $22.50 (INCUR).

Silver, Gold Inlaid, . 25.00 (INCURSION).

No. 177.

Silver, ... $21.50 (HUMOR).

Silver and Gold Inlaid, . 24.00 (HUMOROUS).

No. 173.

Silver, ... $27.50 (HOST).

Silver, Gold Inlaid, . 30.00 (HOSTAGE).

GOLD AND SILVER PLATE.

No. 195.

Old Silver, . . . $22.50 (INDELIBLE).

Silver, Gold Inlaid, . 25.00 (INDEMNITY).

No. 178.

Silver, ... $24.00 (HUDDLE).

Silver, Gold Inlaid, . . 26.00 (HUE).

No. 197.

Silver, ... $24.50 (INCURVE).

Silver, Gold Inlaid, . 27.50 (INDEED).

No. 154.

Silver, ... $18.00 (HUSH).

Silver, Gold Inlaid, . 20.00 (HUSK).

GOLD AND SILVER PLATE.

No. 223.
Enameled Copper Base, Silver Trimmings.
Crystal Cut, . $7.75 (MAGNETISM).
Non-Tarnishable.

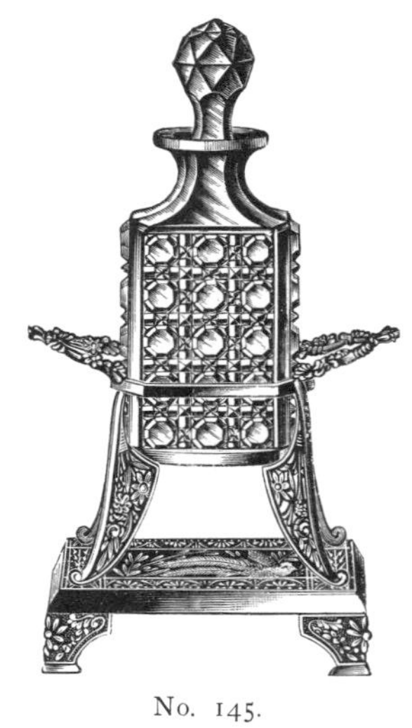

No. 145.
Old Silver, . $6.00 (IMITATE).

No. 222.
Enameled Copper Base, Silver Trimmings.
Cut Glass, . $9.50 (MAGNITUDE).
Non-Tarnishable.

No. 225.
Enameled Copper Base, Silver Trimmings.
Crystal, . $15.00 (MAHOGANY).
Non-Tarnishable.

No. 224.
Enameled Copper Base, Silver Trimmings.
Assorted Colors, . $12.50 (MAIL-COACH).
Non-Tarnishable.

No. 221.
Old Silver, ... $14.50 (MARVELOUS).
Old Silver, Gold Inlaid, . 16.00 (MASQUERADE).
Non-Tarnishable.

No. 215. With Jewel Drawer.
Old Silver, ... $20.00 (MAMELUKE).
Old Silver, Gold Inlaid, . 22.50 (MAMMOTH).
Non-Tarnishable.

GOLD AND SILVER PLATE.

No. 181.

Silver, . . . $7.25 (IGNOBLE).
Silver, Gold Inlaid, . 8.00 (ILLEGAL).

No. 96.

Crystal, . . $12.00 (HYSON).

No. 201.

Old Silver, . . . $15.00 (MOSAIC).
X Gold Inlaid, . . 17.50 (NEAT).

No. 194.

Silver, . . . $13.50 (INCRUST).
Silver, Gold Inlaid, 15.00 (INCUMBENT).

No. 143, . . $10.50 (ICICLE).

No. 136.

Silver, . . $10.50 (IGNITE).

No. 153.

Silver, Gold Inlaid, . $15.00 (HUSSAR).

GOLD AND SILVER PLATE.

No. 170.

Silver, . . . $10.50 (IMAGE).
Silver, Gold Inlaid, 12.00 (IMBIBE).

No. 147.

Silver, Gold Inlaid, . $10.50 (ILLUME).

No. 185. SCENT JAR.

Silver, . . $13.50 (HUMMOCK).
Silver, Gold Inlaid, 15.00 (HUMDRUM).

No. 210.

Silver, ... $13.50 (MOSQUE).
Silver, Gold Inlaid, . 15.00 (MOTH).

No. 186. TOILET.

Silver, ... $15.00 (HUNCH).
Silver, Gold Inlaid, . 17.50 (HUMORIST).

GOLD AND SILVER PLATE.

No. 220.

Old Silver, . . $11.00 (MARKSMAN).
Old Silver, Gold Inlaid, 12.50 (MARITIME).
Non-Tarnishable.

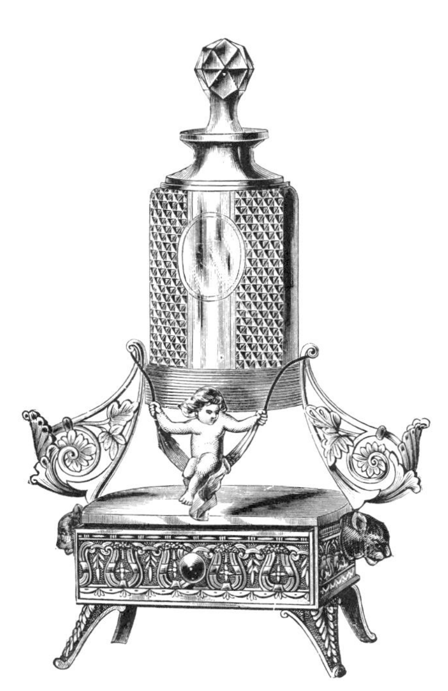

No. 116. COMBINATION.

Jewel Case and Cologne, $13.50 (IMMURE).

No. 115. COMBINATION.

Jewel Case and Cologne, $12.00 (IMPALE).

No. 184.

Silver, . . $10.00 (HYACINTH).
Silver, Gold Inlaid, 12.00 (HYDRA).

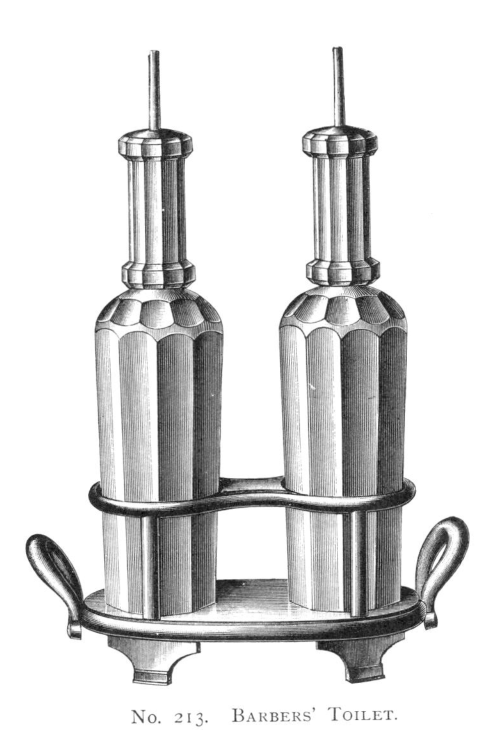

No. 213. BARBERS' TOILET.

Silver, . . $10.00 (MARMALADE).

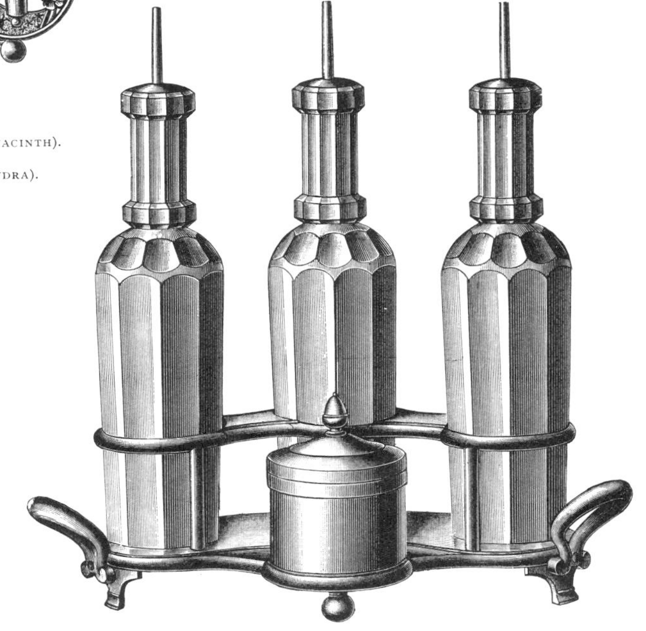

No. 214. BARBERS' TOILET.

Silver, . . $15.00 (MANIFESTO).

TRADE MARK.
WHITE METAL.

GOLD AND SILVER PLATE.

TRADE MARK.
NICKEL SILVER.

No. 161. Engraved, . $4.50 (IMPLANT).

No. 128, . $6.50 (IMPANEL).

No. 162, . $6.00 (IMPETUS).

No. 166, . $4.00 (IMPOST).

No. 163, $4.50 (IMPLY).

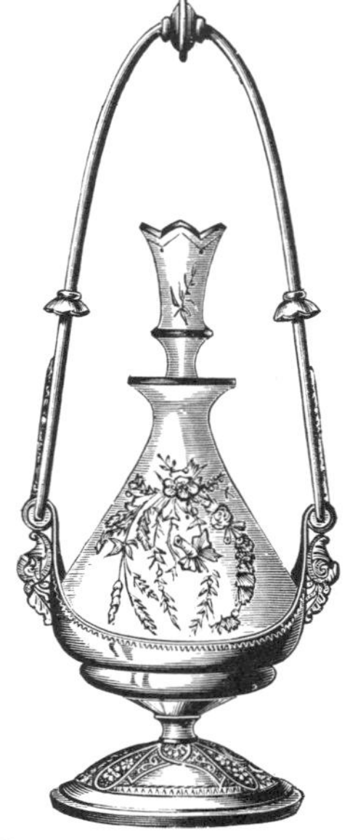

No. 97, . $5.00 (IMPEL).

No. 168, . $4.00 (IMPORT).

No. 74, . $6.50 (IMPLORE).

No. 121, . $5.50 (IMPEND).

No. 120, . $5.00 (IMPEACH).

No. 155. Fine Cut.
Silver, Gold Inlaid, $13.50 (IMPACT).

GOLD AND SILVER PLATE.

(ONE-THIRD SIZE.)

No. 150, . $2.50 (IMPRESS).

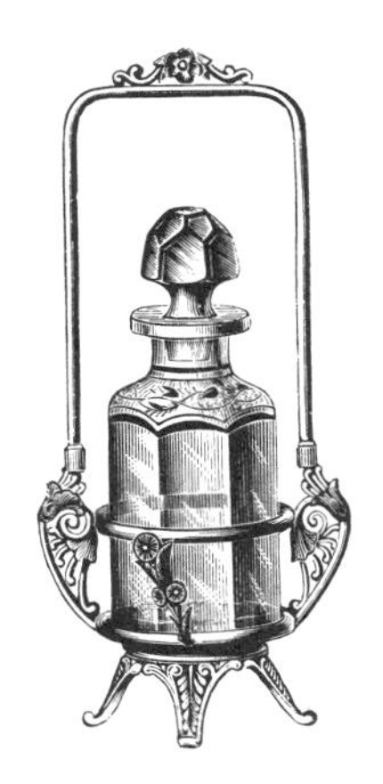

No. 139, . $3.50 (IMPUGN).

No. 149, . $2.50 (IMPROVE).

No. 83, . $2.00 (IMPRINT).

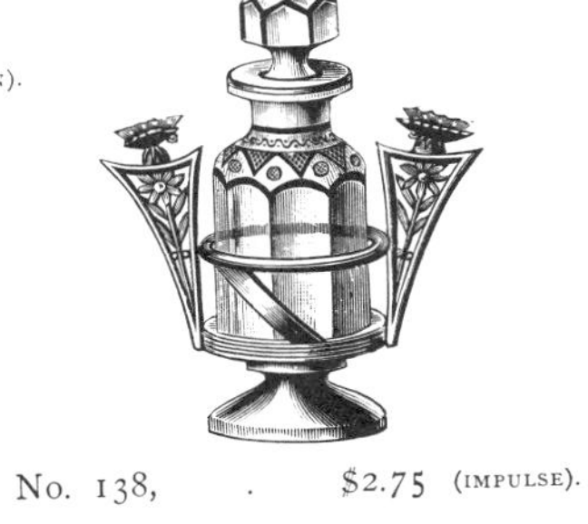

No. 138, . $2.75 (IMPULSE).

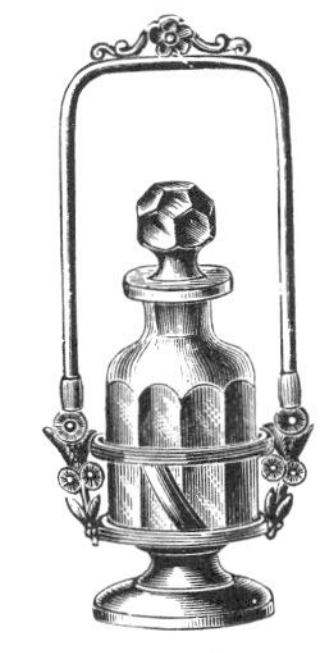

No. 137, . $2.50 (IMPROVISE).

No. 140, . $4.00 (IMPUNITY).

No. 80 (2 oz. Bottle), $2.00 (IMPRISON).
No. 79 (3 oz. Bottle), 3.00 (IMPROBABLE).
No. 73 (6 oz. Bottle), 4.00 (IMPROMPTU).

No. 101, . . $4.00 (IMPULSIVE).

No. 142. Silver, Gold Inlaid, $4.00 (IMPOSING).

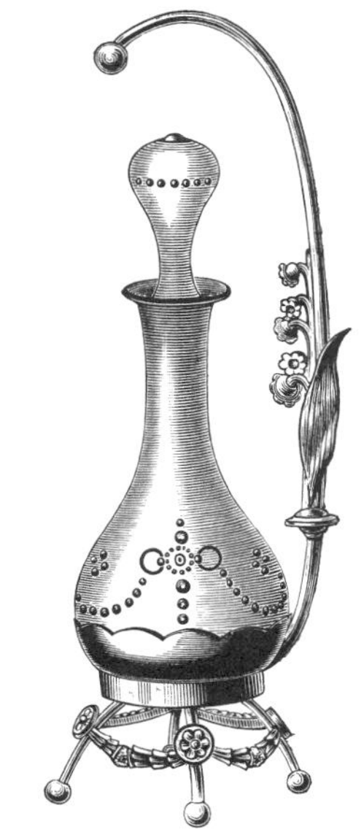

No. 100, . . $3.50 (IMPUTE).

GOLD AND SILVER PLATE.

(HALF SIZE.)

No. 192.

Silver, . . $5.00 (INDENT).
Silver, Gold Inlaid, 6.00 (INDENTURE).

No. 207.

Hammered, . . $4.00 (ATLAS).
Hammered, Gold Inlaid, 5.00 (ATROPHY).

No. 187.

Silver, . . . $5.00 (INDEX).
Silver, Gold Inlaid, 6.00 (INDIAN).

No. 191.

Silver, ... $4.75 (INDUCT).
Silver, Gold Inlaid, . 5.50 (INDULGE).

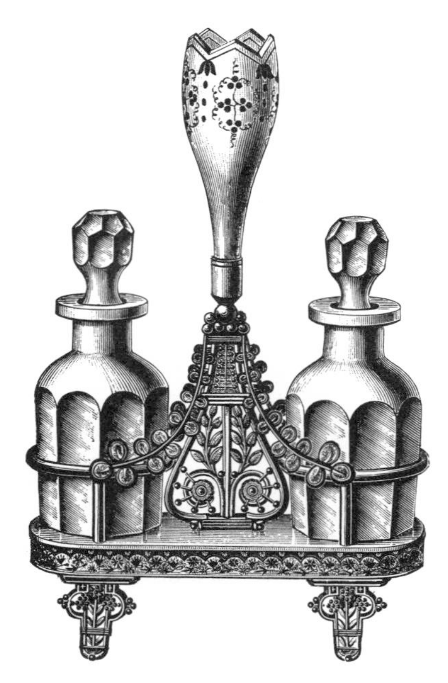

No. 188.

Silver, . . . $7.50 (INDIRECT).
Silver, Gold Inlaid, 8.50 (INDITE).

No. 190.

Silver, . . . $7.00 (INDICT).
Silver, Gold Inlaid, 8.00 (INDIGO).

No. 198.

Silver, . . . $6.50 (INDICATE).
Silver, Gold Inlaid, 8.00 (INDICATION).

(HALF-SIZE.)

No. 219.

Silver, . . $5.00 (MANDREL).
Silver, Gold Inlaid, 5.75 (MANGROVE).
Non-Tarnishable.

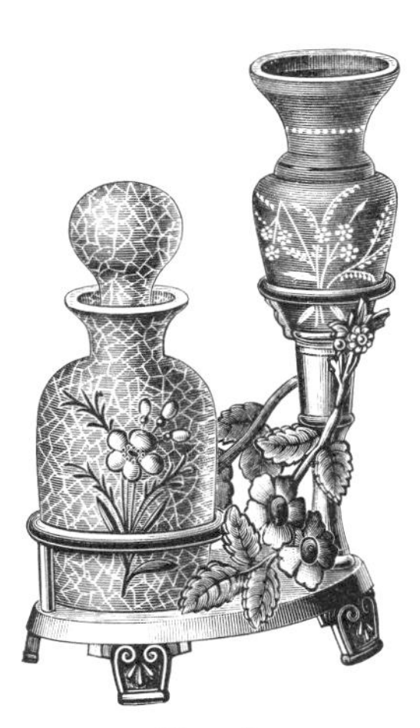

No. 189.

Silver, . . $5.00 (INDURATE).
Silver, Gold Inlaid, 6.00 (INDUSTRY).

No. 218.

Silver, . . $4.75 (MANUMIT).
Silver, Gold Inlaid, 5.50 (MANUSCRIPT).
Non-Tarnishable.

No. 203.

Silver, . . . $5.50 (ATTRACT).
Silver and Gold Inlaid, 6.50 (ATTUNE).

No. 208.

Silver, . . . $4.50 (AUCTION).
Silver and Gold Inlaid, 5.00 (AUDIBLE).

No. 204.

Silver, . . . $5.00 (ATTACH).
Silver and Gold Inlaid, 6.00 (ATTEST).

No. 202.

Silver, . . . $6.50 (AURICLE).
Silver and Gold Inlaid, 7.50 (AUSTERE).

No. 209.

Silver, . . . $6.00 (AUDITOR).
Silver and Gold Inlaid, 7.00 (AURORA).

GOLD AND SILVER PLATE.

(HALF SIZE.)

No. 217.

Silver, ... $3.50 (MARINER).
Silver, Gold Inlaid, . 4.00 (MANFULLY).

(Non-Tarnishable.)

No. 193.

Silver, ... $3.00 (INDORSE).
Silver, Gold Inlaid, . 3.50 (INDUCE).

No. 216.

Silver, ... $3.25 (MOVABLE).
Silver, Gold Inlaid, . 3.75 (MANNERISM).

No. 159, $4.00 (INCISION).

No. 160, . $4.50 (INCITE).

No. 157, . $4.00 (INCLINE).

No. 158, $3.75 (INBRED).

No. 179.
Silver, . . $4.00 (INCENSE).
Silver and Gold, 4.50 (INCENTIVE).

No. 180.
Silver, . . $4.00 (INCANT).
Silver and Gold, 4.50 (INCH).

No. 156, . $3.75 (INCIDENT).

VASES, FLOWER STANDS, ETC.

ALSO SEE ART WORK.

(ONE-THIRD SIZE.)

No. 60. JARDINIERE.
Silver, . . $16.00 (INITIAL).
Silver, Gold Inlaid, 18.00 (INITIATE).

No. 70. JARDINIERE.
Silver, ... $16.50 (NITROGEN).
Silver, Gold Inlaid, . 18.00 (NITROUS).

No. 372. VASE.
Silver and Gold, . $13.50 (INROAD).

No. 418. VASE.
Silver, . . $20.00 (NOCTURN).
Silver, Gold Inlaid, 22.50 (NODDLE).

No. 69. JARDINIERE.
Old Silver, . . $30.00 (NOBLE).
Gold Inlaid, . . 35.00 (NOBLESSE).

No. 64. JARDINIERE.
Silver, . . $22.50 (INGULF).
Silver, Gold Inlaid, 25.00 (INHABIT).

GOLD AND SILVER PLATE.

No. 425.
Silver, . . $2.50 (SYSTEMATIC).
Old Silver, . 3.00 (SYREN).

No. 63. FLOWER STAND.
Silver, Gold Inlaid, $7.50 (INTERLUDE).

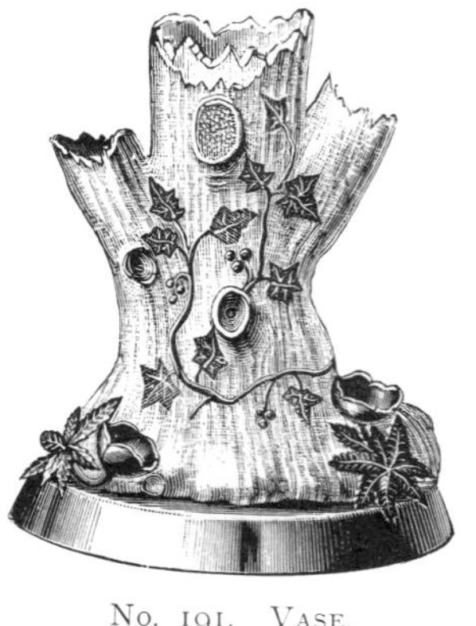

No. 191. VASE.
Silver, $5.00 (INTERCEPT).

No. 24. FLOWER STAND.
Silver, . . $4.75 (INTERNAL).

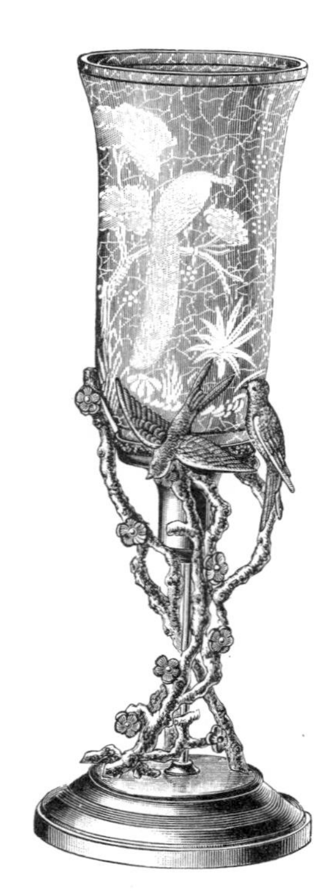

No. 376.
Silver, ... $12.00 (INSECT).
Silver and Gold, . 13.50 (INSECURE).

No. 44. FLOWER STAND.
Silver, . $7.75 (INTERMIX).

No. 367.
Silver, ... $10.25 (INSTILL).
Silver, Gold Inlaid, . 12.00 (INSTINCT).

GOLD AND SILVER PLATE.

(ONE-THIRD SIZE.)

No. 365, . . $7.50 (INSTEAD).
Silver, Gold Inlaid, 9.00 (INSTEP).

No. 379.
Silver, . . $6.00 (INSTALL).
Silver and Gold, 7.50 (INSTANCE).

No. 366, . . $10.75 (INSTANT).
Silver, Gold Inlaid, 12.50 (INSTANTER).

No. 6600. No. 6500.

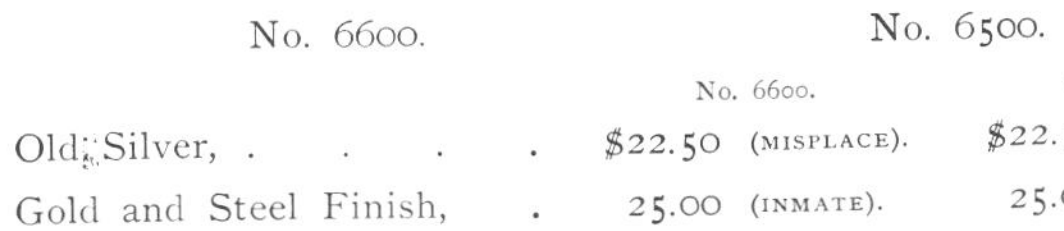

	No. 6600.	No. 6500.
Old Silver, ...	$22.50 (MISPLACE).	$22.50 (MISPRINT).
Gold and Steel Finish, .	25.00 (INMATE).	25.00 (INMOST).

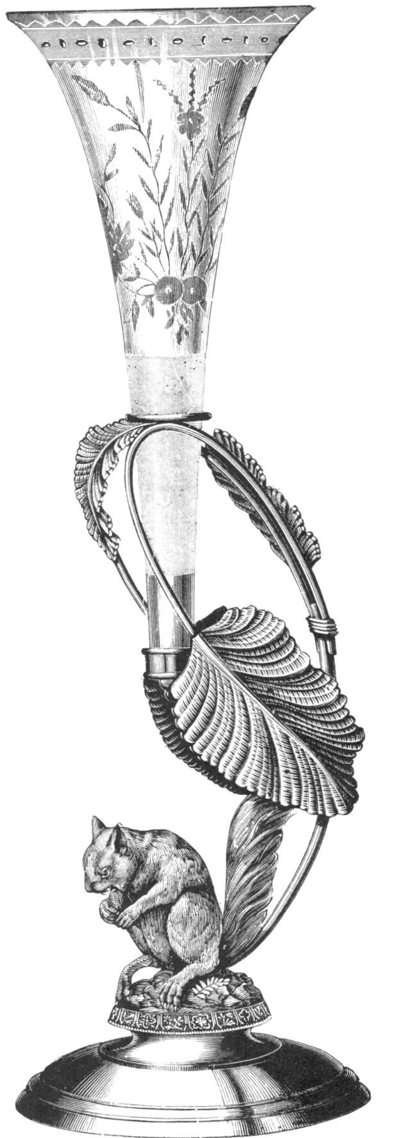

No. 301, . $16.50 (INLET).

No. 300, . $22.00 (INNATE).

GOLD AND SILVER PLATE.

(HALF SIZE.)

No. 428.
Old Silver, . . $7.25 (MORASS).
Old Silver, Gold Inlaid, 8.00 (MORESQUE).
Non-Tarnishable.

No. 417.
Silver, ... $10.50 (NONCHALANT).
Silver, Gold Inlaid, . 12.00 (NOOK).

No. 422.
Old Silver, . . $6.00 (MARAUDER).
Old Silver, Gold Inlaid, 7.00 (MARIGOLD).
Non-Tarnishable.

No. 339.
Silver, Gold Inlaid, . $10.00 (NONCE).

No. 354.
Silver, Gold Inlaid, . $14.00 (KIND).

No. 415. Ruby Glass.
Old Silver, . $6.75 (NOONDAY).

GOLD AND SILVER PLATE.

(HALF SIZE.)

No. 431.
Old Silver, . $6.00 (MONITION).
(Coral Rose Glass.)
Non-Tarnishable.

No. 423.
Old Silver, ... $7.50 (MOLTEN).
Old Silver, Gold Inlaid, . 8.50 (MOLLIENT).
Non-Tarnishable.

No. 429.
Old Silver, . $13.50 (MONITORY).
Non-Tarnishable.

No. 424.
Old Silver, ... $8.00 (MORAVIAN).
Old Silver, Gold Inlaid, . 9.00 (MONOTONY).
Non-Tarnishable.

No. 416.
Silver, ... $7.00 (NOMAD).
Silver, Gold Inlaid, . 8.00 (NOMADIC).

GOLD AND SILVER PLATE.

(HALF SIZE.)

No. 421.
Silver, . $5 00 (MORIBUND).

No. 55. FLOWER STAND.
Silver, . $6.00 (KEPT).

No. 408.
Silver, . . $5.00 (LEND).
Silver, Gold Inlaid, 6.00 (LENGTH).

No. 307.
Gold and Silver, . $7.50 (LAKE).

No. 409.
Silver, . . $7.50 (LEGIBLE).
Silver, Gold Inlaid, 9.00 (LEGION).

No. 409 furnished in both right and left-hand figure.

No. 283, . $7.50 (LAGOON).

GOLD AND SILVER PLATE.

(HALF SIZE.)

No. 65.
Silver, . . $6.50 (LANDED).
Silver, Gold Inlaid, 7.50 (LANDSCAPE).

No. 267, . $7.50 (KNIT).

No. 299, . $6.75 (KNOLL).

No. 315, . $4.50 (LARD).

No. 329.
Silver, Gold Inlaid, . $6.00 (KNEE).

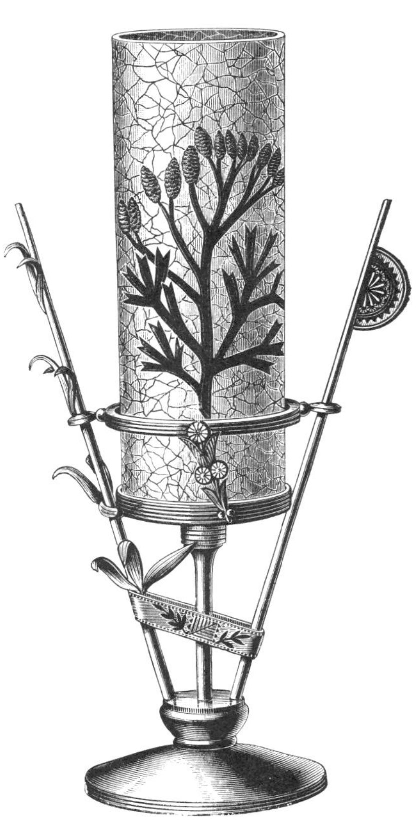

No. 327.
Silver, Gold Inlaid, . $6.00 (KIRK).

Trade Mark.
White Metal.

GOLD AND SILVER PLATE.

Trade Mark.
Nickel Silver.

(Half Size.)

No. 371, . $4.00 (laconic).

No. 427.
Old Silver, . $4.00 (modulate).
Non-Tarnishable.

No. 432.
Old Silver, . $5.00 (moulding).
Non-Tarnishable.

No. 419.
Old Silver, . $3.00 (moulder).
Non-Tarnishable.

No. 420.
Old Silver, . $3.50 (modern).
Non-Tarnishable.

Flower Stand.
No. 41, . $4.25 (lance).

Flower Stand.
No. 42, . $5.25 (lancet).

Flower Stand.
No. 51, . $4.75 (invade).

GOLD AND SILVER PLATE.

(HALF SIZE.)

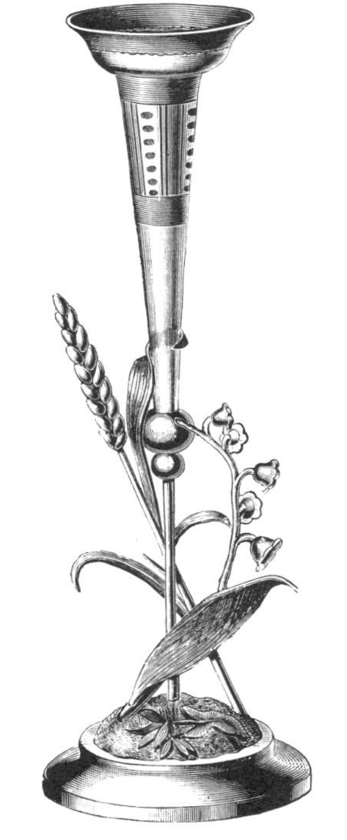

No. 360. . $3.50 (LATHE).

No. 320, . $4.50 (LATITUDE).

No. 323, . $5.00 (KORAN).

No. 289, . $4.00 (LAWN).

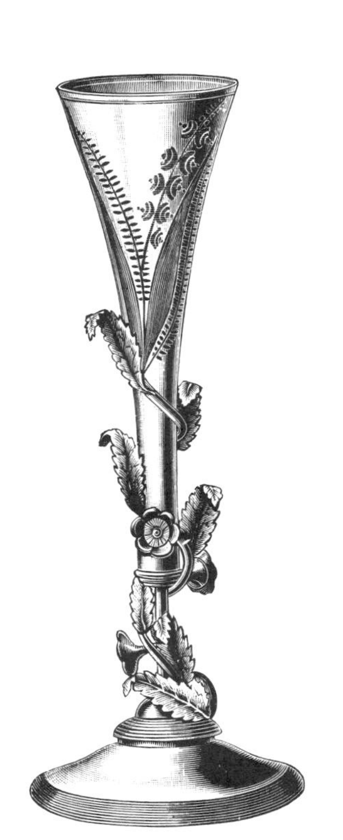

No. 318, . $3.50 (LAUNCH).

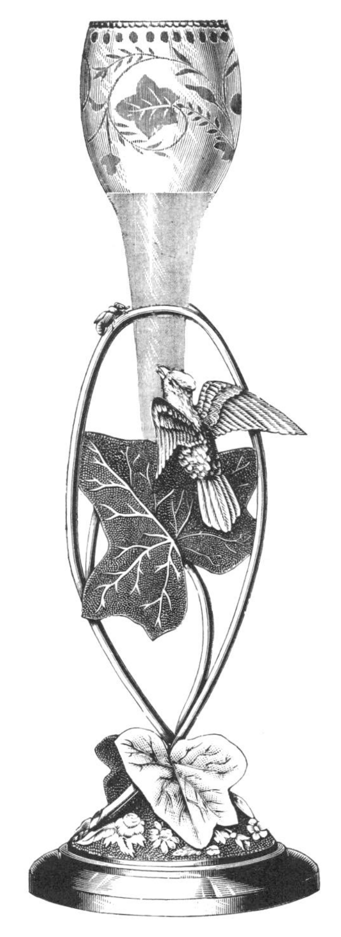

No. 296, . $5.25 (LATCH).

No. 295, . $5.50 (LATE).

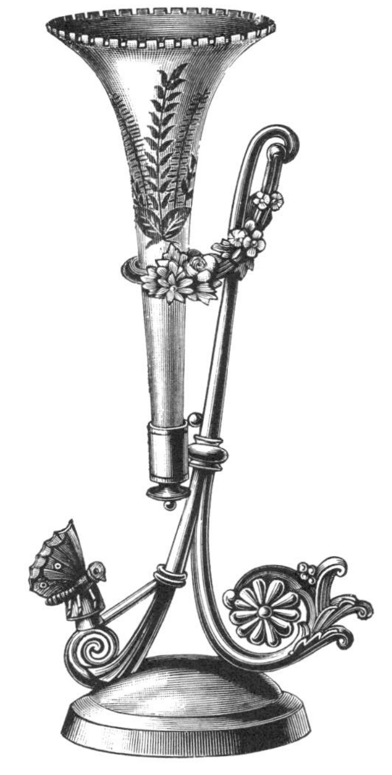

No. 308, . $3.25 (LAVISH).

GOLD AND SILVER PLATE.

(HALF SIZE.)

No. C.

Silver, . $1.50 (INVASION).

No. 385.

Chased, Gold Lined, . . . $2.75 (INVENT).
Chased, Gold Inlaid and Gold Lined, 3.25 (INVENTORY).

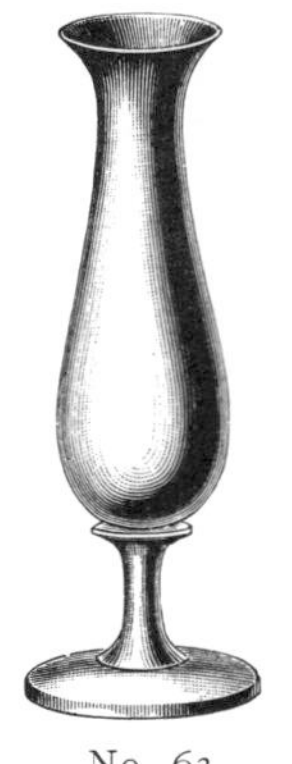

No. 63.

Gold Lined, . $2.00 (INVEST).

No. 270.

Gold and Steel Finish, . $3.75 (SOLELY).

No. 86.

Plain, . . . $2.00 (INVISIBLE).
Gold Lined, . 2.25 (INVITE).

No. 387.

Chased, Gold Lined, . . . $3.25 (JOURNAL).
Chased, Gold Inlaid and Gold Lined, 4.00 (JOURNEY).

No. 273.

Engraved, ... $4.50 (JACKET).
Gold and Steel Finish, . 6.00 (JAPAN).

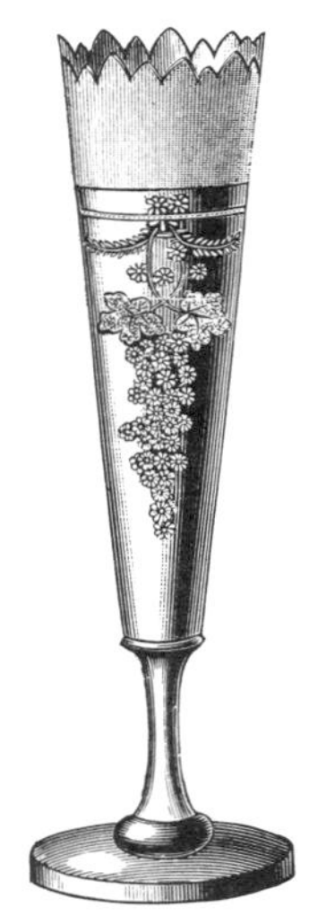

No. 85. Height, $5\frac{1}{4}$ inches.
Satin, Engraved, . $2.50 (ISSUE).

No. 84. Height, 6 inches.
Satin, Engraved, . $3.00 (ITEM).

No. 272.

Engraved, ... $4.50 (JAUNT).
Gold and Steel Finish, . 6.00 (JEAN).

GOLD AND SILVER PLATE.

(HALF SIZE.)

No. 386.

Gold Lined, . . . $3.00 (JEST).

Gold Inlaid and Gold Lined, 3.50 (JOCKEY).

No. 384.

Gold Lined, . . . $2.00 (JOCOSE).

Gold Inlaid and Gold Lined, 2.50 (JOIN).

No. 271.

Engraved, ... $4.00 (JUMP).

Gold and Steel Finish, . 5.00 (JUNE).

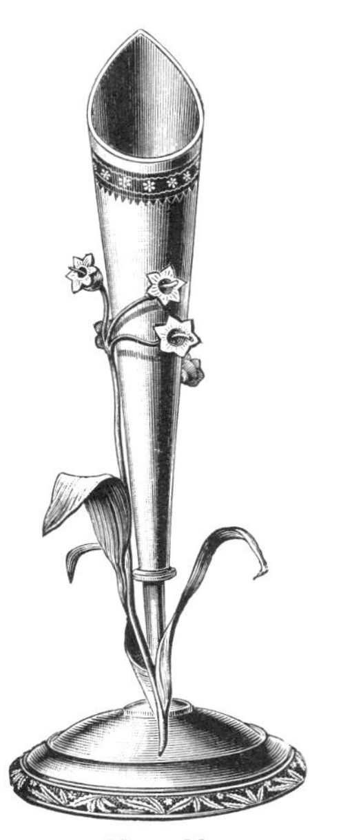

No. 388.

Gold Inlaid, . $4.00 (ISOLATE).

No. 382.

Silver, Gold Inlaid, . $3.75 (JUNIOR).

Gold and Steel Finish.

No. 252. Height, 7 inches, . $5.00 (JUSTICE).

No. 251. Height, 10 inches, . 7.50 (JUVENILE).

No. 250. Height, 12 inches, . 9.00 (KEDGE).

No. 253.

Old Silver, . . . $4.00 (JUNK).

Silver, Gold Inlaid, . 5.00 (JUROR).

No. 435. Height, $8\frac{1}{4}$ inches.

Persian Chased, . . . $25.00 (MILDLY).

Persian Chased, XX Gold Inlaid, 35.00 (MILEAGE).

No. 434. Height, 5 inches.

Persian Chased, . . . $11.00 (MINDFUL).

Persian Chased, XX Gold Inlaid, 15.00 (MILITANT).

No. 274.

Engraved, Gold Lined, . . $7.75 (KEEL).

Gold and Steel Finish, Gold Lined, 9.75 (KEEP).

Trade Mark.
WHITE METAL.

GOLD AND SILVER PLATE.

Trade Mark.
NICKEL SILVER.

(Half Size.)

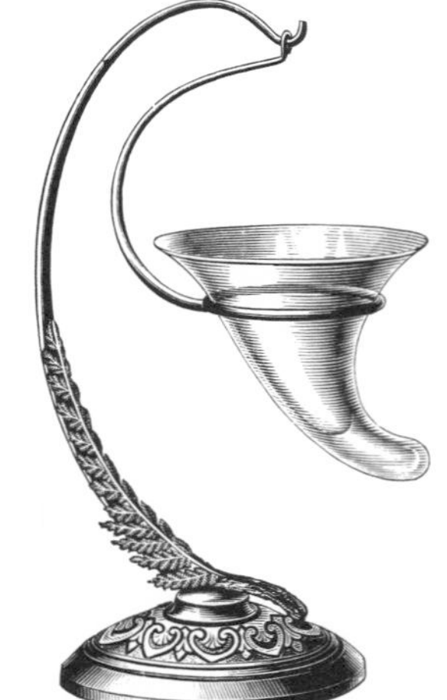

No. 248, . $1.50 (layer).

No. 234, . $2.00 (leach).

No. 249, . $1.50 (lead).

No. 242.
Silver, $2.50 (interest).

No. 426.
Silver, . . $3.50 (misname).
Old Silver, . 4.00 (misnomer).
Non-Tarnishable.

No. 399.
Silver, . $3.00 (leisure).

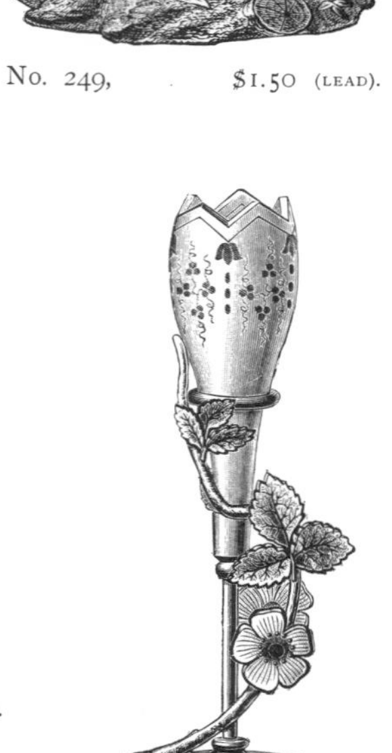

No. 400.
Silver, . $3.25 (lemon).

No. 333, . $2.75 (league).

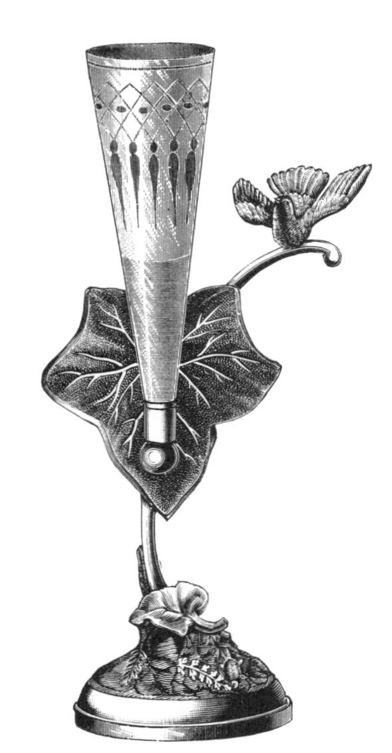

No. 286, . $3.25 (learn).

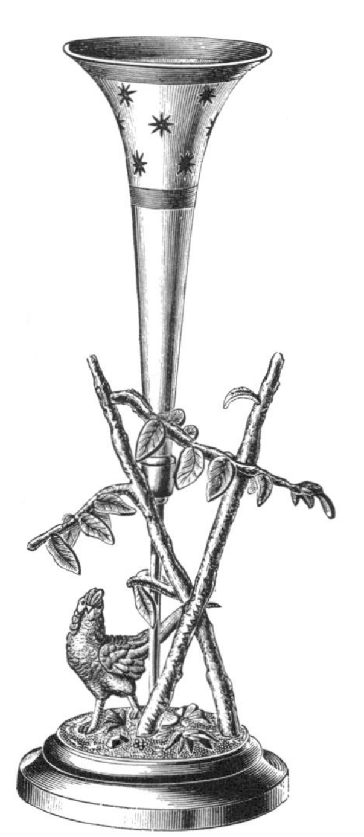

No. 361, . $3.75 (lease).

No. 285, . $2.75 (leaf).

GOLD AND SILVER PLATE.

FLOWER STANDS.

(HALF SIZE.)

No. 52.
Flower Stand, . $5.00 (INTWINE).

No. 57.
Silver, Gold Inlaid, . $6.50 (INTHRALL).

No. 53.
Flower Stand, . $6.00 (INTRUST).

No. 59.
Gold and Silver, . $10.00 (INTRICATE).

No. 40.
Silver, . $10.00 (INTRINSIC).

WAITERS.

(ONE-THIRD SIZE.)

All 24 and 26 inch Waiters Chased to match Tea Sets if desired.

No. 82—20 INCH. CHASED.

Satin, . $30.00 (MISDOING). Chased, . $36.00 (MISDIRECT). Patent Plate Glass Protector, . $4.50 extra (SCAPEMENT).

No. 107—26 INCH.

Satin, Engraved, . $60.00 (MISCHIEF). Patent Plate Glass Protector, . $7.00 extra (SALTNESS).

No. 9927. PLACQUE.
Moorish, Gold Inlaid, $27 50 (NEGATIVE.) Moorish, Old Silver, $23.50 (NEEDFUL).
(Size 11 x 11 inches.)

No. 322 — 14 INCH WAITER.
Satin Engraved, XX Gold Inlaid, $24.00 (NAVIGATOR).
Patent Plate Glass Protector, $2.00 extra (NOBILITY).

No. 86½ — 26 INCH WAITER.
Satin Rose Engraved, XX Gold Inlaid, $85.00 (ELLIPSE). Satin Rose Engraved, $60.00 (ELK).
Patent Plate Glass Protector, $7.50 extra (NOISELESS).

GOLD AND SILVER PLATE.

No. 99. Satin, Shield.

22 inch. Satin, Shield, . $35.00 (metheglin). Hammered, . $41.00 (methodic). Patent Plate Glass Protector, . $5.25 extra (mezzotint).
24 inch. Satin, Shield, . 40.00 (microphone). Hammered, . 47.00 (midland). Patent Plate Glass Protector, . 6.00 extra (migratory).

No. 80—26 inch. Chased, . $60.00 (elevate).
Patent Plate Glass Protector, $7.50 extra (elevator).

No. 105. Satin, Engraved.

22 inch.	Satin, Shield, . $35.00 (midge).	Satin, Engraved, . $42.00 (midship).	Patent Plate Glass Protector, . $5.25 extra (mightily).
24 inch.	Satin, Shield, . 40.00 (mildew).	Satin, Engraved, . 48.00 (milestone).	Patent Plate Glass Protector, . 6.00 extra (milliner).

No. 86—26 inch. Chased.

Satin, . $50.00 (trap). Chased, . $60.00 (transport). Chased, X Gold Inlaid, . $70.00 (elocution). Chased, XX Gold Inlaid, . $80.00 (elongate).

Patent Plate Glass Protector, . $7.50 extra (elm).

GOLD AND SILVER PLATE.

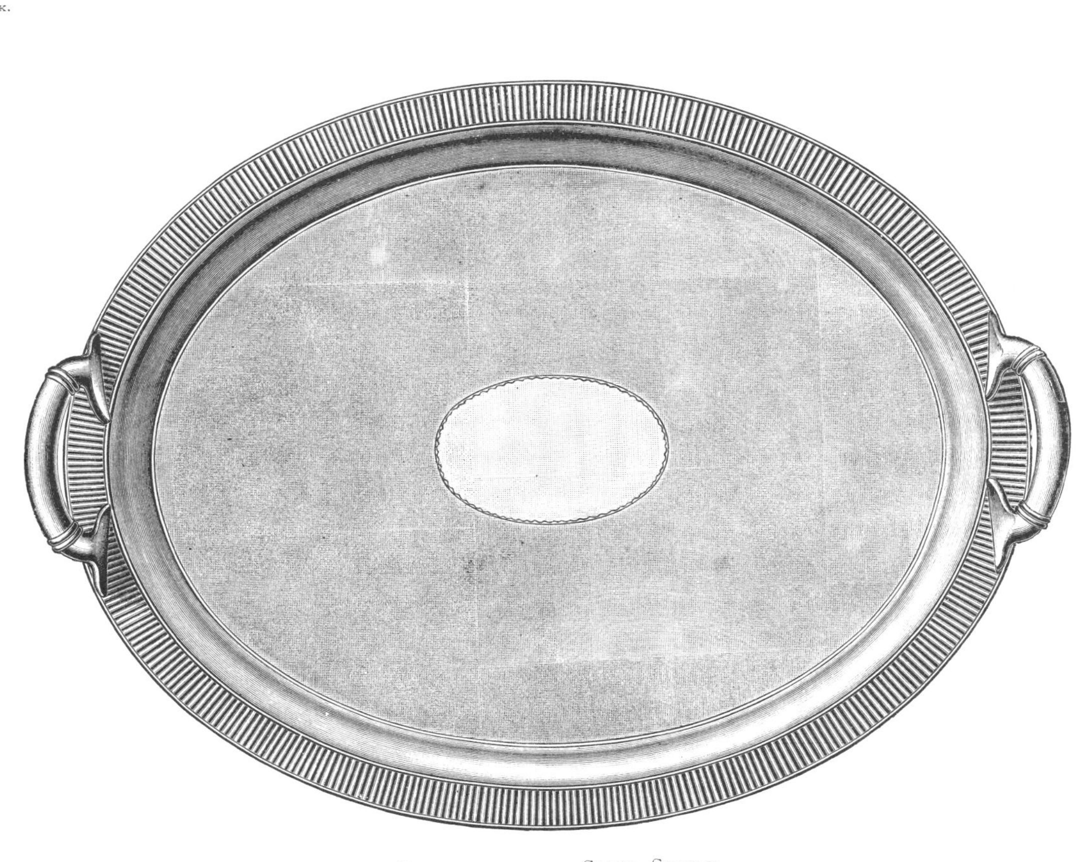

No. 95—21 inch. Satin, Shield.

Satin, Shield, . $25.00 (minutely). Hammered, . $30.00 (minority). Patent Plate Glass Protector, . $5.25 extra (sambo).

No. 109—24 inch.

Chased, . $50.00 (minikin). Patent Plate Glass Protector, . $6.00 extra (sameness).

GOLD AND SILVER PLATE.

No. 76. SATIN.

22 INCH. Satin, . $35.00 (BULLION). Hammered, . $41.00 (MINEVER). Patent Plate Glass Protector, . $5.25 extra (BULLETIN).
24 INCH. Satin, . 40.00 (MILLSTONE). Hammered, . 47.00 (SANITY). Patent Plate Glass Protector, . 6.00 extra (SANDY).

No. 26—28 INCH.
Chased, . . $65.00 (BLUSH).
Patent Plate Glass Protector, . $8.00 extra (BOA).

Trade Mark.
WHITE METAL.

Trade Mark
NICKEL SILVER.

No. 4. Satin.

20 inch, . $20.00 (bonnet). 22 inch, . $27.00 (bonfire). 24 inch, . $30.00 (boneset). 26 inch, . $35.00 (bookish).

No. $4\frac{1}{2}$. With Plain Border and Handles, same price.

No. 67. Satin, Shield. 22 inch, . $33.50 (scape). 24 inch, . $37.50 (bond).

GOLD AND SILVER PLATE.

No. 112—18 inch. Satin, Engraved.

Satin, ... $17.50 (sapsago).

Satin, Engraved, . 20.00 (sarcastic).

Also used for Child's Tray.

Patent Plate Glass Protector, . $4.00 extra (sapless).

No. 64—11 inch. Hammered, Chased.

Hammered, ... $10.50 (bootjack).

Hammered, Chased, . . . 12.50 (bootless).

Hammered, Chased, XX Gold Inlaid, 15.50 (booty).

Patent Plate Glass Protector, . $1.75 extra (sober).

No. 98. Satin, Shield.

	Satin, Shield.	Hammered.	Patent Plate Glass Protector, extra.
9 inch, .	$6.00 (satire).	$7.50 (satinet).	$0.75 (satiric).
11 inch, .	6.50 (satrap).	8.25 (satyr).	1.00 (sausage).
13 inch, .	8.25 (savage).	10.25 (savagely).	1.50 (scaldic).
15 inch, .	11.25 (savor).	13.75 (scamble).	2.25 (scanty).
17 inch, .	13.50 (saucy).	16.50 (scandent).	3.00 (sneeze).

No. 88—16 inch. Chased.

Satin, . . . $16.50 (deflect).

Chased, . . 18.50 (deforce).

Patent Plate Glass Protector, . $2.50 extra (element).

No. 75. CHASED.

12 inch, $14.00 (BUNG). Patent Plate Glass Protector, $2.00 extra (BUNION).
14 inch, 16.00 (BUNGLE). Patent Plate Glass Protector, 2.25 extra (BUNK).

No. 111—16 INCH. SATIN, ENGRAVED.

Satin, ... $16.00 (SALIVATE).
Satin, Engraved, ... 18.50 (SABIAN).
Satin, Engraved, Old Silver Border, 19.50 (SACKAGE).
Patent Plate Glass Protector, $3.00 extra (SAILYARD).

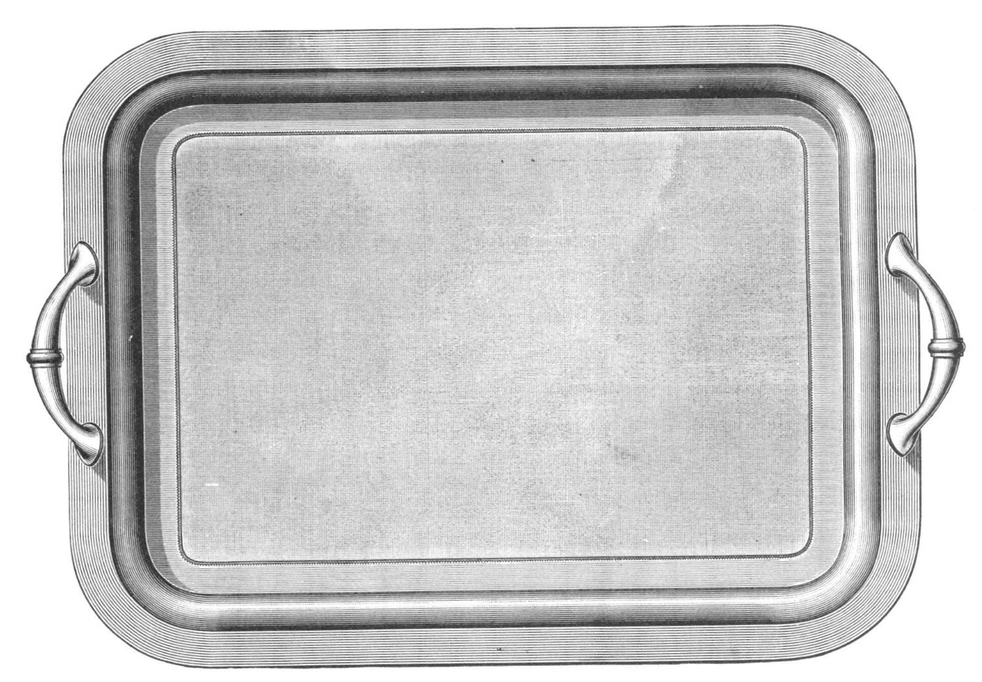

No. 79. SATIN.

17 inch, . . . $17.00 (EMBANK).
Patent Plate Glass Protector, $3.25 extra (EMBARGO).

No. 78—11 INCH. HAMMERED.

Satin, . . $11.00 (ELOPE).
Hammered, . 12.50 (ELOQUENCE).
Without Handles, $2.00 less.
Patent Plate Glass Protector, $1.75 extra (ELUCIDATE).

No. 67. SATIN, SHIELD.

		Satin, Shield.		Hammered.	
9 inch,	.	$6.00	(SANDIVER).	$7.75	(SAPOROUS).
11 inch,	.	6.50	(SAPWOOD).	8.50	(SATANIC).
13 inch,	.	7.25	(SCATHFUL).	9.75	(SCYTHIAN).
15 inch,	.	9.50	(SEA-GOD).	12.50	(SEA-GAGE).
17 inch,	.	12.50	(SEAROOM).	15.00	(SEASICK).

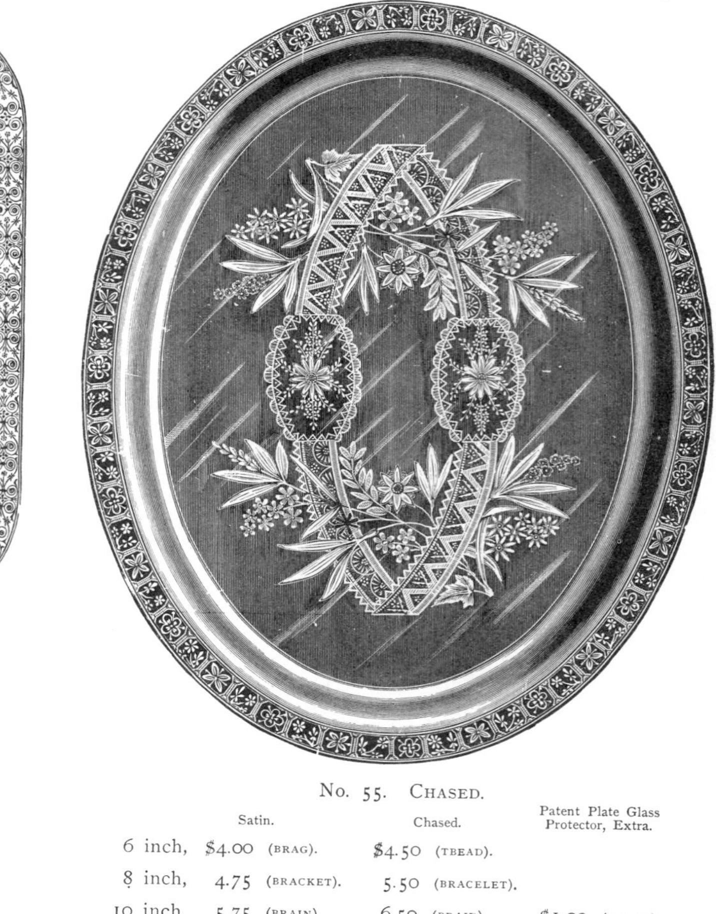

No. 55. CHASED.

	Satin.		Chased.		Patent Plate Glass Protector, Extra.	
6 inch,	$4.00	(BRAG).	$4.50	(TBEAD).		
8 inch,	4.75	(BRACKET).	5.50	(BRACELET).		
10 inch,	5.75	(BRAIN).	6.50	(BRAID).	$1.00	(SHADE).
12 inch,	7.50	(BRAY).	8.50	(BRAWL).	1.50	(SHAGREEN).
14 inch,	10.50	(BREACH).	11.50	(BRAZEN).	2.25	(SILEX).
16 inch,	12.50	(BRAKE).	14.00	(BRAND).	3.00	(SILENT).
18 inch,	16.00	(SEXTILE).	17.50	(BRASS).	3.75	(SMIRK).

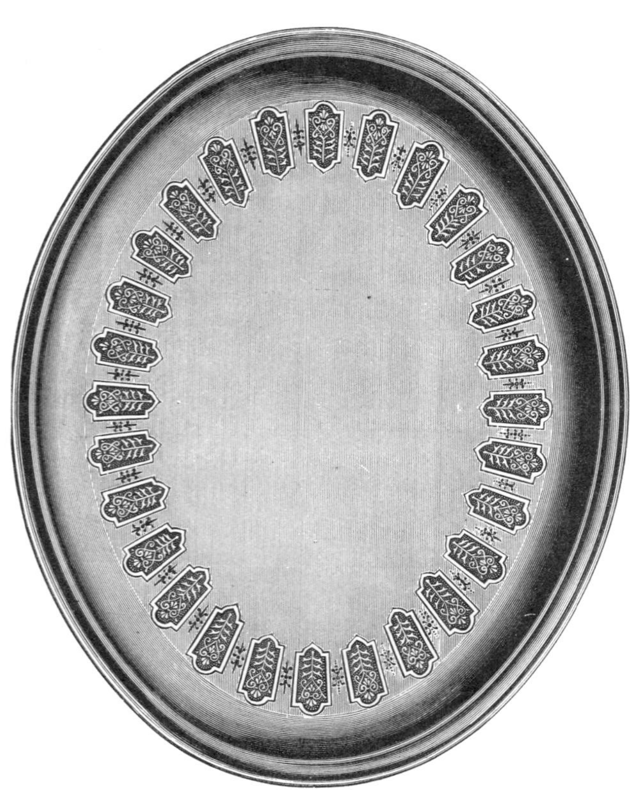

No. 011. CHASED. NICKEL SILVER.

		Satin.		Chased.	
13 inch,	.	$11.00	(SALIC).	$12.00	(REEF).
15 inch,	.	14.00	(SAPID).	15.00	(SAPOR).
17 inch,	.	17.00	(SASH).	18.00	(REEL).

No. 72—17 INCH. CHASED.

Without Handles, . $17.00 (BULB).

With Handles, . . 19.00 (BUILD).

Patent Plate Glass Protector, . $2.50 extra (BULGE).

GOLD AND SILVER PLATE.

No. 83—17 INCH. CHASED.

Satin, . $14.00 (SEASONING). Chased, . $16.00 (SECEDER). Patent Plate Glass Protector, . $3.00 extra (SECLUSION).

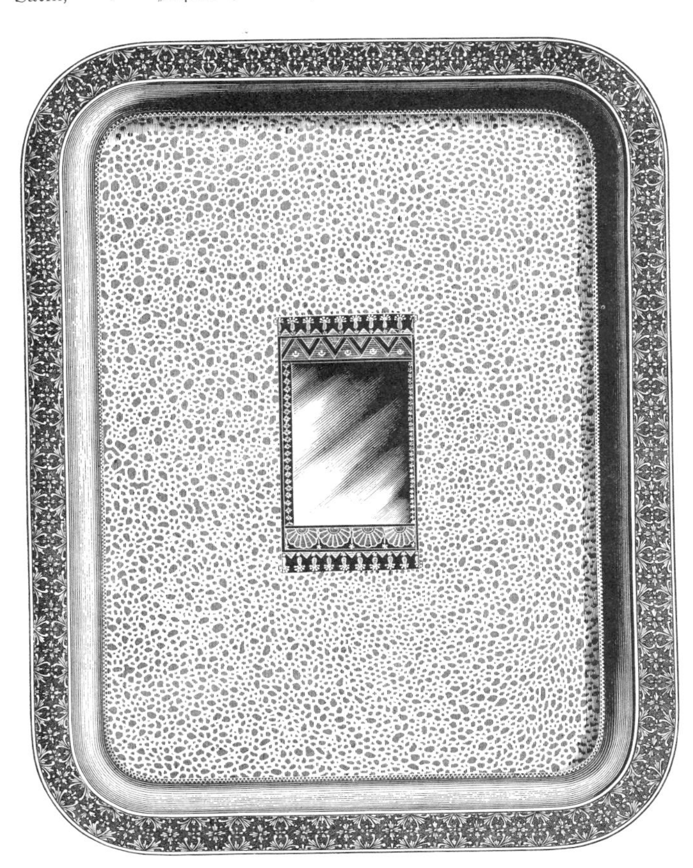

No. 60. DAMASCENE SHIELD.

	Satin, Shield.	Damascene, Shield.
9 inch, .	$6.25 (BREVET).	$7.00 (BRIDE).
11 inch, .	7.25 (BREW).	8.00 (BRIDGE).
13 inch, .	9.00 (BRIBE).	10.00 (BRIDAL).
15 inch, .	12.00 (BRICK).	13.25 (BRIEF).
17 inch, .	14.00 (BRICKBAT).	15.50 (BRIG).

No. 89. SATIN, SHIELD.

	Satin, Shield.	Hammered.	Patent Plate Glass Protector, Extra.
9 inch, .	$6.50 (SECONDLY).	$8.00 (SECONDARY).	
11 inch, .	7.25 (SEDITIOUS).	9.00 (SEDENTARY).	
13 inch, .	9.00 (SELFISH).	11.00 (SELF-MADE).	$2.00 (SERVILE).
15 inch, .	12.00 (SENIORITY).	14.50 (SELF-WILL).	2.50 (SERPENT).
17 inch, .	14.00 (SENTENCE).	17.00 (SELFSAME).	3.25 (SEPTUM).

GOLD AND SILVER PLATE.

No. 3½. Satin.

10 inch, $4.50 (bolus). 14 inch, $8.75 (bombshell).
12 inch, 6.00 (bonbon). 16 inch, 10.50 (bondman).

No. 3. Satin.

10 inch, $4.50 (bombay). 14 inch, $8.75 (bolton).
12 inch, 6.00 (bonhomme). 16 inch, 10.50 (bologna).

No. 65. Satin, Shield.

6 inch, $4.25 (brigade). 12 inch, $7.50 (brine).
8 inch, 4.75 (bright). 14 inch, 10.50 (bring).
10 inch, 5.75 (brim). 16 inch, 12.50 (brink).

No. 5. Satin.

12 inch, $6.00 (bolivia). 14 inch, $8.75 (bonded). 16 inch, $10.50 (bombard).

No. 5½. With Plain Border (see No. 3½).

12 inch, $6.00 (boland). 14 inch, $8.75 (bondage). 16 inch, $10.50 (bombast).

TRADE MARK.
WHITE METAL.

GOLD AND SILVER PLATE.

TRADE MARK.
NICKEL SILVER.

No. 102—11 INCH. SATIN, ENGRAVED.
Satin, . . $10.00 (SHAMEFUL).
Satin, Engraved, 11.50 (SHARPER).

Patent Plate Glass Protector,
$2.00 extra (SHARPNESS).

No. 97. BROCADE, X CHASED.
Hammered, . . . $11.00 (SHADINESS).
Brocade, X Chased, . 13.00 (SHADOWY).

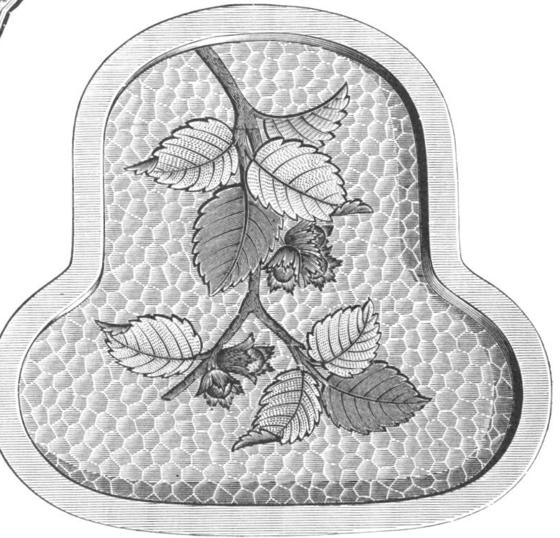

No. 91—10 INCH. HAMMERED, CHASED.
Hammered, Old Silver, ... $11.50 (EMBER).
Hammered, Chased, Old Silver, . . 13.50 (EMBLEM).
Hammered, Chased, Old Silver, Gold Inlaid, 15.50 (EMBODY).
Patent Plate Glass Protector, . . $2.00 extra (EMBOGUE).

No. 19. SATIN, ENGRAVED.
Satin, Shield, . . $10.50 (BOUND).
Satin, Engraved, . . 13.50 (BOUGHT).
Patent Plate Glass Protector, . $3.00 extra (SEPARATE).

No. 106—12 INCH. SATIN, ENGRAVED.
Showing Patent Plate Glass Protector partly removed.
Satin, . $10.00 (SENSATIONAL). Satin, Engraved, . $12.50 (SENSIBILITY).
Patent Plate Glass Protector, . $2.00 extra (SEPARATOR).

THE PATENT PLATE GLASS PROTECTOR, a piece of beveled plate glass cut to fit the Waiter, which, placed upon it and being transparent, shows the design clearer than when removed; also affording perfect protection from all wear, scratches, etc.; making a much more durable Waiter than when used without it. This Patent applies to Waiters of all shapes and sizes.

GOLD AND SILVER PLATE.

No. 101—10 INCH. SATIN, ENGRAVED.

Satin, . . . $8.50 (SHARER).

Satin, Engraved, . 10.00 (SHAVING).

Patent Plate Glass Protector, $1.75 extra (SHEEN).

No. 100—11 inch. MOORISH.

Satin, Old Silver, . . $12.50 (SHEEPSKIN).

Moorish, Old Silver, . 14.00 (SHELL-FISH).

Moorish, XX Gold Inlaid, 20.00 (SHIFTLESS).

Patent Plate Glass Protector, $1.75 extra (SHINING).

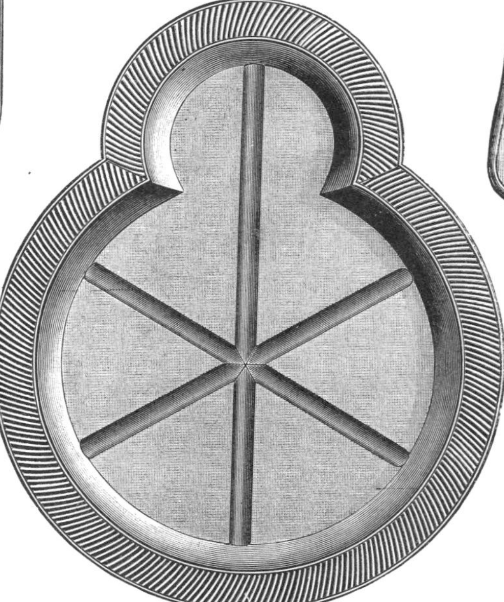

No. 317. SATIN.

Satin, . . $6.25 (SHIPPING). Hammered, . 7.00 (SHORTER).

Patent Plate Glass Protector, $2.00 extra (SHOVEL).

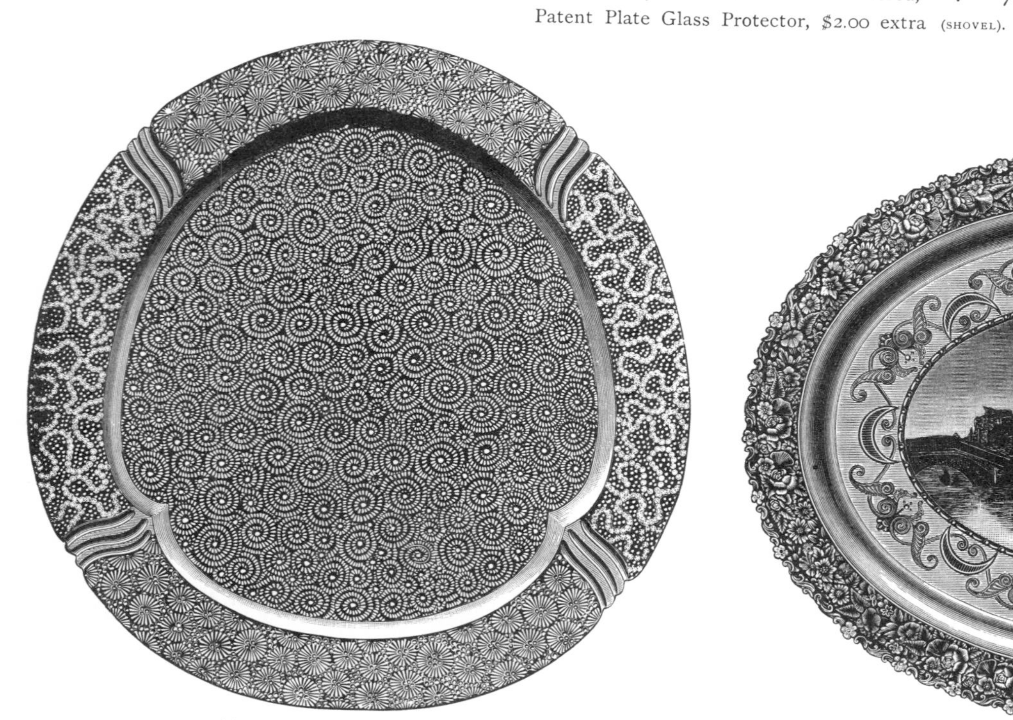

No. 103—12 INCH. MOORISH.

Moorish, Old Silver, . $13.50 (SHOWERY).

Gold Inlaid, . . . 19.50 (SIDERAL).

Patent Plate Glass Protector, $2.00 extra (SIGNALLY).

No. 110—15 INCH. VENETIAN.

Satin, ... $16.00 (SHREWISH).

Satin, Old Silver Border, 17.00 (SIGNALIZE).

Patent Plate Glass Protector, $2.25 extra (SOOTHE).

Venetian, ... $18.00 (SHRIEK).

Venetian, Old Silver Border, 19.00 (SILICON).

Venetian, XX Gold Inlaid, 23.00 (SYLLABUB).

WHITE METAL.

GOLD AND SILVER PLATE.

NICKEL SILVER.

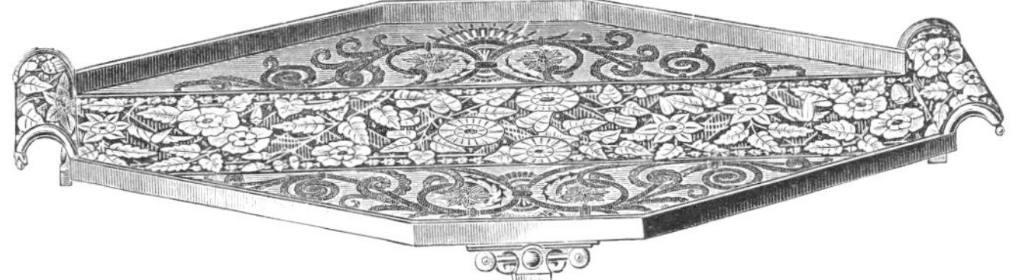

No. 90—12 INCH. CHASED.

Plain, ... $11.00 (EMULGENT).
Chased, ... 12.50 (EMULSION).
Chased, X Gold Inlaid, 14.00 (ENCUMBER).
Patent Plate Glass Protector, . $2.50 extra (SMARTNESS).

No. 104—7 INCH. MOORISH.

Moorish, Old Silver, . $6.50 (SATE).
Moorish, Gold Inlaid, . 8.50 (SPRAT).
atent Plate Glass Protector, $1.00 extra (STUPOR).

No. 64—7 INCH. INDIA CHASED.

Satin, ... $5.50 (BUMP).
Satin, Gold Inlaid, . 7.50 (BUMPER).
India Chased, . . 6.00 (BUNCH).
India Chased, Gold Inlaid, 8.00 (BUNDLE).
Patent Plate Glass Protector, $1.00 extra (STUBBY).

No. 84—12 INCH. SATIN C.

Satin C, ... $13.50 (ELUDE).
Satin C, X Gold Inlaid, 16.50 (ELUSIVE).
Satin C, XX Gold Inlaid, 19.50 (EMANATE).
Patent Plate Glass Protector, . $2.00 extra (EMBALM).

No. 319—9 INCH. SATIN, OLD SILVER BORDER.

Satin, ... $6.00 (SPRIG).
Satin, Old Silver Border, 6.75 (SPATTER).

No. 81—7 INCH. CHASED.

Satin, . . $6.00 (EMBOSS).
Chased, . . 7.00 (EMBRACE).

No. 318—7 INCH.

Moorish, Old Silver, $4.00 (SOFTLY). Moorish, Gold Inlaid, $6.00 (SOFTNESS).
Patent Plate Glass Protector, . $0.75 extra (SOLECISM).

Trade Mark.
WHITE METAL.

GOLD AND SILVER PLATE.

Trade Mark.
NICKEL SILVER.

No. 310—10 inch. Chased.

	10 Inch.		12 Inch.	
Satin, . .	$4.50	(burden).	$6.00	(bureau).
Chased, . .	5.50	(burdock).	7.00	(burg).
Patent Plate Glass Protector, extra,	1.50	(burgess).	2.00	(burgher).

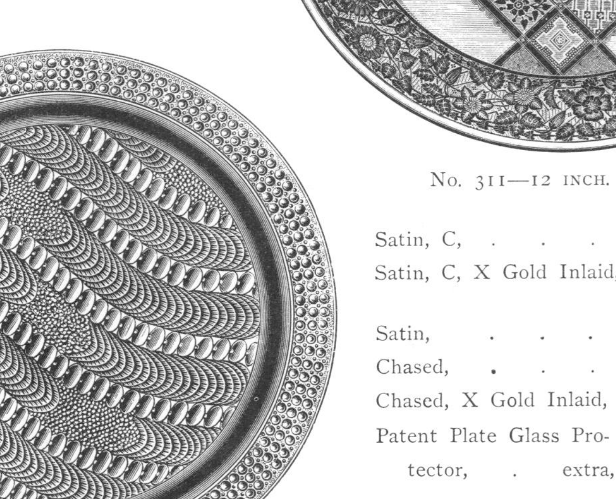

No. 311—12 inch. Chased.

8 Inch.		
Satin, C, ...	$4.00	(engineer).
Satin, C, X Gold Inlaid,	6.00	(engird).
12 Inch.		
Satin, ...	$6.50	(endeavor).
Chased, ...	7.50	(endowment).
Chased, X Gold Inlaid,	10.00	(endurance).
Patent Plate Glass Protector, . extra,	2.00	(engraft).

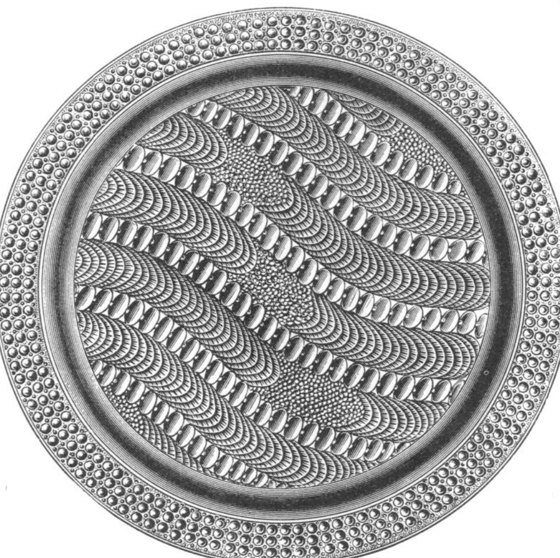

No. 320—11 inch.

Moorish, Old Silver, . $7.00 (simplicity).
Moorish, Gold Inlaid, . 9.00 (simplest).
Patent Plate Glass Protector, $1.50 extra (snugly).

No. 316—11 inch.

Satin, Shield, . $3.50 (simulate).
Hammered, . 4.50 (simulation).
Patent Plate Glass Protector, $1.50 extra (sincerely).

No. 308—11 inch.

Chased, . $6.00 (bootee).
Patent Plate Glass Protector, $1.50 extra (bonito).

GOLD AND SILVER PLATE.

No. 302—10 INCH.
Chased, . . . $6.00 (BROW).
Patent Plate Glass
Protector, . extra, 1.50 (BROWSE).

No. 301—10 INCH.
Chased, . . . $6.00 (BROIL).
Patent Plate Glass
Protector, . extra, 1.50 (BROKER).

No. 303—12 INCH.
Feather Chased, . $8.50 (BRUIN).
Patent Plate Glass
Protector, . extra, 2.00 (BRUIT).

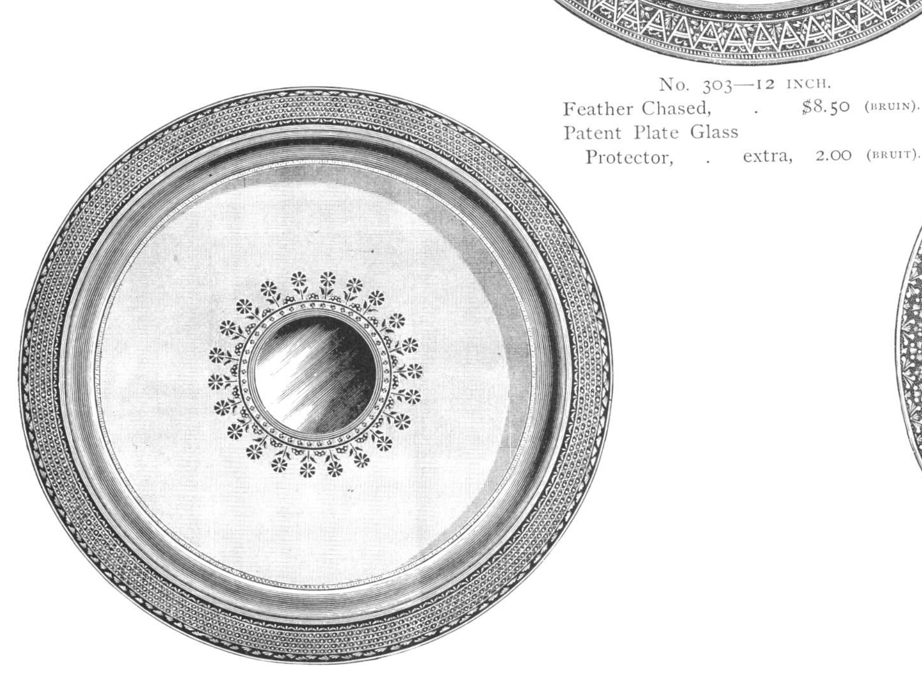

No. 306. SATIN, SHIELD.

10 inch, ... $4.50 (BREAD).
12 inch, ... 5.50 (BREAKER).

No. 39½. CHASED.

	Satin, Shield.	Chased.	Patent Plate Glass Protector, Extra.
6 inch,	$2.50 (BUFFALO).	$3.00 (BUCK).	$0.50 (SINISTER).
7 inch,	3.00 (BUFFET).	3.75 (BUBBLE).	.75 (SINUATE).
8 inch,	3.50 (SKYSAIL).	4.50 (SKINNER).	1.00 (SKYLIGHT).
9 inch,	4.00 (BUG).	5.00 (BRUTE).	1.25 (SLACKEN).
10 inch,	4.50 (BUGGY).	5.50 (BRUSH).	1.50 (SLAPJACK).
12 inch,	5.50 (BUGLE).	6.50 (BRUNT).	2.00 (SMUGGLER).

GOLD AND SILVER PLATE.

No. 10. Child's Tray.
Chased B, . . $13.50 (bonus).
Patent Plate Glass Protector, . $3.75 extra (book).

No. 2. Crumb Tray.
Chased B, . . $8.75 (boom).

No. 1. Crumb Brush.
Chased, ... $6.00 (prism).
Hammered, Old Silver, . 6.00 (slimness).
Satin, Engraved, . . 6.00 (smallness).

No. 5. Hammered Crumb Tray.
Satin, ... $7.50 (emergency).
Hammered, Old Silver, 8.50 (emersion).
Satin, Engraved, . 8.50 (slenderly).

No. 9½. Child's Tray.
Damascene, Chased, . . $10.50 (boot).
No. 9. Same shape with different border.
Minerva, Chased, . . . $9.00 (booth).

Trade Mark.
WHITE METAL.

GOLD AND SILVER PLATE.

Trade Mark.
NICKEL SILVER.

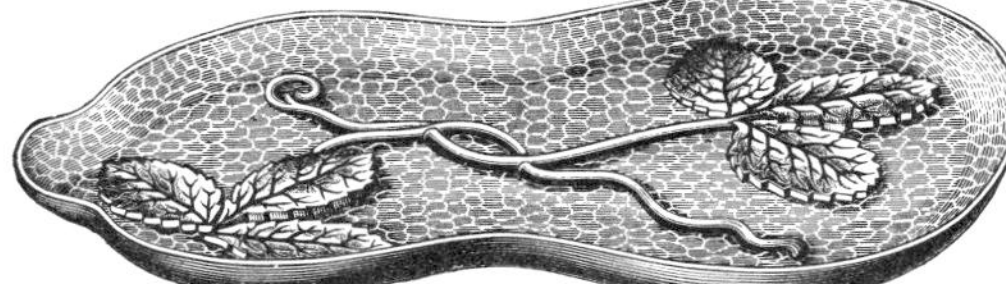

No. 11—7 inch. Card Waiter.

Hammered, Old Silver, . . $4.00 (start).
Hammered and Applied, Old Silver, 4.50 (staid).
Hammered and Applied, Gold Inlaid, 5.50 (scarp).

No. 7. Crumb Tray.

Satin, ... $9.50 (speculum).
Satin, Engraved, . . 10.50 (spelling).
Satin, Engraved, Old Silver, 11.00 (spheroid).

No. 8. Crumb Tray.

Satin, Old Silver, . . $8.50 (spheric).
Satin, Engraved, Old Silver, 9.50 (spotless).

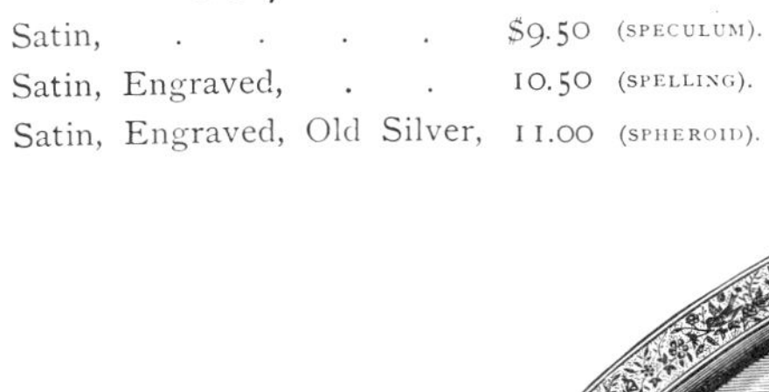

No. 11. Child's Tray.

Satin, . $14.50 (elfin). Chased, . $17.00 (elicit).
Patent Plate Glass Protector, . $3.75 extra (elixir).

No. 13. Crumb Tray.

Satin, . . . $7.50 (splashy).
Satin, Engraved, . 8.50 (sprawl).

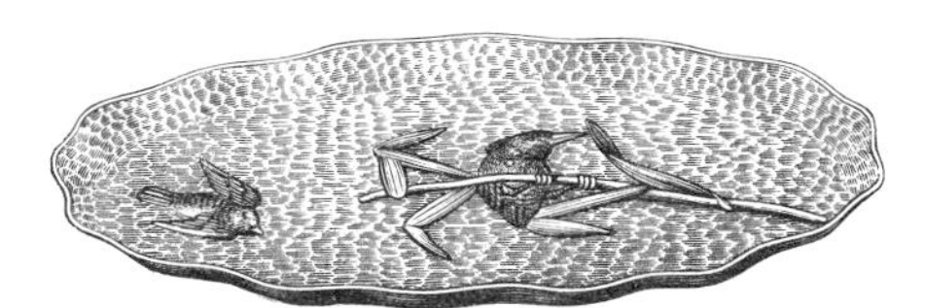

No. 10—6 inch. Card Waiter.

Hammered, Old Silver, . . $3.00 (specious).
Hammered and Applied, Old Silver, 3.50 (spectral).
Hammered and Applied, Gold Inlaid, 4.50 (specular).

8½ inch.

Satin, ... $4.00 (subsoil).
Hammered, Old Silver, . . 5.00 (subtend).
Hammered and Applied, Old Silver, 5.50 (succinct).
Enameled Copper, . . . 3.50 (succulent).

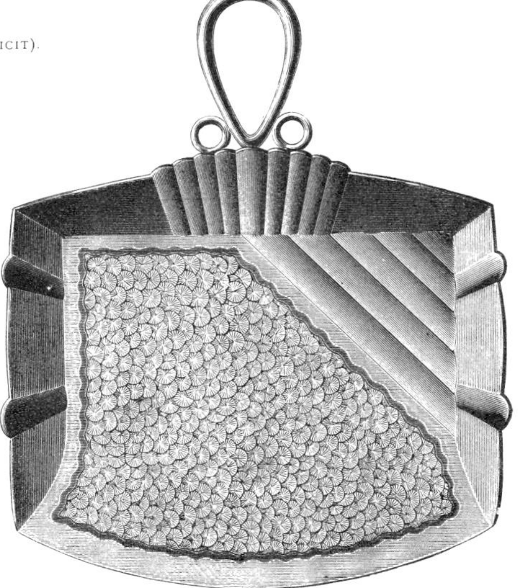

No. 6. Crumb Tray.

Satin, . . . $8.00 (spirit).
Crystal, Chased, . 8.50 (splay).
Satin, Engraved, . 9.00 (spongy).

NICKEL SILVER WAITERS.

No. 06030—26 INCH. Satin, $100.00 (SLEEPER). Engraved, $140.00 (REDRESS).

No. 06020—26 INCH. Satin, . $100.00 (SLEEPING). Engraved, . $140.00 (REDUCE).

NICKEL SILVER, SILVER SOLDERED.

GOLD AND SILVER PLATE.

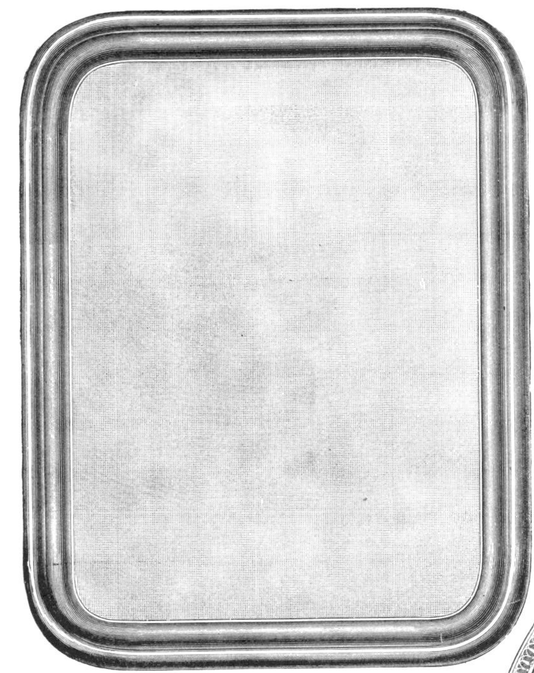

No. 06014. Satin.

Size	Price	Code
10 inch,	$16.00	(stature).
12 inch,	20.00	(statedly).
14 inch,	25.00	(stated).
16 inch,	32.00	(starry).

No. 06015. Cash Waiter.

7 inch, . . $6.50 (reed).

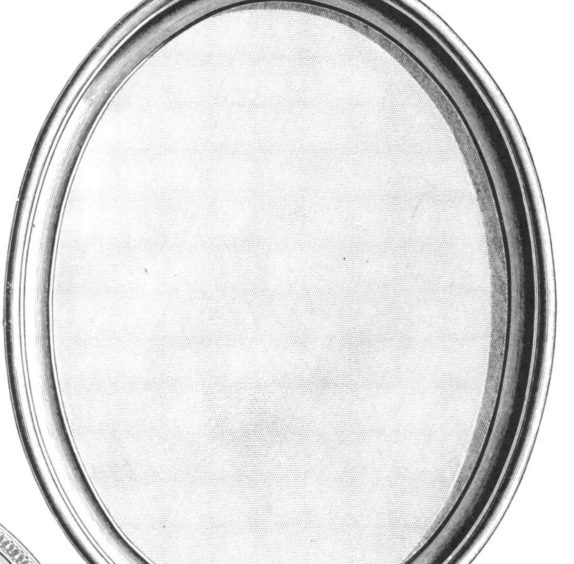

No. 06013. Plain or Satin.

Size	Price	Code
12 inch,	$16.00	(redundant).
14 inch,	20.00	(re-echo).
16 inch,	25.00	(reduction).
18 inch,	31.00	(smartly).

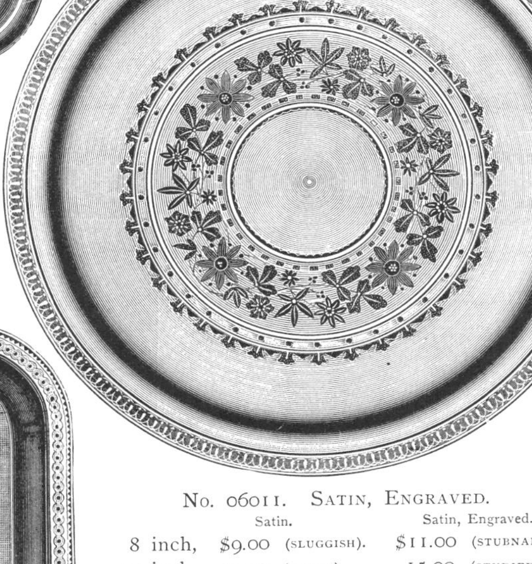

No. 06011. Satin, Engraved.

Size	Satin	Code	Satin, Engraved	Code
8 inch,	$9.00	(sluggish).	$11.00	(stubnail).
10 inch,	12.00	(reeve).	15.00	(studied).
12 inch,	15.00	(reflection).	18.50	(stumble).

No. 06016.

Size	Satin	Code	Satin, Engraved	Code
9 inch,	$15.00	(starless).	$18.00	(staging).
11 inch,	19.00	(starchly).	22.50	(staccato).
13 inch,	24.00	(standish).	29.00	(stabling).
15 inch,	30.00	(standing).	37.00	(sprucely).
17 inch,	37.00	(staidness).	46.00	(spyglass).

No. 010. Crumb Tray.

Finish	Price	Code
Satin, . . .	$10.50	(springy).
Satin, Engraved, .	12.50	(spright).

No. 06012.

Size	Satin	Code	Satin, Engraved	Code
12 inch,	$17.50	(sprout).	$21.00	(seaport).
14 inch,	22.00	(splendor).	27.00	(seaweed).
16 inch,	27.00	(spondee).	34.00	(spicery).
18 inch,	33.00	(sporadic).	42.00	(spirally).

NICKEL SILVER, SILVER SOLDERED.

FLAT WARE.

TRADE MARK.

For Spoons, Forks, Etc.:	For SECTIONAL Plating:
1847.-Rogers Bros.-A 1. ®	**1847.-Rogers Bros.-XII.** ®

The above cut is printed on the label of each box containing the genuine 1847.—ROGERS BROS.—® goods.

All goods bearing the above trade mark are plated with Pure Silver on the best quality of 18 per cent. Nickel Silver, are warranted in every respect, are accurately weighed before and after plating to conform to the following standard, and are Stamped as follows:

EXTRA OR STANDARD PLATE.

(Plated 20 per cent. heavier than the ordinary market standard.)

	EXTRA OR STANDARD PLATE.	DOUBLE PLATE.	TRIPLE PLATE.
TEA SPOONS, ...	1847.—ROGERS BROS.—A 1. ®	1847.—ROGERS BROS.—4. ®	1847.—ROGERS BROS.—6. ®
DESSERT SPOONS AND DESSERT FORKS,	1847.—ROGERS BROS.—A 1. ®	1847.—ROGERS BROS.—6. ®	1847.—ROGERS BROS.—9. ®
TABLE SPOONS AND MEDIUM FORKS, .	1847.—ROGERS BROS.—A 1. ®	1847.—ROGERS BROS.—8. ®	1847.—ROGERS BROS.—12. ®

Sectional Plate is Stamped "XII" in addition to above.

Forks furnished with Cutting Tines if desired (see Price-list).

LABELS.

The different grades of Plating are labeled on each half-dozen package as follows, each grade having a different color.

Extra Plate. On Nickel Silver. 1847.—ROGERS BROS.—A 1. Meriden, Conn.	Double Plate. On Nickel Silver. 1847.—ROGERS BROS.—A 1. Meriden, Conn.	Triple Plate. On Nickel Silver. 1847.—ROGERS BROS.—A 1. Meriden, Conn.
Extra and XII Plate. On Nickel Silver. 1847.—ROGERS BROS.—XII. Meriden, Conn.	Double and XII Plate. On Nickel Silver. 1847.—ROGERS BROS.—XII. Meriden, Conn.	Triple and XII Plate. On Nickel Silver. 1847.—ROGERS BROS.—XII. Meriden, Conn.

We would invite attention to our round spring-tempered Shank, on Spoons, Forks, etc., which increases their strength where most required, and adds much to the lasting quality of the goods.

"XII" SECTIONAL PLATE.

Attention is invited to this Patent Process for Electro-Plating Spoons and Forks, by which the parts most exposed to wear (see below) receive an extra coating of silver three times the usual thickness, rendering the goods more economical than those of other manufacturers.

This Sectional Plate is recommended for hard service, being worth many times the additional cost in durability. The great advantage will be readily seen, as Spoons and Forks (not Sectional Plated) always wear through on these exposed points, while the plate is yet good upon other parts of the article. All Spoons and Forks stamped "1847.—ROGERS BROS.—XII. ®" are plated as above in addition to the regular plate. This method of plating is applied to the Extra, Double, and Triple Plate, as required. The extra cost, on Tea Spoons, is 75 cents; on Dessert Spoons and Forks, $1.13; on Table Spoons, Table and Medium Forks, $1.50 per dozen. (See Price-list.)

When desired, we can furnish for Hotels, Steamships, Clubs, etc., goods of extra weight of metal, which, with our heavy spring-tempered Shank, and plated by the "XII" process, are the most durable for all purposes where hard usage is necessary.

The Sectional or "XII" process will add three times to the durability of goods so plated.

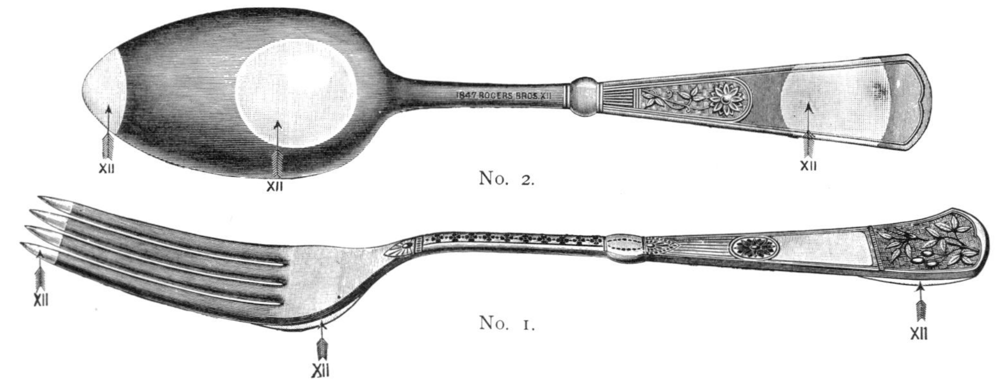

No. 2.

No. 1.

The above cuts, Nos. 1 and 2, show the points (XII) most exposed to wear, and where the extra quantity of silver is deposited by the patent process. The appearance, when finished, is the same as the Standard Plate.

N. B.—In ordering, *order "XII,"* and NOT *No.* 12, as *No.* 12 indicates Standard Triple Plate.

Every letter, syllable, and device of our trade mark has been appropriated and is being imitated by unprincipled parties who wish to take advantage of our reputation. Customers are sending us these goods, supposing them to be our make, and we find they are inferior blanks poorly plated, and stamped in such a way as to mislead the unsuspecting public. Our standard plate is 20 per cent. heavier than we represent it to be, and the unequaled reputation we have enjoyed for over a third of a century, with constantly increasing sales, shows conclusively that they are the best in the world.

1847.-ROGERS BROS.-A 1. 1847.-ROGERS BROS.-XII.

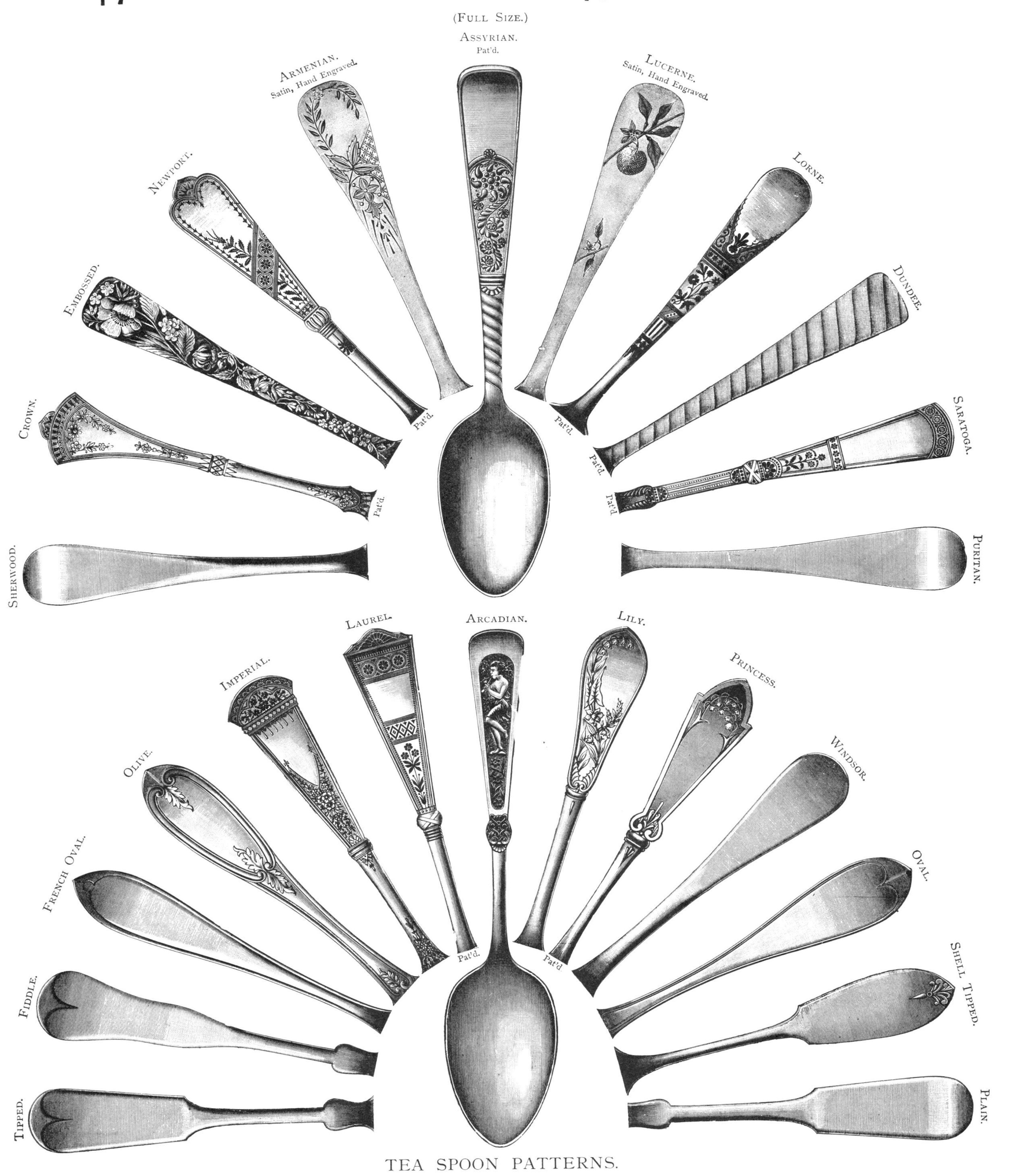

TEA SPOON PATTERNS.

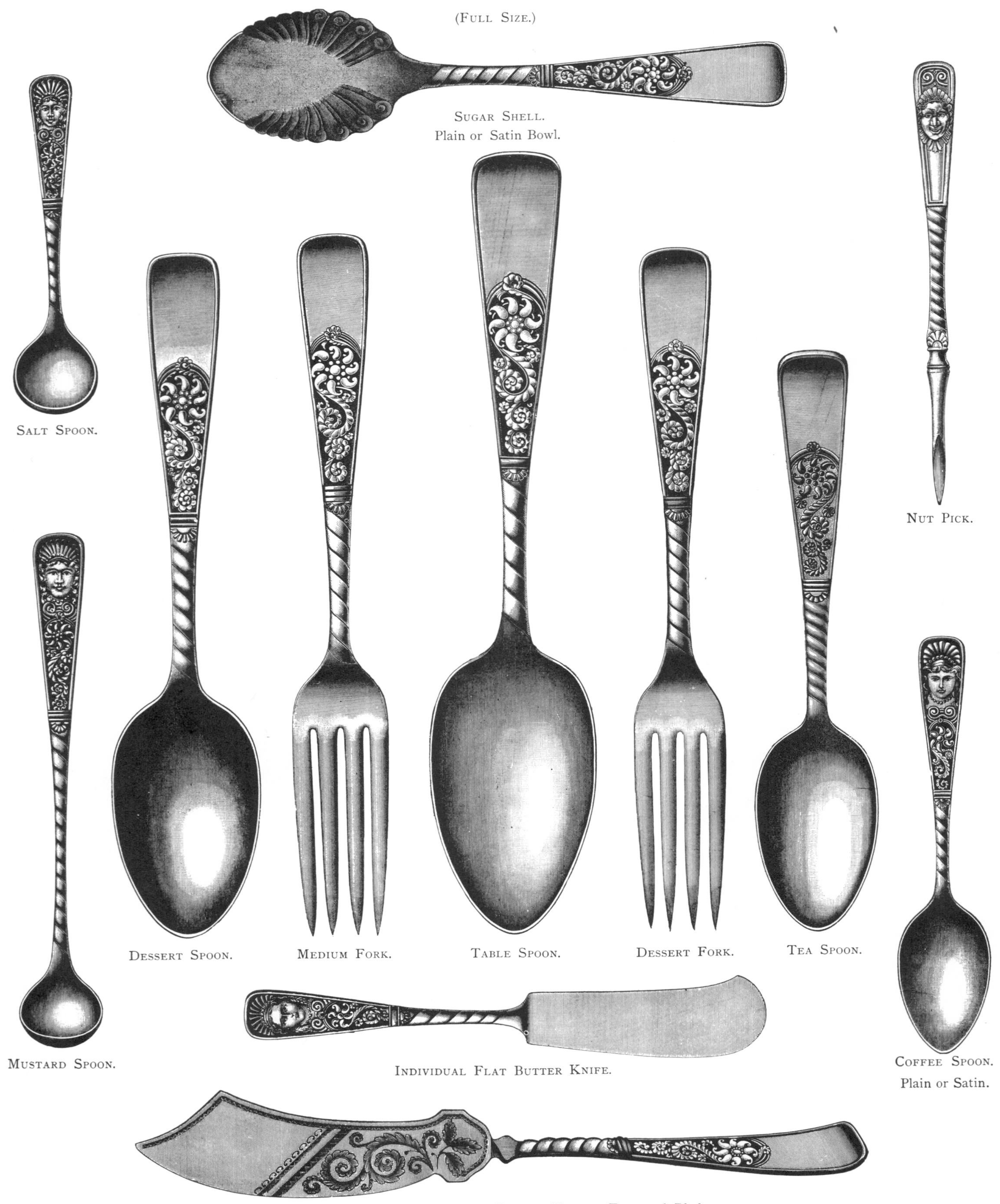

TWIST OR REVERSED HANDLE BUTTER KNIFE. Engraved Blade.

ASSYRIAN PATTERN.

(Patented.)

For complete Price-List see pages 422–428.

(Full Size.)

Sugar Tongs.

Sugar Tongs. Tête-à-Tête.

Asparagus Tongs. Hollow Handle.

Child's Knife. Chased Blade.

Pickle Fork. Long Handle.

Oyster Fork.

Salad Fork.

Salad Spoon.

Child's Fork.

ASSYRIAN PATTERN.

(Patented.)

For complete Price-List, see pages 422–428.

1847.-ROGERS BROS.-A 1. 1847.-ROGERS BROS.-XII.

(FULL SIZE.)

ICE CREAM KNIFE.
Satin, Hand Engraved.
Hollow Handle.

CAKE KNIFE.
Satin, Hand Engraved.

BERRY SPOON. Plain or Satin Bowl.

CHEESE SCOOP.
Satin, Hand Engraved.
Hollow Handle.

PIE KNIFE.
Satin, Hand Engraved.
(Also made with Hollow Handle.)

ASSYRIAN PATTERN.

(Patented.)

For complete Price-List see pages 422–428.

(Full Size.)

Gravy or Platter Spoon.

Fish Fork.

Fish Knife. Satin, Hand Engraved. (Also made with Hollow Handle.)

ASSYRIAN PATTERN.

(Patented.)

For complete Price-List see pages 422–428.

Crumb Knife. Hollow Handle, Satin, Hand Engraved. (Also made with Flat Handle.)

(FULL SIZE.)

CREAM LADLE.
Plain or Satin Bowl.

GRAVY LADLE. Plain or Satin Bowl.

OYSTER LADLE.
Satin, Hand Engraved.

MEDIUM LADLE.
Plain or Satin Bowl.

SOUP LADLE. Satin, Hand Engraved.

ASSYRIAN PATTERN.

(Patented.)

For complete Price-List, see pages 422–428.

1847.-ROGERS BROS.-A1.

Assyrian
Fish Knife.
Assyrian
Cake Knife.
Assyrian
Sugar Shell.
Arcadian
Soup Ladle.
Arcadian
Sugar Shell.
Assyrian
Fish Fork.
Arcadian
Pie Knife.
$1.75 each.
$1.75 each.
$6.50 each.
$5.50 each.
$7.25 each.
$5.50 each.
$6.50 each.

1847.-ROGERS BROS.-A 1. 1847.-ROGERS BROS.-XII.

ARCADIAN PATTERN.

For complete Price-List see pages 422–428.

1847.-Rogers Bros.-A I. 1847.-Rogers Bros.-XII.

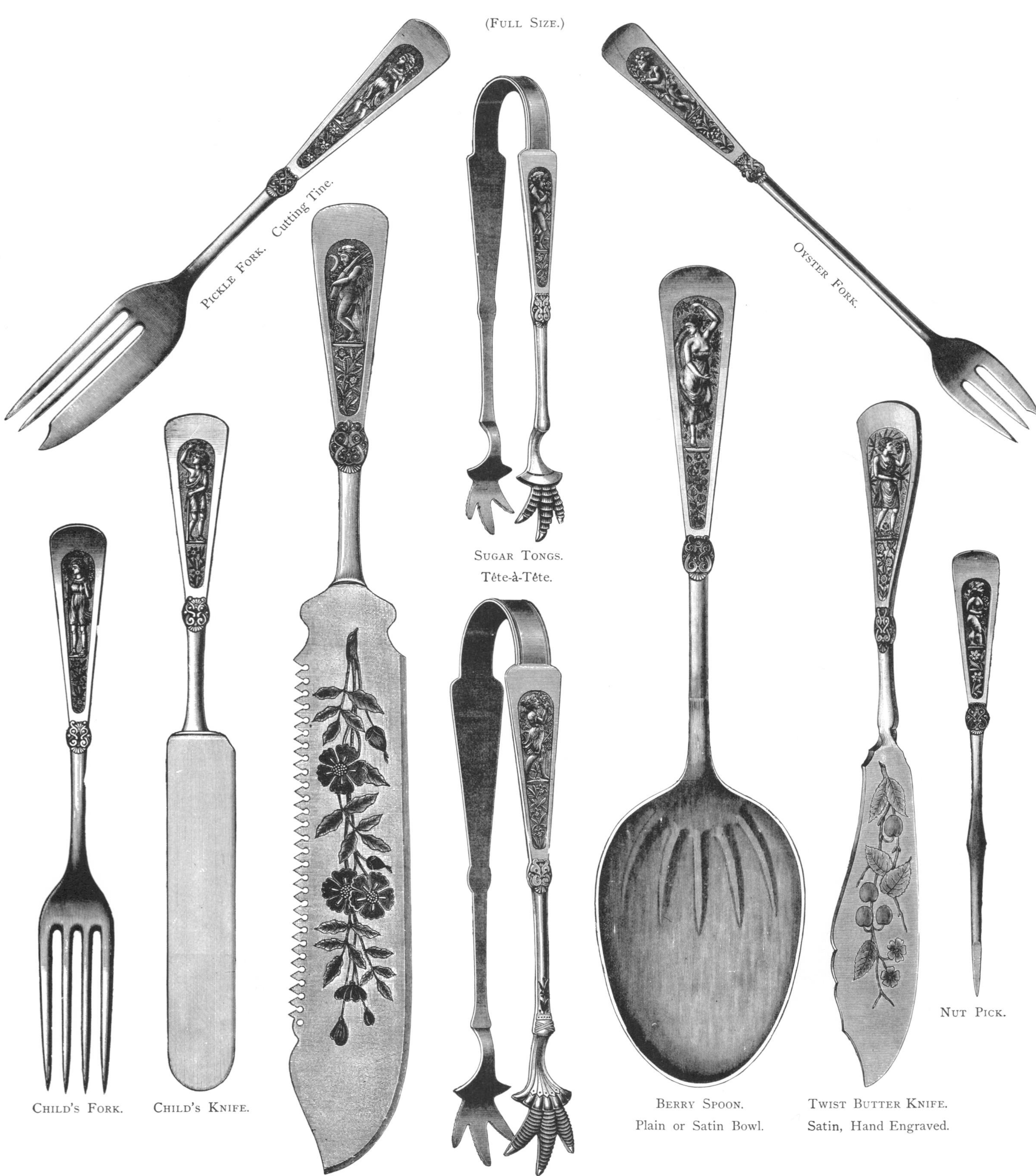

ARCADIAN PATTERN.

For complete Price-List see pages 422–428.

1847.-Rogers Bros.-A 1. 1847.-Rogers Bros.-XII.

(Full Size.)

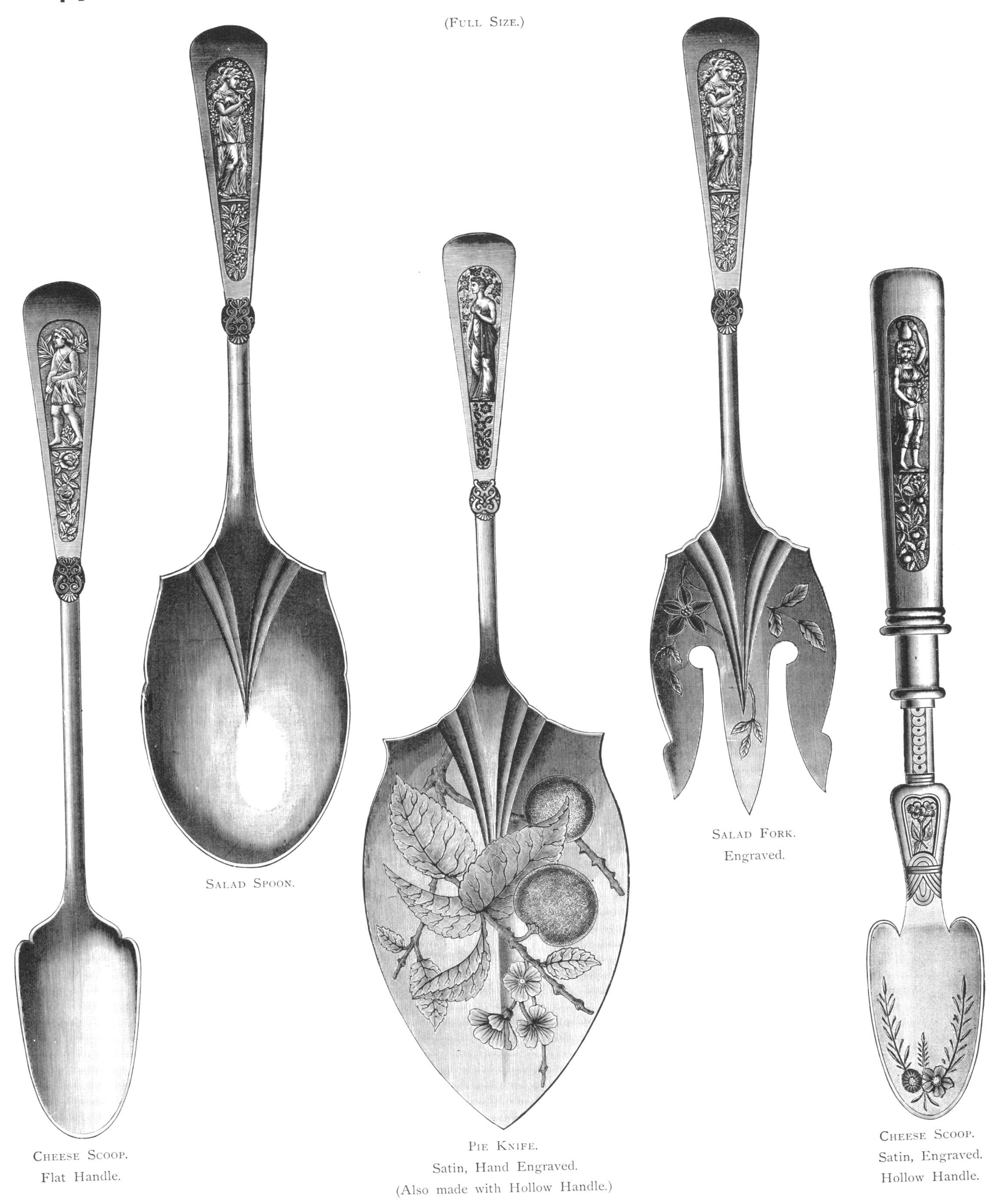

Salad Spoon.

Salad Fork.
Engraved.

Cheese Scoop.
Flat Handle.

Pie Knife.
Satin, Hand Engraved.
(Also made with Hollow Handle.)

Cheese Scoop.
Satin, Engraved.
Hollow Handle.

ARCADIAN PATTERN.

For complete Price-List see pages 422–428.

1847.-Rogers Bros.-A 1. 1847.-Rogers Bros.-XII.

(Full Size.)

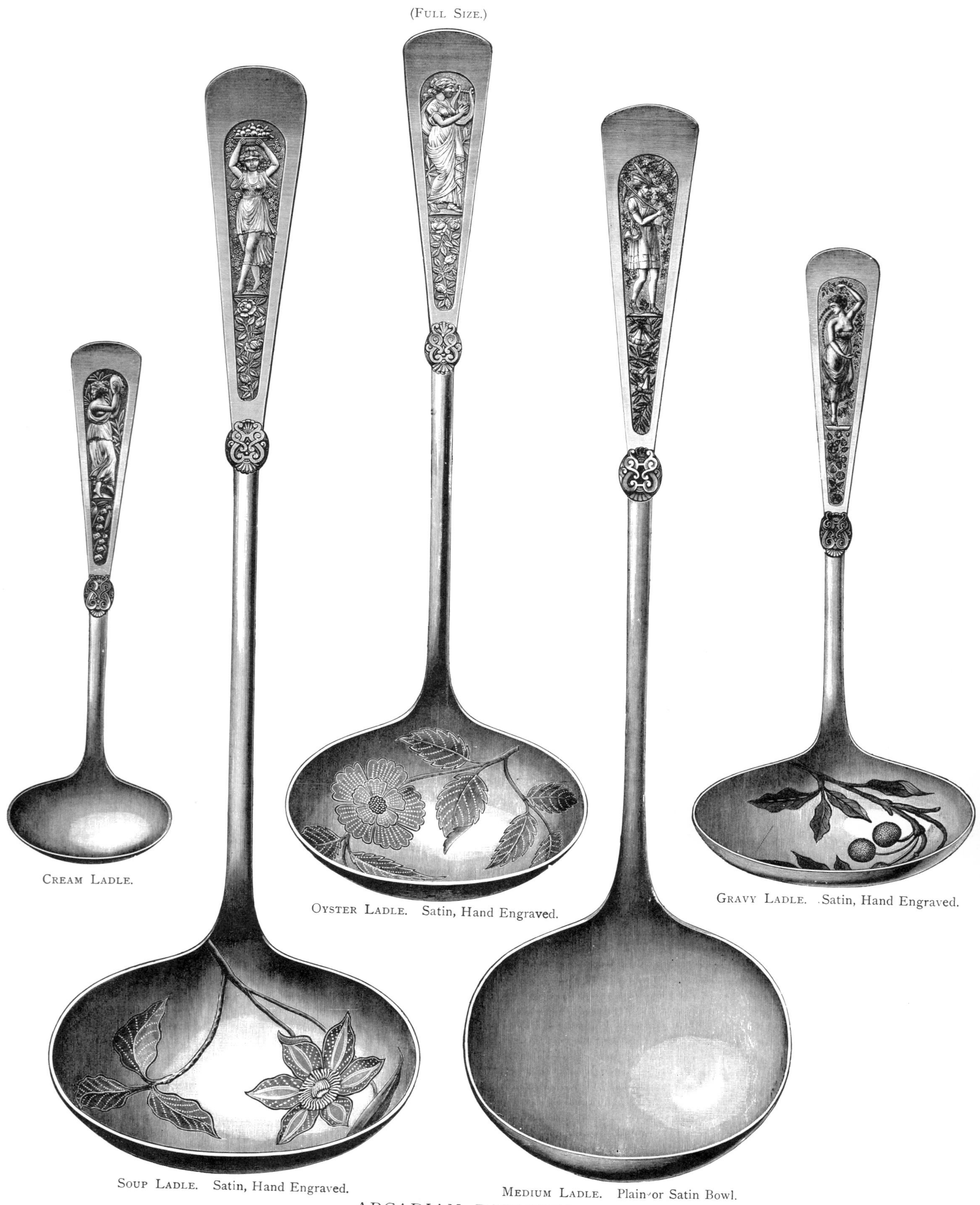

Cream Ladle.

Oyster Ladle. Satin, Hand Engraved.

Gravy Ladle. Satin, Hand Engraved.

Soup Ladle. Satin, Hand Engraved.

Medium Ladle. Plain or Satin Bowl.

ARCADIAN PATTERN.

For complete Price-List see pages 422–428.

(FULL SIZE.)

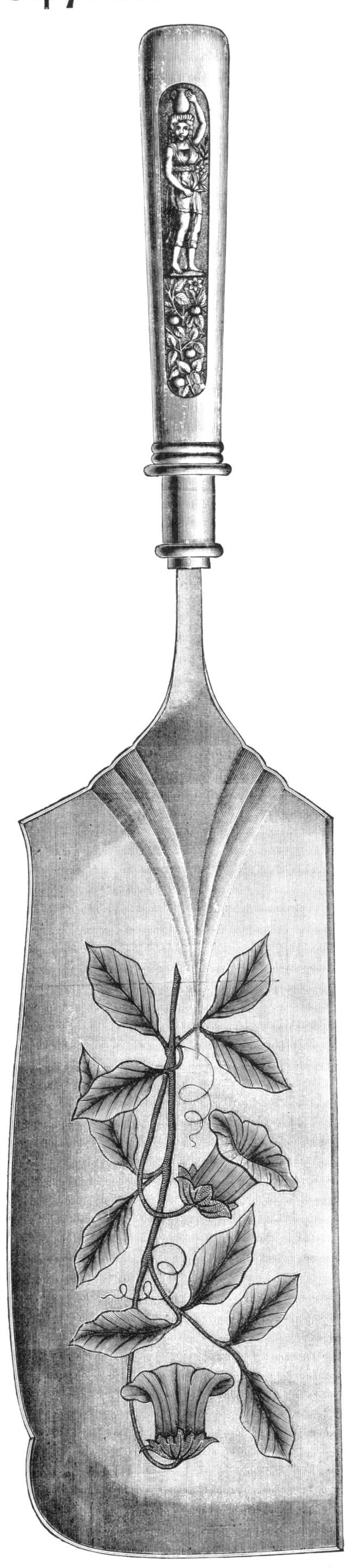

CRUMB KNIFE. Satin, Hand Engraved. Hollow Handle.

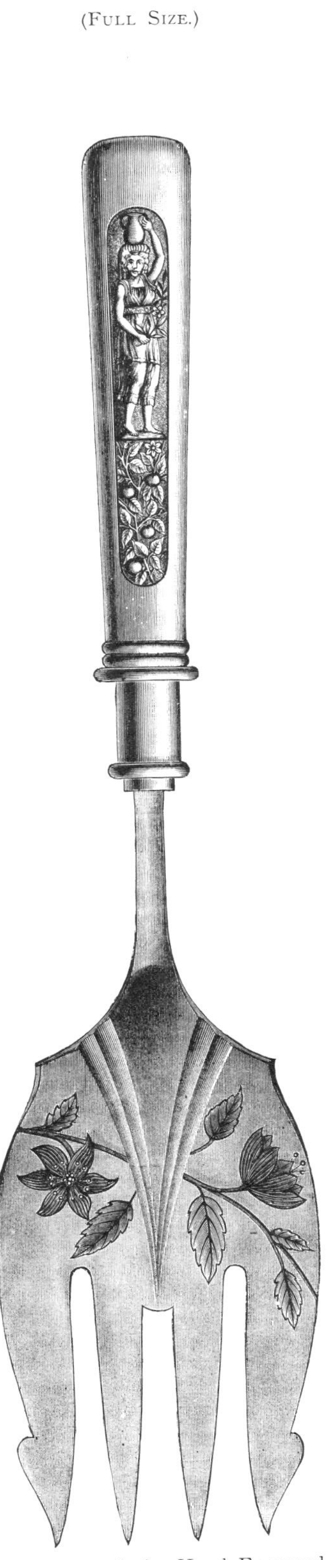

FISH FORK. Satin, Hand Engraved. Hollow Handle.

(Also made with Flat Handles.)

ARCADIAN PATTERN.

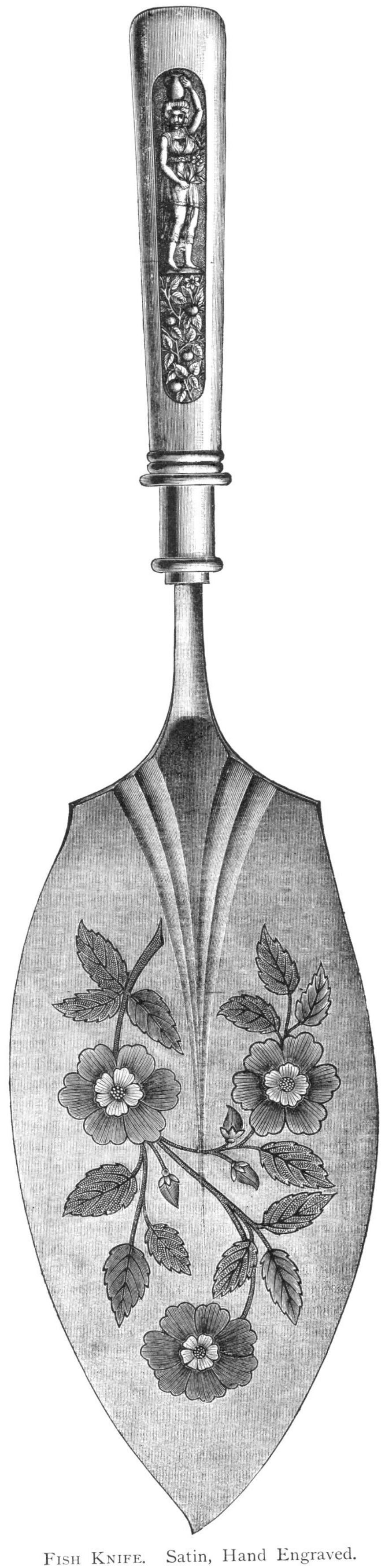

FISH KNIFE. Satin, Hand Engraved. Hollow Handle.

For complete Price-List see pages 422-428.

1847.-Rogers Bros.-A 1. 1847.-Rogers Bros.-XII.

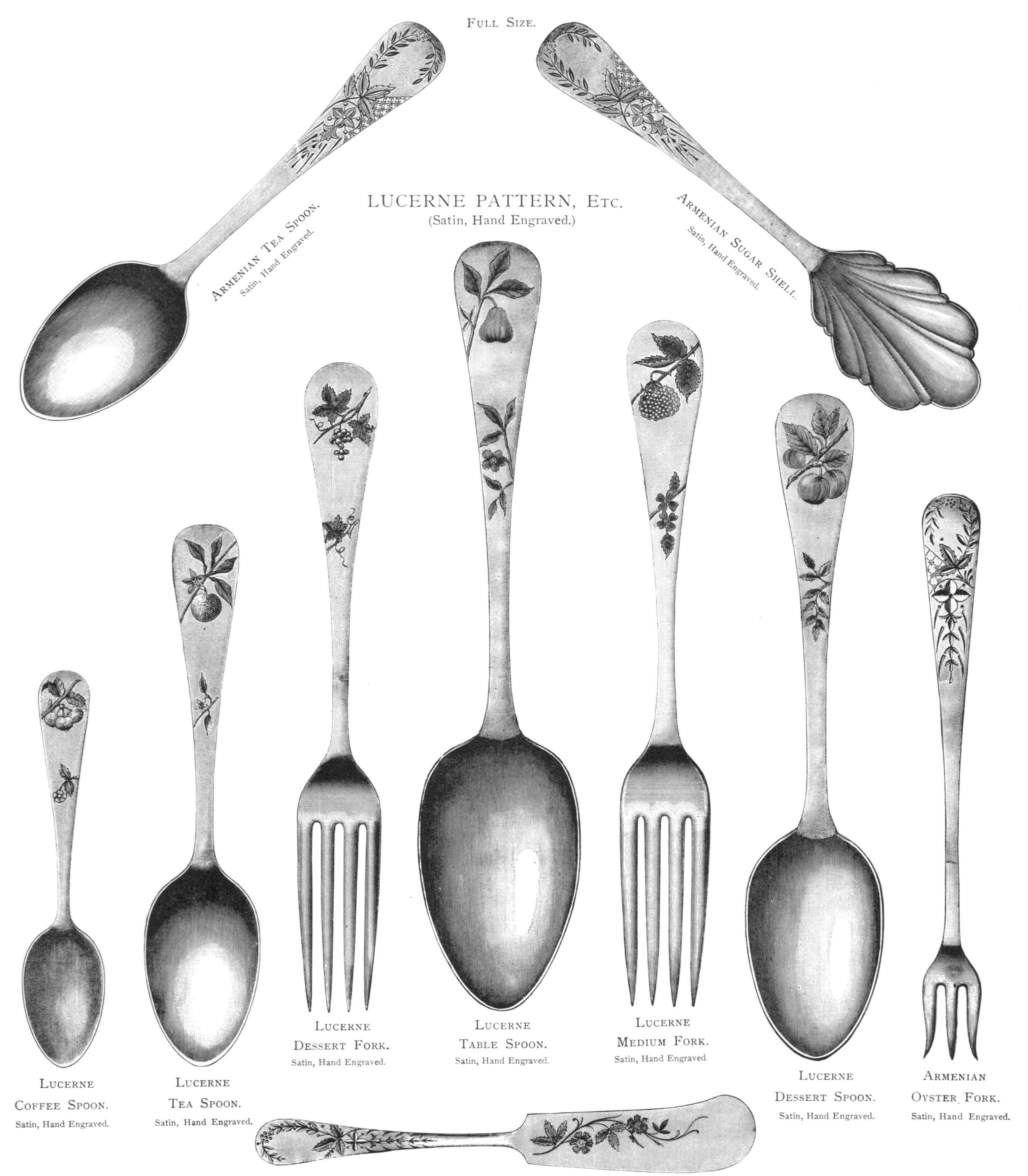

For complete Price-List see pages 422–428.

1847.-Rogers Bros.-A 1. 1847.-Rogers Bros.-XII.

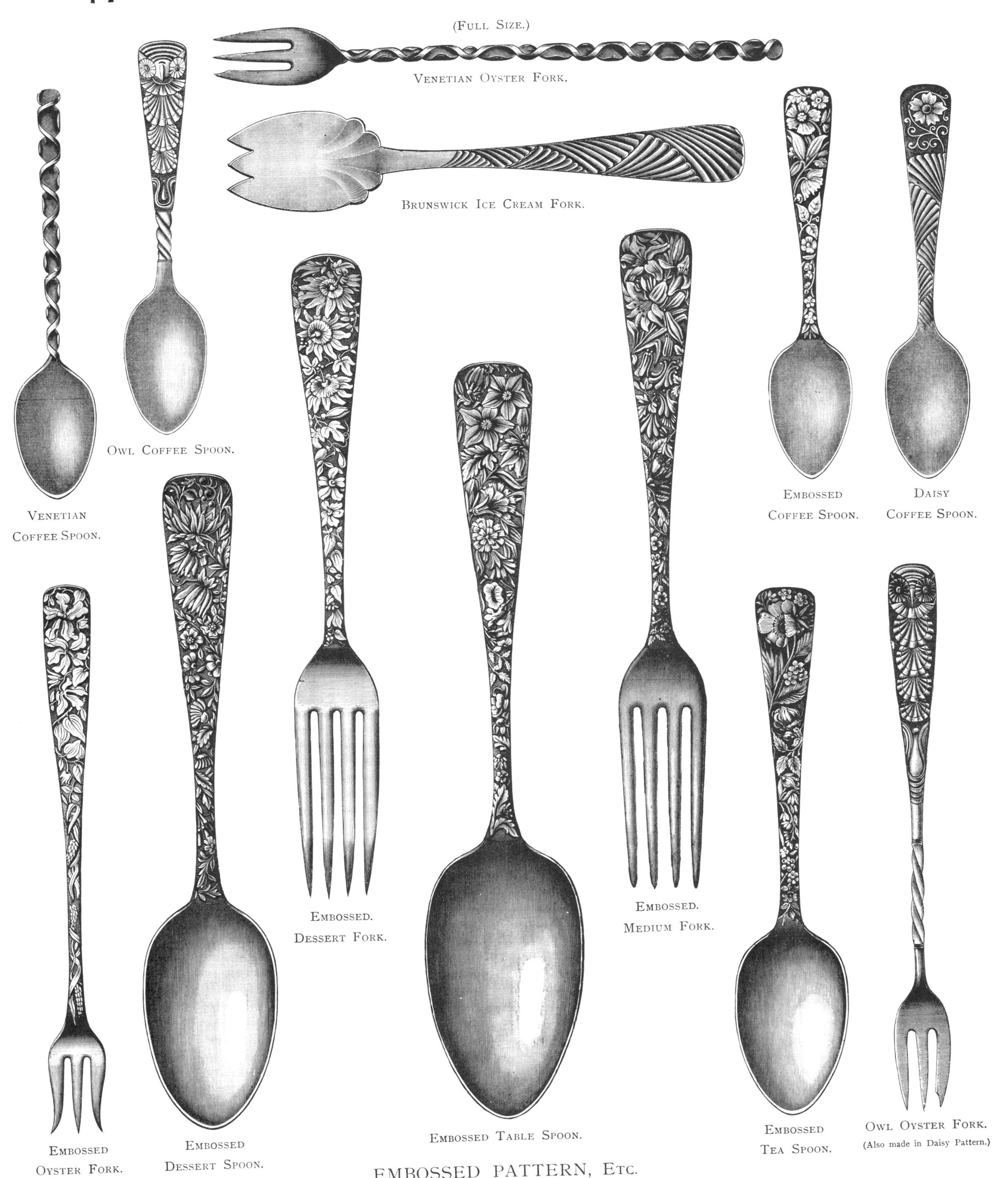

EMBOSSED PATTERN, Etc.

For complete Price-List see pages 422–428.

1847.-Rogers Bros.-A 1. 1847.-Rogers Bros.-XII.

DUNDEE PATTERN.

(Patented.)

For complete Price-List see pages 422–428.

1847.-Rogers Bros.-A 1. 1847.-Rogers Bros.-XII.

(Full Size.)

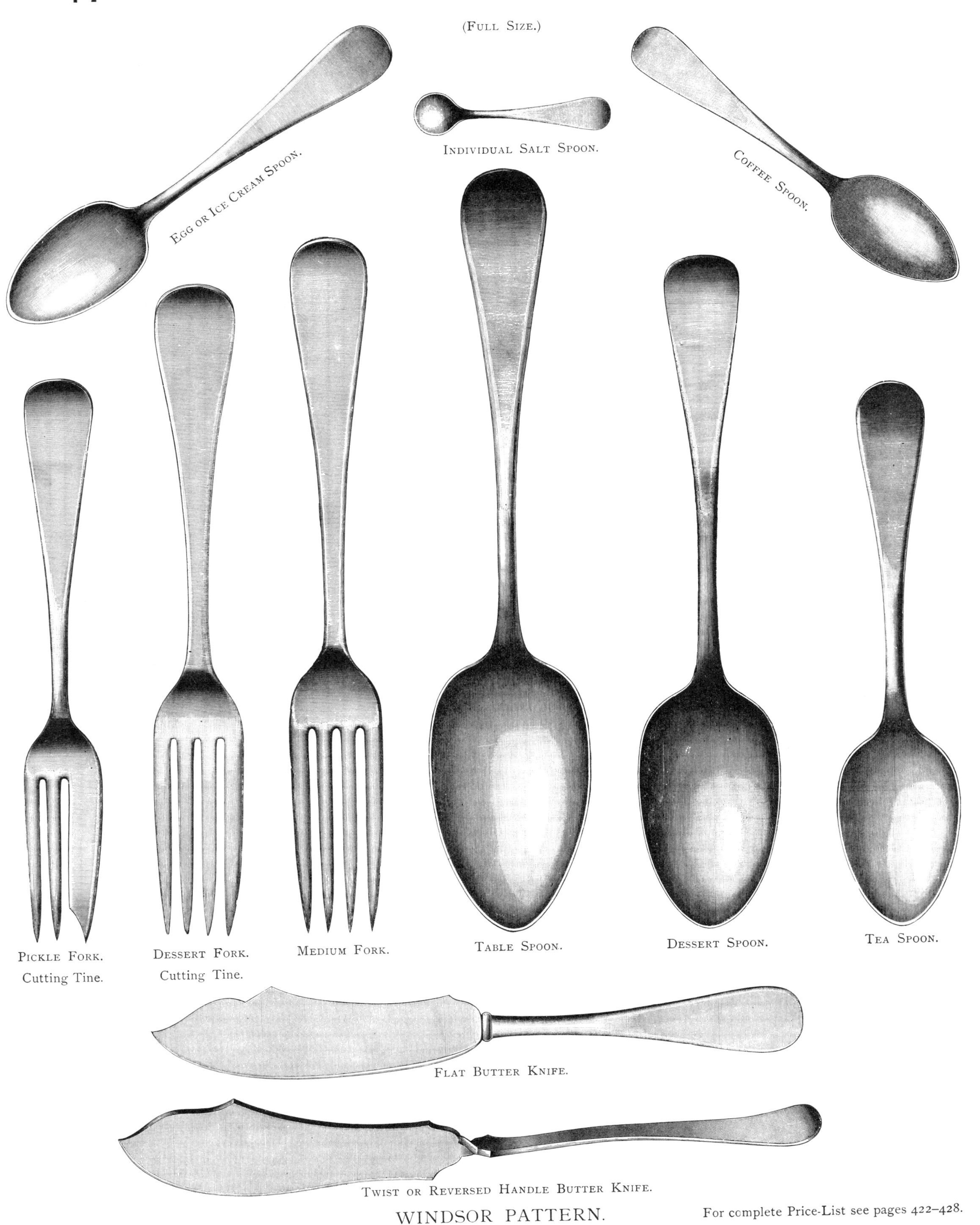

WINDSOR PATTERN.

For complete Price-List see pages 422–428.

1847.-Rogers Bros.-A 1. 1847.-Rogers Bros.-XII.

(Full Size.)

WINDSOR PATTERN.

For complete Price-List see pages 422–428.

1847.-Rogers Bros.-A 1.

1847.-Rogers Bros.-XII.

(Full Size.)

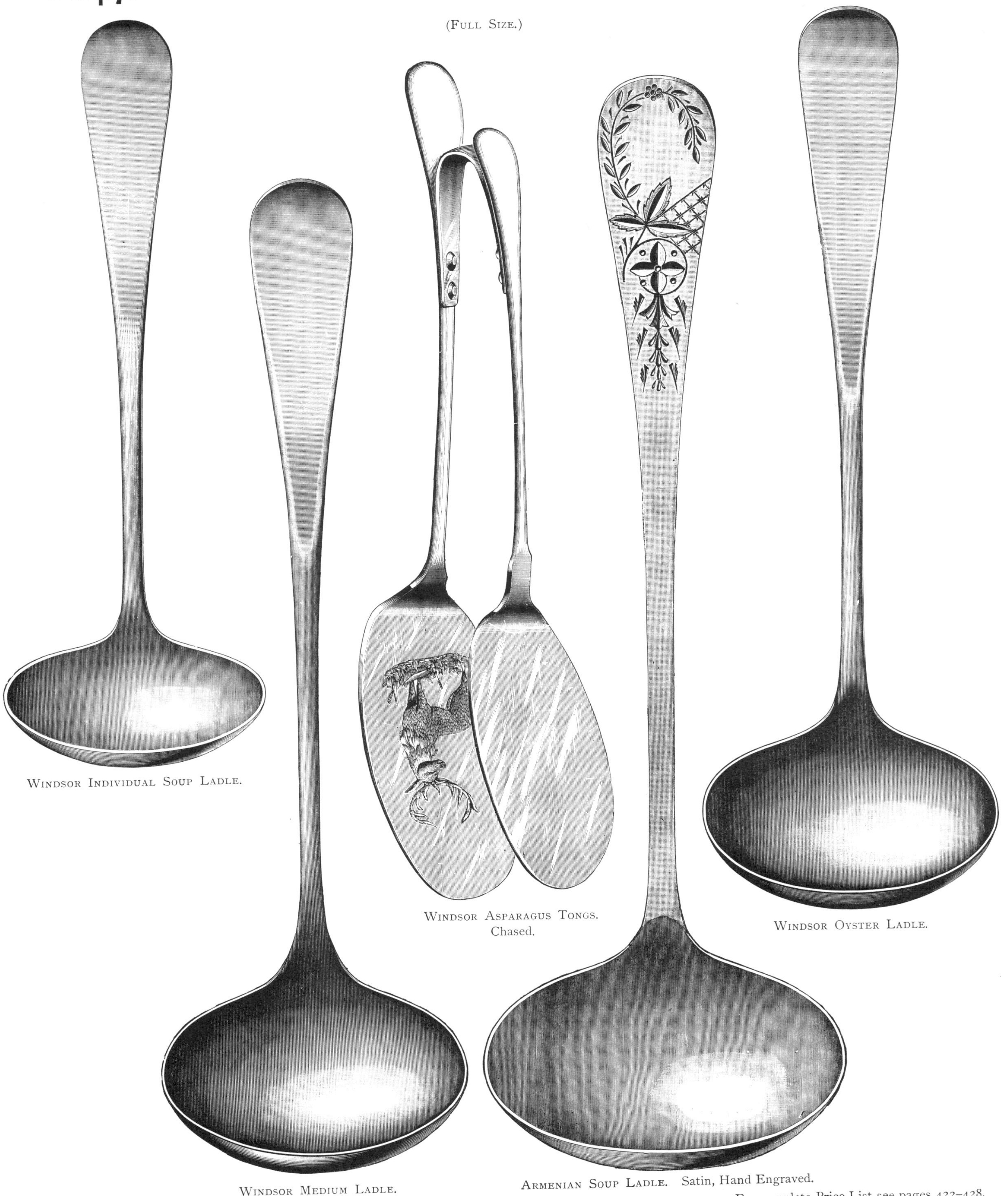

Windsor Individual Soup Ladle.

Windsor Asparagus Tongs. Chased.

Windsor Oyster Ladle.

Windsor Medium Ladle.

Armenian Soup Ladle. Satin, Hand Engraved.

For complete Price-List see pages 422–428.

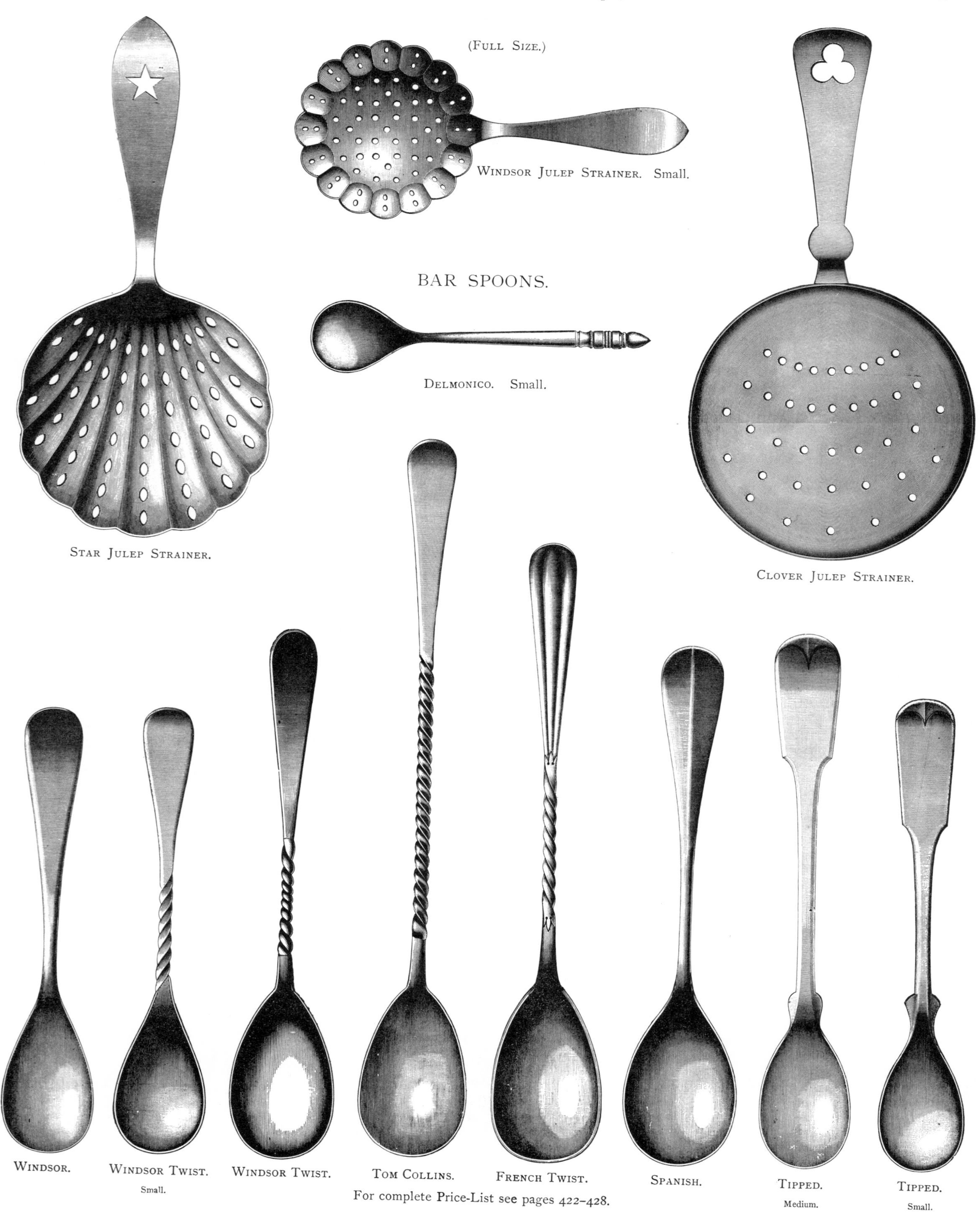

For complete Price-List see pages 422–428.

1847.-Rogers Bros.-A 1. 1847.-Rogers Bros.-XII.

(Full Size.)

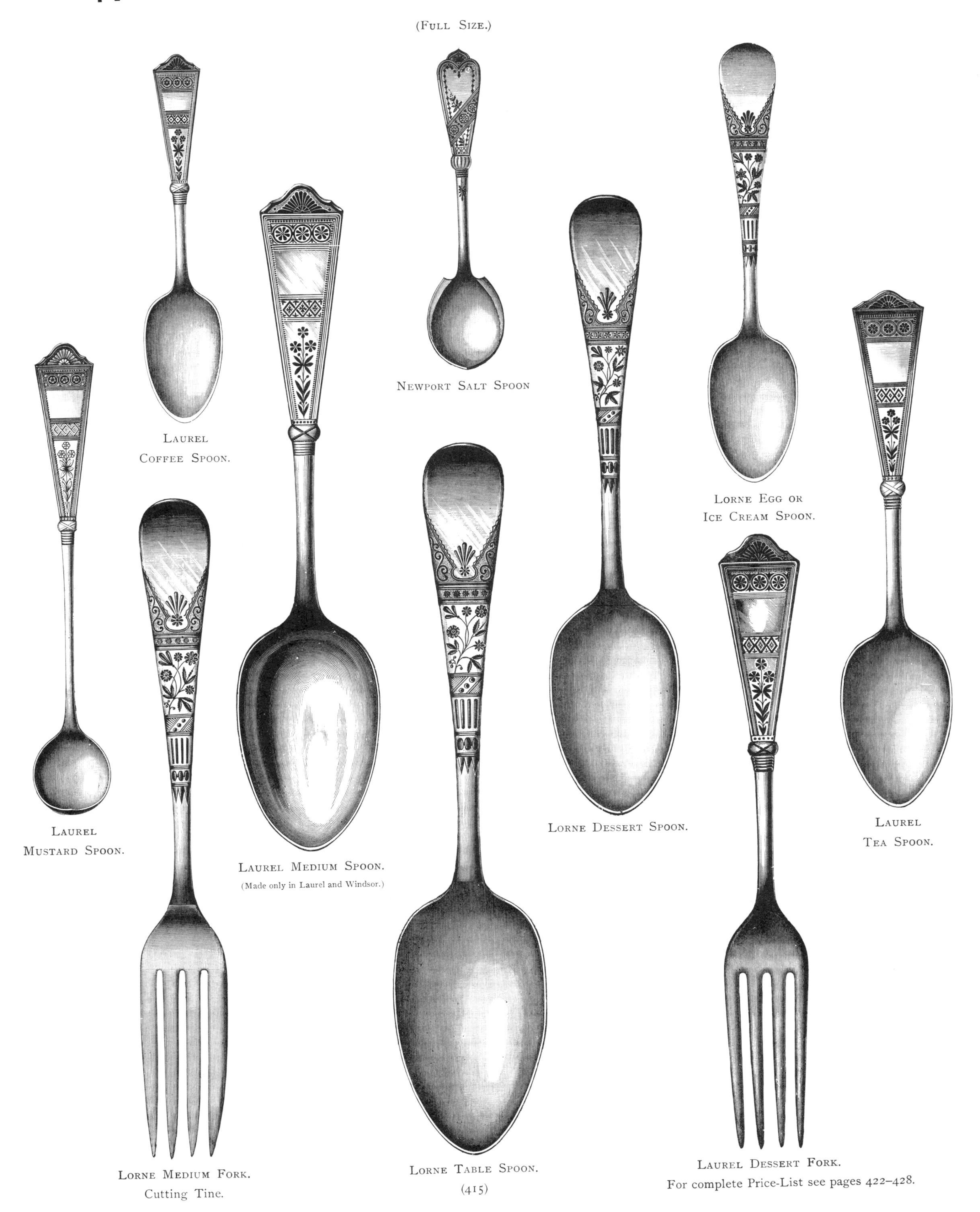

Laurel Coffee Spoon.

Newport Salt Spoon

Lorne Egg or Ice Cream Spoon.

Laurel Mustard Spoon.

Laurel Medium Spoon.
(Made only in Laurel and Windsor.)

Lorne Dessert Spoon.

Laurel Tea Spoon.

Lorne Medium Fork.
Cutting Tine.

Lorne Table Spoon.

Laurel Dessert Fork.

For complete Price-List see pages 422–428.

1847.-Rogers Bros.-A 1. 1847.-Rogers Bros.-XII.

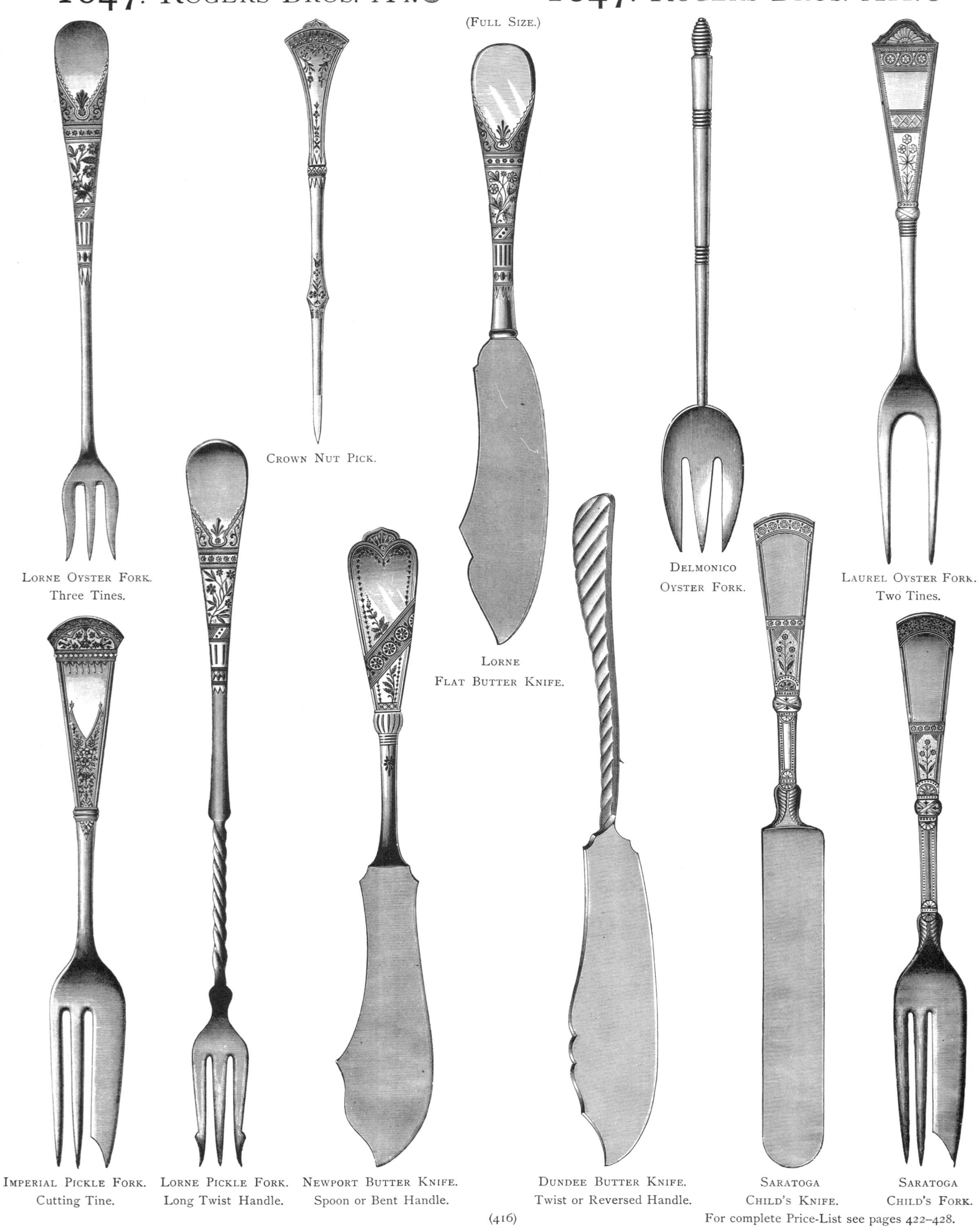

(Full Size.)

Lorne Oyster Fork. Three Tines.

Crown Nut Pick.

Lorne Flat Butter Knife.

Delmonico Oyster Fork.

Laurel Oyster Fork. Two Tines.

Imperial Pickle Fork. Cutting Tine.

Lorne Pickle Fork. Long Twist Handle.

Newport Butter Knife. Spoon or Bent Handle.

Dundee Butter Knife. Twist or Reversed Handle.

Saratoga Child's Knife.

Saratoga Child's Fork.

For complete Price-List see pages 422–428.

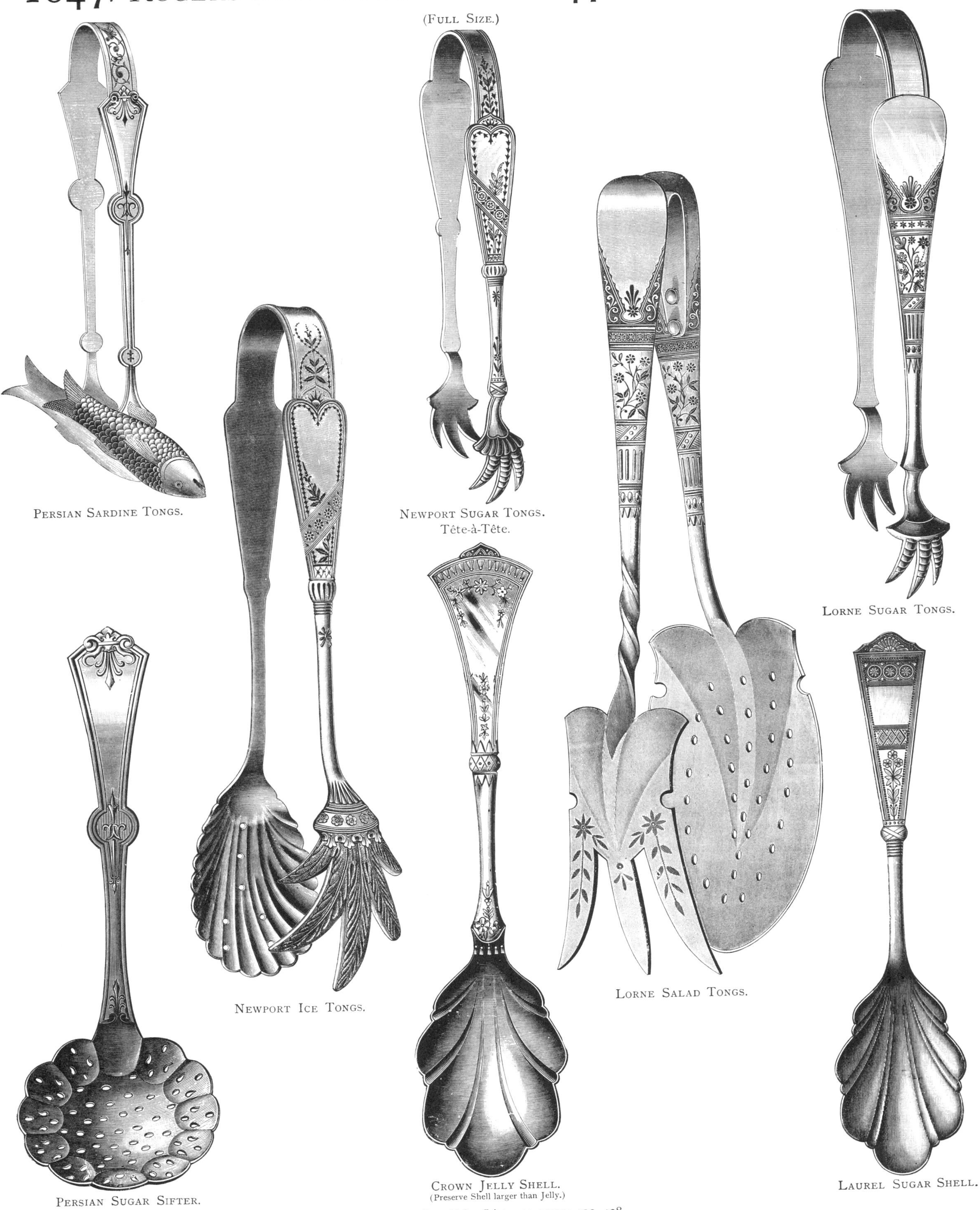

PERSIAN SARDINE TONGS.

NEWPORT SUGAR TONGS.
Tête-à-Tête.

LORNE SUGAR TONGS.

NEWPORT ICE TONGS.

LORNE SALAD TONGS.

PERSIAN SUGAR SIFTER.

CROWN JELLY SHELL.
(Preserve Shell larger than Jelly.)

LAUREL SUGAR SHELL.

For complete Price-List, see pages 422–428.

(Full Size.)

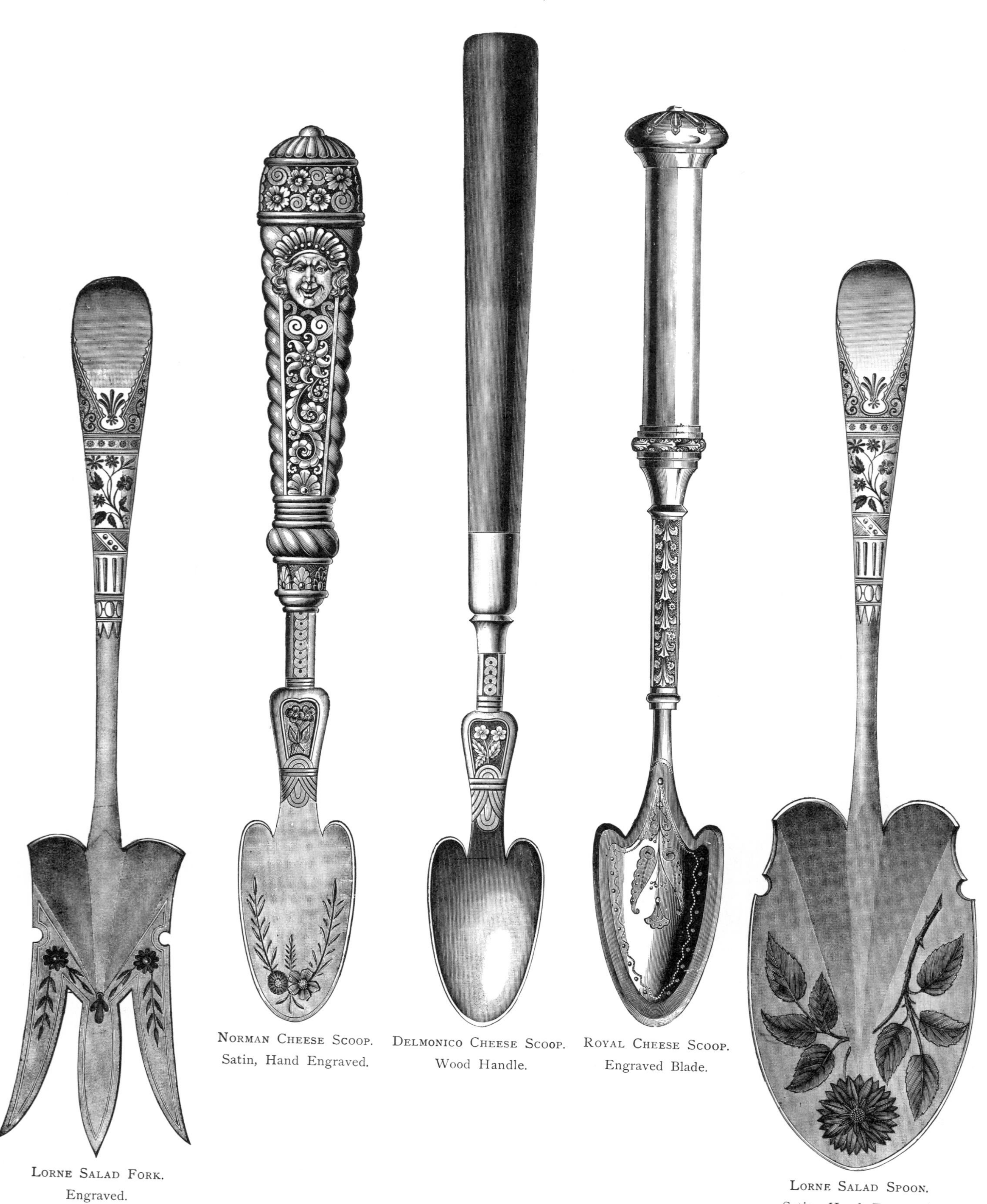

Lorne Salad Fork.
Engraved.

Norman Cheese Scoop.
Satin, Hand Engraved.

Delmonico Cheese Scoop.
Wood Handle.

Royal Cheese Scoop.
Engraved Blade.

Lorne Salad Spoon.
Satin, Hand Engraved.

For complete Price-List see pages 422–428.

(Full Size.)

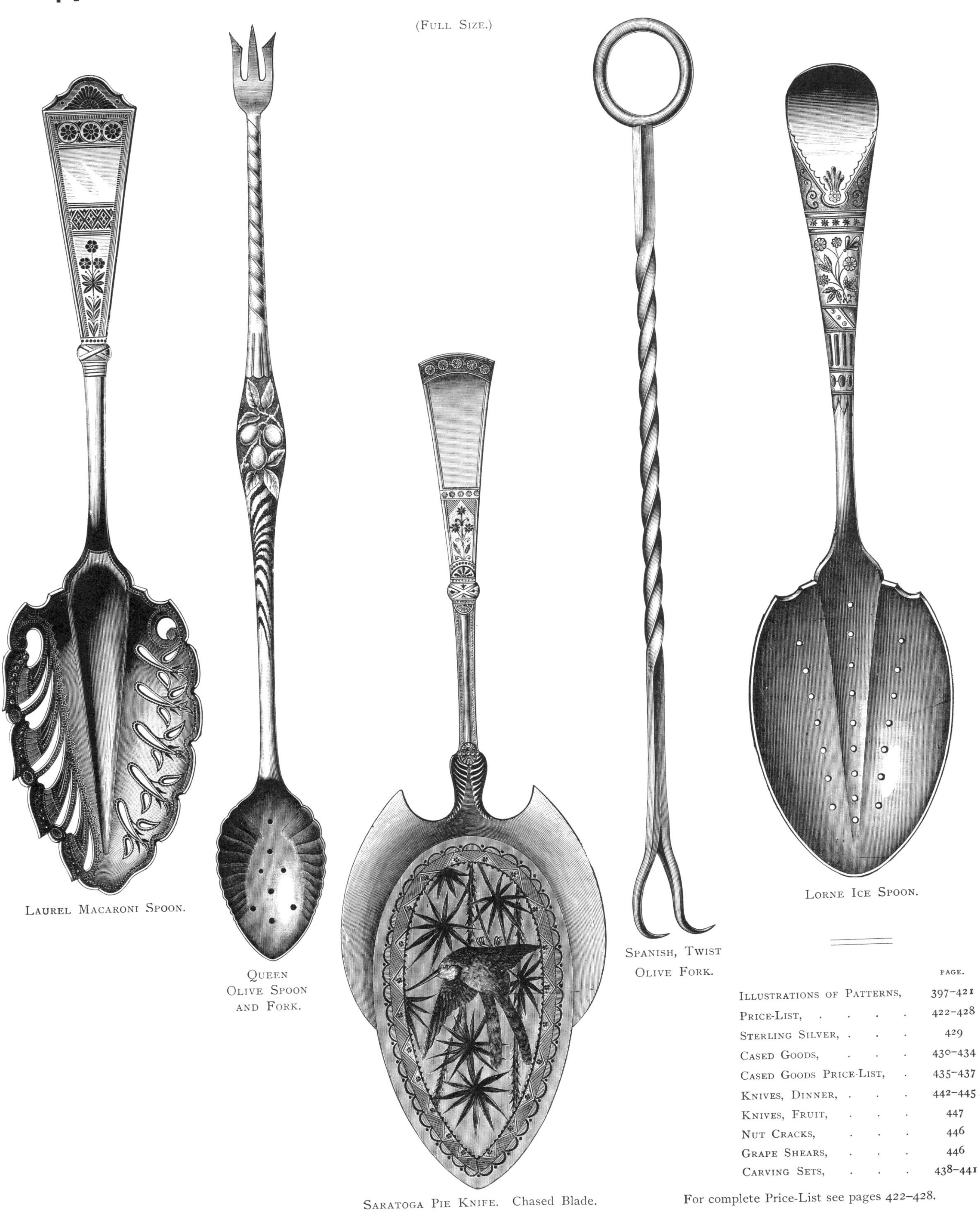

Laurel Macaroni Spoon.

Queen Olive Spoon and Fork.

Saratoga Pie Knife. Chased Blade.

Spanish, Twist Olive Fork.

Lorne Ice Spoon.

For complete Price-List see pages 422–428.

(FULL SIZE).

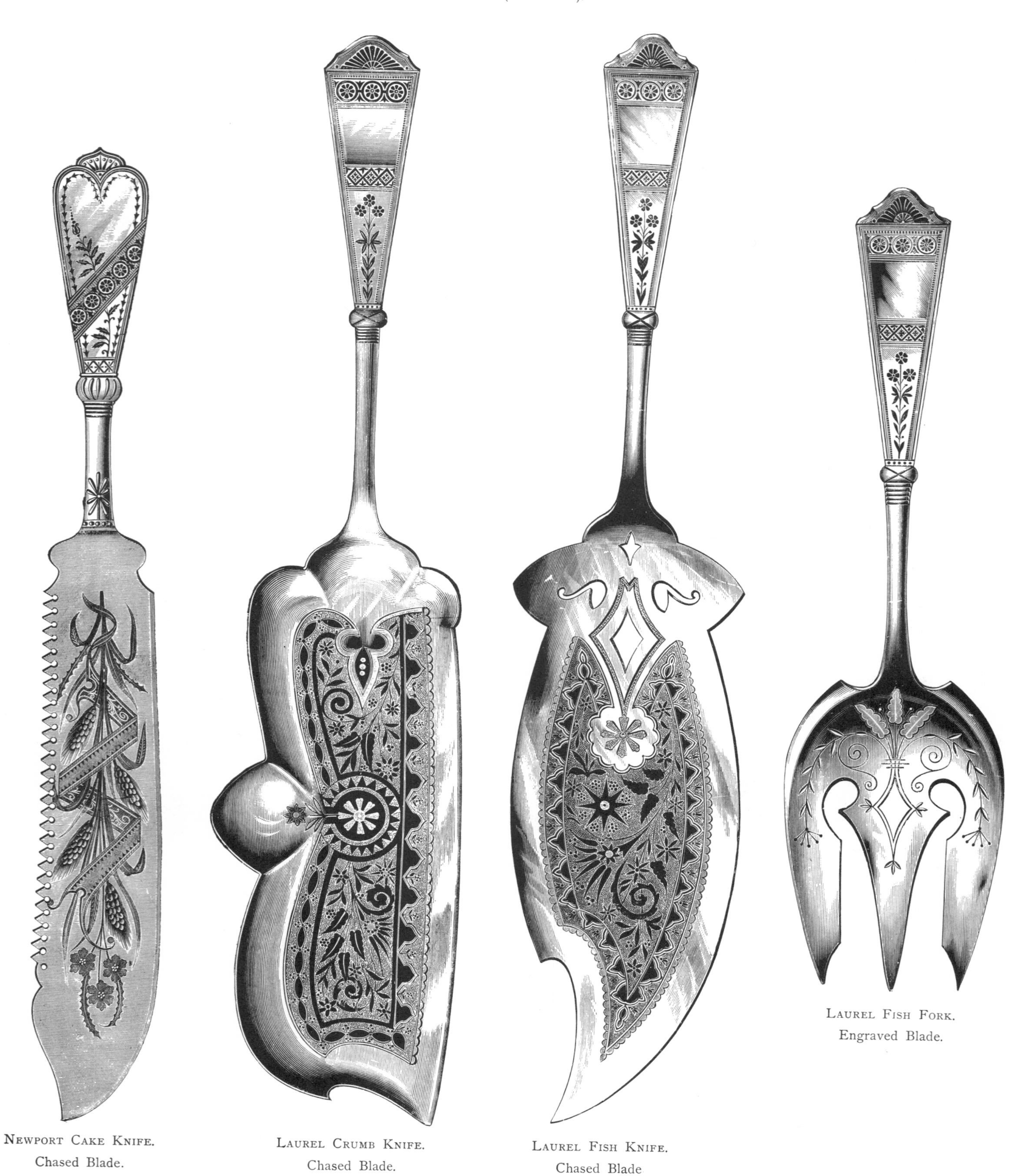

NEWPORT CAKE KNIFE.
Chased Blade.

LAUREL CRUMB KNIFE.
Chased Blade.

LAUREL FISH KNIFE.
Chased Blade

LAUREL FISH FORK.
Engraved Blade.

For complete Price-List see pages 422–428.

1847.-Rogers Bros.-A 1. 1847.-Rogers Bros.-XII.

(Full Size.)

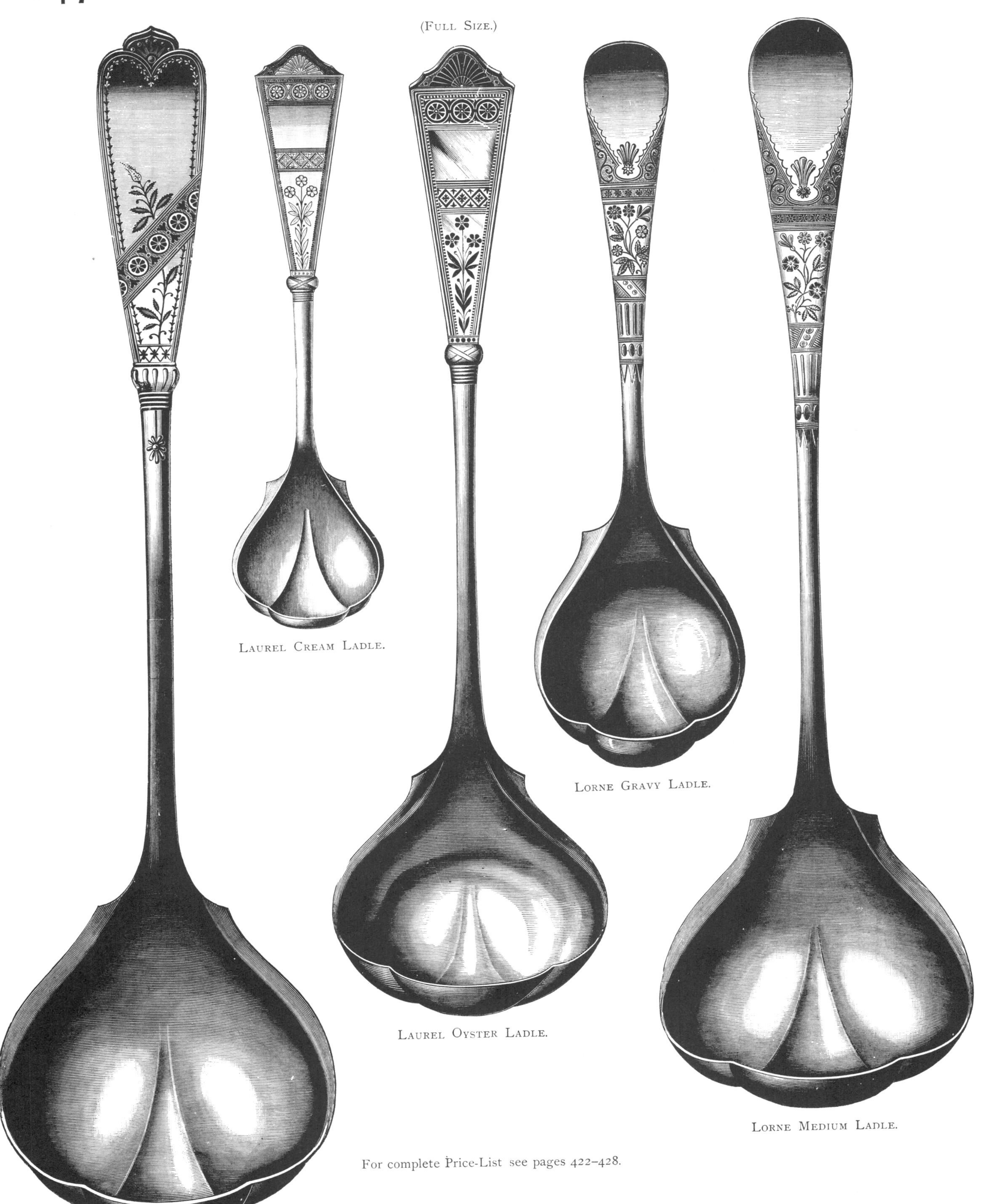

Laurel Cream Ladle.

Lorne Gravy Ladle.

Laurel Oyster Ladle.

Lorne Medium Ladle.

Newport Soup Ladle.

For complete Price-List see pages 422–428.

1847.-Rogers Bros.-A 1. 1847.-Rogers Bros.-XII.

PRICE-LIST OF SPOONS, FORKS, ETC.

ALL PRICES GIVEN ARE BY THE DOZEN.

Each Telegraphic Word indicates *one dozen* of the kind it prefixes, in *Extra Plate;* larger quantity and different grade of plate should be specified, etc.

TEA SPOONS.

Telegraphic Words.	Patterns.	Extra Plate. No. 2.	Double Plate. No. 4.	Triple Plate. No 6.	Sectional or XII Plate. Extra and XII Plate. No. 2 XII.	Double and XII Plate. No. 4 XII.	Triple and XII Plate. No. 6 XII.
(SCION).	Plain,	$4.00	$5.25	$6.50			
(SCISSOR).	Tipped,						
(DISSEMBLE).	Shell Tipped,						
(SCOFF).	Fiddle,	4.25	5.50	6.75	$5.00	$6.25	$7.50
(FIREBRAND).	Puritan,						
(SCOOP).	Oval,						
(SCOPE).	French Oval,	4.50	5.75	7.00	5.25	6.50	7.75
(SCORCH).	Olive,						
(SCORPION).	Persian,						
(SCOT).	Lily,						
(SCOTTISH).	Princess,						
(SCOUR).	Windsor,						
(SCOURGE).	Crown,						
(SCOUT).	Laurel,						
(FELDSPAR).	Saratoga,	4.75	6.00	7.25	5.50	6.75	8.00
(SCOW).	Newport,						
(SCRAMBLE).	Lorne,						
(SCRAP).	Imperial,						
(DISSENSION).	Arcadian,						
(DISSERVE).	Assyrian,						
(DISSONANT).	Dundee,						
(DISTANTLY).	Embossed,						
(DISTRAIN).	Embossed, Old Silver,						
(DIURNAL).	Assyrian, " "	5.25	6.50	7.75	6.00	7.25	8.50
(DIVERGE).	Lucerne,						
	(Satin, Hand Engraved.)	8.25	9.50	10.75	9.00	10.25	11.50
(DIVERSION).	Armenian,						
	(Satin, Hand Engraved.)	8.75	10.00	11.25	9.50	10.75	12.00

TABLE SPOONS.

Telegraphic Words.	Patterns.	Extra Plate. No. 4.	Double Plate. No. 8.	Triple Plate. No. 12.	Sectional or XII Plate. Extra and XII Plate. No. 4 XII.	Double and XII Plate. No. 8 XII.	Triple and XII Plate. No. 12 XII.
(SCULPTOR).	Plain,	$8.00	$10.50	$13.00			
(SCUPPER).	Tipped,						
(DISLOCATE).	Shell Tipped,						
(SCUTTLE).	Fiddle,	8.50	11.00	13.50	$10.00	$12.50	$15.00
(FIREPLACE).	Puritan,						
(SEAFOWL).	Oval,						
(SEAL).	French Oval,	9.00	11.50	14.00	10.50	13.00	15.50
(SEALER).	Olive,						
(SEAMLESS).	Persian,						
(SEANCE).	Lily,						
(SEAR).	Princess,						
(SEARCH).	Windsor,						
(SEASIDE).	Crown,						
(SEASON).	Laurel,						
(FENNEL).	Saratoga,	9.50	12.00	14.50	11.00	13.50	16.00
(SEAT).	Newport,						
(SECEDE).	Lorne,						
(SECLUDE).	Imperial,						
(DOCTRINE).	Arcadian,						
(DOGMATIST).	Assyrian,						
(DOGSTAR).	Dundee,						
(DOGWATCH).	Embossed,						
(DONATIVE).	Embossed, Old Silver						
(DONJON).	Assyrian, " "	10.50	13.00	15.50	12.00	14.50	17.00
(DOOMSDAY).	Lucerne,						
	(Satin, Hand Engraved.)	15.50	18.00	20.50	17.00	19.50	22.00
(DOUBLER).	Armenian,						
	(Satin, Hand Engraved.)	16.50	19.00	21.50	18.00	20.50	23.00

DESSERT SPOONS.

Telegraphic Words.	Patterns.	No 3.	No. 6.	No. 9.	No. 3 XII.	No. 6 XII.	No. 9 XII.
(SCRAPER).	Plain,	$7.00	$9.00	$11.00			
(SCRATCH).	Tipped,						
(DIVERT).	Shell Tipped,						
(SCRAWL).	Fiddle,	7.50	9.50	11.50	$8.63	$10.63	$12.63
(FIRMAMENT).	Puritan,						
(SCREW).	Oval,						
(SCRAPING).	French Oval,	8.00	10.00	12.00	9.13	11.13	13.13
(SCRIBBLE).	Olive,						
(SCRIPT).	Persian,						
(SCROLL).	Lily,						
(SCRUB).	Princess,						
(SCRUBBY).	Windsor,						
(SCRUPLE).	Crown,						
(SCRUTINY).	Laurel,						
(FENCIBLE).	Saratoga,						
(SCUD).	Newport,	8.50	10.50	12.50	9.63	11.63	13.63
(SCUFFLE).	Lorne,						
(SCULLER).	Imperial,						
(DIVEST).	Arcadian,						
(DIVIDEND).	Assyrian,						
(DIVIDER).	Dundee,						
(DIVISION).	Embossed,						
(DIVISOR).	Embossed, Old Silver,						
(DIVULGE).	Assyrian, " "	9.25	11.25	13.25	10.38	12.38	14.38
(DOCILITY).	Lucerne,						
	(Satin, Hand Engraved.)	13.50	15.50	17.50	14.63	16.63	18.63
(DOCKYARD).	Armenian,						
	(Satin, Hand Engraved.)	14.50	16.50	18.50	15.63	17.63	19.63

MEDIUM SPOONS.

Size between Dessert and Table.

Telegraphic Words.	Patterns.	No. 4.	No. 8.	No. 12.	No. 4 XII.	No. 8 XII.	No. 12 XII.
(SECRECY).	Windsor,	$9.00	$11.50	$14.00	$10.50	$13.00	$15.50
(SECRETE).	Laurel,						

FRENCH OR DESSERT COFFEE SPOONS.

Plain or Satin Bowls.

Telegraphic Words.	Patterns.	Extra Plate. No. 2.	Double Plate. No. 4.	Triple Plate. No. 6.
(DISJUNCT).	Puritan,	$4.25	$5.50	$6.75
(SHRED).	Oval,	4.50	5.75	7.00
(SHREWD).	Olive,			
(SHRIMP).	Persian,			
(SHRINE).	Lily,			
(SHRIVEL).	Windsor,			
(SHRUB).	Princess,			
(SHUCK).	Crown,			
(SHUDDER).	Laurel,			
(SHUN).	Saratoga,	4.75	6.00	7.25
(SHUT).	Newport,			
(SHUTTLE).	Lorne,			
(SHUNT).	Lorne, extra small,			
(DING-DONG).	Arcadian,			
(DIPHTHONG).	Assyrian,			
(DIPLOMATIC).	Dundee,			
(DISAFFECT).	Embossed,			
(DISCERNER).	Embossed, Old Silver,			
(DISCOMPOSE).	Assyrian, " "			
(DISCOUNTER).	Owl, " "	5.00	6.25	7.50
(DISCOVERY).	Daisy, " "			
(DISCREETLY).	Venetian,			
(DISCURSION).	Lucerne,	5.75	7.00	8.25
	(Satin, Hand Engraved.)	8.25	9.50	10.75
(DISGUISER).	Armenian,			
	(Satin, Hand Engraved.)	8.75	10.00	11.25

Bowls, Gold Lined, . . $3.00 per dozen extra.

OLIVE SPOON OR FORK.

Telegraphic Words.	Patterns.	No. 4.	No. 8.	No. 12.
(FILLIBEG).	Spanish (Olive Fork),	$15.00	$18.00	$21.00
(FERRULE).	Queen (Spoon and Fork),	42.00	51.00	60.00

1847.-Rogers Bros.-A 1.

EGG OR ICE CREAM SPOONS.

Telegraphic Words.	Patterns.	Extra Plate. No. 2.	Double Plate. No. 4.	Triple Plate. No. 6.
(shore).	Oval,	$4.50	$5.75	$7.00
(short).	Olive,			
(shot).	Persian,			
(shoulder).	Lily,			
(shout).	Princess,			
(shove).	Crown,			
(shower).	Laurel,	4.75	6.00	7.25
(show).	Saratoga,			
(showy).	Newport,			
(shrew).	Lorne,			
(emergent).	Arcadian,			
(emigrant).	Assyrian,			
(eminence).	Assyrian, Old Silver,	5.00	6.25	7.50
(eminently).	Armenian, (Satin, Hand Engraved.)	8.75	10.00	11.25
	Bowls Gold Lined,	$3.00 per dozen extra.		

MUSTARD SPOONS.

Telegraphic Words.	Patterns.	No. 2.	No. 4.	No. 6.
(shield).	Tipped,	$4.25	$5.50	$6.75
(shift).	Fiddle,			
(shine).	Oval,	4.50	5.75	7.00
(shingle).	Olive,			
(shire).	Persian,			
(shiver).	Lily,			
(shoal).	Princess,			
(shock).	Windsor,			
(shoddy).	Crown,	4.75	6.00	7.25
(shoe).	Laurel,			
(shod).	Saratoga,			
(shone).	Newport,			
(shop).	Lorne,			
(emphasis).	Arcadian,			
(emphatic).	Assyrian,			
(employer).	Assyrian, Old Silver,	5.00	6.25	7.50
(emulation).	Armenian, (Satin, Hand Engraved.)	8.75	10.00	11.25
	Bowls Gold Lined,	$2.00 per dozen extra.		

SALT SPOONS.

Telegraphic Words.	Patterns.	No. 2.	No. 4.	No. 6.
(sheaf).	Tipped,			
(shear).	Fiddle,	$3.75	$5.00	$6.25
(enchanter).	Windsor, Individual,			
(enchase).	Arcadian, "			
(sheave).	Oval,	4.00	5.25	6.50
(shed).	Olive,			
(shelf).	Persian,			
(shell).	Lily,			
(shellac).	Princess,			
(shelter).	Windsor,			
(shelve).	Crown,	4.25	5.50	6.75
(shepherd).	Laurel,			
(shelly).	Saratoga,			
(sherbet).	Newport,			
(sheriff).	Lorne,			
(encompass).	Assyrian,			
(endless).	Dundee,			
(energetic).	Assyrian, Old Silver,	4.50	5.75	7.00
(enervate).	Armenian, (Satin, Hand Engraved.)	8.25	9.50	10.75
	Bowls Gold Lined,	$2.00 per dozen extra.		

BAR SPOONS (small size).

Telegraphic Words.	Patterns.	No. 2.	No. 4.	No. 6.
(shyness).	Tipped,	$4.25	$5.50	$6.75
(episcopal).	Delmonico,			
(sibyl).	Oval,			
(sickle).	Windsor,	4.50	5.75	7.00
(side).	Windsor, Twist,			
(sidelong).	Lorne,			
(siege).	Olive,	4.75	6.00	7.25
(siesta).	Tipped, medium,			

BAR SPOONS (large size).

Telegraphic Words.	Patterns.	No. 3.	No. 6.	No. 9.
(sign).	Tipped,	5.00	6.50	8.00
(sight).	Oval,	5.50	7.00	8.50
(sieve).	Olive,			
(sifter).	Persian,	6.00	7.50	9.00
(signet).	Spanish,			
(signify).	Windsor Twist,	7.50	9.00	10.50
(silence).	Twist,	8.50	10.00	11.50
(silesia).	French Twist,			
		No. 4.	No. 8.	No. 12.
(silk).	Threaded, large bowl,	7.50	9.50	11.50
(episode).	Tom Collins, ex. long,	9.00	11.00	13.00

1847.-Rogers Bros.-XII.

BERRY OR NUT SPOONS.

Telegraphic Words.	Patterns.	Extra Plate. No. 4.	Double Plate. No. 8.	Triple Plate. No. 12.
(silvan).	Oval,	$21.00	$27.00	$33.00
(similar).	Olive,			
(simoon).	Persian,			
(simple).	Lily,			
(since).	Princess,			
(simplify).	Windsor,			
(sincere).	Crown,			
(sinecure).	Laurel,	24.00	30.00	36.00
(sincerity).	Saratoga,			
(single).	Newport,			
(singer).	Lorne,			
(equable).	Arcadian,			
(equality).	Assyrian,			
(dace).	Dundee,			
(dactyl).	Assyrian, Old Silver,	26.00	32.00	38.00
(daffodil).	Armenian, (Satin, Hand Engraved.)	33.00	39.00	45.00
	Bowls Gold Lined,	$9.00 per dozen extra.		
	" Satin, Hand Engraved,	9.00 " " "		
	" Satin, Hand Engraved, Gold Inlaid,	24.00 " " "		
(dahlia).	Plush Cases,	3.00 each.		

MACARONI SPOONS.

Telegraphic Words.	Patterns.	No. 4.	No. 8.	No. 12.
(sinew).	Laurel,	$42.00	$51.00	$60.00
(sine).	Lorne,			
(daintily).	Arcadian,			

SALAD SPOONS.

Telegraphic Words.	Patterns.	No. 4.	No. 8.	No. 12.
(sinewy).	Lorne,			
(dairy).	Arcadian,	$30.00	$36.00	$42.00
(dabble).	Assyrian,			
(flagitious).	Assyrian, Old Silver,	32.00	38.00	44.00

GRAVY OR PLATTER SPOONS (long handle).

Telegraphic Words.	Patterns.	No. 4.	No. 8.	No. 12.
(singe).	Oval,	$36.00	$45.00	$54.00
(dally).	Windsor,	42.00	51.00	60.00
(dandler).	Assyrian,			
(daphne).	Assyrian, Old Silver,	45.00	54.00	63.00

DESSERT FORKS.

Telegraphic Words.	Patterns.	Extra Plate. No. 3.	Double Plate. No. 6.	Triple Plate. No. 9.	Sectional or XII Plate. Extra and XII Plate. No. 3 XII.	Double and XII Plate. No. 6 XII.	Triple and XII Plate. No. 9 XII.
(sect).	Tipped,	$7.50	$9.50	$11.50	$8.63	$10.63	$12.63
(section).	Fiddle,						
(fisherman).	Puritan,						
(security).	Oval,	8.00	10.00	12.00	9.13	11.13	13.13
(sectional).	French Oval,						
(sedan).	Olive,						
(sedge).	Persian,						
(sediment).	Lily,						
(sedition).	Princess,						
(sedlitz).	Windsor,						
(seductive).	Crown,						
(seed).	Laurel,	8.50	10.50	12.50	9.63	11.63	13.63
(sedulous).	Saratoga,						
(seedling).	Newport,						
(seedy).	Lorne,						
(seeing).	Imperial,						
(darkish).	Arcadian,						
(darkly).	Assyrian,						
(dash-board).	Dundee,						
(dateless).	Embossed,						
(date tree).	Assyrian, Old Silver,	9.25	11.25	13.25	10.38	12.38	14.38
(dauber).	Embossed, " "						
(daybook).	Lucerne, (Satin, Hand Engraved.)	13.50	15.50	17.50	14.63	16.63	18.63
(daybreak).	Armenian, (Satin, Hand Engraved.)	14.50	16.50	18.50	15.63	17.63	19.63

PIE OR DESSERT FORKS (cutting tines).

Telegraphic Words.	Patterns.	No. 3.	No. 6.	No. 9.	No. 3 XII.	No. 6 XII.	No. 9 XII.
(seedsman).	Tipped,	$7.50	$9.50	$11.50	$8.63	$10.63	$12.63
(seek).	Windsor,						
(seel).	Laurel,						
(seeker).	Saratoga,	8.50	10.50	12.50	9.63	11.63	13.63
(seem).	Lorne,						
(seer).	Newport,						
(dazzle).	Armenian, (Satin, Hand Engraved.)	14.50	16.50	18.50	15.63	17.63	19.63

1847.-Rogers Bros.-A 1.

MEDIUM FORKS.

Telegraphic Words.	Patterns.	Extra Plate. No. 4.	Double Plate. No. 8.	Triple Plate. No. 12.	Sectional or XII Plate. Extra and XII Plate. No. 4 XII.	Double and XII Plate. No. 8 XII.	Triple and XII Plate. No. 12 XII.
(SEESAW).	Tipped,						
(SEETHE).	Fiddle,	$8.50	$11.00	$13.50	$10.00	$12.50	$15.00
(FITNESS).	Puritan,						
(SEINE).	Oval,						
(SELECTION).	French Oval,	9.00	11.50	14.00	10.50	13.00	15.50
(SEIZE).	Olive,						
(SELECT).	Persian,						
(SELF).	Lily,						
(SELLER).	Princess,						
(SELVAGE).	Windsor,						
(SEMBLANCE).	Crown,						
(SEMINARY).	Laurel,						
(SEMITIC).	Saratoga,						
(SEMITONE).	Newport,	9.50	12.00	14.50	11.00	13.50	16.00
(SENATE).	Lorne,						
(SENATOR).	Imperial,						
(DISMISS).	Arcadian,						
(DISMOUNT).	Assyrian,						
(DISPARITY).	Dundee,						
(DISPASSION).	Embossed,						
(DISPLEASE).	Assyrian, Old Silver,						
(DISPENSARY).	Embossed, " "	10.50	13.00	15.50	12.00	14.50	17.00
(DISPIRIT).	Lucerne, (Satin, Hand Engraved.)	15.50	18.00	20.50	17.00	19.50	22.00
(DISPOSAL).	Armenian, (Satin, Hand Engraved.)	16.50	19.00	21.50	18.00	20.50	23.00

MEDIUM FORKS (CUTTING TINES).

Telegraphic Words.	Patterns.	No. 4.	No. 8.	No. 12.	No. 4 XII.	No. 8 XII.	No. 12 XII.
(SENIOR).	Tipped,	$8.50	$11.00	$13.50	$10.00	$12.50	$15.00
(SENNA).	Windsor,						
(SENSATION).	Laurel,						
(SENSATE).	Saratoga,	9.50	12.00	14.50	11.00	13.50	16.00
(SENSE).	Lorne,						
(SENSIBLE).	Newport,						
(DISPOSITION).	Armenian, (Satin, Hand Engraved.)	16.50	19.00	21.50	18.00	20.50	23.00

TABLE FORKS.

Telegraphic Words.	Patterns.	No. 4.	No. 8.	No. 12.	No. 4 XII.	No. 8 XII.	No. 12 XII.
(SENTIMENT).	Tipped,	$9.00	$11.50	$14.00	$10.50	$13.00	$15.50
(SENTRY).	Oval,	9.50	12.00	14.50	11.00	13.50	16.00
(SEPARATE).	Olive,	10.00	12.50	15.00	11.50	14.00	16.50

PICKLE FORKS (CUTTING TINES).

Telegraphic Words.	Patterns.	Extra Plate. No. 3.	Double Plate. No. 6.	Triple Plate. No. 9.
(SEXTANT).	Tipped,	$6.50	$8.00	$9.50
(SEXTON).	Oval,	7.00	8.50	10.00
(SEXTUPLE).	Olive,			
(SHAD).	Persian,			
(SHAFT).	Lily,			
(SHAGGY).	Princess,			
(SHAKE).	Crown,			
(SHALLOP).	Windsor,			
(SHAMBLE).	Laurel,	7.50	9.00	10.50
(SHALLOW).	Saratoga,			
(SHAMPOO).	Lorne,			
(SHANK).	Newport,			
(SHAMROCK).	Imperial,			
(DISPRAISE).	Arcadian,			

PICKLE FORKS (LONG HANDLE)

Telegraphic Words.	Patterns.	No. 3.	No. 6.	No. 9.
(SHANTY).	Tipped,	$9.50	$11.00	$12.50
(SEWERAGE).	French Antique,			
(SHAPE).	Oval,	10.00	11.50	13.00
(SHARE).	Crown,			
(SHARPEN).	Saratoga,			
(SHARK).	Laurel, Twist,			
(SHARP).	Newport, "	10.50	12.00	13.50
(SHAPELY).	Lorne, "			
(SHADOW).	Persian, "			
(DISPUTANT).	Assyrian,			
(DISQUALIFY).	Assyrian, Old Silver,	11.50	13.00	14.50

1847.-Rogers Bros.-XII.

CHILD'S (ALSO USED AS BEEF) FORKS.

Telegraphic Words.	Patterns.	Extra Plate. No. 3.	Double Plate. No. 6.	Triple Plate. No. 9.
(SERVANT).	Tipped,	$6.00	$7.50	$9.00
(SERVE).	Oval,	6.50	8.00	9.50
(SERVICE).	Olive,			
(SETON).	Persian,			
(SETTEE).	Lily,			
(SETTING).	Princess,			
(SETTLER).	Crown,			
(SEVENTH).	Windsor,			
(SEVER).	Laurel,	7.00	8.50	10.00
(SEVERE).	Saratoga,			
(SEVERANCE).	Newport,			
(SEVERITY).	Lorne,			
(SEVENTHLY).	Imperial,			
(DISREGARD).	Arcadian,			
(EAGERLY).	Assyrian,			
(EAGLET).	Assyrian, Old Silver,	7.75	9.25	10.75
(EARLOCK).	Armenian, (Satin, Hand Engraved.)	12.00	13.50	15.00

OYSTER FORKS (TWO TINES).

Telegraphic Words.	Patterns.	No. 3.	No. 6.	No. 9.
(SEPOY).	Tipped,	$6.00	$8.00	$10.00
(SEPTEMBER).	Oval,	6.50	8.50	10.50
(SEQUEL).	Olive,			
(SEQUENCE).	Persian,			
(SEQUIN).	Lily,			
(SERAGLIO).	Princess,			
(SERAPH).	Crown,			
(FLAGRANCY).	Windsor,	7.00	9.00	11.00
(SERE).	Laurel,			
(EARWIG).	Newport,			
(SERAPHIM).	Saratoga,			
(SERENELY).	Lorne,			

OYSTER FORKS (THREE TINES).

Telegraphic Words.	Patterns.	No. 3.	No. 6.	No. 9.
(SERENADE).	Delmonico,			
(EARRING).	Lorne,			
(EARTHLY).	Windsor,			
(EASTERN).	Arcadian,	$8.00	$10.00	$12.00
(EBB-TIDE).	Assyrian,			
(ECLECTIC).	Dundee,			
(ECSTASY).	Embossed,			
(EDGETOOL).	Owl, Old Silver,			
(EDGEWISE).	Daisy, " "			
(EDILE).	Assyrian, " "	9.00	11.00	13.00
(EDUCATION).	Embossed, " "			
(EDUCTION).	Venetian,	10.50	12.50	14.50
(EFFECTOR).	Armenian, (Satin, Hand Engraved.)	14.00	16.00	18.00

ICE CREAM FORKS.

Telegraphic Words.	Patterns.	No. 3.	No. 6.	No. 9.
(EFFICIENT).	Brunswick (Satin Bowls),	$10.50	$12.50	$14.50
(EGGNOG).	Brunswick, (Satin, Engraved Bowls.)	15.00	17.00	19.00
(ELDERLY).	Plush Cases, holding ½ dozen,	$3.75 each.		
(ELECT).	Plush Cases, holding 1 dozen,	4.75 "		

FISH FORKS (ENGRAVED BLADES).

Telegraphic Words.	Patterns.	No. 4.	No. 8.	No. 12.
(SERENE).	Olive,			
(SERF).	Princess,			
(SERGE).	Persian,			
(SERGEANT).	Crown,			
(SERIAL).	Laurel,			
(SEROON).	Saratoga,	$42.00	$51.00	$60.00
(SERIES).	Newport,			
(SERIOUS).	Lorne,			
(EJECTMENT).	Windsor,			
(ELABORATE).	Arcadian,			
(ELATION).	Assyrian,			
(ELECTIVE).	Assyrian, Old Silver,	44.00	53.00	62.00
(ELECTORAL).	Armenian, (Satin, Hand Engraved.)	54.00	63.00	72.00
(ELECTRIFY).	Arcadian (Hollow Handle)			
(ELEGANT).	Assyrian, " "	54.00	63.00	72.00

SALAD FORKS (ENGRAVED BLADES).

Telegraphic Words.	Patterns.	No. 4.	No. 8.	No. 12.
(ELEGIAC).	Lorne,			
(ELEGIST).	Arcadian,	$30.00	$36.00	$42.00
(ELEPHANT).	Assyrian,			
(ELEVATION).	Assyrian, Old Silver,	32.00	38.00	44.00
(ELFLOCK).	Arcadian (Hollow Handle)			
(ELIMINATE).	Assyrian " "	42.00	48.00	54.00

1847.-ROGERS BROS.-A 1.

SUGAR SIFTERS.

Telegraphic Words.	Patterns.	Extra Plate. No. 4.	Double Plate. No. 8.	Triple Plate. No. 12.
(SPANGLE).	Oval,	$16.50	$22.50	$28.50
(SPANIARD).	Olive,	18.00	24.00	30.00
(SPAR).	Persian,			
	Bowls Gold Lined,	$6 00 per dozen extra.		

SUGAR SHELLS.

Telegraphic Words.	Patterns.	No. 3.	No. 6.	No. 9.
(SOCKET).	Crown, Tête-à-Tête,	$6.00	$7.25	$8.50
(SNEER).	Tipped,			
(DEANSHIP).	Puritan,	6.50	8.50	10.50
(DEBENTURE).	Shell Tipped,			
(SNIPE).	Fiddle,			
(SNUFF).	Oval,	8.75	10.75	12.75
(SNUG).	Olive,			
(SOAP).	Persian,			
(SOAR).	Lily,			
(SOCIABLE).	Princess,			
(SOCIAL).	Windsor,			
(SOCIETY).	Crown,			
(SODA).	Laurel,			
(SODIUM).	Saratoga,	9.00	11.00	13.00
(SOFA).	Newport,			
(SOFTEN).	Lorne,			
(SOIREE).	Imperial,			
(DECAGON).	Arcadian,			
(DECALOGUE).	Assyrian,			
(DECENT).	Dundee,			
(DECENTLY).	Embossed,			
(DECEPTIVE).	Assyrian, Old Silver,	9.75	11.75	13.75
(DECIDE).	Embossed, " "			
(DECIDED).	Armenian, (Satin, Hand Engraved.)	14.00	16.00	18.00
	Bowls Gold Lined,	$4.00 per dozen extra.		
	" Satin, Hand Engraved,	6.00 " " "		
	" Satin, Hand Engraved, Gold Inlaid,	12.00 " " "		

JELLY SHELLS.

Telegraphic Words.	Patterns.	No. 4.	No. 8.	No. 12.
(SOJOURN).	Oval,	$10.50	$13.00	$15.50
(SOLACE).	Olive,			
(SOLAR).	Persian,	12.00	14.50	17.00
(SOLDER).	Princess,			
(SOLDIER).	Crown,			
(SOLICIT).	Crown (Spoon-Shaped Bowl),			
	Bowls Gold Lined,	$6.00 per dozen extra.		

PRESERVE SHELLS.

LARGER THAN JELLY.

Telegraphic Words.	Patterns.	No. 4.	No. 8.	No. 12.
(SOLIDLY).	Oval,	$16.50	$22.50	$28.50
(SOLITARY).	Olive,			
(SOLO).	Persian,			
(SOLUTION).	Princess,	18.00	24.00	30.00
(SOLVE).	Crown,			
(SOMBER).	Laurel,			
(SOMERSET).	Saratoga,			
	Bowls Gold Lined,	$9.00 per dozen extra.		

SUGAR TONGS.

Telegraphic Words.	Patterns.	No. 4.	No. 8.	No. 12.
(SOWER).	Persian, Tête-à-Tête,			
(SPACE).	Windsor, " "			
(SPACIOUS).	Newport, " "	$18.00	$21.00	$24.00
(SPAN).	Lorne, " "			
(DEDUCTIVE).	Arcadian, " "			
(DEEM).	Assyrian, " "			
(DEEPEN).	Assyrian, " Old Silver, "	19.50	22.50	25.50
(DEFENDANT).	Armenian, " " (Satin, Hand Engraved.)	27.00	30.00	33.00

Telegraphic Words.	Patterns.	No. 4.	No. 8.	No. 12.
(SORCERER).	Princess, medium size,	$22.00	$25.00	$27.00
(SOREL).	Oval,	24.00	30.00	36.00
(SORTIE).	Olive,			
(SOUND).	Persian,			
(SOURCE).	Princess,			
(SOUTH).	Windsor,			
(SOUTHERN).	Crown,	25.50	31.50	37.50
(SOUVENIR).	Laurel,			
(SOUTHING).	Saratoga,			
(SOVEREIGN).	Newport,			
(SPADE).	Lorne,			
(DECK).	Arcadian,			
(DECKER).	Assyrian,			
(DECOCTION).	Assyrian, Old Silver,	27.50	33.50	39.50
(DECOLOR).	Armenian, (Satin, Hand Engraved.)	37.50	43.50	49.50

1847.-ROGERS BROS.-XII.

SARDINE TONGS.

Telegraphic Words.	Patterns.	Extra Plate. No. 4.	Double Plate. No. 8.	Triple Plate. No. 12.
(SONNET).	Persian,	$18.00	$24.00	$30.00

ICE TONGS.

Telegraphic Words.	Patterns.	No. 4.	No. 8.	No. 12.
(DEFENCE).	Lorne,	$42.00	$51.00	$60.00
(DEFICIENT).	Newport,			

ASPARAGUS TONGS.

Telegraphic Words.	Patterns.	No. 4.	No. 8.	No. 12.
(SOPHIST).	Persian,	$48.00	$60.00	$72.00
(SOPRANO).	Windsor, Chased,	54.00	66.00	78.00
(DEMURELY).	Assyrian (Hollow Handle),	108.00	118.00	130.00

SALAD TONGS.

SATIN ENGRAVED.

Telegraphic Words.	Patterns.	No. 4.	No. 8.	No. 12.
(DENTED).	Lorne,	$72.00	$84.00	$96.00
(DENTISTRY).	Assyrian,			

CAKE CUTTERS.

PLAIN, SATIN, OR CHASED BLADES, SAW EDGE.

Telegraphic Words.	Patterns.	No. 4.	No. 8.	No. 12.
(SPARK).	Oval,	$39.00	$48.00	$57.00
(SPARROW).	Olive,			
(SPATULA).	Persian,			
(SPAVIN).	Princess,			
(SPEAK).	Crown,			
(SPECIAL).	Laurel,	42.00	51.00	60.00
(SPEAR).	Saratoga,			
(SPECIE).	Newport,			
(SPECIFIC).	Lorne,			
(DEPENDANT).	Arcadian,			
(DEPICTURE).	Assyrian,			
(DEPLETION).	Assyrian, Old Silver,	44.00	53.00	62.00
	Blades, Satin, Hand Engraved,	$9.00 per dozen extra.		
	" Satin, Hand Engraved, Gold Inlaid,	24.00 " " "		
(DEPLUME).	Plush Cases,	2.75 each.		

INDIVIDUAL BUTTER KNIVES.

SOLID OR FLAT HANDLE.

Telegraphic Words.	Patterns.	No. 3.	No. 6.	No. 9.
(DERELICT).	Windsor,	$9.00	$11.00	$13.00
(DERIVATION).	Assyrian,			
(DERVISH).	Assyrian, Old Silver,	9.75	11.75	13.75
(DESERTER).	Armenian, (Satin, Hand Engraved.)	14.00	16.00	18.00
	Hand Engraved Blades,	$6.00 per dozen extra.		

BUTTER KNIVES.

SOLID OR FLAT HANDLE.

Telegraphic Words.	Patterns.	No. 3.	No. 6.	No. 9.
(SKEIN).	Oval, small,	$8.00	$10.00	$12.00
(SKEPTIC).	Oval,	8.50	10.50	12.50
(SKETCH).	Olive, small,			
(SKEWER).	Olive,			
(SKIFF).	Persian,			
(SKILL).	Lily,			
(SKILLET).	Princess,			
(SKILFUL).	Windsor,	9.00	11.00	13.00
(SKIM).	Crown,			
(SKIP).	Laurel,			
(SKIN).	Saratoga,			
(SKIPPER).	Newport,			
(SKIRMISH).	Lorne,			
(DEVIOUSLY).	Armenian, (Satin, Hand Engraved.)	14.00	16.00	18.00

SPOON OR BENT HANDLE.

Telegraphic Words.	Patterns.	No. 3.	No. 6.	No. 9.
(SKIRT).	Tipped,	$8.00	$10.00	$12.00
(SKITTISH).	Oval,	8.50	10.50	12.50
(SLAB).	Olive,			
(SLAKE).	Crown,			
(SLAM).	Laurel,	9.00	11.00	13.00
(SLAG).	Saratoga,			
(SLANG).	Newport,			
(SLANT).	Lorne,			

1847.-Rogers Bros.-A 1.

BUTTER KNIVES.—*Continued.*

TWIST OR REVERSED HANDLE.

Telegraphic Words.	Patterns.	Extra Plate. No. 3.	Double Plate. No. 6.	Triple Plate. No. 9.
(ELLIPTIC).	Tipped,			
(SLAP).	Fiddle,			
(ELOQUENT).	Puritan,	10.00	12.00	14.00
(ELVISH).	Shell Tipped,			
(SLASH).	Oval,			
(SLAT).	Olive,			
(SLAY).	Persian,			
(SLED).	Lily,			
(SLEDGE).	Princess,			
(SLEEK).	Windsor,			
(SLEEP).	Crown,			
(SLEET).	Laurel,			
(SLEEPY).	Saratoga,	10.50	12.50	14.50
(SLEEVE).	Newport,			
(SLEIGH).	Lorne,			
(SLENDER).	Imperial,			
(EMANATION).	Arcadian,			
(EMBARK).	Assyrian,			
(EMBATTLE).	Dundee,			
(EMBELLISH).	Embossed,			
(EMBLAZON).	Assyrian, Old Silver,			
(EMBOLDEN).	Embossed, " "	11.25	13.25	15.25
(EMBOWER).	Lucerne,			
	(Satin, Hand Engraved.)	15.50	17.50	19.50
(EMBRASURE).	Armenian,			
	(Satin, Hand Engraved.)	16.00	18.00	20.00

Chased Blades, ... $4.00 per dozen extra.
Satin, Engraved, Gold Inlaid Blades, 18.00 " "

CHILD'S KNIVES.

FLAT HANDLE (ALSO USED AS SMALL TEA OR FRUIT KNIVES).

Telegraphic Words.	Patterns.	No. 3.	No. 6.	No. 9.
(SLICE).	Oval,	$8.50	$10.00	$11.50
(SLIDE).	Olive,			
(SLIM).	Persian,			
(SLING).	Lily,			
(SLIP).	Princess,			
(SLIPSHOD).	Crown,			
(SLIVER).	Laurel,			
(SLOE).	Saratoga,	9.00	10.50	12.00
(SLOOP).	Newport,			
(SLOPE).	Lorne,			
(SLIPPER).	Imperial,			
(DUSTMAN).	Arcadian,			
(DUTIFUL).	Assyrian,			
(DWELLER).	Assyrian, Old Silver,	9.75	11.25	12.75
(DYNAMIC.).	Armenian,			
	(Satin, Hand Engraved.)	14.50	16.00	17.50

Chased Blades, ... $6.00 per dozen extra.

PIE KNIVES.

PLAIN, SATIN, OR CHASED BLADES.

Telegraphic Words.	Patterns.	No. 4.	No. 8.	No. 12.
(SIPHON).	Antique,			
(SINGULAR).	Oval,	$39.00	$48.00	$57.00
(SIREN).	Olive,			
(SIRNAME).	Persian,			
(SIRUP).	Lily,			
(SISTER).	Princess,			
(SITTING).	Windsor,			
(SITUATE).	Crown,			
(SIXTEENTH).	Laurel,			
(SIXFOLD).	Saratoga,	42.00	51.00	60.00
(SIXTH).	Newport,			
(SIZABLE).	Lorne,			
(SKATE).	Imperial,			
(ENGRASP).	Arcadian,			
(ENIGMATIC).	Assyrian,			
(ENORMOUS).	Dundee,			
(ENROOT).	Assyrian, Old Silver,	44.00	53.00	62.00
(ENSNARE).	Armenian,			
	(Satin, Hand Engraved.)	51.00	60.00	69.00
(DUCKLING).	Arcadian (Hollow Handle),			
(DUELIST).	Assyrian, " "	54.00	63.00	72.00

Blades, Satin, Hand Engraved, . . $9.00 per dozen extra.
" Satin, Hand Engraved, Gold Inlaid, 24.00 " "
(ENFILADE). Plush Cases, ... 3.00 each.

1847.-Rogers Bros.-XII.

FISH KNIVES.

PLAIN, SATIN, OR CHASED BLADES.

Telegraphic Words.	Patterns.	Extra Plate. No. 4.	Double Plate. No. 8.	Triple Plate. No. 12.
(SMACK).	Oval,	$39.00	$48.00	$57.00
(SMART).	Olive,			
(SMATTER).	Persian,			
(SMELT).	Princess,			
(SMILE).	Crown,			
(SMITE).	Laurel,			
(SMOKER).	Saratoga,	42.00	51.00	60.00
(SMITH).	Newport,			
(SMOKE).	Lorne,			
(ENTIRELY).	Windsor,			
(ENTREATY).	Arcadian,			
(ENUNCIATE).	Assyrian,			
(ENVIABLE).	Assyrian, Old Silver,	44.00	53.00	62.00
(EPICUREAN).	Armenian,			
	(Satin, Hand Engraved.)	54.00	63.00	72.00
(EPIDEMIC).	Arcadian (Hollow Handle),			
(EPIGRAPH).	Assyrian, " "	54.00	63.00	72.00

Blades, Satin, Hand Engraved, . . $12.00 per dozen extra.
" Satin, Hand Engraved, Gold Inlaid, 36.00 " "
(ENGAGED). Plush Cases, ... 3.25 each.

CRUMB KNIVES.

PLAIN, SATIN OR CHASED BLADES.

Telegraphic Words.	Patterns.	No. 4.	No. 8.	No. 12.
(SMOOTH).	Oval,	$45.00	$57.00	$69.00
(SMOULDER).	Olive,			
(SNACK).	Persian,			
(SNAFFLE).	Princess,			
(SNAG).	Crown,			
(SNAIL).	Laurel,			
(SNAKE).	Saratoga,	48.00	60.00	72.00
(SNAP).	Newport,			
(SNARE).	Lorne,			
(DROPLET).	Windsor,			
(DRUIDESS).	Arcadian,			
(DRUMMER).	Assyrian,			
(DUALITY.)	Assyrian, Old Silver,	50.00	62.00	74.00
(DUBIOUSLY).	Armenian,			
	(Satin, Hand Engraved.)	60.00	72.00	84.00
(DRAINAGE).	Arcadian (Hollow Handle),			
(DRAMATIST).	Assyrian, " "	60.00	72.00	84.00

Blades, Satin, Hand Engraved, . . $12.00 per dozen extra.
" Satin, Hand Engraved, Gold Inlaid, 36.00 " " "
(DISMAST). Plush Cases, ... 3.75 each.

ICE CREAM KNIVES.

Telegraphic Words.	Patterns.	No. 4.	No. 8.	No. 12.
(SNARL).	Persian (Spoon-shaped Blade),			
(SNATCH).	Princess, " "			
(SNATH).	Crown, " "	$24.00	$30.00	$36.00
(SNORE).	Lorne, " "			
(DAYLIGHT).	Newport, " "			

Gold Lined, ... $12.00 per dozen extra.

Telegraphic Words.	Patterns.	No. 4.	No. 8.	No. 12.
(DAYSTAR).	Assyrian (Hollow Handle), Satin Blade,	60.00	72.00	84.00
(DISMAY).	Assyrian, " " Engraved "	72.00	84.00	96.00

CREAM OR SAUCE LADLES.

Telegraphic Words.	Patterns.	No. 4.	No. 8.	No. 12.
(STEM).	Tipped,	$10.50	$13.50	$16.50
(STENCIL).	Oval,	12.00	15.00	18.00
(STEP).	Olive,			
(STILE).	Persian,			
(STILETTO).	Lily,			
(STILL).	Princess,			
(STILT).	Windsor,			
(STING).	Crown,			
(STIPEND).	Laurel,	13.50	16.50	19.50
(STINT).	Saratoga,			
(STIPPLE).	Newport,			
(STIRRUP).	Lorne,			
(DIGESTER).	Arcadian,			
(DIGITAL).	Assyrian,			
(DIGRAPH).	Assyrian, Old Silver,	14.50	17.50	20.50
(DIGEST).	Armenian,			
	(Satin, Hand Engraved.)	18.50	21.50	24.50

Bowls Gold Lined, ... $6.00 per dozen extra.
" Satin, Hand Engraved, . . 6.00 " "
" Satin, Hand Engraved, Gold Inlaid, 18.00 " "
(DECIMATE). Plush Cases, ... 2.62 each.

1847.-ROGERS BROS.-A 1.

GRAVY LADLES.

Telegraphic Words.	Pattern.	Extra Plate. No. 4.	Double Plate. No. 8.	Triple Plate. No. 12.
(STARE).	Tipped,	$15.00	$19.50	$24.00
(STARK).	Oval,	16.50	21.00	25.50
(STARTLE).	Olive,			
(STATION).	Persian,			
(STATISTIC).	Lily,			
(STATUE).	Princess,			
(STAUNCH).	Windsor,			
(STAVE).	Crown,	18.00	22.50	27.00
(STAY).	Laurel,			
(STEADY).	Saratoga,			
(STEAD).	Newport,			
(STEAK).	Lorne,			
(STEAM).	Imperial,			
(DICKER).	Arcadian,			
(DICTIONARY).	Assyrian,			
(DECURION).	Assyrian, Old Silver,	20.00	24.50	29.00
(DIFFUSELY).	Armenian, (Satin, Hand Engraved.)	27.00	31.50	36.00

Bowls Gold Lined, $9.00 per dozen extra.
" Satin, Hand Engraved, 9.00 " "
" Satin, Hand Engraved, Gold Inlaid, 24.00 " "

(DECORATOR). Plush Cases, 3.00 each.

OYSTER LADLES.

Telegraphic Words.	Pattern.	No. 4.	No. 8.	No. 12.
(SQUIRE).	Tipped,	$33.00	$42.00	$51.00
(STABLE).	Oval,	36.00	45.00	54.00
(STACK).	Olive,			
(STAGE).	Persian,			
(STAGNANT).	Lily,			
(STAIN).	Princess,			
(STAKE).	Windsor,			
(STALK).	Crown,			
(STALL).	Laurel,	39.00	48.00	57.00
(STALKER).	Saratoga,			
(STALWART).	Newport,			
(STAMP).	Lorne,			
(STAND).	Imperial,			
(DEFTLY).	Arcadian,			
(DEFECTION).	Assyrian,			
(DEMITINT).	Assyrian, Old Silver,	42.00	51.00	60.00
(DEMOTIC).	Armenian, (Satin, Hand Engraved.)	51.00	60.00	69.00

Bowls Gold Lined, $10.00 per dozen extra.
" Satin, Hand Engraved, 10.00 " "
" Satin, Hand Engraved, Gold Inlaid, 27.00 " "

(DEFICIT). Plush Cases, $5.00 each.

MEDIUM LADLES.

Telegraphic Words.	Pattern.	No. 4.	No. 8.	No. 12.
(SPREAD).	Tipped,	$42.00	$54.00	$66.00
(SPRING).	Oval,	45.00	57.00	69.00
(SPRINKLE).	Olive,			
(SPRUCE).	Persian,			
(SPRY).	Lily,			
(SPUNK).	Princess,			
(SPUR).	Windsor,			
(SPURN).	Crown,			
(SPURT).	Laurel,	48.00	60.00	72.00
(SPUTTER).	Saratoga,			
(SQUAB).	Newport,			
(SQUADRON).	Lorne,			
(SQUANDER).	Imperial,			
(DISHFUL).	Arcadian,			
DISJOINTLY).	Assyrian,			
(DIMINUTION).	Dundee,			
(DILAPIDATE).	Assyrian, Old Silver,	51.00	63.00	75.00
(DULCIFY).	Armenian, (Satin, Hand Engraved.)	60.00	72.00	84.00

Bowls Gold Lined, $12.00 per dozen extra.
" Satin, Hand Engraved, 12.00 " "
" Satin, Hand Engraved, Gold Inlaid, 30.00 " "

(DEXTROUS). Plush Cases, 5.50 each.

1847.-ROGERS BROS.-XII.

SOUP LADLES.

Telegraphic Words.	Patterns.	Extra Plate. No. 4.	Double Plate. No. 8.	Triple Plate. No. 12.
(SPINNER).	Tipped,	$45.00	$57.00	$69.00
(SPIRAL).	Oval,	48.00	60.00	72.00
(SPIRE).	Olive,			
(SPLASH).	Persian,			
(SPLENDID).	Lily,			
(SPLICE).	Princess,			
(SPLINT).	Windsor,			
(SPOKE).	Crown,			
(SPONGE).	Laurel,	51.00	63.00	75.00
(SPOKEN).	Saratoga,			
(SPONSOR).	Newport,			
(STOCKING).	Lorne,			
(SPONTOON).	Imperial,			
(DETENT).	Arcadian,			
(DETER).	Assyrian,			
(DETRIMENT).	Assyrian, Old Silver,	54.00	66.00	78.00
(STOIC).	Armenian, (Satin, Hand Engraved.)	63.00	75.00	87.00

Bowls Gold Lined, $15.00 per dozen extra.
" Satin, Hand Engraved, 12.00 " "
" Hand Engraved, Gold Inlaid, 36.00 " "

(DETECTER). Plush Cases, 6.00 each.

INDIVIDUAL SOUP LADLES.

(SIZE BETWEEN GRAVY AND OYSTER.)

Telegraphic Words.	Pattern.	No. 4.	No. 8.	No. 12.
(DESIRABLE).	Windsor,	$27.00	$34.50	$42.00

PUNCH LADLES.

Telegraphic Words.	Pattern.	No. 4.	No. 8.	No. 12.
(STONE).	Persian (Long Twist Handle),	$96.00	$108.00	$120.00

Bowls Gold Lined, $18.00 per dozen extra.

CHEESE SCOOPS.

Telegraphic Words.	Pattern.	No. 4.	No. 8.	No. 12.
(FANLIGHT).	Arcadian (Flat Handle),	$30.00	$39.00	$48.00
(FANTASTIC).	Delmonico (Wood ").	33.00		
(FARCICAL).	Oval (Flat "),	36.00	45.00	54.00
(FARRAGO).	Royal, (Hollow "),			
(FASTENING).	Arcadian (" "),	51.00	63.00	75.00
(FASTIDIOUS).	Assyrian (" "),			
(FAVORABLE).	Norman (" "),	66.00	75.00	84.00

Engraved Blades, $6.00 per dozen extra.

JULEP STRAINERS.

Telegraphic Words.	Pattern.	No. 4.	No. 8.	No. 12.
(STONY).	Windsor, small,	$9.00	$11.00	$13.00
(EPACT).	Clover,	12.00	15.00	18.00
(STOKER).	Star,			
(STOLID).	Olive,	13.50	16.50	19.50

NUT PICKS.

Telegraphic Words.	Pattern.	No. 2.	No. 4.	No. 6.
(SPECK).	Oval,	$4.50	$5.75	$7.00
(SPECTRUM).	Olive,			
(SPEED).	Persian,			
(SPELL).	Lily,			
(SPENCER).	Princess,			
(SPERM).	Windsor,			
(SPHERE).	Crown,	4.75	6.00	7.25
(SPHINX).	Laurel,			
(SPICY).	Saratoga,			
(SPICE).	Newport,			
(SPIDER).	Lorne,			
(DETAIN).	Arcadian,			
(FLAGSTONE).	Assyrian,			
(DISFAVOR).	Assyrian, extra heavy,	5.75	7.00	8.25
(DISHONOR).	Assyrian, Old Silver,	6.00	7.25	8.50
(DISFIGURE).	Armenian, (Satin, Hand Engraved.)	8.75	10.00	11.25

(SPIKE). Plush Cases, holding ½ dozen, $1.38 each.
(SPIGOT). Plush Cases, holding 1 dozen, 2.00 "

1847.-Rogers Bros.-A 1.

1847.-Rogers Bros.-XII.

EXTRA HEAVY SPOONS AND FORKS.

WITH SPRING TEMPERED SHANKS.

For Hotels, Steamships, Etc.

TEA SPOONS.

Telegraphic Words.	Patterns.	Extra Plate. No. 2.	Double Plate. No. 4.	Triple Plate. No. 6.	Sectional or XII Plate. Extra and XII Plate. No. 2 XII.	Double and XII Plate. No. 4 XII.	Triple and XII Plate. No. 6 XII.
(STOOL).	French Threaded,	$4.75	$6.00	$7.25	$5.50	$6.75	$8.00
(STOPPER).	Oval,	5.50	6.75	8.00	6.25	7.50	8.75
(STORAGE). (STORK).	Windsor, Sherwood,	5.75	7.00	8.25	6.50	7.75	9.00

DESSERT SPOONS.

Telegraphic Words.	Patterns.	No. 3.	No. 6.	No. 9.	No. 3 XII.	No. 6 XII.	No. 9 XII.
(STORY).	French Threaded,	$9.00	11.00	13.00	$10.13	$12.13	$14.13
(STORM).	Oval,	9.50	11.50	13.50	10.63	12.63	14.63
(STOUT). (STOVE).	Windsor, Sherwood,	10.00	12.00	14.00	11.13	13.13	15.13

TABLE SPOONS.

Telegraphic Words.	Patterns.	No. 4.	No. 8.	No. 12.	No. 4 XII.	No. 8 XII.	No. 12 XII.
(STRAND).	French Threaded,	$10.00	$12.50	$15.00	$11.50	$14.00	$16.50
(STRAIN).	Oval,	11.00	13.50	16.00	12.50	15.00	17.50
(STRANGE) (STRAP).	Windsor, Sherwood,	11.50	14.00	16.50	13.00	15.50	18.00

DESSERT FORKS.

Telegraphic Words.	Patterns.	No. 3.	No. 6.	No. 9.	No. 3 XII.	No. 6 XII.	No. 9 XII.
(STRAW).	French Threaded,	$9.00	$11.00	$13.00	$10.13	12.13	14.13
(STRATA).	Oval,	9.50	11.50	13.50	10.63	12.63	14.63
(STREAK). (STREAM).	Windsor, Sherwood,	10.00	12.00	14.00	11.13	13.13	15.13

MEDIUM FORKS.

Telegraphic Words.	Patterns.	No. 4.	No. 8.	No. 12.	No. 4 XII.	No. 8 XII.	No. 12 XII.
(STRENGTH).	French Threaded,	$10.75	$13.25	$15.75	$12.25	$14.75	$17.25
(STREET).	Oval,	11.00	13.50	16.00	12.50	15.00	17.50
(STRESS). (STRICT).	Windsor, Sherwood,	11.50	14.00	16.50	13.00	15.50	18.00

TABLE FORKS.

Telegraphic Words.	Patterns.	No. 4.	No. 8.	No. 12.	No. 4 XII.	No. 8 XII.	No. 12 XII.
(STRIP).	French Threaded,	$11.25	$13.75	$16.25	$12.75	$15.25	$17.75
(STRING).	Oval,	11.50	14.00	16.50	13.00	15.50	18.00
(STROKE). (STROLL).	Windsor, Sherwood,	12.00	14.50	17.00	13.50	16.00	18.50

Also, Sherwood Coffee, Mustard, and Salt Spoons; Pickle, Oyster, and Child's Forks; Sugar Shells, Butter Knives, and Nut Picks. Price same as Windsor.

REPLATING

Spoons, Forks, Knives, Etc.

TEA, EGG, MUSTARD, AND SALT SPOONS.

	Extra Plate. Per dozen.	Double Plate. Per dozen.	Triple Plate Per dozen.
Plain and Tipped,	$1.75	$2.50	$3.25
Persian, Olive, Oval, etc.,	2.00	2.75	3.50

DESSERT SPOONS AND FORKS, AND SUGAR SHELLS.
BAR SPOONS, CHILD'S KNIVES AND FORKS, PICKLE FORKS.

	Extra Plate.	Double Plate.	Triple Plate
Plain and Tipped,	$2.62	$3.75	$4.87
Persian, Olive, Oval, etc.,	3.00	4.00	5.00

TABLE SPOONS, FORKS, AND BUTTER KNIVES.

	Extra Plate.	Double Plate.	Triple Plate
Plain and Tipped,	$3.50	$5.00	$6.50
Persian, Olive, Oval, etc.,	4.00	5.50	7.00
Cream Ladles, Gravy Ladles, Berry Spoons, Sugar Tongs,	8.00	11.25	14.50
Cake Knives, Pie Knives, Fish Knives, Oyster Ladles,	16.75	22.50	28.25
Medium Ladles, Soup Ladles, Crumb Knives,	20.00	27.25	34.50

Refinishing all Spoons and Forks before Plating, unless otherwise ordered, 80 cents per dozen extra.

Refinishing Gravy Ladles and Berry Spoons, $2.50 per dozen extra.

Refinishing Cake, Pie, Fish Knives, and Oyster Ladles, $3.00 per dozen extra.

Refinishing Medium and Soup Ladles, $3.50 per dozen extra.

KNIVES.

	Per dozen.
Metal Handle Knives, Dessert size,	$3.75
Metal Handle Knives, Medium and Table size,	4.25
Ivory Handle Knives, Dessert size,	3.75
Ivory Handle Knives, Medium and Table size,	4.25
Refinishing Knives,	1.00

GERMAN SILVER GOODS.

NOT PLATED.

Extra Weight and Quality.

		Per gross.
(STRONG).	Plain Tea Spoons,	$21.00
(STRUNG).	Tipped Tea Spoons,	22.50
(STRUT).	Plain Dessert Spoons,	31.00
(STUCCO).	Tipped Dessert Spoons,	34.00
(STUDENT).	Plain Table Spoons,	42.00
(STUDIO).	Tipped Table Spoons,	45.00
(STUDY).	Tipped Dessert Forks,	44.00
(STUMP).	Tipped Medium Forks,	48.00

Put up in new and attractive style, tied up in sets, and packed three dozen Teas or two dozen Table in a box.

STERLING SILVER.

GUARANTEED $\frac{925}{1000}$ FINE.

(FULL SIZE.)

EMBOSSED. TIPPED. FIGURED FRENCH. SHELL TIPPED. ARCADIAN. ARMENIAN. NEWPORT. LORNE. ST. GEORGE.

Satin, Hand Engraved.

PRICE-LIST.

$1.35 per ounce. No extra charge for making, except Fancy Pieces.	Satin, Engraved, Handles. Extra.	Old Silver, Extra.
Tea Spoons,	$2.00	.25
Dessert "	3.00	.50
Table "	3.50	.75
Dessert Forks,	3.00	.50
Medium "	3.50	.75

The following goods, $1.30 per ounce, and *extra for making, as follows:*

			Engraved, Extra.	Gilt, Extra.		
Salt Spoons,	per doz.,	$3.50		$1.00	$2.00	.25
Mustard "	"	3.50		1.00	2.00	.25
Coffee "	"	3.50		1.50	2.00	.25
Child's Knives,	"	10.00			3.00	.75
Child's Forks,	"	5.00			3.00	.75
Pickle "	"	5.00			3.00	.75
Butter Knives,	"	10.00	$6.00		3.00	.75
Sugar Shells,	"	10.00	6.00	2.50	3.00	.75
Berry Spoons,	each,	1.25	.50	.75	.50	.25
Cream Ladles,	"	1.00	.40	.50	.25	.15
Gravy "	"	1.50	.50	.75	.50	.20
Oyster "	"	3.50	.75	1.00	.75	.25
Soup "	"	4.50	1.00	1.50	1.00	.25
Pie Knives,	"	2.50	.75	1.50	.75	.25
Fish "	"	3.00	.75	1.50	.75	.25
Cake, "	"	2.50	.75	1.50	.75	.25
Crumb "	"	3.00	1.00	1.75	.75	.25
Sugar Tongs, Large,	"	2.00			.75	.25
Sugar " Tête-à-Tête,	"	1.50			.50	.25

TERMS, NET CASH, 10 DAYS.

USUAL WEIGHTS PER DOZEN.

		Tip, Fiddle, Shell Tip, Figured French. Ounces.	Lorne, St. George, Newport, Embossed. Laurel. Ounces.	Arcadian, Windsor, Armenian. Ounces.
Tea Spoons,	per doz.,	6 to 8	8 to 9	8 to 10
Table "	"	14 " 18	18 " 20	20 " 24
Dessert "	"	12 " 16	16 " 18	18 " 20
Medium Forks,	"	16 " 18	18 " 20	20 " 24
Dessert "	"	12 " 15	16 " 18	18 " 20
Salt Spoons,	"	3 " 4	3 " 4	3 " 4
Mustard Spoons,	"	5 " 6	5 " 6	5 " 6
Coffee "	"	4 " 6	4 " 6	4 " 6
Child's Knives,	each,	1¼ " 1½	1¼ " 1½	1¼ " 1½
Child's Forks,	"	¾ " 1	¾ " 1	¾ " 1
Pickle "	"	1½	1½	1¾
Berry Spoons,	"	2 " 2¼	2 " 2¼	2¼ " 2¾
Cream Ladles,	"	1¼ " 1½	1¼ " 1½	1¼ " 1½
Gravy "	"	2¼ " 2½	2½ " 2¾	2½ " 2¾
Oyster "	"	4 " 4¼	4 " 4½	4¼ " 4½
Soup "	"	5 " 5½	5½ " 6	5½ " 6
Pie Knives,	"	2¼ " 2½	2½ " 3	2½ " 3
Fish "	"		3¼ " 3¾	3¼ " 3¾
Cake "	"		3¼ " 3½	3¼ " 3½
Crumb "	"		4 " 5	4 " 5
Sugar Tongs,	"			
Sugar " Tête-à-Tête,	"		1 " 1¼	1 " 1¼
		Dwts.	Dwts.	Dwts.
Butter Knives,	"	26 to 30	28 to 35	30 to 35
Sugar Shells,	"	12 " 14	13 " 15	14 " 19

PRICES SUBJECT TO CHANGE WITHOUT NOTICE.

PLUSH AND MOROCCO CASES

CONTAINING 1847.–ROGERS BROS.–A I SPOONS, FORKS, KNIVES, ETC.

(FOR FULL DESCRIPTION OF COMBINATIONS SEE PAGES 436–437.)

In ordering, state the number of Case and Pattern desired. The number indicates the Combination, but not the Pattern.

Discount same as Flat Ware.

(ONE-THIRD SIZE.)

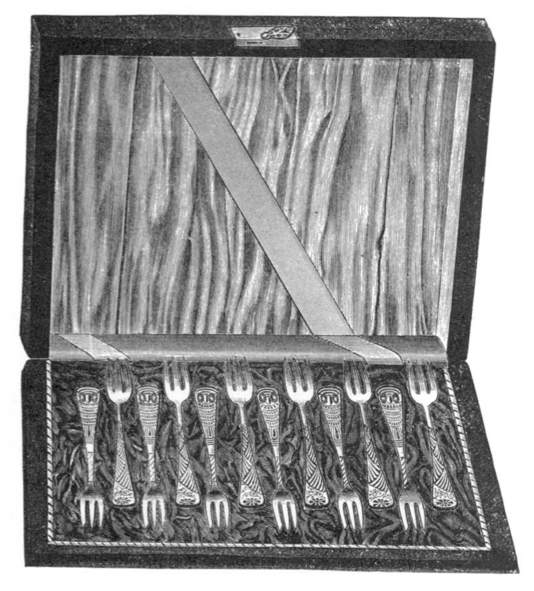

Six Each Owl and Daisy Oyster Forks.

No. 254. Morocco, complete, . $14.25 (EXCLUSION).
No. 2540. Plush, " . 14.25 (EXCLAIMER).

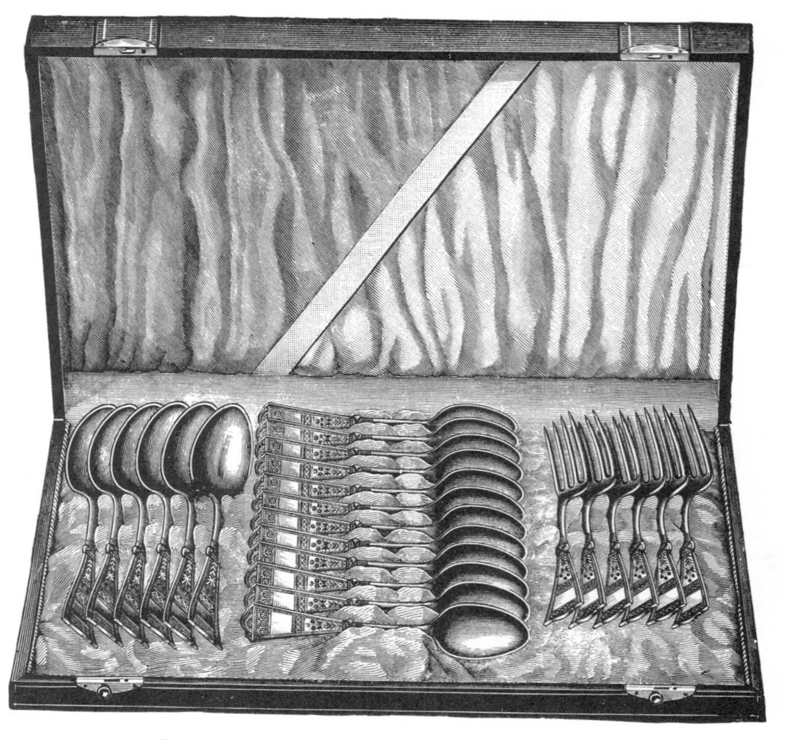

Twelve Laurel Tea Spoons, Six Table Spoons, Six Medium Forks.

No. 102. Morocco, complete, $24.50 (TACKLE).
No. 1020. Plush, " 24.50 (EXCESSIVE).

Twelve Crown Tea Spoons, Six Table Spoons, Six Dessert Spoons, Twelve Medium Forks.

No. 103. Morocco, complete, . $38.25 (TABLE).
No. 1030. Plush, " . 38.25 (EXERTION).

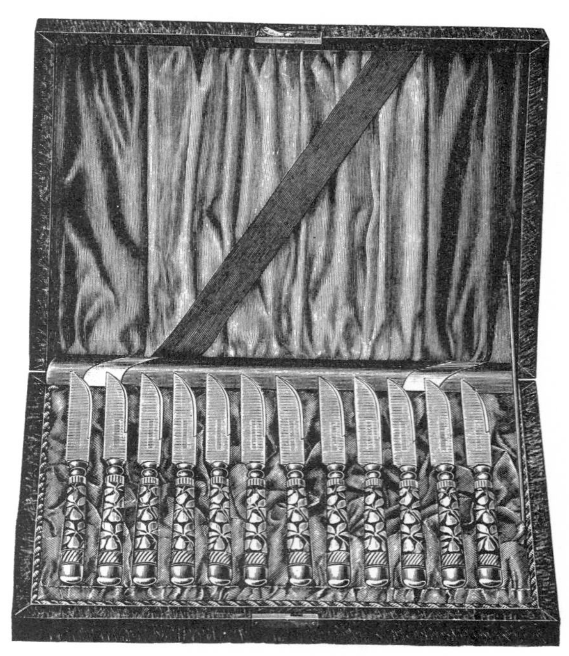

Twelve No. 32 Arabesque Old Silver Fruit Knives.

No. 262. Morocco, complete, . $13.75 (EROSION).
No. 2620. Plush, " . 13.75 (EXHIBITION).

For complete Price-List see pages 436–437.

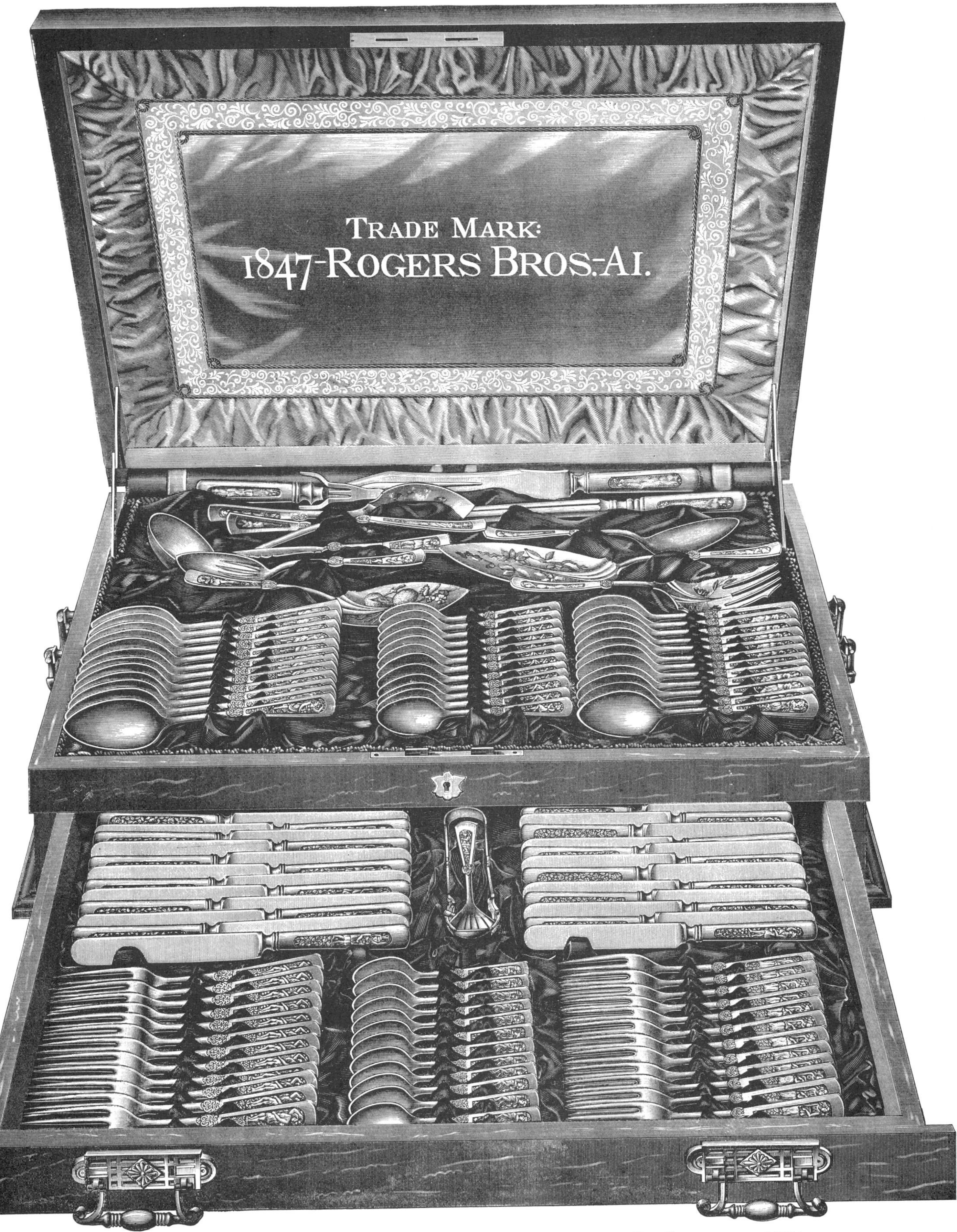

FINE BLACK WALNUT CHEST, WITH DRAWER, CONTAINING ONE HUNDRED AND TEN PIECES, AS FOLLOWS:

Twelve Arcadian Medium Knives, twelve Arcadian Dessert Knives, twelve each Table Spoons, Medium Forks, Dessert Forks, Dessert Spoons, Tea Spoons, Coffee Spoons, one each Soup Ladle, Berry Spoon, Sugar Shell, Sugar Tongs, Twist Butter Knife, Ice Tongs, Salad Spoon, Salad Fork, Pie Knife, Fish Knife, Fish Fork, Arcadian Carver, Fork, and Steel.

No. 259. Complete, Goods Standard Plate, $220.00 (EXPERTLY). Goods Triple Plate, $256.00 (EXPECTANCE).

For complete Price-List see pages 436–437.

1847.-ROGERS BROS.-A 1.

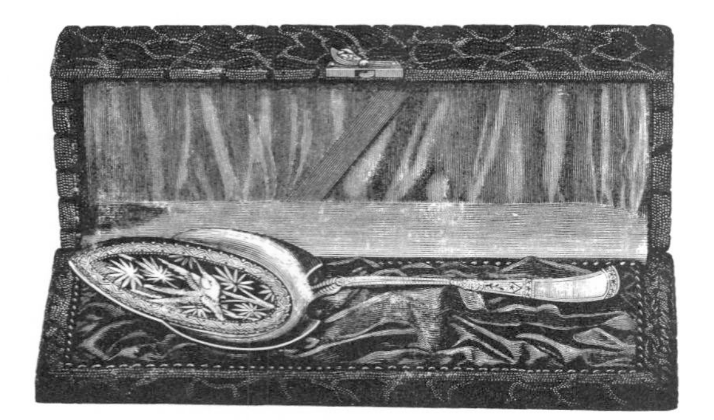

Saratoga Pie Knife.
No. 95. Morocco, complete, . $6.50 (EXCELLENT).
No. 950. Plush, " . 6.50 (EXCEEDING).

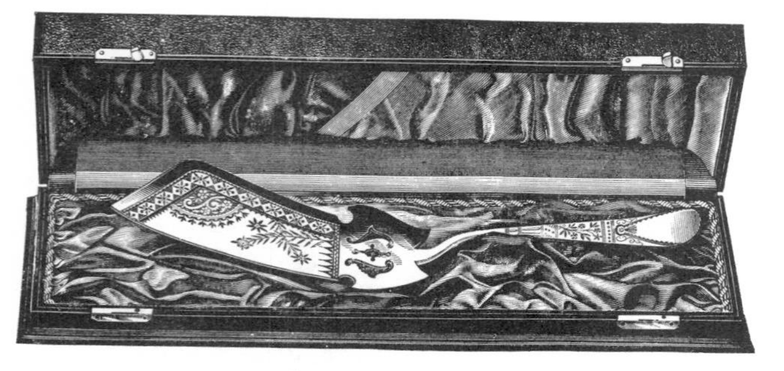

Lorne Fish Knife.
No. 94. Morocco, complete, . $6.75 (TALLOW).
No. 940. Plush, " . 6.75 (EVENTUATE).

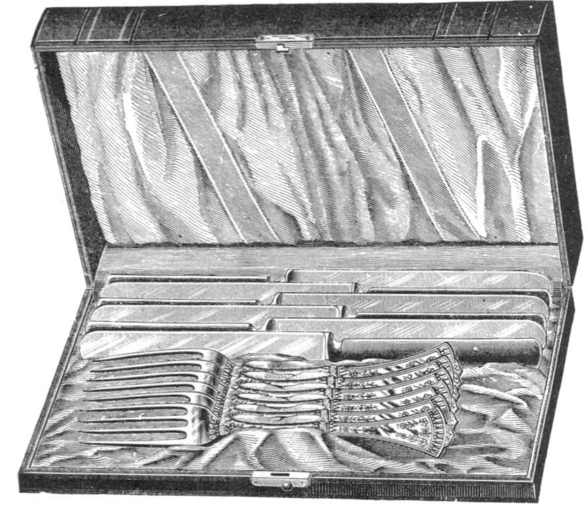

Six each, No. 12 Medium Knives and Crown Medium Forks.
No. 154. Morocco, complete, . $14.25 (TARTAR).
No. 1540. Plush, " . 14.25 (EXASPERATE).

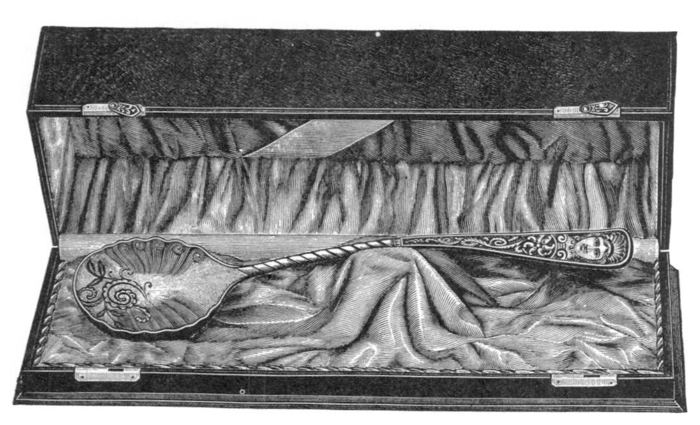

Assyrian Medium Ladle.
No. 97. Morocco, complete, . $9.50 (TASSEL).
No. 970. Plush, " . 9.50 (ESCARPMENT).

1847.-ROGERS BROS.-XII.

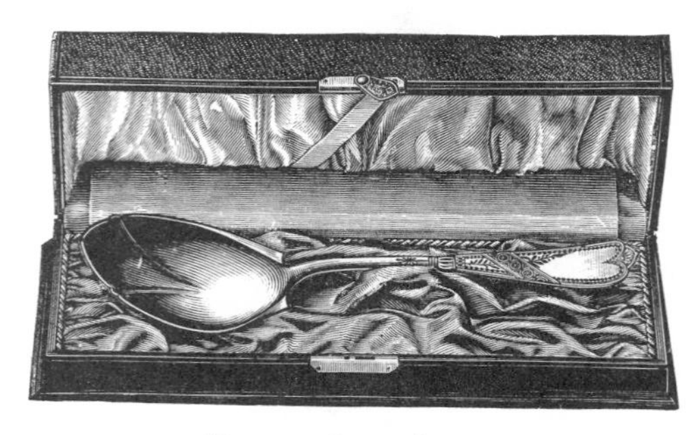

Newport Berry Spoon.
No. 135. Morocco, complete, . $5.00 (TARRY).
No. 1350. Plush, " . 5.00 (EVIDENTLY).

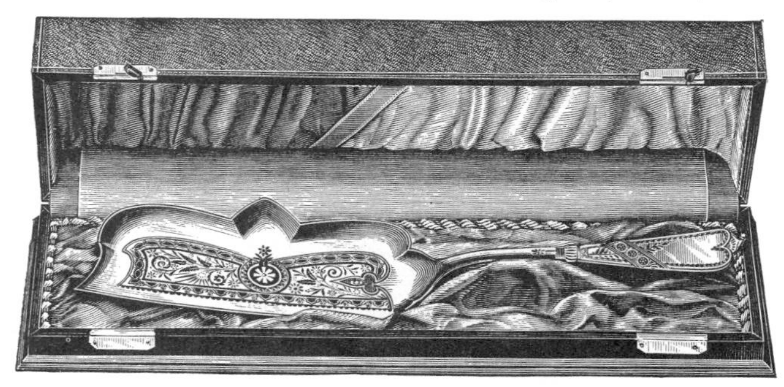

Newport Crumb Knife.
No. 96. Morocco, complete, . $7.75 (TALLY).
No. 960. Plush, " . 7.75 (ESCAPEMENT).

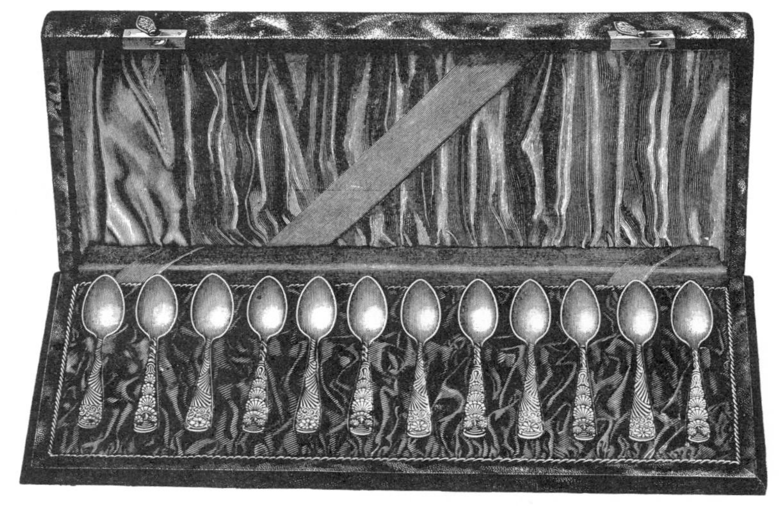

Six each, Old Silver, Owl and Daisy Coffee Spoons.
No. 145. Morocco, complete, . $11.00 (TABOO).
No. 1450. Plush, " . 11.00 (EXCEPTIONAL).

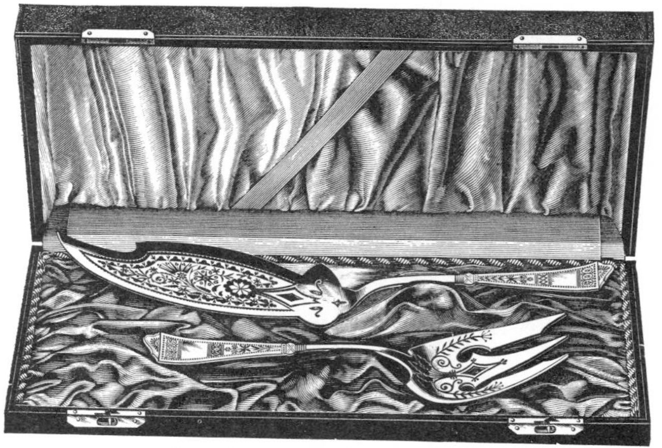

Laurel Fish Knife and Fork.
No. 109. Morocco, complete, . $12.25 (TABLET).
No. 1090. Plush, " . 12.25 (ESCUTCHEON).

For complete Price-List see pages 436–437.

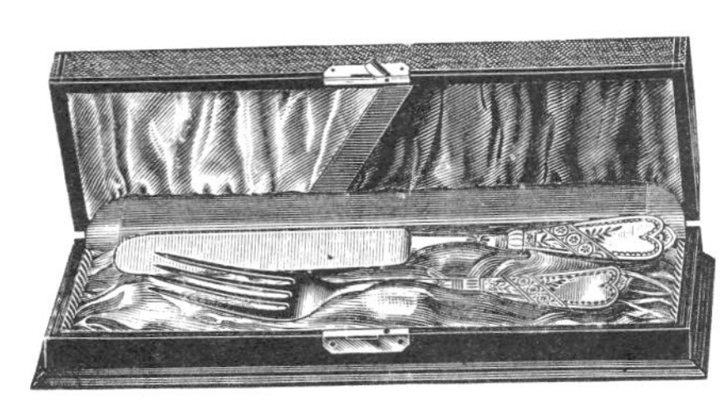

Newport Child's Knife and Fork.

No. 114. Morocco, complete, . $3.00 (TASTY).
No. 1140. Plush, " . 3.00 (EUCHRE).

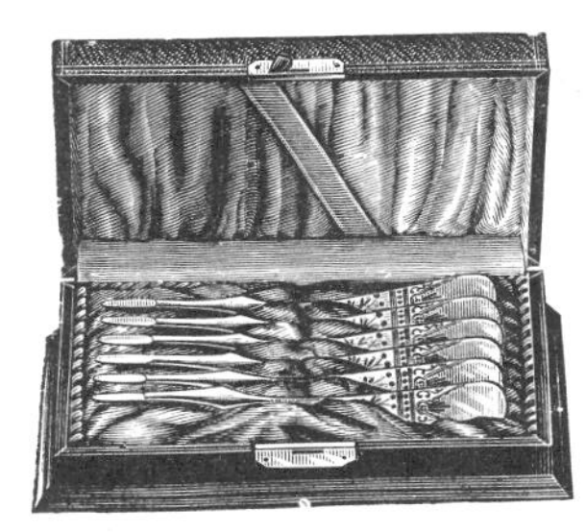

Six Lorne Nut Picks.

No. 91. Morocco, complete, . $3.75 (TAPIOCA).
No. 910. Plush, " . 3.75 (ESPLANADE).

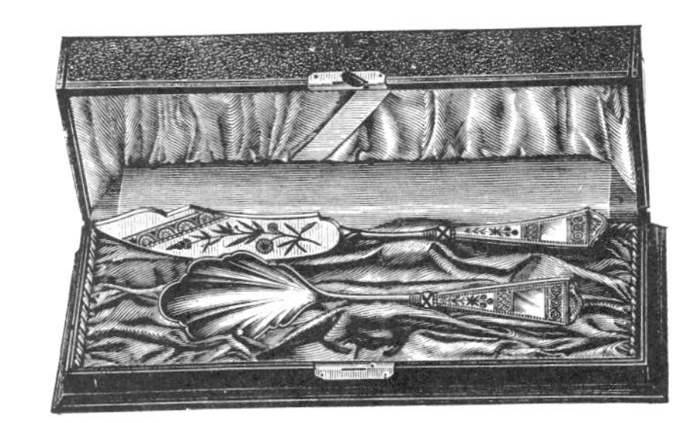

Laurel Sugar Shell and Twist Butter Knife.

No. 159. Morocco, complete, . $3.75 (TANDEM).
No. 1590. Plush, " . 3.75 (EXORCISE).
No. 1590½. Plush, Butter Knife, with Chased Blade, $4.00 (FERVID).

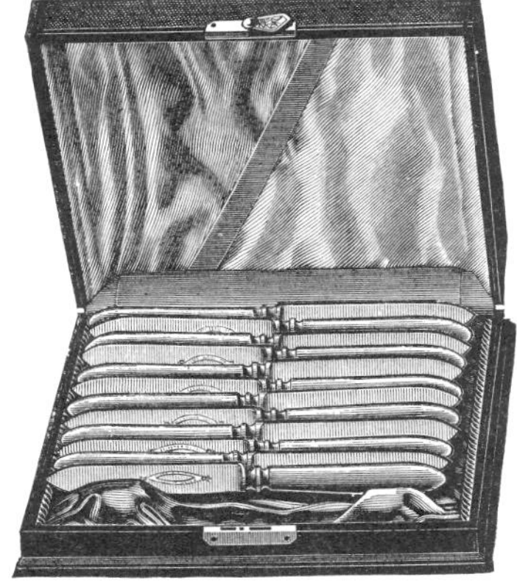

Twelve No. 26 Fruit Knives.

No. 193. Morocco, complete, . $8.75 (TANGLE).
No. 1930. Plush, " . 8.75 (ETHEREAL).

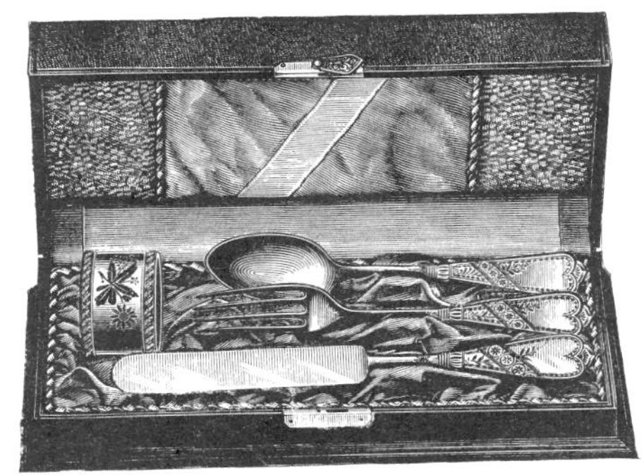

Newport Knife, Fork, Spoon, and Napkin Ring.

No. 117. Morocco, complete, . $5.25 (TAXABLE).
No. 1170. Plush, " . 5.25 (ERUPTION).

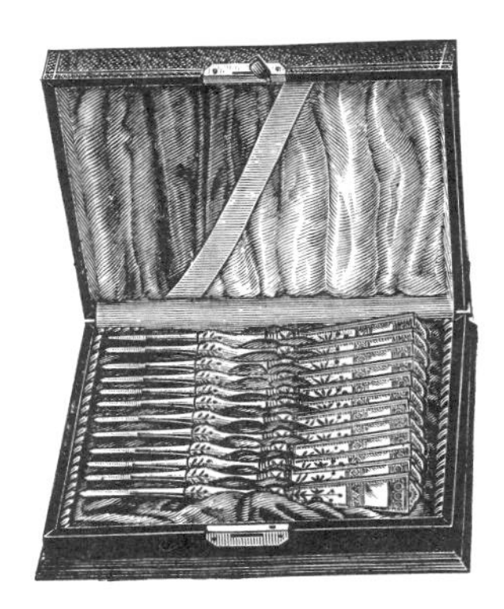

Twelve Laurel Nut Picks.

No. 90. Morocco, complete, . $6 75 (TAPER).
No. 900. Plush, " . 6.75 (EXISTENCE).

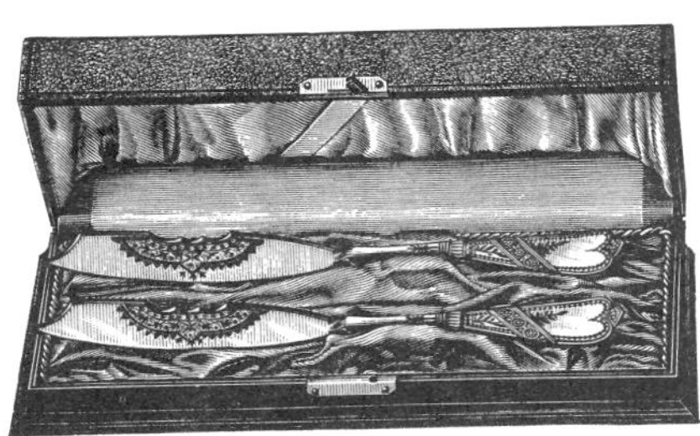

Two Newport Twist Butter Knives.

No. 138. Morocco, complete, . $4.00 (TANGENT).
No. 1380. Plush, " . 4.00 (ETERNIZE).
No. 1380½. Plush, Butter Knives, with Chased Blades, 4.50 (EUPHONY).

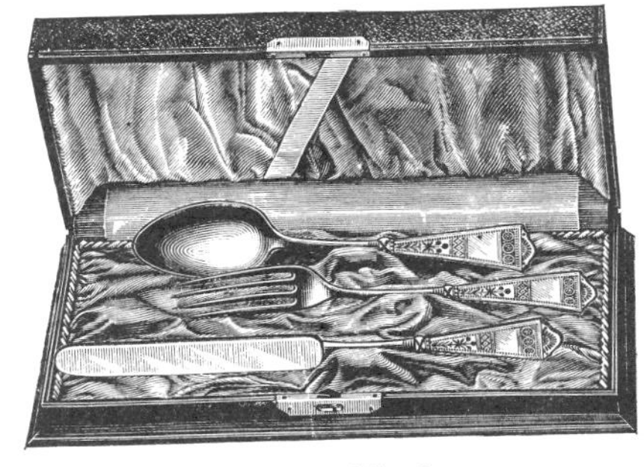

Laurel Child's Set.

No. 116. Morocco, complete, . $3.75 (TEACH).
No. 1160. Plush, " . 3.75 (ERRONEOUS).

Lorne Gravy Ladle.

No. 137. Morocco, complete, . $4.50 (TANK).
No. 1370. Plush, " . 4.50 (EXHAUSTER).

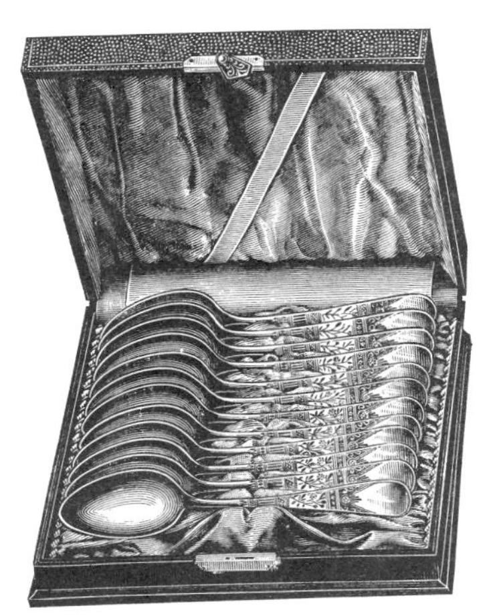

Twelve Lorne Tea Spoons.

No. 163. Morocco, complete, . $8.50 (TABULAR).
No. 1630. Plush, " . 8.50 (ESTABLISH).

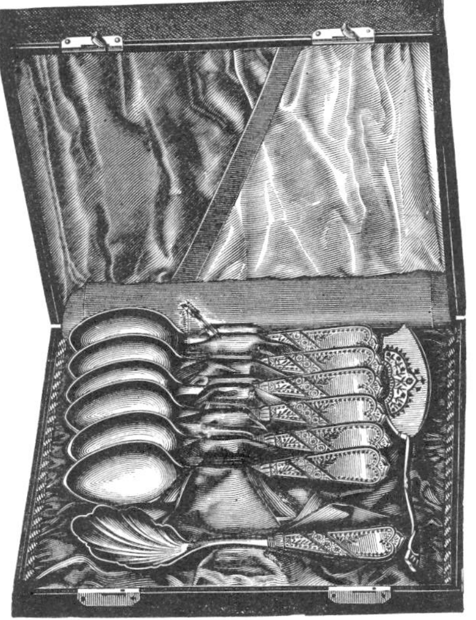

Six Newport Tea Spoons, Sugar Shell, and Twist Butter Knife.

No. 160. Morocco, complete, . $8.75 (TACTIC).
No. 1600. Plush, " . 8.75 (EXPANSION).
No. 1600½. Plush, Butter Knife, with Chased Blade, 9.00 (FERRYMAN).

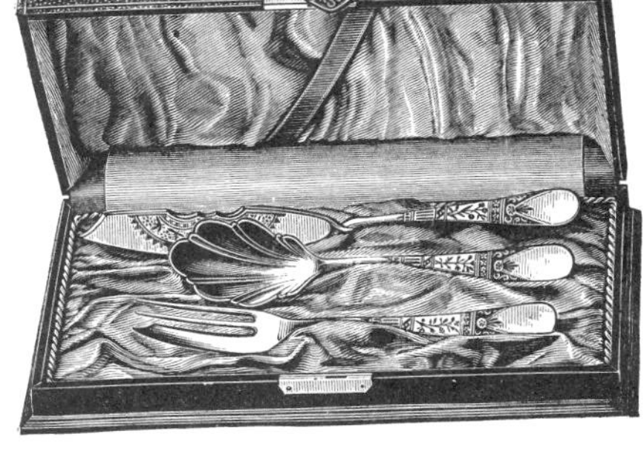

Lorne Sugar Shell, Pickle Fork, and Twist Butter Knife.

No. 158. Morocco, complete, . $5.00 (TAMER).
No. 1580. Plush, " . 5.00 (EXEMPLIFY).
No. 1580½. Plush, Butter Knife, with Chased Blade, 5.25 (FINANCIAL).

For complete Price-List see pages 436, 437.

BLACK CASES, SATIN LINED.

(One-Third Size.)

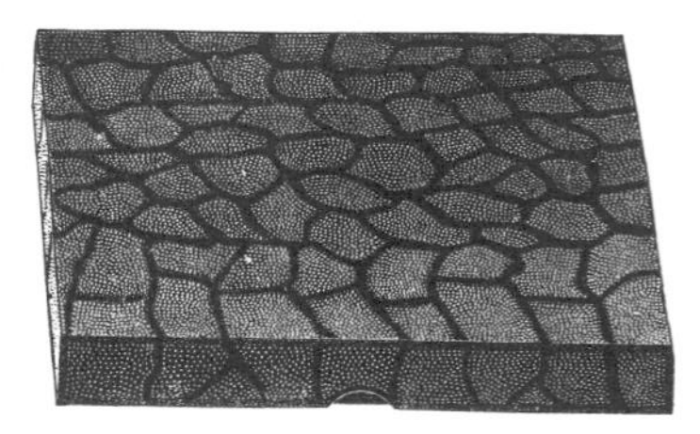

No. 42. View showing Case closed.

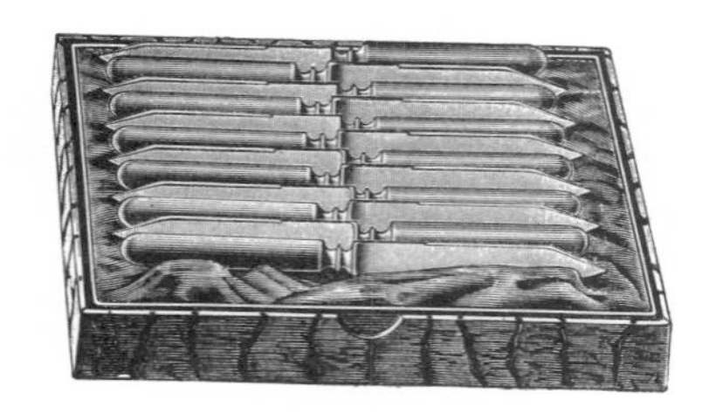

Twelve No. 26 Fruit Knives.
No. 42. Complete, . $6.10 (excitement).

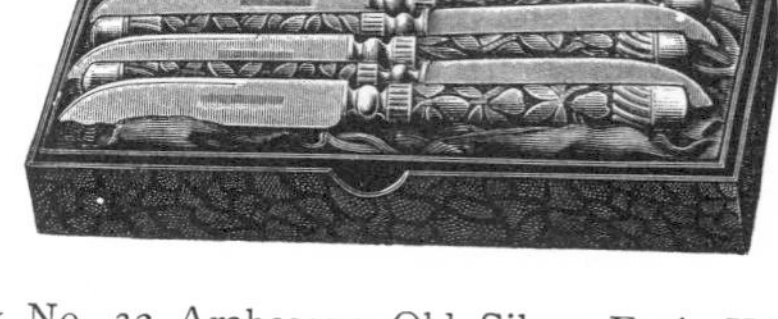

Six No. 32 Arabesque Old Silver Fruit Knives.
No. 52. Complete, . $4.75 (expertly).

Arcadian Child's Set.
No. 28. Complete, . $2.50 (experience).

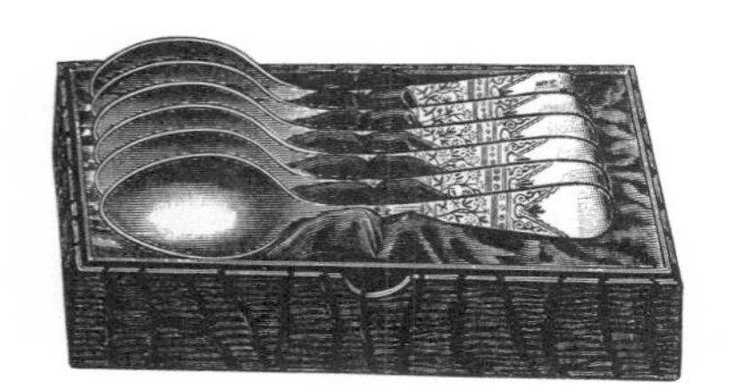

Six Lorne Tea Spoons.
No. 29. Complete, . $3.12 (expectance).

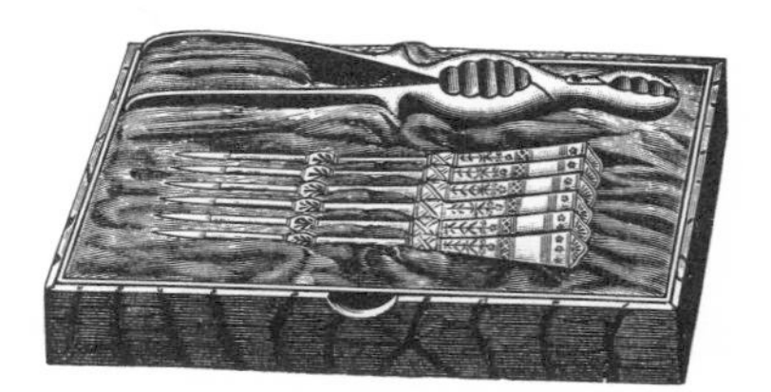

Six Laurel Nut Picks and One Nut Crack.
No. 36. Complete, . $4.37 (gratuitous).

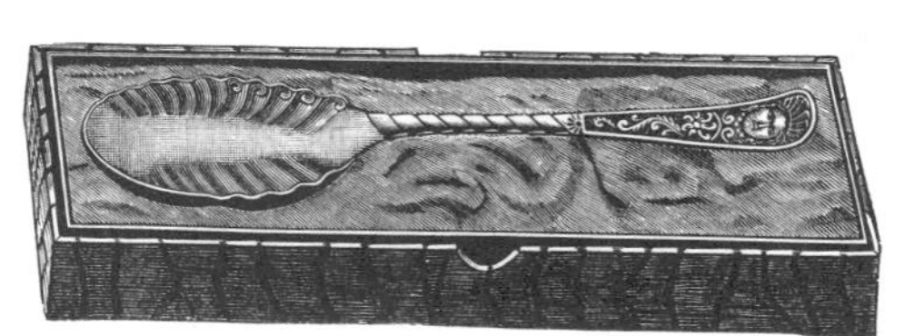

Assyrian Berry Spoon.
No. 20. Complete, . $3.00 (experiment).

Arcadian Pie Knife.
No. 21. Complete. . $4.50 (expedition).

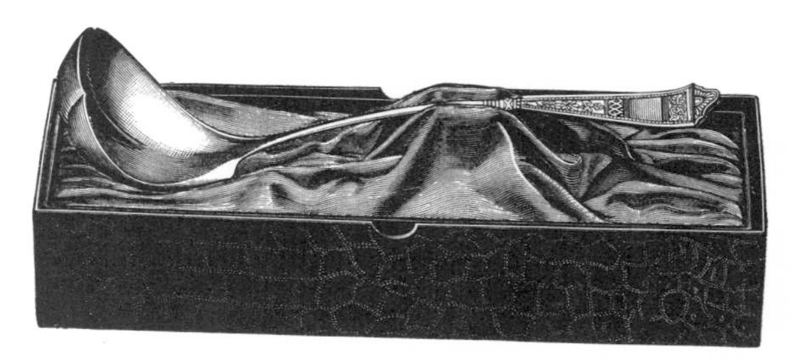

Laurel Medium Ladle.
No. 24. Complete, . $5.25 (gratuity).

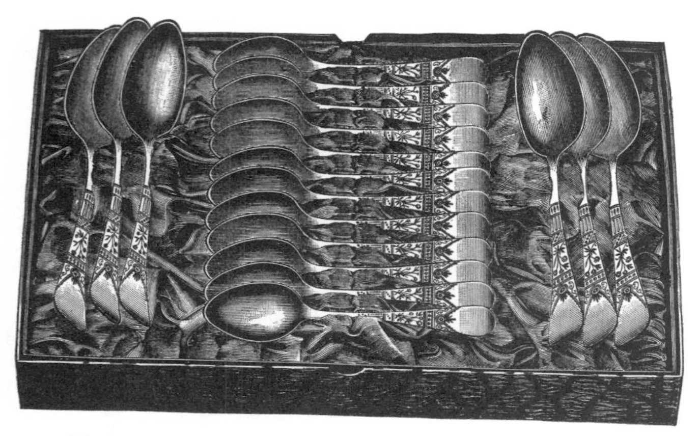

Twelve Lorne Tea Spoons and Six Lorne Table Spoons.
No. 41. Complete, . $11.50 (grayhound).

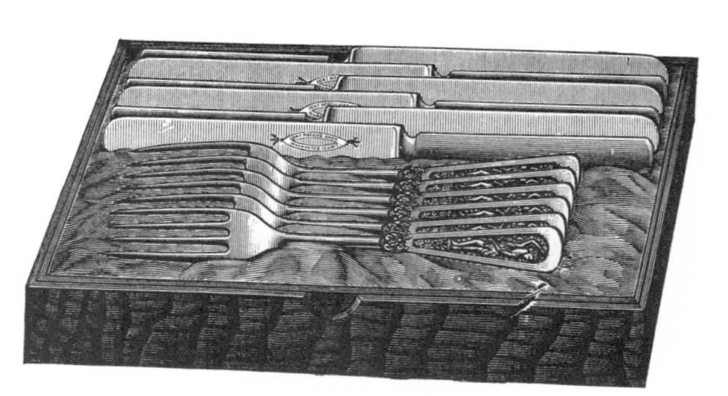

Six Arcadian Medium Forks and Six No. 12 Medium Knives.
No. 40. Complete, . $10.25 (greatness).

For complete Price-List see page 435.

BLACK CASES, SATIN LINED.

A VERY DESIRABLE CASE WHERE A CHEAPER ARTICLE THAN EITHER PLUSH OR MOROCCO IS DESIRED.

Lined with Fine Satin, and covered with Imitation of Morocco.

containing

1847.–Rogers Bros.–A 1 Goods.

In ordering, state the number of Case and Pattern desired. The number indicates the combination, but not the pattern.

In using Telegraph Code, state whether Plush or Morocco.

No. of Case.	Description of Goods in Case.	Price of Goods Complete in case.	Telegraphic Words.
	CASES CONTAINING ONE PIECE.		
20	Berry Spoon,	$3.00	(fertilize).
21	Pie Knife,	4.50	(festivity).
56	Crumb Knife,	5.40	(feudalism).
22	Cake Knife,	4.25	(fidelity).
54	Gravy Ladle,	2.25	(fierceness).
23	Oyster Ladle,	4.40	(figurative).
24	Medium Ladle,	5.25	(fighter).
25	Soup Ladle,	5.65	(filiation).
	CASES CONTAINING TWO PIECES.		
26	Sugar Shell and Twist Butter Knife,	2.37	(expire).
27	Fish Knife and Fork,	8.25	(explorer).
	CASE CONTAINING THREE PIECES.		
28	Child's Knife, Fork, and Spoon,	2.50	(explosion).
	CASES CONTAINING SIX PIECES.		
29	Tea Spoons,	3.12	(exponent).
30	Coffee Spoons,	3.12	(exposition).
31	Table Spoons,	5.85	(expositor).
51	Medium Forks,	5.85	(exposure).
34	A 1 Nut Picks,	3.00	(expression).
	CASE CONTAINING SEVEN PIECES.		
36	Six A 1 Nut Picks, one Nut Crack,	4 37	(extension).
	CASES CONTAINING TWELVE PIECES.		
37	Tea Spoons,	5.85	(extortion).
38	Coffee Spoons,	5.75	(extremely).
45	A 1 Nut Picks,	5.75	(exuberant).
	CASE CONTAINING EIGHTEEN PIECES.		
41	Twelve Tea Spoons, six Table Spoons,	11.50	(eyewater).

The following Prices are for Cases only.

goods at lowest market prices.

CASES TO CONTAIN:

No. of Case.	Pieces.		Price of Case only.	Telegraphic Words.
32	6	No. 12 Medium Knives,	$1.10	(facet).
33	6	No. 26 Solid Steel Plated Fruit Knives,	.75	(facility).
52	6	No. 32 Solid Steel Plated Fruit Knives,	.75	(factiously).
47	6	No. 44 Nut Picks,	.75	(faintly).
49	6	No. 12 Dessert Knives,	1.00	(faithful).
35	7	Six No. 44 Nut Picks, one Nut Crack,	1.00	(fallacy).
39	12	No. 12 Medium Knives,	1.75	(fallow).
48	12	No. 12 Dessert Knives,	1.60	(famously).
40	12	Six No. 12 Medium Knives, six Medium Forks,	1.75	(fanatical).
42	12	No. 26 Solid Steel Plated Fruit Knives,	1.10	(equitable).
53	12	No. 32 Solid Steel Plated Fruit Knives,	1.10	(equinox).
43	12	Six No. 44 Nut Picks, six No. 22 Solid Steel Fruit Knives,	1.10	(feeder).
46	12	No. 44 Nut Picks,	1.10	(febrile).
50	13	Six Nut Picks, six No. 26 Solid Steel Fruit Knives, one Nut Crack,	1.50	(fearless).
44	14	Twelve No. 44 Nut Picks, two No. 4 Nut Cracks,	1.50	(fearful).

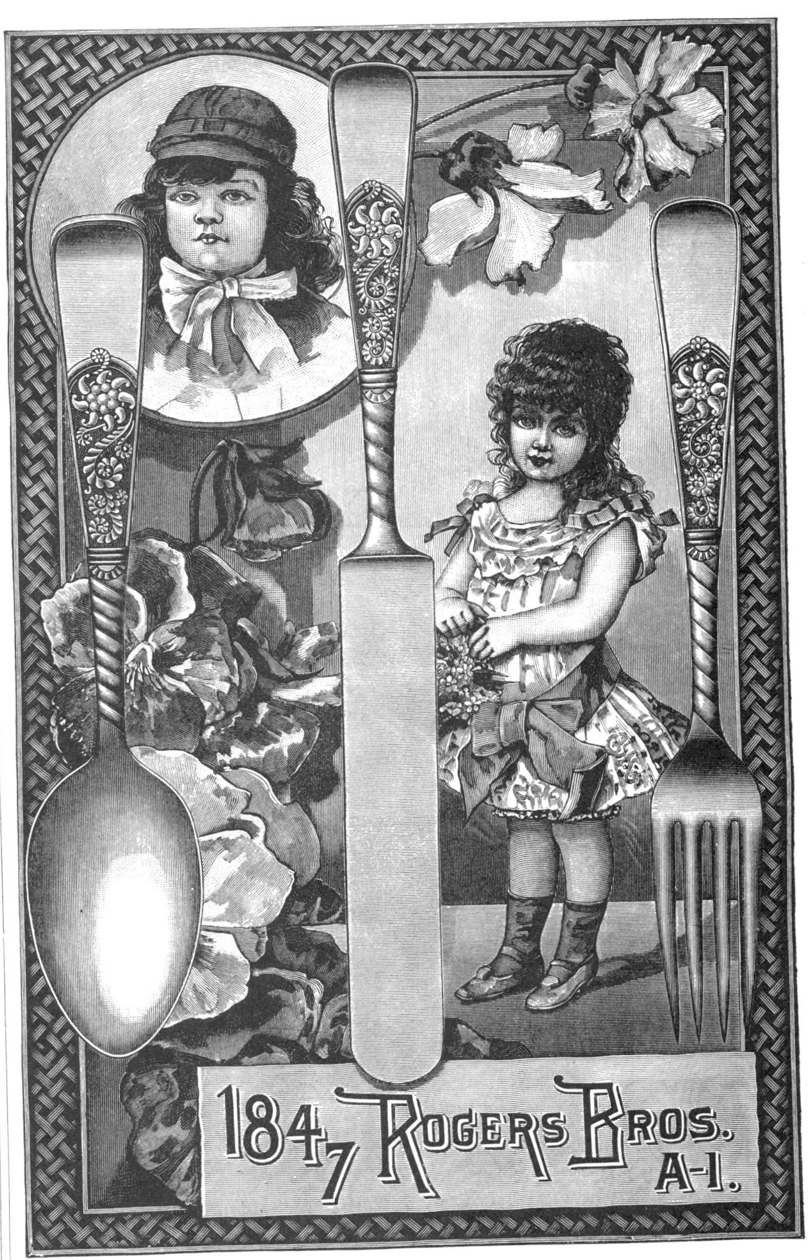

No. 192. Child's Set, on Card.

Assyrian Pattern,	$1.75	(wade).
Tipped Pattern, with Steel Plated Knife,	1.38	(wager).

This Card is handsomely lithographed in colors.

(Full size.)

No. 116. Child's Set, in Card Board Case.

Lined with Colored Down.

Lorne Pattern, complete, $1.75 each (expiation).

(One-third size.)

PRICE-LIST

OF

FINE SATIN LINED PLUSH AND MOROCCO CASES,

CONTAINING 1847.–ROGERS BROS.–A 1 GOODS.

THIS LIST DOES NOT CONTAIN ANY IMITATION CASES.

In ordering state the *number* of Case and *pattern* desired. The number indicates the combination, but not the pattern. When using Telegraph Code, state whether Plush or Morocco.

PRICES OF CASES AND WARE COMPLETE.

DISCOUNT SAME AS FLAT WARE.

CASES CONTAINING ONE PIECE.

No. of Plush Case.	No. of Morocco Case.	Description of Goods in Case.	Price of Case and Ware Complete.	Telegraphic Words.
920	92	Cake Knife, ...	$6.25	(TELLER).
930	93	Cream Ladle, ...	3.75	(TEMPER).
940	94	Fish Knife, ...	6.75	(TEMPLE).
950	95	Pie Knife, ...	6.50	(TENDER).
960	96	Crumb Knife, ...	7.75	(TENDON).
970	97	Medium Soup Ladle, ...	9.50	(TENDRIL).
980	98	Soup Ladle, ...	10.25	(TENEMENT).
990	99	Oyster Ladle, ...	8.25	(TENNIS).
1370	137	Gravy Ladle, ...	4.50	(TENOR).
1350	135	Berry Spoon, ...	5.00	(TENSE).
1390	139	Sugar Shell, ...	2 50	(TENSION).
2050	205	Ice Cream Knife (spoon-shaped blade), .	5.00	(TENTH).
2170	217	Sugar Tong, ...	4 25	(TENURE).
2330	233	Butter Knife, twist handle, . . .	2.75	(TEPID).
2410	241	Macaroni Spoon, ...	6.50	(TEPOR).
2420	242	Salad Spoon, ...	5 75	(TEPIDITY).
2430	243	Royal Cheese Scoop, ...	7.75	(TERMINATE).
2570	257	Arcadian Cheese Scoop H. H., . .	7.75	(NAIAD).

CASES CONTAINING TWO PIECES.

No. of Plush Case.	No. of Morocco Case.	Description of Goods in Case.	Price of Case and Ware Complete.	Telegraphic Words.
1380	138	Butter Knives, Twist Handles, . . .	$4.00	(TERM).
1590	159	Sugar Shell and Twist Butter Knife, .	3.75	(TERRACE).
1080	108	Pie and Cake Knife, ...	12.25	(TERRIER).
1090	109	Fish Knife and Fork, ...	12.25	(TERSE).
1130	113	Gravy and Cream Ladle, ...	6.25	(TEST).
1140	114	Child's Knife and Fork, ...	3.00	(TESTIFY).
1150	115	Child's Fork and Spoon, ...	2.75	(TETHER).
2130	213	Sugar Shell and Cream Ladle, . . .	4.75	(TEXTURE).
2180	218	Fish and Pie Knife, ...	12.25	(THANK).
2240	224	Child's Fork and Pearl Handle Knife, .	4.75	(THATCH).

CASES CONTAINING THREE PIECES.

No. of Plush Case.	No. of Morocco Case.	Description of Goods in Case.	Price of Case and Ware Complete.	Telegraphic Words.
1290	129	Two Nut Cracks, One Nut or Fruit Spoon,	$9.00	(THAW).
1510	151	Berry Spoon, Sugar Sifter and Cream Ladle,	9.25	(THEME).
1580	158	Sugar Shell, Pickle Fork, and Twist Butter Knife, ...	5.00	(THEN).
1160	116	Child's Knife, Fork and Spoon, . .	3.75	(THEORY).
1180	118	Twist Butter Knife, Sugar Shell and Cream Ladle, ...	5.75	(THERE).
1470	147	Cream Ladle, Sugar Shell, and Pair Sugar Tongs, ...	7.75	(THEREFORE).
2060	206	Child's Spoon, Fork, and Pearl Handle Knife, ...	5.50	(THEREIN).
2070	207	Child's Spoon, Fork, and Steel Plated Child's Knife, ...	3.50	(THESIS).
2280	228	One Mustard and two Salt Spoons, .	3.25	(THIMBLE).

CASES CONTAINING FOUR AND FIVE PIECES.

SCHOOL SETS.

No. of Plush Case.	No. of Morocco Case.	Description of Goods in Case.	Price of Case and Ware Complete.	Telegraphic Words.
1170	117	Knife, Fork, Spoon, and Napkin Ring,	$5.25	(THING).
1250	125	Tea and Dessert Spoons, Knife, Fork, and Napkin Ring, ...	6.75	(THIRST).
1810	181	Tea and Dessert Spoon, Dessert Knife, Fork, and Napkin Ring, ...	7.00	(THONG).
1070	107	Fish Knife, Pie Knife, Oyster, Soup and Gravy Ladles, ...	28.75	(THORAX).

CASES CONTAINING SIX PIECES.

No. of Plush Case.	No. of Morocco Case.	Description of Goods in Case.	Price of Case and Ware Complete.	Telegraphic Words.
910	91	Nut Picks, ...	$3.75	(THOROUGH).
1680	168	Dessert Forks, ...	8.00	(THREAT).
1660	166	Medium Forks, ...	8.75	(THRICE).
1640	164	Table Spoons, ...	8.75	(THRIFTY).
1800	180	Tea Spoons, ...	5.50	(THRONG).
1801	180½	Coffee Spoons, ...	5.25	(THROW).
1940	194	Dessert Spoons, ...	8.00	(THRUSH).
2530	253	Owl or Daisy Oyster Forks, ...	8.25	(NAIL).

CASES CONTAINING SEVEN PIECES.

No. of Plush Case.	No. of Morocco Case.	Description of Goods in Case.	Price of Case and Ware Complete.	Telegraphic Words.
1100	110	Six A 1 Nut Picks, one Nut Crack, .	7.00	(TIDAL).
1320	132	Six Nut Cracks, one Nut or Fruit Spoon,	13.00	(TIDE).

CASES CONTAINING EIGHT PIECES.

No. of Plush Case.	No. of Morocco Case.	Description of Goods in Case.	Price of Case and Ware Complete.	Telegraphic Words.
1710	171	Six A 1 Nut Picks, one Nut Crack, and Nut or Fruit Spoon, ...	$11.50	(TIER).
1600	160	Six Tea Spoons, Sugar Shell, and Twist Butter Knife, ...	8.75	(TIERCE).

CASES CONTAINING NINE AND ELEVEN PIECES.

No. of Plush Case.	No. of Morocco Case.	Description of Goods in Case.	Price of Case and Ware Complete.	Telegraphic Words.
1270	127	Two Nut Cracks, six Nut Picks, and Nut or Berry Spoon, ...	$12.50	(TIGER).
1610	161	Six Tea Spoons, Sugar Spoon, Mustard Spoon, Two Salt Spoons, and Twist Butter Knife, ...	11.00	(TILE).

CASES CONTAINING TWELVE PIECES.

No. of Plush Case.	No. of Morocco Case.	Description of Goods in Case.	Price of Case and Ware Complete.	Telegraphic Words.
1450	145	Coffee Spoons, lying flat (Case extra size),	$10 75	(TIME).
1650	165	Table Spoons, ...	15.50	(TINGE).
1630	163	Tea Spoons, ...	8.50	(TINKER).
1631	163½	Coffee Spoons, ...	8.00	(TINSEL).
1690	169	Dessert Forks, ...	13.25	(TIPPLE).
1670	167	Medium Forks, ...	14.50	(TIRADE).
2540	254	Oyster Forks, Owl or Daisy, . . .	14.25	(NATIONAL).
2630	263	Six Owl Oyster Forks, six Daisy Coffee Spoons, ...	12.25	(FINDER).
900	90	A 1 Nut Picks, ...	6.75	(TIRE).
1950	195	Dessert Spoons, ...	13.25	(TONTINE).
2150	215	Six Tea Spoons, six Table Spoons, .	13.00	(TOPAZ).
2210	221	Six Table Spoons, six Medium Forks, .	15.50	(TOPIC).

CASES CONTAINING THIRTEEN PIECES.

No. of Plush Case.	No. of Morocco Case.	Description of Goods in Case.	Price of Case and Ware Complete.	Telegraphic Words.
1110	111	Twelve A 1 Nut Picks and Nut Crack,	$9.75	(NADIR).
1330	133	Twelve Ice Cream Spoons and Ice Cream Knife, ...	15.25	(TORPID).
1340	134	Twelve Coffee Spoons, pair Small Sugar Tongs, ...	14.50	(TORRENT).
1500	150	Twelve Oyster Forks (two tines), pair Sardine Tongs, ...	14 00	(TORSA).
2140	214	Twelve Nut Picks, and Nut or Berry Spoon,	12.75	(TOUCH).
2290	229	Twelve Tea Spoons, pair Sugar Tongs,	13.00	(TOURNEY).

1847.-Rogers Bros.-A 1.

CASES CONTAINING FOURTEEN AND FIFTEEN PIECES.

No. of Plush Case.	No. of Morocco Case.	Description of Goods in Case.	Price of Case and Ware Complete.	Telegraphic Words.
1120	112	Twelve A 1 Nut Picks, two Nut Cracks,	$10.75	(TOWAGE).
1440	144	Twelve Coffee Spoons, Cream Spoon, and pair Sugar Tongs, . . .	16.25	(TOWARD).
2080	208	Twelve Tea Spoons, Sugar Shell, and Twist Butter Knife, . . .	14.25	(TOWEL).
1260	126	Twelve A 1 Nut Picks, two Nut Cracks, and Nut or Berry Spoon, . .	17.75	(TOWN).
1460	146	Twelve Coffee Spoons, Cream Spoon, Sugar Shell, pair small Sugar Tongs,	17.00	(TRACE).

CASES CONTAINING SEVENTEEN AND EIGHTEEN PIECES.

No. of Plush Case.	No. of Morocco Case.	Description of Goods in Case.	Price of Case and Ware Complete.	Telegraphic Words.
1860	186	Six Tea Spoons, three Table Spoons, six Medium Forks, one each Twist Butter Knife and Sugar Shell, .	$21.00	(TRAFFIC).
1010	101	Twelve Tea Spoons, six Table Spoons,	19.25	(TRAGIC).
1960	196	Twelve Medium Forks, six Table Spoons,	24.00	(TRAIL).

CASES CONTAINING TWENTY-FOUR PIECES.

No. of Plush Case.	No. of Morocco Case.	Description of Goods in Case.	Price of Case and Ware Complete.	Telegraphic Words.
1020	102	Twelve Tea Spoons, six Table Spoons, six Medium Forks, ...	$24.50.	(TRANQUIL).
1880	188	Twelve Table Spoons, twelve Tea Spoons,	25.50	(TRANSFUSE).
1850	185	Six each, Tea Spoons, Table Spoons, Dessert Spoons, Medium Forks, .	28.00	(TRANSIT).
2110	211	Twelve Dessert Forks, twelve Medium Forks, ...	30.75	(TRANSOM).

CASES CONTAINING THIRTY-SIX, THIRTY-SEVEN, AND THIRTY-NINE PIECES.

No. of Plush Case.	No. of Morocco Case.	Description of Goods in Case.	Price of Case and Ware Complete.	Telegraphic Words.
1030	103	Twelve Tea Spoons, six Table Spoons, six Dessert Spoons, twelve Medium Forks, ...	$38.25	(TRAVEL).
1040	104	Twelve Tea Spoons, six Table Spoons, six Dessert Spoons, twelve Medium Forks and Soup Ladle, . . .	47.00	(TRAVESTY).
1050	105	Twelve Tea Spoons, six Table Spoons, six Dessert Spoons, twelve Medium Forks, Soup Ladle, and two Twist Butter Knives, ...	49.50	(TRAY).

1847.-Rogers Bros.-XII.

CASE CONTAINING FORTY-ONE PIECES.

No. of Plush Case.	No. of Morocco Case.	Description of Goods in Case.	Price of Case and Ware Complete.	Telegraphic Words.
1060	106	Twelve Tea Spoons, six Table Spoons, six Dessert Spoons, twelve Medium Forks, Soup Ladle, two Butter Knives, and two Sugar Shells, .	$51.75	(TREACLE).

Extra Fine Hard Wood Polished Chest, with Drawer, containing forty-eight pieces.

No. of Case.	Description of Goods in Case.	Price. Complete.	Telegraphic Words.
184	Twelve Tea Spoons, six Table Spoons, six Dessert Spoons, twelve Medium Forks, twelve Dessert Forks, ...	$96.00	(TREATISE).

Extra Fine Hard Wood Polished Case, with Drawer, containing fifty-eight pieces.

No. of Case.	Description of Goods in Case.	Price. Complete.	Telegraphic Words.
258	Six each, Laurel Medium Knives, Laurel Dessert Knives, Table Spoons, Medium Forks, Dessert Forks, Dessert Spoons, Tea Spoons, Coffee Spoons; one each, Soup Ladle, Berry Spoon, Sugar Shell, Twist Butter Knife, Asparagus Tong, Salad Spoon, Salad Fork, and Laurel Carver, Fork and Steel, . .	$138.00	(NAME).

Fine Black Walnut Chest, with Drawer, containing one hundred and ten pieces.

No. of Case.	Description of Goods in Case.	Price. Complete.	Telegraphic Words.
259	Twelve each, Arcadian Medium Knives, Arcadian Dessert Knives, Table Spoons, Medium Forks, Dessert Forks, Dessert Spoons, Tea Spoons, Coffee Spoons; one each, Soup Ladle, Berry Spoon, Sugar Shell, Sugar Tong, Twist Butter Knife, Ice Tong, Salad Spoon, Salad Fork, Pie Knife, Fish Knive, Fish Fork, Arcadian Carver, Fork and Steel,	$220.00	(NAMELY).

THE FOLLOWING PRICES ARE FOR CASES ONLY.

Discount same as Flat Ware. Goods at Lowest Market Prices.

CASES TO CONTAIN THREE PIECES.

No. of Plush Case.	No. of Morocco Case.	Description of Goods in Case.	Price of Case only.	Telegraphic Words.
1520	152	Windsor Carver, Fork and Steel, . .	$5.75	(THEATRE).
2440	244	Laurel or Nevada Carver, Fork and Steel,	5.75	(THINE).

CASES TO CONTAIN FIVE PIECES.

No. of Plush Case.	No. of Morocco Case.	Description of Goods in Case.	Price of Case only.	Telegraphic Words.
2450	245	Laurel or Arcadian Carver, Fork, Steel, and Game Carver and Fork, .	$9.50	(THIRSTY).

CASES TO CONTAIN SIX PIECES.

No. of Plush Case.	No. of Morocco Case.	Description of Goods in Case.	Price of Case only.	Telegraphic Words.
2460	246	No. 44 Nut Picks, ...	$2.00	(THRALL).
1220	122	Medium Knives, No. 12, ...	4.25	(THOUGHT).
1210	121	Dessert Knives, No. 12, ...	3.25	(THREAD).
2120	212	Fruit Knives, No. 17, 22, or 25, Solid Steel, Plated, ...	2.25	(THYME).
2380	238	Fruit Knives, No. 26, Solid Steel Plated,	2.25	(TICKET)
2510	251	Fruit Knives, No. 32, Solid Steel Plated,	2.25	(NAPTHA).
2610	261	Fruit Knives, No. 32, Solid Steel Plated, lying flat (Case extra size), . .	3.75	(TENET).

CASES TO CONTAIN SEVEN PIECES.

No. of Plush Case.	No. of Morocco Case.	Description of Goods in Case.	Price of Case only.	Telegraphic Words.
2500	250	Six 44 Nut Picks, one Nut Crack, .	$3.75	(NARRATE).

CASES TO CONTAIN TWELVE PIECES.

No. of Plush Case.	No. of Morocco Case.	Description of Goods in Case.	Price of Case only.	Telegraphic Words.
2220	222	Six Dessert and six Medium Knives, No. 12,	$5.75	(TOPMOST).
1230	123	Medium Knives, No. 12, ...	5.75	(TILLER).
1200	120	Dessert Knives, No. 12, ...	4.00	(TIMBER).
1570	157	Six Dessert Knives No. 12, six Dessert Forks,	4.00	(TIMBRELL).
1540	154	Six Medium Knives, No. 12, six Medium Forks, ...	5.75	(TIMID).
2470	247	No. 44 Nut Picks, ...	2.75	(TOAD).
1930	193	Fruit Knives, No. 17, 22, 25 or 26, Solid Steel Plated, ...	3.75	(TOMATO).

CASES TO CONTAIN TWELVE PIECES.—*Continued.*

No. of Plush Case.	No. of Morocco Case.	Description of Goods in Case.	Price of Case only.	Telegraphic Words.
2520	252	Fruit Knives, No. 32, Solid Steel Plated,	4.00	(NARRATIVE).
1190	119	Table Knives, No. 12, ...	5.75	(TONSURE).
2340	234	Six 44 Nut Picks, six No. 22 Fruit Knives, Solid Steel Plated, . .	3.75	(TOPPLE).
2360	236	Six 44 Nut Picks, six No. 26 Fruit Knives, Solid Steel Plated, . .	3.75	(TORCH).
2620	262	Fruit Knives, No. 32, Solid Steel Plated, lying flat (Case extra size), . .	5.75	(NATIVITY).

CASE TO CONTAIN THIRTEEN PIECES.

No. of Plush Case.	No. of Morocco Case.	Description of Goods in Case.	Price of Case only.	Telegraphic Words.
2550	255	Six Fruit Knives, No. 26, six A 1 Nut Picks, one Nut Crack, . . .	$4.75	(NATURAL).

CASES TO CONTAIN TWENTY-FOUR AND TWENTY-SIX PIECES.

No. of Plush Case.	No. of Morocco Case.	Description of Goods in Case.	Price of Case only.	Telegraphic Words.
1700	170	Twelve Dessert Knives, No. 12, twelve Dessert Forks, ...	$9.00	(TRAMPLE).
1550	155	Twelve Medium Knives, No. 12, twelve Medium Forks, ...	9.75	(TRANCE).
2370	237	Twelve No. 44 Nut Picks, twelve No. 26 Fruit Knives, Solid Steel, . .	9.00	(TRANSFER).
2350	235	Twelve No. 44 Nut Picks, twelve No. 22 Fruit Knives, Solid Steel, . .	9.00	(TRANSFIX).
2100	210	Six Medium Knives, No. 12, twelve Tea Spoons, six Medium Forks, .	14.50	(TRANSMUTE).
2230	223	Six each Dessert and Medium Knives, No. 12, six each Dessert and Medium Forks, ...	12.25	(TRANSPIRE).
2600	260	Twelve A 1 Nut Picks, twelve No. 32 Fruit Knives, two Nut Cracks, .	9.00	(TRANSPORT.)

N. B.—Dealers are not entirely restricted to these combinations. We will make any arrangement of pieces desired. Cases made for special orders will cost more for the same number of pieces than those on list.

CARVING SETS.

(Full Size.)

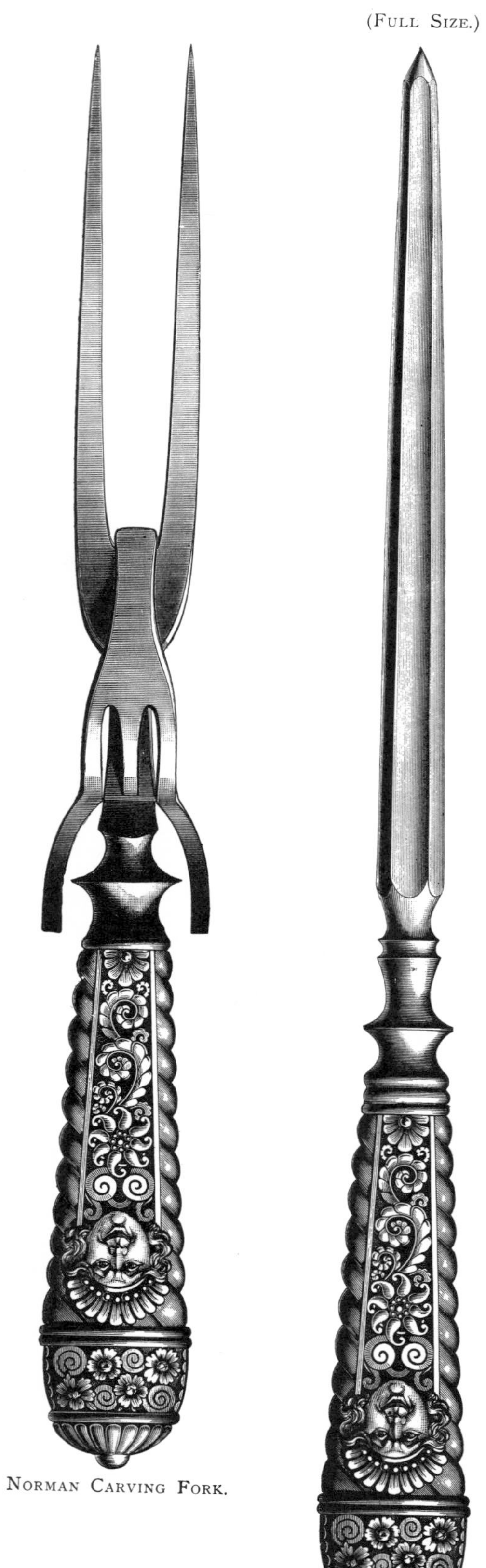

Norman Carving Fork.

Norman Steel.

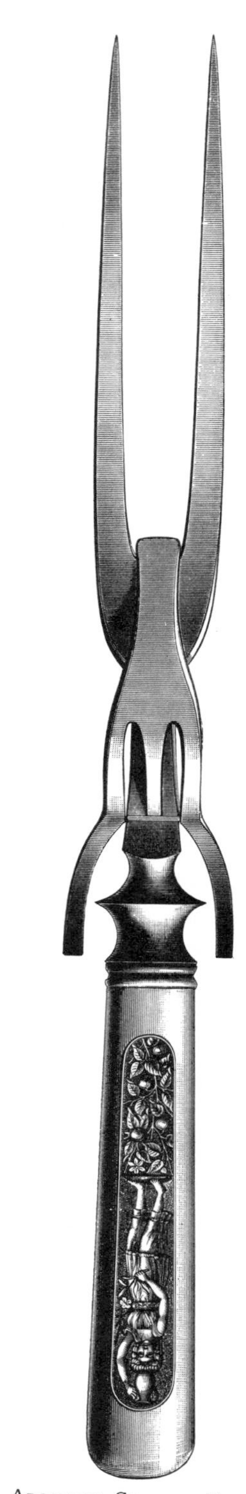

Arcadian Carving Fork.

Norman Carver.

Arcadian Carver.

CARVING SETS.

HOLLOW, NICKEL SILVER HANDLES, HARD SOLDERED, STEEL BLADES.

When desired, Carvers and Steels furnished with only the Handles Plated.

	Carver.	Fork.	Steel.	Set Complete.
Arcadian, .	$5.50 (formerly).	$4.75 (forthwith).	$4.75 (fossilize).	$15.00 (grandly).
Norman, .	8.00 (formulate).	6.00 (fortnight).	6.00 (fraternize).	20.00 (grandeur).

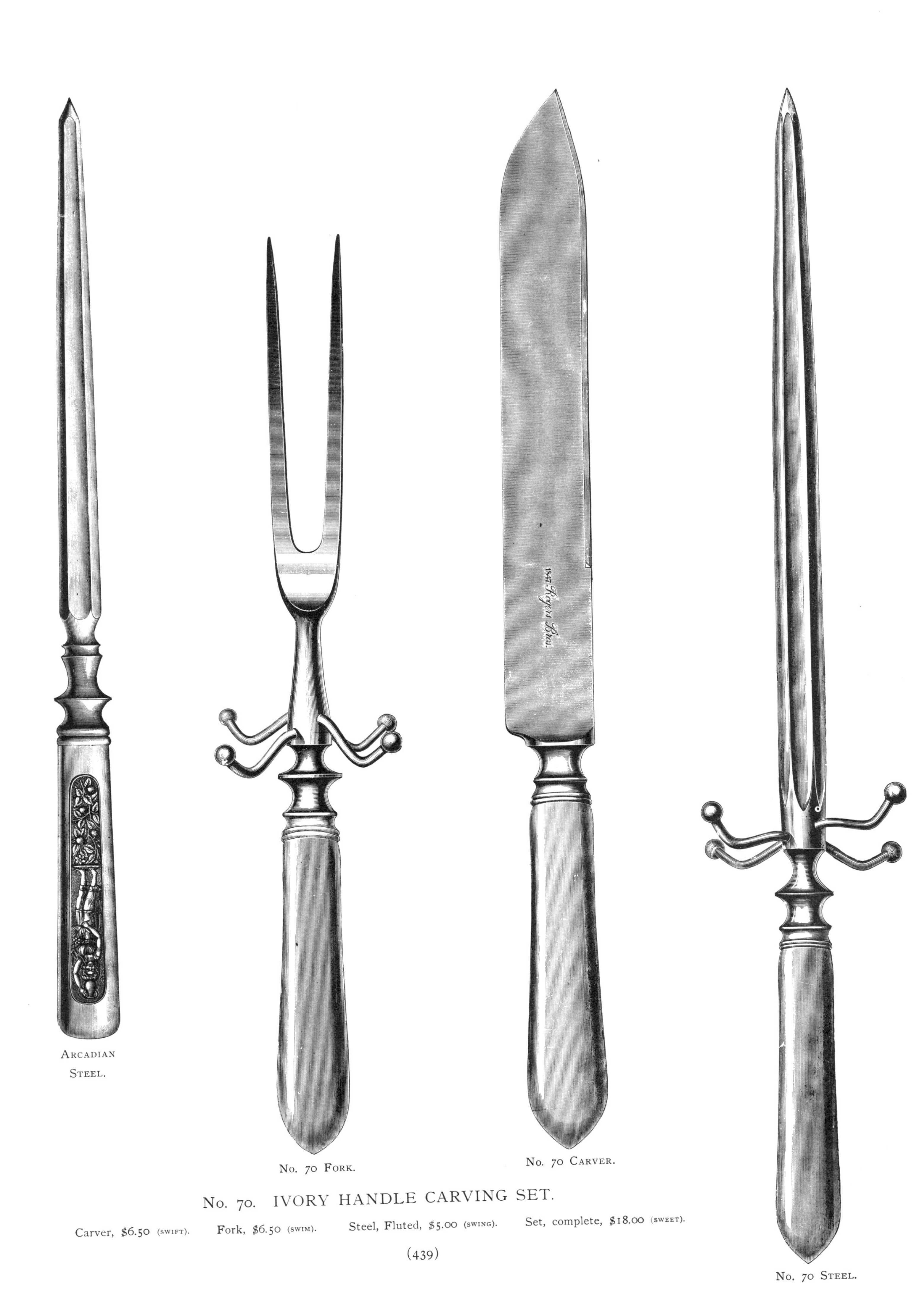

Arcadian Steel.

No. 70 Fork.

No. 70 Carver.

No. 70 Steel.

No. 70. IVORY HANDLE CARVING SET.

Carver, $6.50 (swift). Fork, $6.50 (swim). Steel, Fluted, $5.00 (swing). Set, complete, $18.00 (sweet).

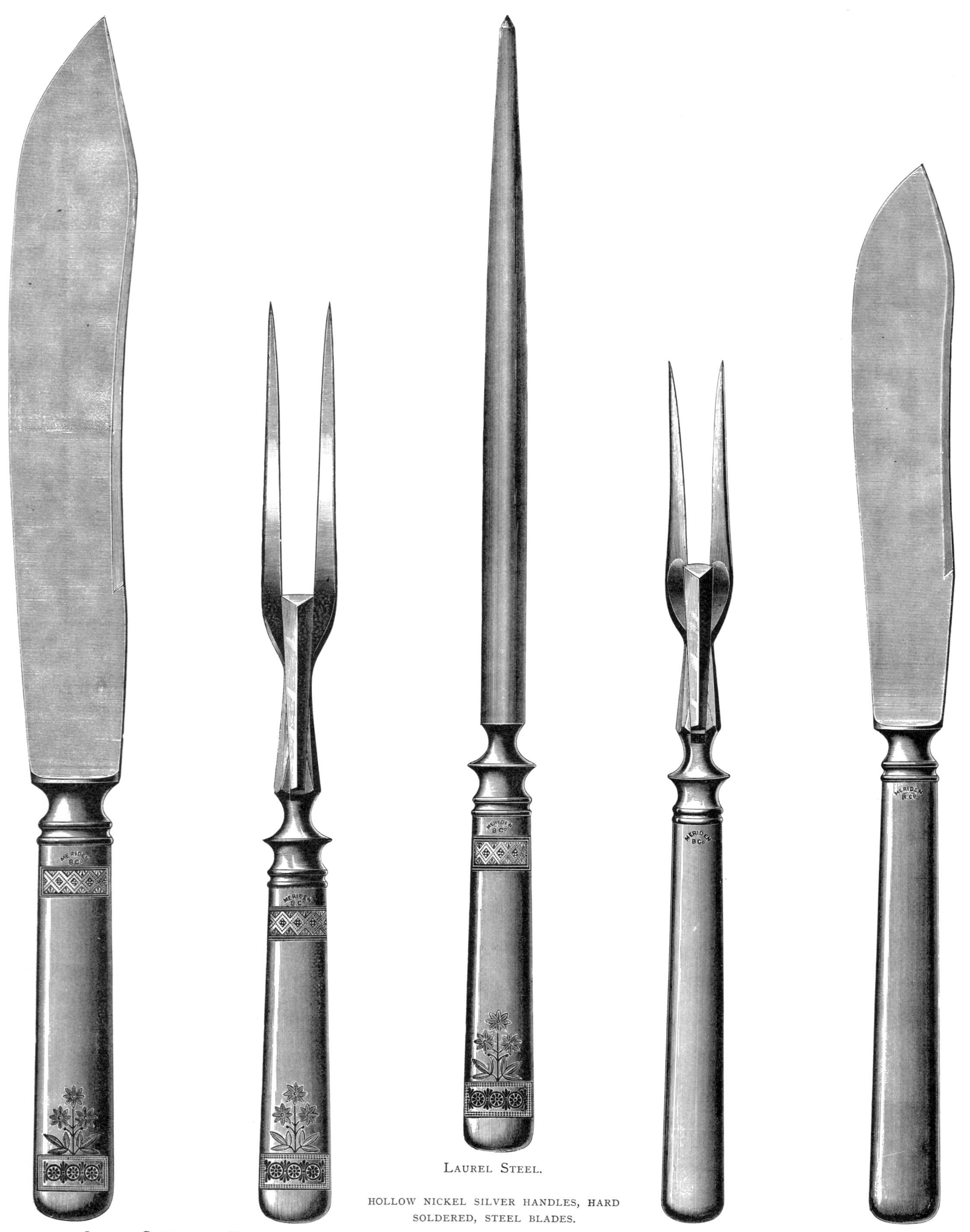

LAUREL CARVER AND FORK.

LAUREL STEEL.

HOLLOW NICKEL SILVER HANDLES, HARD SOLDERED, STEEL BLADES.

SWISS GAME CARVER AND FORK.

When desired, Carvers and Steels furnished with only the handles plated.

CARVING SETS.

	Carver.	Fork.	Steel.	Set Complete.
Swiss,	$5.00 (SUTLER).	$4.25 (SWAB).	$4.25 (SWAG).	$13.50 (SWAIN).
Laurel,	5.50 (SWALLOW).	4.75 (SWAMP).	4.75 (SWAN).	15.00 (SWARD).

GAME SETS.

	Carver.	Fork.	Steel.	Set Complete.
Swiss,	$4.75 (FRAGILITY).	$4.00 (IGNITION).	$4.25 (FOXHUNT).	$13.00 (ILLUMINE).
Laurel,	5.25 (FORDABLE).	4.50 (ILLOGICAL).	4.75 (FOXCHASE).	14.50 (ILLUSTRATE).

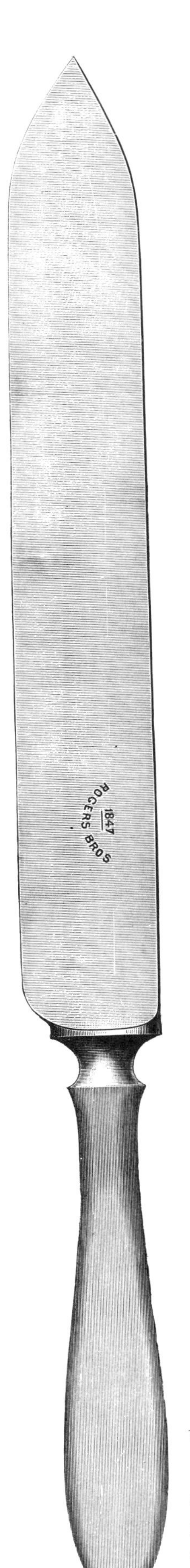

Windsor Carver.

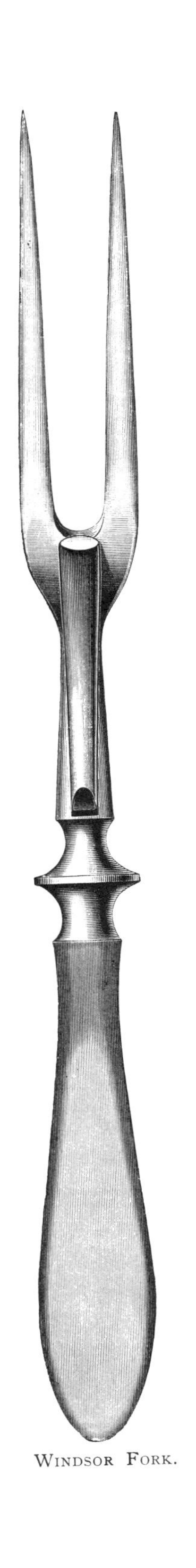

Windsor Fork.

No. 47
Arabesque Steel.

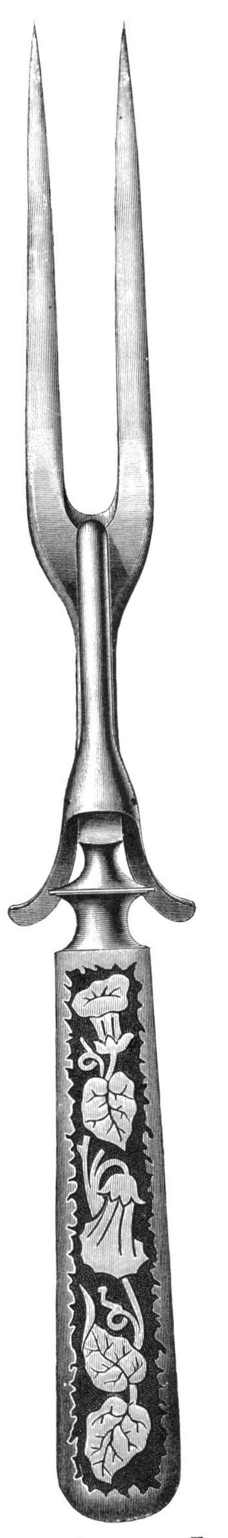

No. 47 Arabesque Fork.

No. 47 Arabesque Carver.

WINDSOR CARVING SET.

Solid Steel, Plated.

Carver,	$4.00	(swath).
Fork,	4.00	(sway).
Steel,	2.00	(sweeping).
Set Complete,	10.00	(sweep).

No. 47 CARVING SET.

Hollow Handle. Steel, Plated.

	Plain or Satin.		Arabesque Old Silver.	
Carver,	$4.50	(forensic).	$5.00	(formation).
Fork,	3.75	(foreland).	4.25	(formality).
Steel,	3.75	(foreigner).	4.25	(formalist).
Set Complete,	12.00	(foreclose).	13.50	(forgiving).

When desired, Carvers and Steels furnished with only the handles plated.

KNIVES.

(FULL SIZE.)

No. 65 MEDIUM. Celluloid Handle.

No. 476 MEDIUM. Ivory Handle.

No. 70 TABLE. Ivory Handle.

No. 669 MEDIUM. Pearl Handle.

DUNDEE FISH KNIFE AND FORK. Hollow Nickel Silver Handles, Hard Soldered.

	DESSERT.	MEDIUM.	TABLE.
No. 65, Celluloid, per dozen,	$11.00 (FURIOUSLY).	$12.50 (FROWARD).	
No. 476, Ivory, "	21.00 (FUMIGATION)	24.00 (FRUITFUL).	$24.00 (FRUSTRATE).
No. 70, Ivory, "	25.50 (FUGLEMAN).	28.50 (FORMER).	28.50 (FREEMASON).
No. 669, Pearl, "	(3 inch,) 39.50 (FROSTY).	(3½ inch,) 46.00 (FRUITY).	
Plush Cases, for one dozen, each,	3.50 (FUGACIOUS).	4.75 (FRECKLE).	

Fish Forks, per dozen, $16.00 (FLAXSEED).
Fish Knives, " 16.00 (FLAPJACK).

HOLLOW HANDLE KNIVES.

NICKEL SILVER HANDLES. PLATED STEEL BLADES.

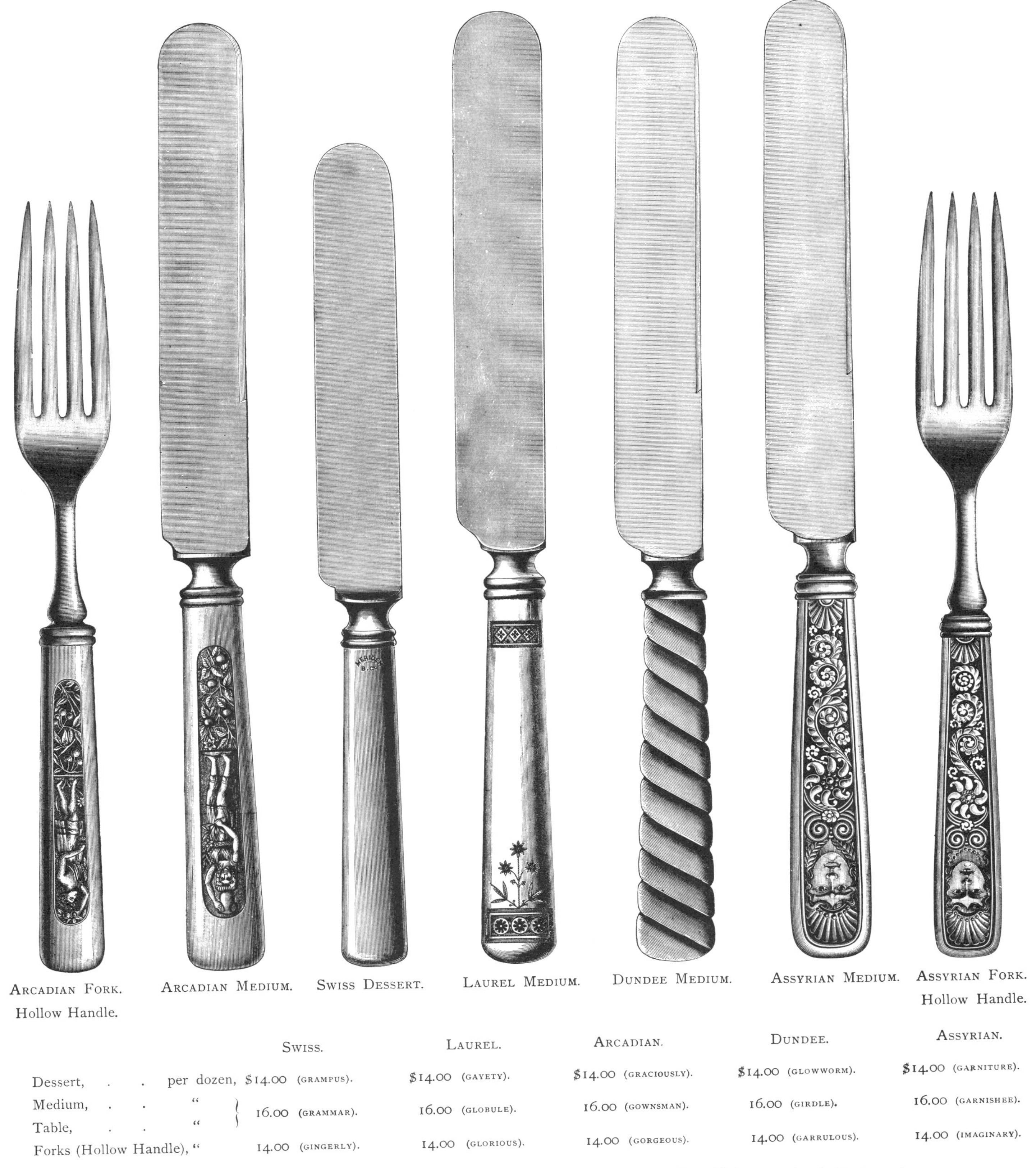

ARCADIAN FORK. Hollow Handle. ARCADIAN MEDIUM. SWISS DESSERT. LAUREL MEDIUM. DUNDEE MEDIUM. ASSYRIAN MEDIUM. ASSYRIAN FORK. Hollow Handle.

	Swiss.	Laurel.	Arcadian.	Dundee.	Assyrian.
Dessert, . . per dozen,	$14.00 (GRAMPUS).	$14.00 (GAYETY).	$14.00 (GRACIOUSLY).	$14.00 (GLOWWORM).	$14.00 (GARNITURE).
Medium, . . " }	16.00 (GRAMMAR).	16.00 (GLOBULE).	16.00 (GOWNSMAN).	16.00 (GIRDLE).	16.00 (GARNISHEE).
Table, . . " }					
Forks (Hollow Handle), "	14.00 (GINGERLY).	14.00 (GLORIOUS).	14.00 (GORGEOUS).	14.00 (GARRULOUS).	14.00 (IMAGINARY).

PLUSH CASES, holding one dozen. Dessert Knives, each, $3.50 (IMAGINE). Medium Knives, each, $4.75 (IMBRUE).

These Knives have Nickel Silver Hard Soldered Handles, Blades of finest tempered Steel, invariably the highest grade of Plate, and are light, durable, and superior to any Knife in the market. We have sold them for more than twenty years, and they have never failed to give entire satisfaction. We would recommend them as being the most economical Knife for general use.

HOLLOW HANDLE STEEL PLATED KNIVES.

No. 47 Satin Fork.
Hollow Handle.

No. 47 Dessert.

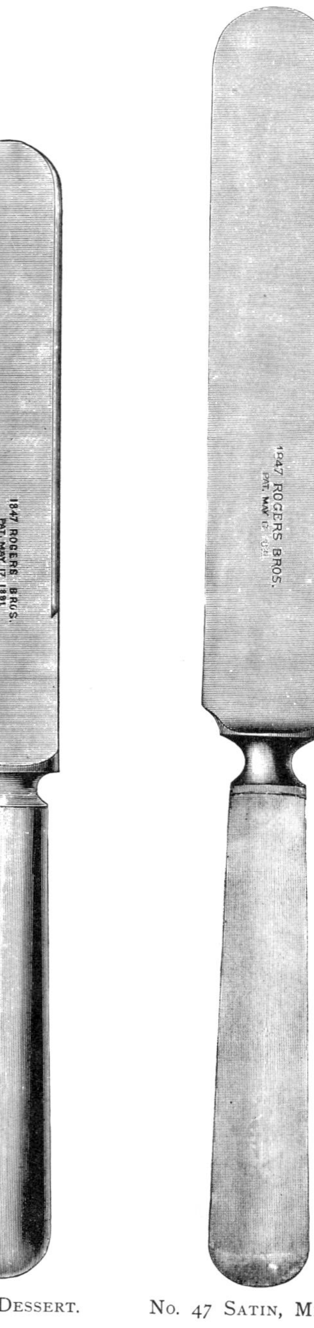

No. 47 Satin, Medium.

No. 47 Assyrian.
Old Silver.

No. 47 Arabesque.
Old Silver.

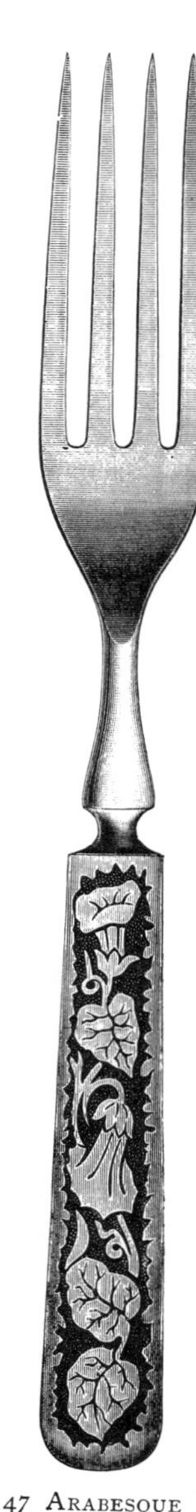

No. 47 Arabesque Fork.
Old Silver.
Hollow Handle.

PRICES PER DOZEN.

		Plain.	Satin.	No. 47 Assyrian.	Assyrian. Old Silver.	Arabesque.	Arabesque. Old Silver.
Dessert,	per dozen,	$8.50 (furlough).	$8.50 (frisket).	$9.00 (frivolous).	$9.50 (fusileer).	$9.00 (futtock).	$9.50 (gardener).
Medium,	"	} 9.00 (frequency).	9.00 (frigidly).	9.50 (furnish).	10.00 (fusilade).	9.50 (gairish).	10.00 (galloway).
Table,	"						
Forks,	"	9.00 (friendly).	9.00 (frighten).	9.50 (furniture).	10.00 (furthest).	9.50 (galley).	10.00 (gallipot).

Attention is invited to our new Hollow Handle Steel Knife, which for lightness, fine finish, and price, has no equal.

The No. 47 Knife illustrated on this page was patented in 1881, five years being taken to perfect it; making the most desirable steel plated Knife ever produced, and one specially adapted for Hotels, Steamers, Clubs, etc. When desired, this Knife is finished with a sharp blade, the handles only being plated.

No. 47 Forks and Carving Sets made under same patent as Knives. For Carving Sets see page 441.

PLATED SOLID STEEL KNIVES.

No. 12 Windsor Dessert. No. 12 Medium. No. 12 Lorne Medium. No. 12 Newport Medium. No. 12 Arabesque Medium. No. 12 Arabesque Medium Fork.

	Windsor, or No. 12 Square.		Lorne.	Newport.	Arabesque, Bright Silver.	Arabesque, Old Silver.
Dessert, per dozen, . .	$5.50 (forceps).	$5.50 (forbid).	$6.00 (forbear).	$6.00 (forager).	$6.00 (foot-face).	$6.50 (footstep).
Medium, " . .	6.00 (foot-hold).	6.00 (foot-ball).	6.50 (fly-wheel).	6.50 (fly-leaf).	6.50 (fluster).	7.00 (fluctuate).
Table, " . .	6.00 (flood-gate).	6.00 (floatage).				
Medium Fork, " . .	6.00 (flirtation).	6.00 (flippancy).			6.50 (fleetness).	7.00 (fledgling).

These Knives are made from a fine quality of steel, are heavily plated, and of excellent finish. They are carefully selected before and after plating, thereby giving the consumer a superior article in every respect, unlike many imitations, which are inferior blanks poorly plated, and look well only when new.

The high standard of this knife will always be maintained, and purchasers are cautioned to examine the trade-mark carefully and avoid the many imitations which are constantly being put on the market.

To meet the wants of all, we have cheaper grades of knives, not bearing our trade-mark, which we guarantee to be fully equal to similar goods made by other manufacturers, and at as low prices.

NUT CRACKS AND GRAPE SHEARS.

(FULL SIZE.)

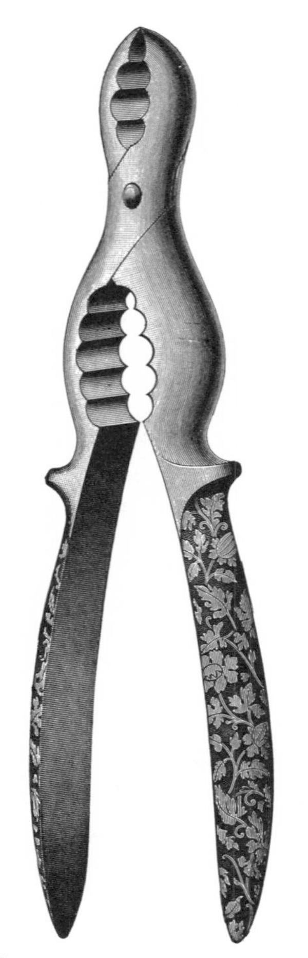

No. 4. NUT CRACK. Steel, Plated.
Per dozen, . . $13.50 (HERMETIC).
Arabesque, Old Silver, 15.00 (HERMITAGE).

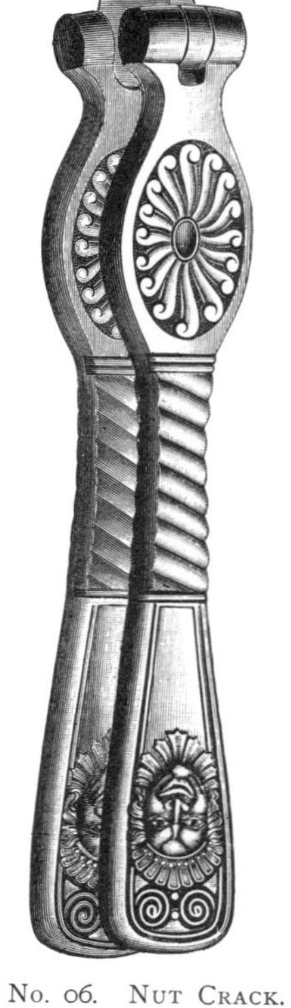

No. 06. NUT CRACK.
Nickel Silver.
Per dozen.
Silver, . $24.00 (HOSTLER).
Old Silver, 26.00 (HURTLE).

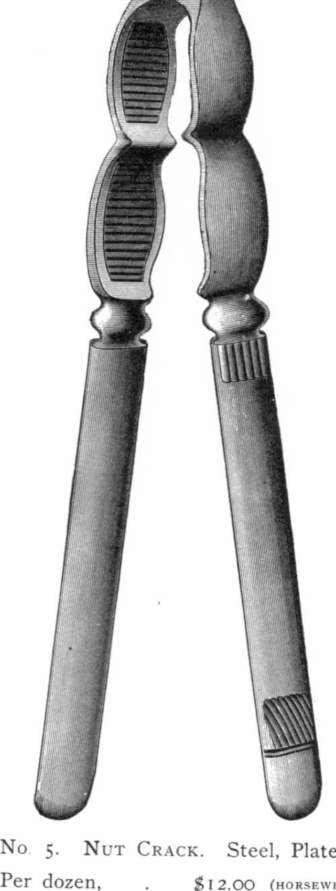

No. 5. NUT CRACK. Steel, Plated.
Per dozen, . $12.00 (HORSEWHIP).

No. 2. NUT CRACK. Steel, Plated.
Per dozen, . . $12.00 (SUBJECT).
Arabesque, Old Silver, 13.50 (HILARIOUS).

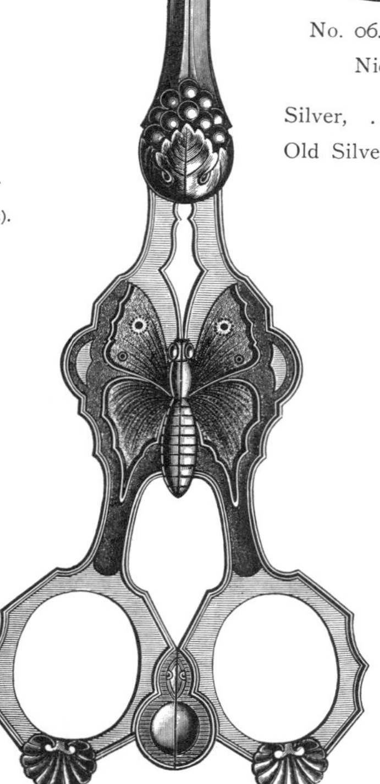

No. 01. GRAPE OR FLOWER SHEARS.
Nickel, . . per pair, $4.50 (SUBVERT).
Silver, . . " 5.50 (SUCCESS).
Silver, Gold Inlaid, " 6.00 (SUCCOR).

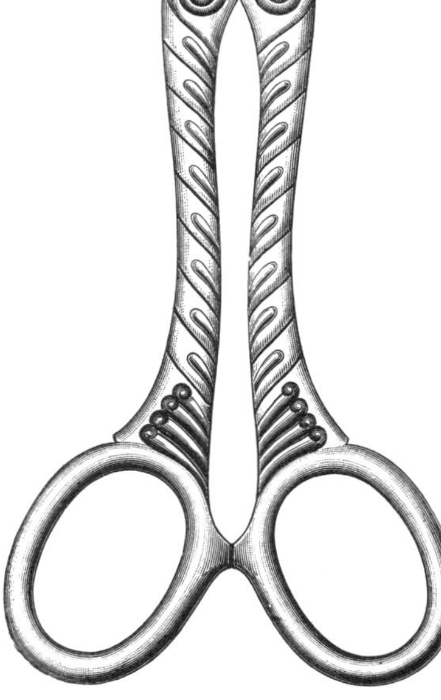

No. 03. GRAPE OR FLOWER SHEARS.
With Steel Cutting Blade.
Silver, . per pair, $5.00 (HOUSEHOLD).

Plated on Nickel Silver.

PLUSH CASES for Grape Shears, . $2.25 extra (SUDDEN).

No. 7. NUT CRACK Steel, Plated.
Per dozen, . $15.00 (LIONESS).

POCKET FRUIT KNIVES.

(Full Size.) (Prices per Dozen.)

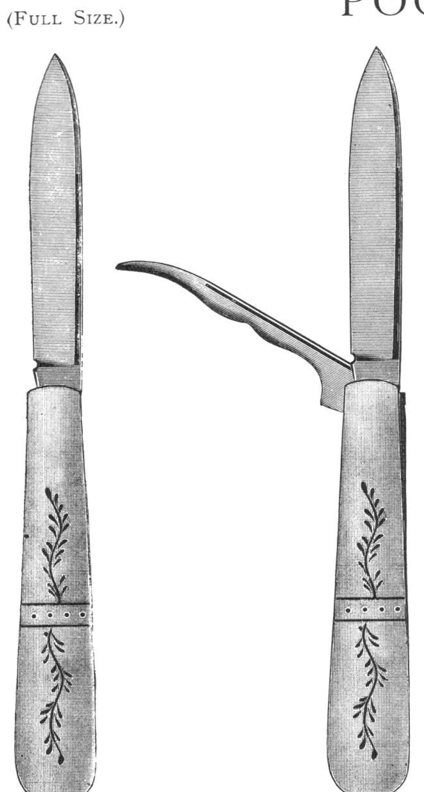

No. 34, without Nut Pick.
Satin, . . $7.50 (gunboat).
Satin, Engraved, 9.00 (gypsum).

No. 35, with Nut Pick.
Satin, . . $9.00 (headlong).
Satin, Engraved, 10.50 (headwind).

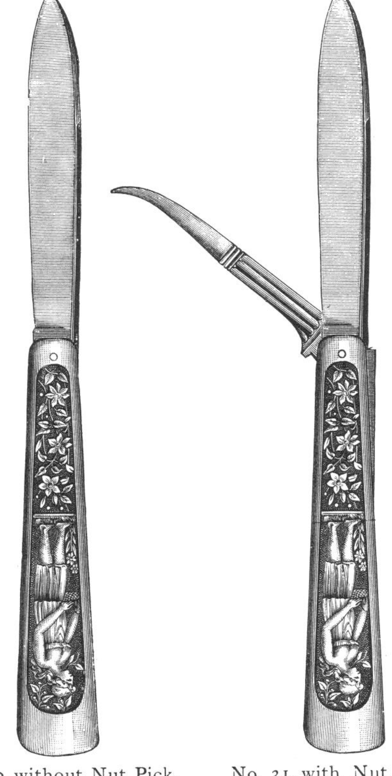

No. 30, without Nut Pick.
$13.50 (harmless).

No. 31, with Nut Pick.
$16.25 (harebell).

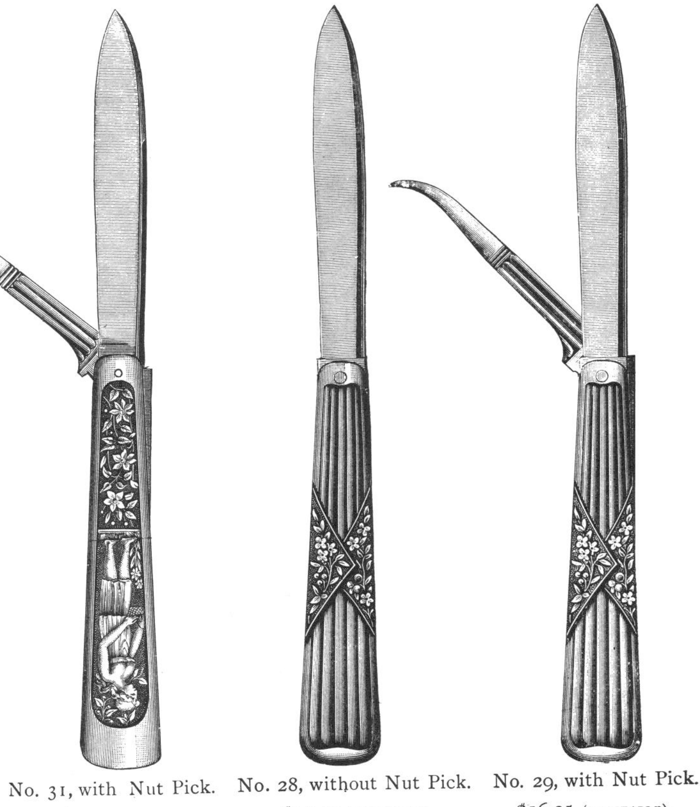

No. 28, without Nut Pick.
$13.50 (hardship).

No. 29, with Nut Pick.
$16.25 (habitable).

SOLID STEEL PLATED FRUIT KNIVES.

(Full Size). (Prices per Dozen.)

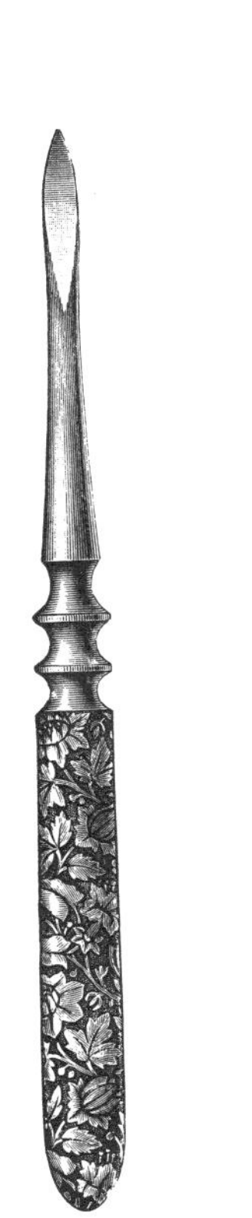

No. 44. Nut Pick.
Plain, . $4.00 (hither).
Arabesque, 4.50 (hoarsely).
Old Silver, 5.00 (gunsmith).

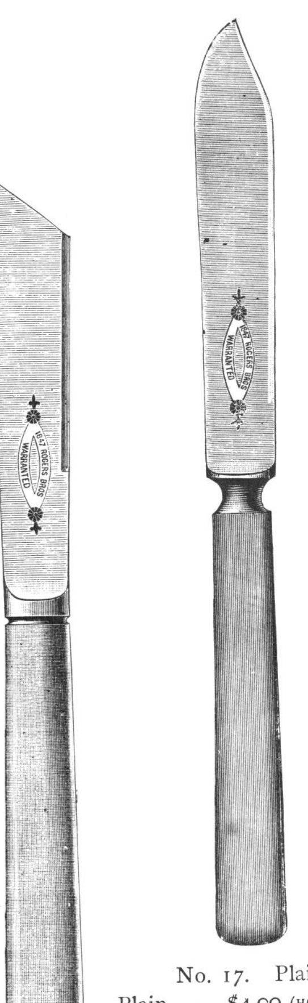

No. 25. Satin.
Satin, $4.00 (horseback).
Plain, 4.00 (guileless).

No. 17. Plain.
Plain, . $4.00 (hornbill).
Arabesque, 4.50 (holdback).
Old Silver, 5.00 (guidance).

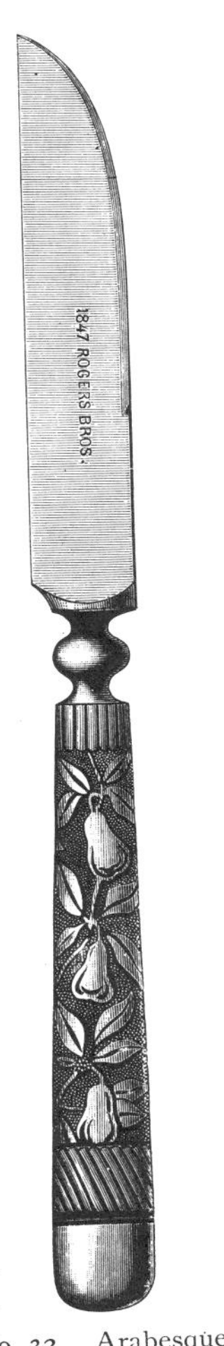

No. 32. Arabesque.
Arabesque, $6.00 (helpmate).
Old Silver, 6.50 (guerilla).

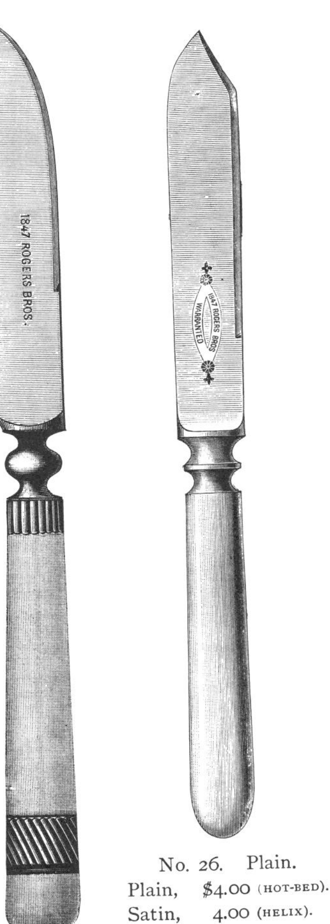

No. 32. Satin.
Plain, $5.50 (herewith).
Satin, 5.50 (heartily).

No. 26. Plain.
Plain, $4.00 (hot-bed).
Satin, 4.00 (helix).

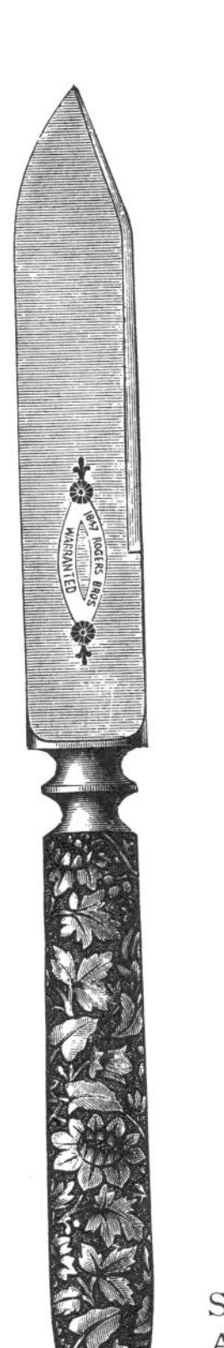

No 26. Arabesque.
Arabesque, $4.50 (historian).
Old Silver, 5.00 (hollyhock).

No. 32. Nut Pick.
Satin, $5.50 (hubbub).
Arabesque, 6.00 (horologe).
Old Silver, 6.50 (horseman).

VASES, ETC. (ADDITIONAL).

(HALF SIZE.)

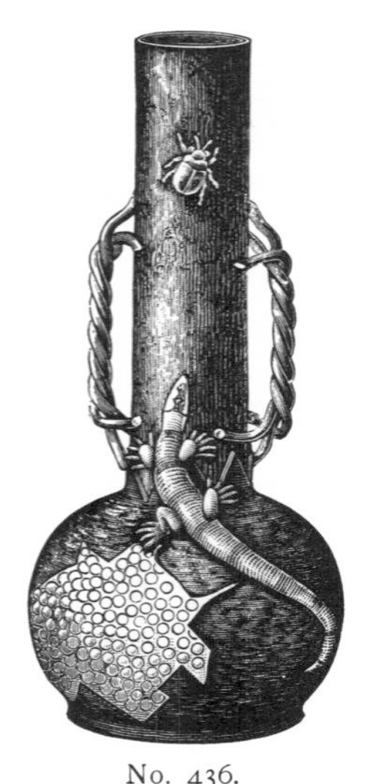

No. 436.

Chased, Old Silver, . . . $8.00 (LOADSTONE).
Chased, Old Silver, Gold Inlaid, 10.00 (LONGEVITY).

No. 437.

Chased, Old Silver, . . . $10.50 (LOVE-KNOT).
Chased, Old Silver, Gold Inlaid, . 12.50 (LOQUACITY).

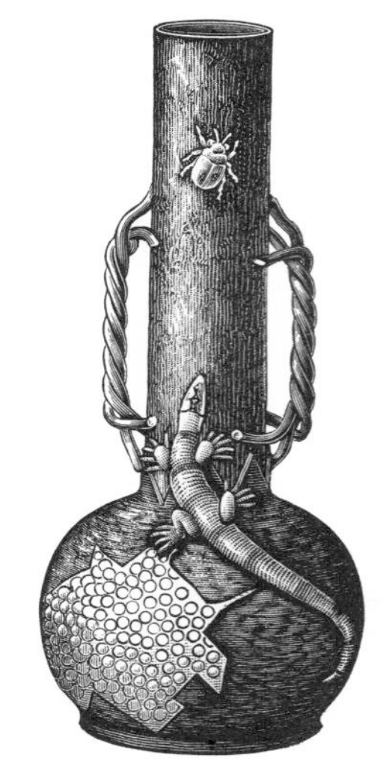

No 436.

Chased, Old Silver, . . . $8.00 (LOWLAND).
Chased, Old Silver, Gold Inlaid, 10.00 (LOUNGER).

No. 16. LETTER SEAL.

Old Silver, . . $2.50 (LOADSTAR).
X Gold Inlaid, . . 3.25 (LOCALITY).

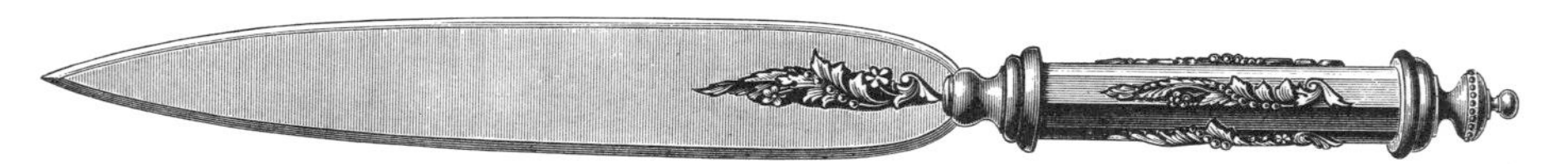

No. 16. PAPER KNIFE.

Old Silver, . . . $4.50 (LOOPHOLE).
X Gold Inlaid, . . 6.00 (LOG-ROLL).

(Half Size.)

No. 21. CHASED SMOKING SET.

	Old Silver.	Gold Inlaid.
Set, complete, ...	$33.50 (LOAD).	$43.50 (LIVERY).
Match Holder, Gold Lined, .	3.00 (SUTTER).	4.00 (SURGERY).
Cigarette Holder, " " . .	4.00 (SUPPOSE).	5.25 (SUPPLANT).
Cigar Holder, " " . .	5.00 (SUNKEN).	6.75 (LOBELIA).
Ash Holder, " " . .	4.00 (LOUDLY).	5.00 (LOCKUP).
Lamp, ...	4.00 (LOTTERY).	5.00 (LOFTILY).
Stand, ...	13.50 (LOCATE).	17.50 (LOGICAL).

(One-Third Size.)

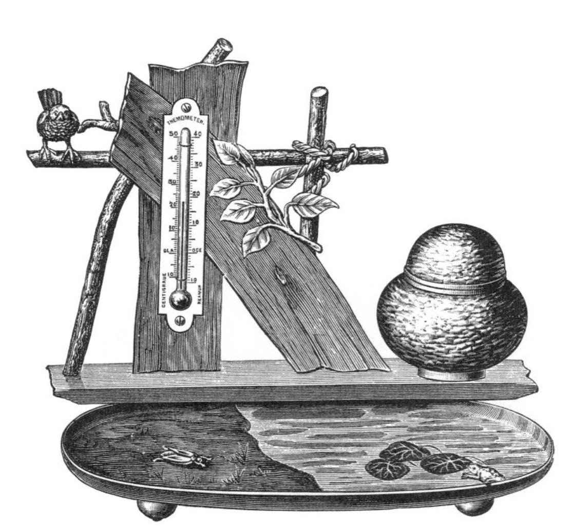

No. 52. INK STAND.

Old Silver, ... $18.00 (SUPERIORITY).
Old Silver, Gold Inlaid, . . 22.50 (SUPERFICIAL).

(One-Third Size.)

TRADE MARK.
WHITE METAL.

CUPS, ETC. (ADDITIONAL).

TRADE MARK.
NICKEL SILVER.

(HALF SIZE.)

No. 174. Etched.

Silver Lined, $3.00 (SUFFLATE).
Gold Lined, . 3.50 (SURPLICE).
Gold Inlaid and
Gold Lined, 4.25 (SUNBURN).

No. 172. Etched.

Silver Lined, $3.50 (SWIMMER).
Gold Lined, . 4.00 (SUSPIRE).
Gold Inlaid and
Gold Lined, 4.75 (SYNCOPE).

No. 173. Etched.

Silver Lined, $3.00 (SWASH).
Gold Lined, . 3.50 (SWALE).
Gold Inlaid and
Gold Lined, 4.25 (SWINGE).

No. 124. Etched.

Silver Lined, $3.00 (SUGAR-CANE).
Gold Lined, . 3.50 (SWORDSMAN).
Gold Inlaid and
Gold Lined, 4.25 (SUFFERING).

No. 100. SOAP BOX.

Etched, Old Silver, . $2.75 (SYNODIC).

No. 10. FLASK.

Etched, Old Silver, . $7.50 (SYMBOLISM).

No. 1. FLASK.

Etched, Old Silver, . $3.50 (SYNOD).

No. 110. BEER MUG.

Porcelain, with Plated Cover, $10.50 (SYLLOGISM).

No. 120. BEER MUG.

Satin, Engraved, ... $22.50 (SYMBOLOGY).
Satin, Engraved, XX Gold Inlaid, 30.00 (SURRENDER).

No. 35. COMBINATION SAFETY MATCH HOLDER AND CIGAR CUTTER.

Old Silver, . $7.50 (SURPRISING).

GOLD AND SILVER PLATE.

No. 25. Ice Hammer and Pick.
Old Silver, . . . $5.00 (luminary).

No. 14. Crumb Tray.
Old Silver, . . $10.50 (lucidness).

No. 2. Crumb Brush.
Old Silver, . . $7.00 (lukewarm).

THE BEST PREPARATIONS FOR CLEANING SILVER.

No. 1 Silver Plate Powder,
FOR CLEANING
Silver and Gold Plate.
Directions.—Use a fine, soft chamois; keep carefully away from dust, and never allow it to be used on anything but the silver. Spread powder on the softest side of the chamois, rub it in well, and it is ready for use; dip the article to be cleaned in hot water, then moisten a small piece of the chamois in alcohol and apply a small portion of the powder, afterwards polishing with a dry chamois. Any particles of the powder that adhere to the chasing or ornaments may be removed with a soft brush, or by washing with castile soap, and rinsing with clean hot water.
Meriden Britannia Co., Meriden, Conn.

Per dozen, $1.50 (wafer).

This Powder is prepared by us, is especially adapted for cleaning and restoring the original luster to Gold and Silver Plate, and all bright metallic surfaces

Neatly put up in packages of one dozen boxes, with full directions for use.

Receipt for Cleaning Tarnished Plated Ware.

Dissolve one-half pound Cyanide of Potassium, one-half pound Salts Tartar in one gallon soft water.

Directions.—Dip the articles in the solution for a few seconds only, and wash with clean hot water. Wipe dry with a soft towel or chamois skin.

CAUTION.—This solution is a deadly poison when taken into the stomach.

M. NIVER'S
POLISHING FLUID.

Per dozen, $6.00 (walnut).

For Cleansing and Polishing Gold, Silver, Plated Ware, and all fine Metallic Surfaces, Mirrors and Plate Glass.

The genuine Polishing Fluid is neatly put up for the trade in bottles containing five fluid ounces, with full directions for use. To avoid counterfeits, see that the words "M. NIVER, Niverville, Columbia County, N. Y.," are blown in the glass of the bottle, and that his signature is upon each label.

Warranted chemically pure, and free from Mercury, Acid, Alkali, Ammonia, Cyanide of Potassium, Grit, or any injurious or poisonous substance, and not to injure or mar the finest surface, hands, or clothing.

MERIDEN BRITANNIA CO.,
Agents.

THOMPSON'S
SILVER POLISHING FLUID.

For cleaning Gold and Silver Plate, Mirrors, and Plate Glass.

Six Fluid Ounces.

Price, per dozen, $3.00 (lustrum).

Warranted to contain neither Ammonia, Acid, Alkali, or anything injurious to metal, hands, or clothing.

Directions.

Shake well before using; moisten a sponge or piece of soft flannel, rub the article to be cleaned briskly, rinse in hot water, and wipe dry with a soft towel or chamois.

Made expressly for the

MERIDEN BRITANNIA CO.

Meriden Britannia Co's
Silver Paste.
A genuine article for cleaning and restoring the original luster to
Gold, Silver
And all Burnished Metals, Mirrors, & Plate Glass.
Price, 25 Cents.
Meriden Britannia Co., Meriden, Conn.

Price, per dozen, $3.00 (warrior).

We consider this preparation equal to anything in the market.

WARRANTED PURE

and free from all poisonous substances, containing neither acid nor alkali.

MERIDEN BRITANNIA CO.,

Sole Manufacturers.

THE FOLLOWING CHANGES HAVE BEEN MADE

IN THE

PRICES OF CALL BELLS

SINCE PRINTING OF CATALOGUE.

	CORRECT PRICES.
No. 086, ...	$10.50 per dozen.
No. 090, Plated, . .	15.00 "
No. 094, ...	15.00 "
No. 1900, Black Base, .	18.00 "
No. 2200, White " .	18.00 "
No. 2250, " " .	20.00 "
No. 6400, Black " .	17.00 "
No. 6450, " " .	17.00 "
No. 6900, Bronze, " .	16.00 "
No. 7100, . . .	13.00 "
No. 7175, . . .	13.00 "
No. 8000, . . .	12.00 "
No. 8050, . . .	12.00 "
No. 8100, . . .	13.00 "
No. 8150, . . .	13.00 "
No. 9000, . . .	20.00 "
No. 9050, . . .	20.00 "

This price list was tipped in between pages 58 and 59 of the original edition.

No. 1200.

Old Silver, ... $18.00 (ORGANIC).

Old Silver, Gold Inlaid, . . 20.00 (ORGANISM).

Clocks Nos. 700, 800, 900, 1000, and 1100 will be furnished with above Gold Inlaid Dials.

This illustration was tipped in between pages 146 and 147 of the original edition.